Algebra 2 Connections
Version 3.0

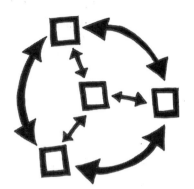

Managing Editors

Judy Kysh
San Francisco State University
San Francisco, CA

Evra Baldinger
Phillip and Sala Burton Academic High School
San Francisco, CA

Contributing Editors

Karen Arth
Central High School East
Fresno, CA

Mark Atkinson
North Salem High School
Salem, OR

Carlos Cabana
San Lorenzo High School
San Lorenzo, CA

John Cooper
Del Oro High School
Loomis, CA

Elizabeth Coyner
Christian Brothers High School
Sacramento, CA

Dolores Dean
Holy Family High School
Broomfield, CO

Ernest Derrera
Roosevelt High School
Johnston, CO

Leslie Dietiker
Michigan State University
East Lansing, MI

Bob Petersen
Rosemont High School
Sacramento, CA

Norm Prokup
The College Preparatory School
Oakland, CA

Barbara Shreve
San Lorenzo High School
San Lorenzo, CA

Estelle Woodbury
San Lorenzo High School
San Lorenzo, CA

Karen Wootton
Odenton, MD

Illustrator

Kevin Coffey
San Francisco, CA

Technical Managers

Bethany Armstrong
Davis, CA

Sarah Maile
Sacramento, CA

Aubrie Maze
Berkeley, CA

Technical Assistants

Daniel Chan
Evan Clark
Elizabeth Fong
Rebecca Harlow
Carolyn Kooi

Brian Chow
Marcos Rojas
Eric Sadur
Tiffany Trujillo

Program Directors

Leslie Dietiker
Michigan State University
East Lansing, MI

Brian Hoey
Christian Brothers High School
Sacramento, CA

Judy Kysh, Ph.D.
Departments of Education and Mathematics
San Francisco State University

Tom Sallee, Ph.D.
Department of Mathematics
University of California, Davis

Contributing Editors to the Parent Guide

Brian Hoey
CPM Educational Program
Sacramento, CA

Sarah Maile
CPM Educational Program
Sacramento, CA

Bob Petersen
Rosemont High School
Sacramento, CA

Karen Wootton
CPM Educational Program
Odenton, MD

Technical Manager

Sarah Maile
CPM Educational Program
Sacramento, CA

3 4 5 6 7 8 9   12 11 10   Version 3.0

Printed in the United States of America   ISBN-13: 978-1-931287-98-2

A Note to Students:

Welcome to Algebra 2! In this course, you will deepen and extend your knowledge of algebra to build a powerful set of mathematical tools for solving problems. Algebra is a way of thinking: a way of investing new situations, discovering relationships and figuring out strategies to apply to problems. You will apply your algebraic tools to a  variety of situations and use them to draw and support your conclusions. Learning to think this way is useful both in mathematical contexts and in other courses, and in life beyond school.

In meeting the challenges of Algebra 2, you will not be working alone. During this course you will collaborate with other students as a member of a study team. Working in a team means speaking up and interacting with others. You will explain your ideas, listen to what others have to say, and ask questions if there is something you do not understand. In algebra, a single problem can often be solved more than one way. You will see problems in different ways than your teammates do. Each of you has something to contribute while you work on the lessons in this course.

Together, your team will complete problems and activities that will help you discover new mathematical ideas and methods. Your teacher will support you as you work, but will not take away your opportunity to think and investigate for yourself. The ideas in the course will be revisited several times and connected to other topics. If something is not clear to you the first time you work with it, keep track of it, but don't worry – you will have more chances to build your understanding as the course continues.

Learning math this way has a significant advantage: as long as you actively participate, make sure everyone in your study team is involved, and ask good questions, you will find yourself understanding mathematics at a deeper level than ever before. By the end of this course, you will have a powerful understanding of properties and principles of functions. You will see how these properties and principles connect with each other so that you can use them together to model real life situations. With your teammates you will meet mathematical challenges you would not have known how to approach before.

We wish you well and are confident that you will enjoy learning Algebra 2!

Sincerely,

The CPM Team

Algebra 2 Connections
Table of Contents
Student Edition

Chapter 5 Solving and Intersections   **219**

Chapter 6 Inverses and Logarithms   **261**

Chapter 7 3-D Graphing and Logarithms

Chapter 8 Trigonometric Functions

Chapter 13 Analytic Trigonometry 669

Checkpoint Materials 703

Glossary 749

Index 777

INVESTIGATIONS AND FUNCTIONS

1

CHAPTER 1   Investigations and Functions

Welcome to Algebra 2! This chapter will introduce you to the ways you will be working as well as several of the big ideas in this course. You will share your current mathematical knowledge with your study team as you work together to solve problems, some of which you will revisit later in the course and connect to new mathematical ideas. You will learn to work with a graphing calculator to help you discover qualities of functions and systems of functions.

This chapter will also introduce you to five Ways of Thinking that are threaded throughout the course. They are: **justifying** (explaining and verifying your ideas), **generalizing** (predicting results for any situation), **choosing a strategy** (deciding which solution methods make sense), **investigating** (gathering information and drawing conclusions), and **reversing** (solving problems backward and forward).

Guiding Questions

Think about these questions throughout this chapter:

How can I work with my team to figure it out?

What questions can I ask about this function?

How can I organize my work?

How can I describe my process?

Finally, this chapter is about problem solving. During this chapter, you will use a variety of problem-solving **strategies** that will remain useful throughout this course, including:

Guessing and Checking	Collecting and Organizing Data	Finding Patterns
Drawing a Graph	Making a Table or List	Working Backward

Chapter Outline

Section 1.1   In this section, you will get to know the members of your study team. You will work with your team to develop skills and techniques for using a graphing calculator to help you explore functions and intersections, and you will present your results to the class.

Section 1.2   Here, you will find multiple ways to represent a geometric relationship, summarize your results, and present your results to the class. You will also analyze the family of linear functions and **investigate** a non-linear function. You will begin to develop your understanding of what it means to **investigate** a function.

1.1.1 How can I work with my team to figure it out?

Solving Puzzles in Teams

Welcome to Algebra 2! This chapter will challenge you to use different problem-solving **strategies**. You will also be introduced to different tools and resources that you can use throughout the course as you **investigate** new ideas, solve problems, and share mathematical ideas.

1-1.   BUILDING WITH YARN

Work with your team to make each of the shapes you see below out of a single loop of yarn. You may make the shapes in any order you like. Before you start, review the team roles that are described on the next page. Use these roles to help your study team work together today. When you make one of the shapes successfully, call your teacher over to show off your accomplishment.

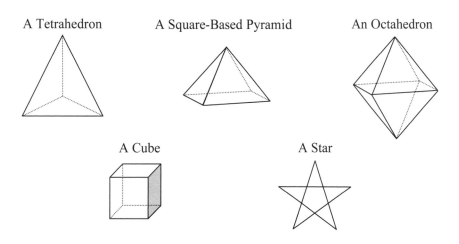

A Tetrahedron   A Square-Based Pyramid   An Octahedron

A Cube   A Star

Team Roles

Resource Manager – If your name comes first alphabetically:

- Make sure your team has all of the necessary materials, such as yarn for problem 1-1 or the resource pages for problem 1-2.

- Ask your teacher a question when the *entire* team is stuck. Before raising your hand, you might ask your team, *"Does anyone have an idea? Should I ask the teacher?"*

- Make sure your team cleans up materials by delegating tasks. You could say, *"I will put away the _____ while you _____ ."*

Facilitator – If your name comes second alphabetically:

- Start your team's discussion by reading the question aloud and then asking, *"Which shape should we start with?"* or *"How can we work together to make this shape?"*

- Make sure that all of the team members get any necessary help. You do not need to answer all of the questions yourself. A good Facilitator regularly asks, *"Do we understand what we are supposed to do?"* and *"Who can answer _____ 's question?"*

Recorder/Reporter – If your name comes third alphabetically:

- Be sure all team members are able to reach the yarn and have access to the resource pages. Make sure resource pages and work that is being discussed are placed in the center of the table or group of desks in a spot where everyone can see them.

- Be prepared to share your team's **strategies** and results with the class. You might report, *"We tried ___ , but it didn't work, so we decided to try ___ ."*

Task Manager – If your name comes fourth alphabetically:

- Remind the team to stay on task and not to talk to students in other teams. You can suggest, *"Let's try working on a different shape,"* or *"Are we ready to try the function machines in a different order?"*

- Keep track of time. Give your team reminders, such as, *"I think we need to decide now so that we will have enough time to ..."*

1-2.   FUNCTION MACHINES

Your teacher will give you a set of four function machines. Your team's job is to get a specific output by putting those machines in a particular order so that one machine's output becomes the next machine's input. As you work, discuss what you know about the kind of output each function produces to help you arrange the machines in an appropriate order. The four functions are reprinted below.

$f(x) = \sqrt{x}$ $g(x) = -(x-2)^2$

$h(x) = 2^x - 7$ $k(x) = -\frac{x}{2} = 1$ $^{-33}$

124

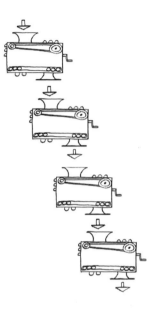

a.   In what order should you stack the machines so that when **6** is dropped into the first machine, and all four machines have had their effect, the last machine's output is **11**?

b.   What order will result in a final output of 131,065 when the first input is 64?

METHODS AND **M**EANINGS

Functions and Relations

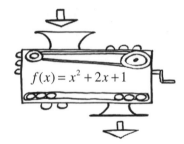

MATH NOTES

A **relation** establishes a relationship between inputs and outputs. A relation is a **function** if there is no more than one output for each input. For example, if a teacher assigns seats alphabetically, the **relation** between each student and his or her seat can be considered a **function**, since no student will receive more than one seat.

Relations and **functions** establish a correspondence between their inputs and outputs. For equations, they establish the relationship between two variables. Some examples are:

$$y = x^2, \ y = \frac{x}{x+3}, \ y = -2x + 5$$

Since the value of y usually depends on x, y is often referred to as the **dependent variable**, while x is called the **independent variable**.

A convenient way to show what a function machine does is to use **function notation**. For the function machine at right, you would write $f(x) = x^2 + 2x + 1$. The f is just the *name* of the function machine; it is not a variable. It could just as well be $Joe(x) = x^2 + 2x + 1$ if the machine happened to be named Joe!

Be careful: $f(x)$ does *not* mean f times x; it is read as "f of x." It means, "The output of the function f resulting from the input x." If you put $x = 3$ into this machine, you would write $f(3) = 3^2 + 2 \cdot 3 + 1 = 16$, or just $f(3) = 16$.

$$f(x) = x^2 + 2x + 1$$

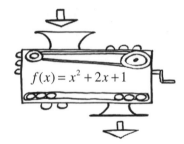

1-3. KEEPING A NOTEBOOK

> You will need to keep an organized notebook for this course. Below is one method of keeping a notebook. Ask your teacher if you should follow these guidelines or if there is another system you should follow.
>
> • The notebook should be a sturdy, three-ring, loose-leaf binder with a hard cover.
>
> • The binder should have dividers to separate it into five sections:
>
> | | |
> |---|---|
> | TEXT | TESTS AND QUIZZES |
> | HOMEWORK | LINED AND GRAPH PAPER |
> | CLASSWORK/NOTES | |
>
> You should put your name inside the front cover of your notebook so it will be returned to you if you lose it. Put your phone number and address (or the school's address, if you prefer) on the inside front cover. It will also help to put your name in large, clear letters on the outside so if someone sees it they can say, *"Hey, Julia, I saw your notebook in the cafeteria under the back table."*
>
> Your notebook will be your biggest asset for this course and will be the primary resource you will use to study, so take good care of it!

1-4. "Find $f(3)$" means to find the output of function $f(x)$ for an input of $x = 3$. For the function $f(x) = \frac{1}{x-2}$, find each of the following values.

   a.   Find $f(4)$. (This means find the output of the function when $x = 4$.)

   b.   Find x when $f(x) = 1$. (This means find the input that gives an output of 1.)

1-5. Angelica is working with function machines. She has the two machines $g(x) = \sqrt{x-5}$ and $h(x) = x^2 - 6$. She wants to put them in order so that the output of the first machine becomes the input of the second. She wants to use a beginning input of 6.

   a.   In what order must she put the machines to get a final output of 5?

   b.   Is it possible for her to get a final output of –5? If so, show how she could do that. If not, explain why not.

1-6.   An average school bus holds 45 people. Sketch a graph showing the relationship between the number of students who need bus transportation and the number of buses required. Be sure to label the axes.

1-7.   In this course, you will learn shortcuts that allow you to sketch many different types of graphs quickly and accurately. However, when the directions ask you to **graph an equation** or to **draw a graph**, this means it is not just a sketch you should do quickly. You need to:

- Use graph paper.
- Scale your axes appropriately.
- Label key points.
- Plot points accurately.

On separate sets of axes, graph each of the following equations. If you do not remember any shortcuts for graphing, you can always make an $x \rightarrow y$ table.

a. $y = -2x + 7$

b. $y = \frac{3}{5}x + 1$

c. $3x + 2y = 6$

d. $y = x^2$

1-8.   The graph for part (d) of problem 1-7 is different from the other three graphs.

a.   Explain how the graph is different from the other three graphs.

b.   What in the equation of part (d) makes its graph different?

c.   What is the graph of part (d) called?

1-9.   Write down everything you know about the equation $y = mx + b$. You should include what this general equation represents, as well as what each of the different letters represents. Be as thorough as possible.

1.1.2 How can I use my graphing calculator?

Using a Graphing Calculator to Explore a Function

In Algebra 1 you learned that multiple representations such as situations, tables, graphs, and equations and their interconnections are useful for learning about functions. A graphing calculator can be a very useful tool for generating different representations quickly. Today, you will use this tool to explore a function. You will describe your function completely to the class.

1-10. Your team will use graphing calculators to learn about one of the following functions.

i. $y = 2\sqrt{9 - x} - 4$ ii. $y = \sqrt{100 - x^2}$

iii. $y = 3\sqrt{x + 4} - 6$ iv. $y = 3\sqrt{4 - x} - 3$

v. $y = -2\sqrt{25 - x^2} + 8$ vi. $y = -3\sqrt{x + 9} + 4$

vii. $y = 2\sqrt{25 - x^2} - 1$ viii. $y = \sqrt{4 - x} - 1$

Your task: Describe your team's function in as much detail as possible. Use your graphing calculator to help you generate a table and a complete graph of your function. Remember that drawing a complete graph means:

- Use graph paper.
- Scale your axes appropriately.
- Label key points.
- Plot points accurately.

As you work, keep your graphing calculators in the middle of your workspace, so that you can compare your screens and all team members can see and discuss your results. Be sure to record what you learn as you explore your function. As a team, you will be preparing a report about your function for the class. Consider the "Discussion Points" below as you work.

Discussion Points

What are the key points on the graph? Where are they exactly?

Are there values of x or y that do not make sense?

How high or low does the graph go?

Did the graphing calculator show an accurate graph?

How can we be sure the graph is complete?

1-11.   Use your graphing calculator to view the graph in the standard window.

a.   Enter the equation in your graphing calculator and view the graph. Use the [TRACE] feature to identify at least five possible integer inputs that give integer values as outputs.

b.   Verify that each integer input gives an integer value as an output, and record these points in a table.

c.   Is there a largest or smallest input value you can use for *x*? Describe and explain any values that cannot be used.

d.   Is there a largest or smallest value for *y*? Describe and explain any values that will not occur as outputs.

e.   Are you sure you have a complete graph? How can you be sure?

———————   *Further Guidance*   ———————
section ends here.

1-12.   When your team has completed a table and drawn a complete graph, prepare a report for the whole class.

The class will get most out of your presentation if you focus on what was particularly interesting about your function or what you learned. Rather than saying, *"We plugged in a 2 and got a 5,"* consider using statements such as, *"We decided to try an input of 2 because we wanted to know what happened to the left of x = 3."*

The following sentence starters can help you make a meaningful and interesting presentation.

"At first we were confused by..."

"This makes sense because..."

"We weren't sure about... , so we tried..."

"Something interesting that we noticed about our graph is..."

As you prepare your presentation, your teacher will provide you with an overhead transparency or poster paper. Reread the task statement of problem 1-10 (labeled "Your task") and be sure to include all relevant information and ideas in your presentation.

 METHODS AND MEANINGS

Linear Equations

A **linear equation** is an equation that forms a line when it is graphed. This type of equation may be written in several different forms. Although these forms look different, they are equivalent; that is, their graphs are all the same line.

Standard Form: An equation in $ax + by = c$ form, such as $-6x + 3y = -18$.

Slope-Intercept Form: An equation in $y = mx + b$ form, such as $y = 2x - 6$.

You can find the **slope** (also known as the **growth factor**) and the **y-intercept** of a line in $y = mx + b$ form quickly. For the equation $y = 2x - 6$, the slope is 2, while the y-intercept is $(0, -6)$.

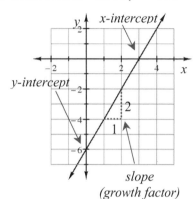

Review & Preview

1-13. Junior is saving money in his piggy bank. He starts with 10 cents and adds two pennies each day. Create an $x \rightarrow y$ table and a graph for the function for which x represents the number of days since Junior started saving money and y represents the total money he has saved.

1-14. Use the Zero Product Property and factoring, when necessary, to solve for x. The Math Notes box for Lesson 1.1.4 or problems 3-111 and 4-80 may be useful, if you need help.

a. $(x + 13)(x - 7) = 0$

b. $(2x + 3)(3x - 7) = 0$

c. $x(x - 3) = 0$

d. $x^2 - 5x = 0$

e. $x^2 - 2x - 35 = 0$

f. $3x^2 + 14x - 5 = 0$

1-15.   Terri's project for the Math Fair was a magnificent black box that she called a function machine. If you put 3 into her machine, the output would be 8. If you put in 10, the output would be 29; and if you put in 20, it would be 59.

3

Terri's

8

a.   What would her machine do to the input 5? What about –1? What about x? Making an input→output table may help you figure this out.

b.   Write a rule for Terri's machine.

1-16.   Nafeesa graphed a line with a slope of 5 and a y-intercept of $(0, -2)$.

a.   Find an equation for her line.   b.   Find the value of x when $y = 0$.

1-17.   In each of the following equations, what is y when $x = 2$? When $x = 0$? Where would the graph of each equation cross the y-axis?

a. $y = 3x + 15$ b. $y = 3 - 3x$

1-18.   Carmichael made a function machine. The inner workings of the machine are visible in the diagram at right. What will the output be in each of the following cases?

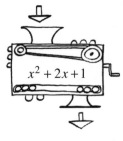

$x^2 + 2x + 1$

a.   If 3 is dropped in?

b.   If –4 is dropped in?

c.   If –22.872 is dropped in?

1-19.   Does the temperature outside depend on the time of day, or does the time of day depend on the temperature outside? This may seem like a silly question, but to sketch a graph that represents this relationship, you first need to decide which axis will represent which quantity.

    a.   When you graph an equation such as $y = 3x - 5$, which variable (the x or the y) *depends* on the other? Which is not dependent? (That is, which is *independent*?) Explain.

    b.   Which variable is *dependent*: temperature or time of day? Which variable is *independent*?

    c.   Sketch a graph (with appropriately named axes) that shows the relationship between temperature outside and time of day.

1-20.   Jill needs to cut a piece off of a 30-foot length of lumber. Create multiple representations ($x \rightarrow y$ table, graph, and equation) for the function with x-values that are the length of the piece Jill cuts off and y-values that are the length of the piece that is left over. Which representation best portrays the situation? Why? Explain.

1-21.   Make a table and graph the function $f(x) = \frac{1}{2}x^2$. Describe all of the possible input and output values.

1-22.   Given $f(x) = -\frac{2}{3}x + 3$ and $g(x) = 2x^2 - 5$, complete parts (a) through (f) below.

    a.   Calculate $f(3)$.   b.   Solve $f(x) = -5$.

    c.   Calculate $g(-3)$.   d.   Solve $g(x) = 9$.

    e.   Solve $g(x) = 8$.   f.   Solve $g(x) = -7$.

1-23.   Gerri made a function machine. Below are four pictures of her machine. (Note that these are all pictures of the same function machine.) Find the rule for Gerri's function machine.

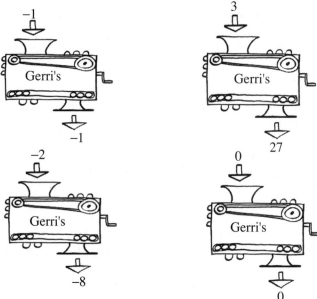

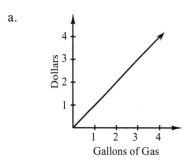

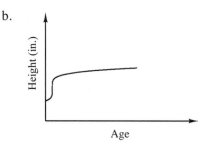

1-24.   Examine each graph below. Based on the shape of the graph and the labels of the axes, write a sentence to describe the relationship that each graph represents. Then state which axis represents the independent variable and which one represents the dependent variable.

a.

Dollars (vertical axis, marked 1, 2, 3, 4)
Gallons of Gas (horizontal axis, marked 1 2 3 4)

b.

Height (in.) (vertical axis)
Age (horizontal axis)

Problem continues on next page. →

1-24.   *Problem continued from previous page.*

c.   d.

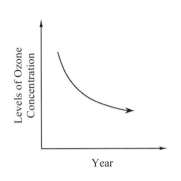

Year

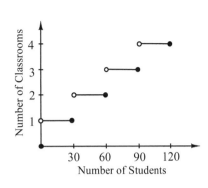

Number of Students

e.   What are all of the possible inputs of the graph in part (d)? What are all of the possible outputs?

1-25.   Gregory planted a lemon tree in his back yard. When he planted the tree, it was 2 feet tall. He noticed that it has been growing 3 inches every week.

a.   Create multiple representations ($x \rightarrow y$ table, graph, and equation) to represent the relationship between the days that have passed and the height of the tree.

b.   If the tree continues growing at this rate, when will it be 6 feet tall? How can you see this in each of the representations?

c.   State the possible inputs and outputs of the graph.

1-26.   Find the error in the solution at right. Explain what the error is and solve the equation correctly. Show how to check your solution to be sure that it is correct.

$$3(x-2)-2(x+7) = 2x+17$$
$$3x-6-2x+14 = 2x+17$$
$$x+8 = 2x+17$$
$$-9 = x$$

Note: The stoplight icon to the right of a problem indicates that there is an error in the problem.

1.1.3 Which values are possible?

Domain and Range

In Lesson 1.1.2 you worked with your graphing calculator to see complete graphs of functions and to determine what information was useful to describe those functions completely. In this lesson you will look at more functions, this time thinking about what input and output values are possible. You will also learn about additional tools on your graphing calculator that allow you to see a complete graph. As you work with your team, remember to ask each other questions such as:

What values are possible?

Can we see the complete graph?

What other information can we use to describe the function?

1-27. Jerrod and Sonia were working with their team on ordering the function machines in problem 1-2. The functions are reprinted for you below.

$f(x) = \sqrt{x}$ $\qquad g(x) = -(x-2)^2$

$h(x) = 2^x - 7$ $\qquad k(x) = -\frac{x}{2} - 1$

a. Jerrod first put an input of 6 into the function $g(x) = -(x-2)^2$ and got an output of -16. He wanted to try $f(x) = \sqrt{x}$ as his next function in the order, but he thinks there might be a problem using -16 as an input. Is there a problem? Explain.

b. Because it is not possible to take the square root of -16, it can be said that -16 is not in the **domain** of the function $f(x)$. The **domain** of a function is the collection of numbers that are possible inputs for that function. With your team, find two other numbers that are *not* part of the domain of $f(x)$. Then describe the domain. In other words, what are all of the numbers that *can* be used as inputs for the function $f(x)$?

c. Sonia claimed that $g(x)$ could not possibly be the last function in the order for problem 1-2. She **justified** her thinking by saying, "*Our final output has to be 11, which is a positive number. The function $g(x)$ will always make its output negative, so it can't come last in the order.*" Discuss this with your team. Does Sonia's logic make sense? How did she know that the output of $g(x)$ would never be positive?

1-28.   Use your graphing calculator to help you draw a complete graph of
$y = (x+1)(x-9)$.

   a.   Describe the graph completely.

   b.   What window settings allow you to see the complete graph?

   c.   How are the settings related to domain and range?

1-29.   Draw a complete graph of $y = (x-12)^2 + 11$.

   a.   What happens when you use the standard window?

   b.   What window settings did you use to see enough of the graph to
         help you visualize and draw a complete graph?

   c.   What are the domain and range of the function?

1-30.   Now you will **reverse** your thinking to create a graph with a given domain and range.

   a.   Sketch a relation that has a domain of all numbers between and including
         −3 and 10 (written $-3 \le x \le 10$) and a range of all numbers between and
         including −4 and 6 (written $-4 \le y \le 6$). You do not have to write an equation
         for your relation. Verify your endpoints with your team. Be creative.

   b.   Sketch a relation with a domain of all real numbers (written $-\infty < x < \infty$) and a
         range of all numbers greater than or equal to –2 (written $y \ge -2$).
         (Note: The symbol ∞ means "infinity.")

1-31.   How can a graphing calculator help you find the solution to a system of equations?
         Consider this system:
$$5x - y = 35$$
$$3x + y = -3$$

   a.   First graph the system in a standard window. Can you see the
         solution on your screen?

   b.   To find the solution you will need to change the window on your calculator.
         Discuss with your team what maximum value, minimum value, and scale you
         should use for the x- and y-axes in order to see the intersection. After you have
         decided, check your conclusion on the graphing calculator.

   c.   Use the [TRACE] button to find the solution from the graphs. Then solve the
         system algebraically.

   d.   Discuss the two methods with your team. Explain which one your team prefers
         and why.

1-32.　What does the graph of $y = x + \frac{1}{(x+2)^2} - 3$ look like?　Graph the

equation on your calculator.　Use the trace and/or zoom buttons to find the *x*- and *y*-intercepts.　What is the domain of this function? What is the range?

1-33.　Use your graphing calculator to help you sketch the graphs of $y = \frac{1}{x} - 4$ and $y = \frac{1}{x-4}$.　Are the graphs the same?　Should they be? Explain why or why not.

1-34.　LEARNING LOG

Throughout this course, you will be asked to reflect on your understanding of mathematical concepts in a Learning Log.　Your Learning Log will contain explanations and examples to help you remember what you have learned throughout the course, as well as questions you are trying to understand and answer.　It is important to write each entry of the Learning Log in your own words so that later you can use your Learning Log as a resource to refresh your memory.　Your teacher will tell you where to write your Learning Log entries and how to structure them.　Remember to label each entry with a title and a date so you can refer to it later.

In your Learning Log today, describe everything you know about domain and range. Include examples to illustrate your ideas.　Title this entry "Domain and Range" and label it with today's date.

(M)ETHODS AND MEANINGS

Domain and Range

MATH NOTES

The set of possible values for the input of a function has a special name. It is called the **domain** of the function.　This set consists of every input value for *x* for which the function is defined.

The **range** of a function is the set of possible values of the output.　This set contains every *y*-value that the function can generate.

Domain and **range** are often written with **inequality notation** as shown in the examples below.

If the domain is any number between and including –2 and 7:　$-2 \le x \le 7$

If the range is any number greater than but excluding 4:　$y > 4$ or $4 < y < \infty$

If the domain is all numbers except for –3:　$x \ne -3$

1-35. Examine $g(x)$ graphed at right.

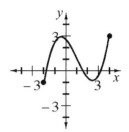

a. Which x-values have points on the graph? That is, describe the domain of $g(x)$.

b. What are the possible outputs for $g(x)$? That is, what is the range?

c. Ricky thinks the range of $g(x)$ is: $-1, 0, 1, 2,$ and 3. Is he correct? Why or why not?

d. Draw a graph for another function with the same domain and range as $g(x)$.

1-36. Consider the functions $f(x) = 3x^2 - 5$ and $g(x) = \sqrt{x-5} + 2$.

a. Find $f(5)$.   b. Find $g(5)$.

c. Find $f(4)$.   d. Find $g(4)$.

e. Find $f(x) + g(x)$.   f. Find $g(x) - f(x)$.

g. Describe the domain of $f(x)$.   h. Describe the domain of $g(x)$.

i. Why is the domain of one of these functions more restrictive than the other?

1-37. Nissos and Chelita were arguing over a math problem. Nissos was trying to explain to Chelita that she had made a mistake in finding the x-intercepts of the function $y = x^2 - 10x + 21$. *"No way!"* Chelita exclaimed. *"I know how to find x-intercepts! You make the y equal to zero and solve for x. I know I did this right!"* Here is Chelita's work:

Step 1: $x^2 - 10x + 21 = 0$, so $(x+7)(x+3) = 0$.

Step 2: Therefore, $x + 7 = 0$ or $x + 3 = 0$.

Step 3: So $x = -7$ or $x = -3$.

Nissos tried to explain to Chelita that she had done something wrong. What is Chelita's error? **Justify** and explain your answer completely.

1-38.   As you have found when using a graphing calculator, equations must be solved for y; that is, they must be written in y-form. Rewrite each equation below so that it can be entered into a graphing calculator.

a. $x = 3y + 6$ b. $x = 5y - 10$

c. $x = y^2$ d. $x = 2y^2 - 4$

e. $x = (y - 5)^2$

1-39.   Write and solve an equation or a system of equations to help you solve the following problem.

A cable 84 meters long is cut into two pieces so that one piece is 18 meters longer than the other. Find the length of each piece of cable.

1-40.   Consider triangles ABC and ADE at right. Give a convincing argument why $\triangle ABC \sim \triangle ADE$. Then use what you know about similar triangles to complete each of the following ratios for the triangles shown below right.

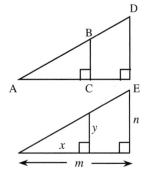

a. $\frac{y}{x} = \frac{?}{?}$ b. $\frac{n}{y} = \frac{?}{?}$

1-41.   Solve each of the following equations. Be sure to check your solutions.

a. $4(x - 1) - 2(3x + 5) = -3x - 1$ b. $3x - 5 = 2.5x + 3 - (x - 4)$

1.1.4 How can I represent intersections?

Points of Intersection in Multiple Representations

Throughout this course, you will represent functions and relations in different ways, and you will find connections between these representations. These connections will give you new ways to **investigate** functions and to **justify** your conclusions.

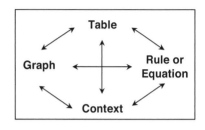

How can these connections help you understand more about systems of equations? In this lesson, you will make connections between ways of representing a system of equations as you use your graphing calculator to find the points of intersection in multiple representations.

1-42. INTERSECTION INVESTIGATION

In Lesson 1.1.3, you used the [TRACE] feature of your graphing calculator to find a point of intersection of two graphs. Can you use other representations as well? What about other **strategies**? Are all **strategies** equally accurate? Which do you prefer?

Your task: Work with your team to find *as many ways as you can* (with *and* without your graphing calculator) to determine the points of intersection of the functions $f(x) = 2x^2 - 5x + 6$ and $g(x) = -2x^2 - x + 30$. Be sure to think about tables, graphs, and equations as you work. Be prepared to teach each of your methods to the class.

Hint: Explore the [TABLE], [TBLSET], and [CALC] features on your graphing calculator.

Discussion Points

How can we find it using graphs?

How can we find it in tables?

How can we find it using equations?

1-43.   Jason and his team were working on finding the points of intersection of
$f(x) = 2x^2 - 5x + 6$ and $g(x) = -2x^2 - x + 30$. He suggested, *"Maybe we could start by looking at the graphs of the functions."*

   a.   Use your graphing calculator to help you graph $f(x)$ and $g(x)$.

   b.   Adjust the viewing window so that you can see all of the points of intersection. How accurately can you approximate the coordinates of these points by looking at the graph? Give it a try.

   c.   Use the [TRACE] feature to get a more accurate approximation of each of the points.

   d.   With your team, explore the [CALC] feature of your graphing calculator. Can you find a way to make the graphing calculator calculate your points of intersection for you? How accurate are your results? Be prepared to teach your method to the class.

1-44.   Aria was in Jason's team. She had another idea and asked, *"Can't we find the points of intersection by comparing the tables of our two functions?"*

   a.   What did Aria mean? How can you find points of intersection by looking at tables?

   b.   Use your graphing calculator to make tables for $f(x)$ and $g(x)$. To do this, you will need to explore the [TABLE] and [TBLSET] features of your calculator.

   c.   Find all of the points of intersection in the tables. How accurate are these results?

   d.   Can you think of any circumstances in which using a table might not be an efficient or accurate **strategy** for finding points of intersection? Explain.

1-45.   Delilah had been listening to Jason and Aria explain their ideas. She said, *"I thought of another way! We know a method for using the equations to find points of intersection even without the graphing calculator, don't we?"*

   a.   What method is Delilah referring to?

   b.   Use Delilah's method to find the points of intersection of these two functions.

———————   *Further Guidance*   ———————
                         section ends here.

1-46.   Rhianna says she can draw different functions that have the same x-intercepts and the same domain and range. Her teammates say, *"No, that's impossible!"* But Rhianna insists, *"It is possible if we just try to sketch the graphs."*

     a.   What if the x-intercepts are $(-5, 0)$, $(2, 0)$, and $(6, 0)$, the domain is $-5 \le x \le 7$, and the range is $-4 \le y \le 10$? Is more than one function possible? Give examples to help explain why or why not.

     b.   What if the x-intercepts are $(-4, 0)$ and $(2, 0)$, the domain is all real numbers, and the range is $y \ge -8$? Is there more than one function possible? Give examples of multiple functions or explain why there can be only one.

METHODS AND MEANINGS

MATH NOTES

Solving a Quadratic Equation

In a previous course, you learned how to solve **quadratic equations** (equations that can be written in the form $ax^2 + bx + c = 0$). Review two methods for solving quadratic equations below.

Some quadratic equations can be solved by **factoring** and using the **Zero Product Property**. For example, because $x^2 - 3x - 10 = (x - 5)(x + 2)$, the quadratic equation $x^2 - 3x - 10 = 0$ can be rewritten as $(x - 5)(x + 2) = 0$. The Zero Product Property states that if $ab = 0$, then $a = 0$ or $b = 0$. So if $(x - 5)(x + 2) = 0$, then $x - 5 = 0$ or $x + 2 = 0$. Therefore, $x = 5$ or $x = -2$.

Another method for solving quadratic equations is using the **Quadratic Formula**. This method is particularly helpful for solving quadratic equations that are difficult or impossible to factor. Before using the Quadratic Formula, the quadratic equation you want to solve must be in standard form (that is, written as $ax^2 + bx + c = 0$).

In this form, a is the coefficient of the x^2-term, b is the coefficient of the x-term, and c is the constant term. The Quadratic Formula is stated at right.

$$x = \frac{-b \pm \sqrt{b^2 - 4ac}}{2a}$$

This formula gives two possible answers, shown by the "$\pm$" symbol. This symbol (read as "plus or minus") is shorthand notation that tells you to calculate the formula twice: once using addition and once using subtraction. Therefore, every Quadratic Formula problem must be simplified twice to give:

$$x = \frac{-b + \sqrt{b^2 - 4ac}}{2a} \quad \text{or} \quad x = \frac{-b - \sqrt{b^2 - 4ac}}{2a}$$

To solve $x^2 - 3x - 10 = 0$ using the Quadratic Formula, substitute $a = 1$, $b = -3$, and $c = -10$ into the formula, as shown below, then simplify.

$$x = \frac{-(-3) \pm \sqrt{(-3)^2 - 4(1)(-10)}}{2(1)} = \frac{3 \pm \sqrt{49}}{2} = \frac{3 \pm 7}{2} \quad \rightarrow \quad x = 5 \text{ or } x = -2$$

1-47.   Use any method to find the point of intersection of $f(x) = 3x - 5$ and $g(x) = -4x + 9$.

1-48.   Compute for $f(x) = \frac{1}{x}$.

    a. $f(\frac{1}{2})$ b. $f(\frac{1}{10})$ c. $f(0.01)$ d. $f(0.007)$

1-49.   Solve each of the following quadratic equations. If you need help, refer to the Math Notes box for this lesson.

    a. $x^2 - 8x + 15 = 0$ b. $2x^2 - 5x - 6 = 0$

1-50.   Consider the points $(-5, 0)$ and $(0, 3)$.

    a.   Plot the points and find the distance between them. Give your answer both in simplest radical form and as a decimal approximation.

    b.   Find the slope of the line that passes through both points.

1-51.   Sketch a few different equilateral triangles. Create multiple representations ($x \rightarrow y$ table, graph, equation) of the function with inputs that are the length of one side of an equilateral triangle and outputs that are its perimeter.

1-52.   Find the error in the solution at right. Identify the error and solve the equation correctly.

$$4.1x = 9.5x + 23.7$$
$$-4.1x = -4.1x$$
$$5.4x = 23.7$$
$$\frac{5.4x}{5.4} = \frac{23.7}{5.4}$$
$$x = 4.39$$

1-53.   Solve each of the following equations.

    a. $3.9x - 2.1 = 11.2x + 51.7$ b. $\frac{1}{5}x - 2 = \frac{13}{25} - 0.7x$

1.2.1 How can I represent a function?

Modeling a Geometric Relationship

Mathematics can be used to model physical relationships to help us understand them better. Mathematical models can assume the form of a series of diagrams, a context, a table, an equation, or a graph. In this course, you will be given situations to explore in which you gather and interpret data. You will learn to **generalize** your information so that you can make predictions about cases not actually tested. In this lesson, you will analyze a geometric relationship and look for connections among its multiple representations.

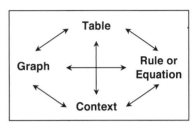

1-54.   ANALYZING DATA FROM A GEOMETRIC RELATIONSHIP

Each team will make paper boxes using the instructions given below. Based on the physical models, your team will represent the relationship between the height of the box and its volume in multiple ways.

Cut a sheet of centimeter grid paper to match the dimensions that your teacher assigns your team. Cut the same size square out of each corner, and fold the sides up to form a shallow box (with no lid) as shown below.

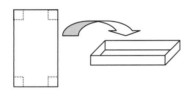

Dimensions	
22 cm × 16 cm	18 cm × 10 cm
22 cm × 14 cm	15 cm × 15 cm
20 cm × 15 cm	15 cm × 10 cm
20 cm × 9 cm	12 cm × 9 cm

Your task: As a team you will **investigate** the relationship between the height of a paper box (the **input**) and its volume (the **output**). You can build as many boxes as necessary to establish this relationship. Be sure to build all of your boxes out of paper of the same size. Record your information using multiple representations—including diagrams, a table, and a graph. Also record any thoughts, observations, and/or general statements that come up in your discussion of the problem.

Discussion Points

How can we collect data for this relationship?

How much data is enough?

What are all the possible inputs for our function?

How are the different representations related?

1-55.   Begin your **investigation** by building several boxes, taking measurements, and
collecting data.

a.   As a team, choose a starting input value. Note that
this value is the same as the *length of the side of
one of the cut-out squares from the corner of your
grid paper* and becomes the height of your box.
Now make the first box and determine its volume.
Label the box with its important information.
Work in the middle of the workspace so that everyone understands what is being
measured or calculated, and be sure everyone agrees on the result before
recording the information in an input→output table on your own paper.

b.   Each team member should now choose a *different* input value and build a new
box or draw a diagram using this new value. Calculate the volume of your box.
Share your input and output values with the rest of your team and record
everyone's data in your input→output table.

c.   Use the data in your table to create a graph to represent the situation.

*Further Guidance
section ends here.*

1-56.   GENERALIZING

Now you will **generalize** your results. **Generalizing** is a mathematical Way of
Thinking for this course. A common way to **generalize** using algebra is to write an
equation.

a.   Draw a diagram of one of your boxes. Since this shape is being used to
generalize, you want it to represent a relationship between *any* possible input and
its output. Therefore, instead of labeling the height with a number, label the
height of this box x.

b.   Work with your team to calculate the volume (or y-value) for a height of x. It
may help you to remember how you calculated the volume when the height was a
number and use the same **strategy** for your new input of x.

Algebra 2 Connections

1-57.   LOOKING FOR CONNECTIONS

Put your $x \to y$ table, graph, and equation in the middle of your workspace. With your team, discuss the questions below.

As you address each question, remember to give reasons when you can. Also, if you make an observation, discuss how that observation relates to your table, graph, and equation.

a.   Are there some input values that would not make sense? Why or why not? How can you tell using the graph? The $x \to y$ table? The equation? The boxes (or diagrams of boxes)?

b.   What are all of the possible outputs (volumes)? Are there any outputs that would not make sense? Why or why not?

c.   Should you connect the points on your graph with a smooth curve? That is, should your graph be *continuous* or *discrete*? Explain.

d.   What is different about your graph from others you have seen in previous courses? What special points or features does it have?

e.   Work with your team to find as many other connections as you can among your geometric models, your table, your equation, and your graph. How can you show or explain each connection?

1-58.   What graph do you get when you use the graphing calculator to draw the graph of your equation? Explain the relationship between this and the graph you made on your own paper.

1-59.   Organize your findings into a stand-alone poster that shows everything you have learned about all of the representations of your function as well as the connections between the representations. Use colors, arrows, words, and any other useful tools you can think of to make sure that someone reading your poster can understand all of your thinking.

METHODS AND **M**EANINGS

Triangle Trigonometry

There are three **trigonometric ratios** you can use to solve for the missing side lengths and angle measurements in any right triangle: tangent, sine, and cosine.

In the triangle below, when the sides are described relative to the angle θ, the opposite leg is y and the adjacent leg is x. The hypotenuse is h regardless of which acute angle is used.

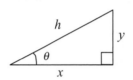

$$\tan \theta = \frac{opposite\ leg}{adjacent\ leg} = \frac{y}{x}$$

$$\sin \theta = \frac{opposite\ leg}{hypotenuse} = \frac{y}{h}$$

$$\cos \theta = \frac{adjacent\ leg}{hypotenuse} = \frac{x}{h}$$

In general, for any uniquely determined triangle, missing sides and angles can be determined by using the **Law of Sines** or the **Law of Cosines**.

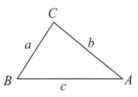

$$\frac{\sin A}{a} = \frac{\sin B}{b} = \frac{\sin C}{c}$$

and

$$c^2 = a^2 + b^2 - 2ab\cos C$$

Review & Preview

1-60.   Make a table and graph for $h(x) = x^3 - 4$. Find the domain, range, and intercepts.

1-61.   For each diagram below, write and solve an equation to find the value of each variable. Give your answer to part (d) in both radical and decimal form. For a reminder of the trigonometry ratios, refer to the Math Notes box for this lesson.

a.
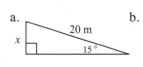

b.
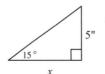

c.

d.

1-62.   Consider the points $(-2, 5)$ and $(5, 2)$ as you complete parts (a) and (b) below.

   a.   Plot the points and find the distance between them. Give your answer both in simplest radical form and as a decimal approximation.

   b.   Find the slope of the line that goes through the two points.

1-63.   Name the domain and range for each of the following functions.

   a.   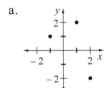   b.   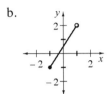   c.   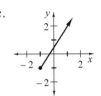   d.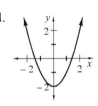

1-64.   Find the error in the solution at right. Explain what the error is and solve the equation correctly. Be sure to check your answer.

$$\frac{5}{x} = x - 4$$
$$x \cdot \frac{5}{x} = x - 4$$
$$5 = x - 4$$
$$x = 9$$

1-65.   Solve each of the following equations. Be sure to check your answers.

   a. $\frac{6}{x} = x - 1$ b. $\frac{9}{x} = x$

1-66.   Compute each of the following values for $f(x) = \frac{1}{x-2}$.

   a. $f(2.5)$ b. $f(1.75)$

   c. $f(2)$ d.   **Justify** your answer for part (c).

1-67.   Graph the following functions and find the x- and y-intercepts.

   a. $y = 2x + 3$ b. $f(x) = 2x + 3$

   c.   How are the functions in (a) and (b) the same? How are they different?

1-68.   A 3-foot indoor kiddy slide must meet the ground very gradually and make an angle of $155°$, as shown in the diagram at right. Find the height of the slide (y) and the length of the floor it will cover (x).

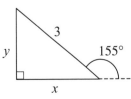

1-69. Write one or two equations to help you solve the following problem.

A rectangle's length is four times its width. The sum of its two adjacent sides is 22 cm. How long is each side?

1-70. Solve each of the following equations.

a. $\frac{3}{x} + 6 = -45$

b. $\frac{x-2}{5} = \frac{10-x}{8}$

c. $(x+1)(x-3) = 0$

1-71. Consider $f(x) = x^2 - 2x + 6$ and $g(x) = 2x + 11$.

a. Use any method to find the points of intersection of $f(x)$ and $g(x)$.

b. Calculate $f(x) + g(x)$.

c. Calculate $f(x) - g(x)$.

1-72. Rearrange each equation below by solving for x. Write each equation in the form $x =$ _____. (Note that y will be in your answer).

a. $y = \frac{3}{5}x + 1$

b. $3x + 2y = 6$

c. $y = x^2$

d. $y = x^2 - 100$

1-73. Consider circles of different sizes. Create multiple representations of the function with inputs that are the radius of the circle and outputs that are its area.

1-74. Consider the equation $4x - 6y = 12$.

a. Predict what the graph of this equation looks like. **Justify** your answer.

b. Solve the equation for y and graph the equation.

c. Explain clearly how to find the x- and y-intercepts.

d. Which form of the equation is best for finding intercepts quickly? Why?

e. Find the x- and y-intercepts of $2x - 3y = -18$. Then use the intercepts to sketch a graph quickly.

1-75.   If the number 1 is the output for Carmichael's function
machine shown at right, how can you find out what number
was dropped in? Find the number(s) that could have been
dropped in.

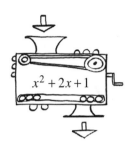

$x^2 + 2x + 1$

1-76.   What value of x allows you to find the y-intercept? Where
does the graph of each equation below cross the y-axis? Write
each answer as an ordered pair.

a. $y = 3x + 6$ b. $x = 5y - 10$

c. $y = x^2$ d. $y = 2x^2 - 4$

e. $y = (x - 5)^2$ f. $y = 3x^3 - 2x^2 + 13$

1-77.   Find the error in the solution at right.
Describe the error and solve the equation
correctly.

$3x + 2 = 10 - 4(x - 1)$

$3x + 2 = 6(x - 1)$

$3x + 2 = 6x - 6$

$8 = 3x$ so $x = \frac{8}{3}$

1.2.2 How can I investigate a function?

Function Investigation

What does it mean to describe a function completely? In this lesson you will graph and **investigate** a family of functions with equations of the form $f(x) = \frac{1}{x-h}$. As you work with your team, keep the multiple representations of functions in mind.

1-78.   INVESTIGATING A FUNCTION, Part One

Your team will **investigate** functions of the form $f(x) = \frac{1}{x-h}$, where h can be any number.

As a team, choose a value for h between -10 and 10. For example, if $h = 7$, then $f(x) = \frac{1}{x-7}$.

Your task: On a piece of graph paper, write down the function you get when you use your h-value. Then make an $x \to y$ table and draw a complete graph of your function. Is there any more information you need to be sure that you can see the entire shape of your graph? Discuss this question with your team and add any new information you think is necessary.

Discussion Points

How can we be sure that our graph is complete?

How can we get output values that are greater than 1 or less than -1?

1-79.   This function is different from others you have seen in the past. To get a complete graph, you will need to make sure your table includes enough information.

   a.   Make an $x \rightarrow y$ table with integer x-values from 5 below your value of h to 5 above your value of h. For example, if you are working with $h = 7$, you would start your table at $x = 2$ and end it at $x = 12$. What do you notice about all of your y-values?

   b.   Is there any x-value that has no y-value for your function? Why does this make sense?

   c.   Plot all of the points that you have in your table so far.

   d.   Now you will need to add more values to your table to see what is happening to your function as your input values get close to your h-value. Choose eight input values that are very close to your value of h on either side. For example, if you are working with $h = 7$, you might choose input values such as 6.5, 6.7, 6.9, 6.99, 7.01, 7.1, 7.3, and 7.5. For each new input value, calculate the corresponding output and add the new point to your graph.

   e.   When you have enough points to be sure that you know the shape of your graph, sketch the curve.

   ——————   *Further Guidance*   ——————
         section ends here.

1-80.   Now you will continue your **investigation** of $f(x) = \frac{1}{x-h}$.

   a.   Each team member should choose a different value of h and make a complete $x \rightarrow y$ table and graph for your new function.

   b.   Examine all of your team's functions. Together, generate a list of questions that you could ask about the functions your team created. Be as thorough as possible and be prepared to share your questions with the class.

   c.   As your teacher records each team's questions, copy them into your Learning Log. Title this entry "Function Investigation Questions" and label it with today's date.

1-81.   INVESTIGATING A FUNCTION, Part Two: SUMMARY STATEMENTS

Now you are ready for the most important part of your **investigation**: summary
statements! Summary statements are a very important part of this course, so your team
will practice making them. A summary statement is a statement about a function *along
with thorough justification*. A strong summary statement should be **justified** with
multiple representations ($x \to y$ table, equation, graph, and situation, if applicable).

a.   Read the example summary statement below, a summary statement about the
range of the function $y = x^2$. Discuss it with your team and decide if it is
justified completely.

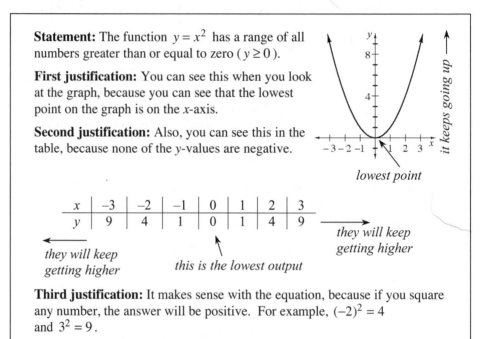

Statement: The function $y = x^2$ has a range of all
numbers greater than or equal to zero ($y \geq 0$).

First justification: You can see this when you look
at the graph, because you can see that the lowest
point on the graph is on the *x*-axis.

Second justification: Also, you can see this in the
table, because none of the *y*-values are negative.

lowest point

x	–3	–2	–1	0	1	2	3
y	9	4	1	0	1	4	9

*they will keep
getting higher*

this is the lowest output

*they will keep
getting higher*

Third justification: It makes sense with the equation, because if you square
any number, the answer will be positive. For example, $(-2)^2 = 4$
and $3^2 = 9$.

b.   Use your "Function Investigation Questions" Learning Log entry from
problem 1-80 to help you make as many summary statements about your
functions as you can. Remember to **justify** each summary statement in as many
ways as possible.

1-82.   SHARING SUMMARY STATEMENTS

With your team, choose one summary statement that you wrote that you find
particularly interesting. On an overhead transparency, write the summary statement
along with its **justification**. Include sketches of graphs, $x \to y$ tables, equations,
circles, arrows, colors, and any other tools that are helpful.

1-83.   What will the graph of $f(x) = \frac{1}{x+25}$ look like?

a.   Discuss this question with your team and make a sketch of what you predict the graph will look like. Give as many reasons for your prediction as you can.

b.   Use your graphing calculator to graph $f(x) = \frac{1}{x+25}$. Do you see what you expected to see? Why or why not?

c.   Adjust the viewing window if needed. When you see the full picture of your graph, make a sketch of the graph on your paper. Label any important points.

d.   How close was your prediction?

1-84.   Use any method to find the points of intersection of $f(x) = 2x^2 - 3x + 4$ and $g(x) = x^2 + 5x - 3$.

1-85.   Solve each equation for x.

a. $-2(x+4) = 35 - (7 - 4x)$ b. $\frac{x-4}{7} = \frac{8-3x}{5}$

1-86.   Make a complete graph of the function $f(x) = \sqrt{x} - 2$, label its x- and y-intercepts, and describe its domain and range.

1-87.   Given $f(x) = 2x - 7$, complete parts (a) through (c) below.

a.   Compute $f(0)$.   b.   Solve $f(x) = 0$.

c.   What do the answers to parts (a) and (b) tell you about the graph of $f(x)$?

1-88.   Solve each equation below for the indicated variable.

a. $y = mx + b$ (for x)   b. $A = \pi r^2$ (for r)

c. $V = LHW$ (for W)   d. $2x + \frac{1}{y} = 3$ (for y)

1-89. What value of y allows you to find the x-intercept? For each of the equations below, find where its graph intersects the x-axis. Write each answer as an ordered pair.

 a. $y = 3x + 6$

 b. $x = 5y - 10$

 c. $y = x^2$

 d. $y = 2x^2 - 4$

 e. $y = (x - 5)^2$

 f. $y = x^3 - 13$

1-90. Make a complete graph of the function $h(x) = 2x^2 + 4x - 6$ and describe its domain and range.

1-91. Find the domain and the range for each of the following functions.

 a. 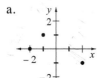   b. 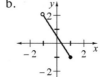   c. 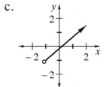   d.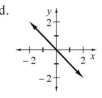

1-92. Carlo got a pet snake as a birthday present. On his birthday, the baby snake was just 26 cm long. He has been watching it closely and has noticed that it has been growing 2 cm each week.

 a. Create multiple representations of the function for which the inputs are the weeks since Carlo's birthday and the outputs are the length of the snake.

 b. If the snake continues to grow at the same rate, when will it be 1 meter (100 cm) long? How can you see this in each representation?

1-93. Create multiple representations of the function $g(x) = \frac{2}{x}$. Then make as many summary statements as you can.

1-94.   Suppose you want to find where the lines $y = 3x + 15$ and $y = 3 - 3x$ cross, and you want to be more accurate than the graphing calculator or graph paper will allow. You can use algebra to find the *point of intersection*.

      a.   If you remember how to do this, find the point of intersection using algebra and be prepared to explain your method to your team tomorrow in class. If you do not remember, then do parts (b) through (e) below.

      b.   Since $y = 3x + 15$ and $y = 3 - 3x$, what must be true about $3x + 15$ and $3 - 3x$ when their y-values are the same?

      c.   Write an equation that does not contain y and solve it for x.

      d.   Use the x-value you found in part (c) to find the corresponding y-value.

      e.   Where do the two lines cross?

1-95.   *Salami and More Deli* sells a 5-foot submarine sandwich for parties. It weighs 8 pounds. Assuming that the weight per foot is constant, what would be the length of a 12-pound sandwich?

1-96.   If $h(x) = x^2 - 5$, where does the graph of $h(x)$ cross the x-axis? Make a sketch of the graph.

1-97.   Graph the following equations.

      a. $y - 2x = 3$ b. $y - 3 = x^2$

      c.   State the x- and y-intercepts for each equation.

      d.   Where do the two graphs cross? Show how you can find these two points without looking at the graphs.

1-98.   Match the laws, rules, or formulas in Column I with the corresponding name from Column II.

Column I   Column II

      a. $x = \frac{-b \pm \sqrt{b^2 - 4ac}}{2a}$ 1.   Law of Cosines

      b. $\frac{\sin A}{a} = \frac{\sin B}{b}$ 2.   Law of Sines

      c. $c^2 = a^2 + b^2$ 3.   Pythagorean Theorem

      d. $c^2 = a^2 + b^2 - 2ab\cos C$ 4.   Quadratic Formula

1.2.3 What do they have in common?

· ·

The Family of Linear Functions

In Lesson 1.2.2, your team **investigated** functions of the form $f(x) = \frac{1}{x-h}$, where h could be any number. You learned that as you changed h, the graph changed, but the basic shape stayed the same. In this lesson, you will think about functions of the form $f(x) = mx + b$.

1-99.   Consider functions of the form $y = mx + b$.

   a.   What do x and y represent in this function? What do m and b represent? Which ones can you change?

   b.   With the rest of the class, explore the effects of m and b on the function $y = mx + b$. What effect does m have on the graph? What effect does b have on the graph?

   c.   For this function, m and b are called **parameters** (as h was for $f(x) = \frac{1}{x-h}$), whereas x and y are called **variables**. With your team, explain the difference between a parameter and a variable.

   d.   What do all of the functions of the form $y = mx + b$ have in common? Since they all have the same basic relationship between x and y, they can be called a **family** of functions.

1-100.   With your team, examine each of group of equations below and discuss what you would see if you drew the graphs of the four equations on one set of axes. Write a description of what you imagine you would see. (You do not actually have to draw them.)

   a. $x + 2y = 10$

$y = -\frac{1}{2}x + 3$

$-4y = 2x + 8$

$y = -\frac{1}{2}x$

   b. $5x + y = -3$

$y = -\frac{1}{2}x - 3$

$3x - 4y = 12$

$5y - 2x = -15$

1-101.   Below, (a) through (f), are six representations of a relationship between an input and an output. With your team, decide whether each relationship is linear and write a clear summary statement **justifying** your decision. If the relationship is linear, graph it and find its equation. If it is not linear, describe the growth.

a.

Pieces of Bread	Grams of Fiber
0	0
1	5
2	10
3	15
4	20

b.   *Killer Fried Chickens charges $7.00 for a basic bucket of chicken and $0.50 for each additional piece. The input is the number of extra pieces of chicken ordered, and the output is the total cost of the order.*

c.

x	y
10	0
5	5
3	7
2	8
1	9
0	10

d.

x	y
10	1
5	2
4	2.5
2	5
1	10
0.5	20

e.   *James planted a bush in his yard. The year he planted it, the bush produced 17 flowers. Each year, the branches of the bush split, so the number of flowers doubles. The input is the year after planting, and the output is the number of flowers.*

f.

x	y
0	–7
2	–2
4	3
6	8
8	13

1-102.   Work with your team to create one new table and one new situation that display linear relationships. Be sure to **justify** how you can tell that your table and situation are linear.

1-103.   Without using a graph, decide whether the relationship shown in the table at right is linear. Write a clear summary statement **justifying** your ideas. Be prepared to share your ideas with the class.

x	y
1	0.5
4	–7
10	–22
15	–34.5

1-104.   LEARNING LOG

In your Learning Log, explain how you can recognize a linear relationship in a table or the description of a situation. Be sure to include examples. Title this entry "Recognizing Linear Relationships" and label it with today's date.

1-105.   Find the slope and intercepts of $3x + 4y = 12$. Sketch a graph.

1-106.   Write an equation for the line that passes through the points $(2, 0)$ and $(0, -3)$. Remember that drawing a diagram (in this case, drawing the graph) can be very helpful.

1-107.   Solve each equation below. Give solutions in both radical and decimal form.

a. $x^2 + 3x - 3 = 0$

b. $3x^2 - 7x = 12$

1-108.   Jason loves to download music. *Downloads R Us* sells songs only in packages of three, and it charges $2.00 for each package of three songs. Jason's favorite group just released their *Greatest Hits* CD, which has 17 songs on it. Jason wants to buy all 17 songs from *Downloads R Us*. How much should Jason expect to pay?

1-109.   Make a sketch of a graph showing the relationship between the number of people on your school's campus and the time of day.

1-110.   For each graph below, what are the domain and range?

a.    b.    c.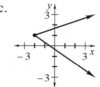

1-111.   Imagine that you add water to the beakers shown below (labeled A, B, and C). Sketch a graph for each beaker to show the relationship between the volume of water added and the height of the water in each beaker. Put all three graphs on one set of axes (you may want to use colored pencils to distinguish the graphs). What are the independent and dependent variables?

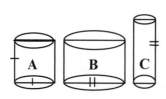   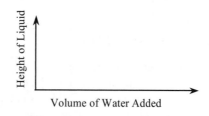

1.2.4 What can I learn about it?

Function Investigation Challenge

In this lesson, you will have a chance to show off your understanding of **investigation** as you work with a new function.

1-112. In this activity you will **investigate** the function $f(x) = \frac{5}{(x^2+1)} - 1$.

a. Take a moment to look over your Learning Log entry entitled "Function Investigation Questions." Are there any questions you should add to your list? Discuss this with your team and make any necessary additions to your Learning Log.

b. Now **investigate** $f(x)$ completely. Be sure to make clear summary statements that are **justified** using multiple representations.

1-113. Recently, Kalani and Lynette took a trip from Vacaville, California to Los Angeles. The graph at right represents their trip.

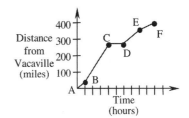

a. Explain what each line segment in the graph represents.

b. About how many miles is it from Vacaville to Los Angeles? How do you know?

c. Using the graph shown above, sketch a graph that would represent their *speed* while traveling. Take your time to think this through carefully and be sure to label the axes.

1-114. Solve each equation below for x.

a. $10 - 2(2x+1) = 4(x-2)$

b. $5 - (2x-3) = -8 + 2x$

1-115.   The right triangle shown at right has a height of 12 cm, and its area is 60 square cm. Find $m\angle B$ and the length of the hypotenuse.

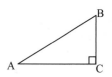

1-116.   The longer leg of a right triangle is three inches more than three times the length of the shorter leg. The area of the triangle is 84 square inches. Find the perimeter of the triangle.

1-117.   Uyregor has a collection of normal, fair dice. He takes one out to roll it.

   a.   What are all possible outcomes that can come up?

   b.   What is the probability that a 4 comes up?

   c.   What is the probability that the number that comes up is less than 5?

1-118.   Stacie says to Cory, *"Reach into this standard deck of playing cards and pull out a card at random. If it is the queen of hearts, I'll pay $5.00."* What is the probability that Cory gets Stacie's $5.00? What is the probability that Stacie keeps her $5.00? **Justify** your answers. (Note: A standard deck of playing cards contains 52 cards, each of which is unique.)

1-119.   Have you ever wondered why so many equations are written with the variables x and y? Suppose you are reaching into a bag that contains all the letters of the English alphabet, and you pull out one letter at random to use as a variable in equations. What is the probability that you pull out an x? If you got the x, now what is the probability that you pull out a y?

Chapter 1 Closure What have I learned?

Reflection and Synthesis

The activities below offer you a chance to reflect on what you have learned in this chapter. As you work, look for concepts that you feel very comfortable with, ideas that you would like to learn more about, and topics with which you need additional help. Look for connections between ideas as well as connections with material you learned previously.

①   TEAM BRAINSTORM

With your team, brainstorm a list for each of the following three categories. Be as detailed as you can. How long can you make your lists? Challenge yourselves. Be prepared to share your team's ideas with the class.

Topics: What have you studied in this chapter? What ideas and words were important in what you learned? Remember to be as detailed as you can.

Investigations: What did you do to **investigate** mathematical relationships? What questions did you ask yourself? List as many aspects of **investigations** as you can.

Connections: How are the topics, ideas, and words that you learned in previous courses connected to the new ideas in this chapter? Again, make your list as long as you can.

②   MAKING CONNECTIONS

Below is a list of the vocabulary used in this chapter. Make sure that you are familiar with all of these words and know what they mean. Refer to the glossary or index for any words that you do not yet understand.

dependent variable	domain	equation
function	**generalize**	graph
independent variable	input	**investigate**
linear	output	range
rule	x-intercept	$x \rightarrow y$ table
y-intercept		

Make a concept map showing all of the connections you can find among the key words and ideas listed above. To show a connection between two words, draw a line between them and explain the connection, as shown in the example below. A word can be connected to any other word as long as there is a **justified** connection. For each key word or idea, provide a sketch of an example.

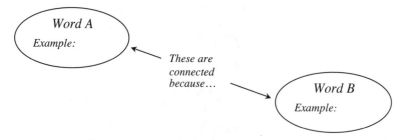

Your teacher may provide you with vocabulary cards to help you get started. If you use the cards to plan your concept map, be sure either to re-draw your concept map on your paper or to attach the vocabulary cards to a poster with all of the connections explained for others to see and understand.

While you are making your map, your team may think of related words or ideas that are not listed above. Be sure to include these ideas on your concept map.

③   GROWTH OVER TIME

This section gives you an opportunity to show growth in your understanding of key mathematical ideas over time as you complete this course. In this section you will complete a problem on its own sheet of paper and will keep it separate from your other work or put it into a portfolio. You will need to refer back to the problem later in the course.

On a separate sheet of paper, explain everything you know about $y = x^2 - 4$ and $y = \sqrt{x + 4}$.

④ SUMMARIZING MY UNDERSTANDING

This section gives you an opportunity to show what you know about certain math topics or ideas.

With your team, make a list of the **big ideas** of this chapter. Discuss the important ideas of the chapter and try to agree on a short list of no more than five big ideas. Be prepared to share your list in a whole class discussion. When the class has reached agreement on a list, continue with parts (a) and (b) below.

a. Write your own description of each big idea.

b. For each big idea, provide one or two representative example problems. Solve each problem completely, using multiple representations, if applicable.

Your teacher may give you a "GO" page to work on (or you can download this from www.cpm.org). "GO" stands for "Graphic Organizer," a tool you can use to organize your thoughts and communicate your ideas clearly.

⑤ WHAT HAVE I LEARNED?

This section will help you determine the types of problems with which you feel comfortable and the types of problems with which you need help. This section will appear at the end of every chapter to help you check your understanding. These problems are intended for you to complete independently and outside of class. Even if your teacher does not assign this section, it is a good idea to try these problems and find out for yourself what you know and what you need to work on.

Solve each problem as completely as you can. The table at the end of this closure section has answers to these problems. It also tells you where you can find additional help and practice with similar problems.

CL 1-120. Given the functions $f(x) = \sqrt{x+4}$ and $g(x) = x^2 - x$, find the value of each expression below.

a. $f(5)$ b. $g(-1)$

c. x if $f(x) = 10$ d. x if $g(x) = 6$

CL 1-121. Describe the domain and range for each function shown below.

a.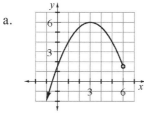

b.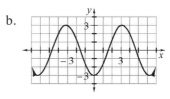

CL 1-122. For each pair of equations below, determine where the graphs intersect.

    a. $y = 3x + 15$

          $y = 3 - 3x$

    b. $y = x^2 - 3x - 8$

          $y = 2$

CL 1-123. Graph the function $f(x) = x^2 - 2x - 8$. Identify the domain and range, identify any special points, and describe any symmetry.

CL 1-124. Graph each equation below and find the x- and y-intercepts.

    a. $y = -\frac{3}{2}x + 8$

    b. $2x - 3y = -6$

CL 1-125. Find an equation for each line described below.

    a.   The line that passes through the point (2, 8) and has a slope of –5.

    b.   The line that passes through the points (–3, 4) and (5, –4).

    c.   The line that passes through the points (–2, 4) and (4, –5).

CL 1-126. Solve each equation below.

    a. $\frac{x+2}{5} = \frac{10-2x}{3}$ b. $\frac{3}{x} - 1 = 8$ c. $\frac{x}{2} + \frac{x}{3} = 7$

CL 1-127. Solve for y.

    a.

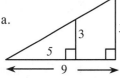

    b.

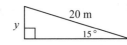

CL 1-128. Micah was given $200 for his birthday. Each week he spends $15 on comic books. In how many weeks will his birthday money be gone?

Create multiple representations ($x \rightarrow y$ table, graph, and equation) for the relationship between the weeks since Micah's birthday and how much money he has left. How does each representation show the solution to the problem?

CL 1-129. Check your answers using the table at the end of this section. Which problems do you feel confident about? Which problems were hard? Have you worked on problems like these in math classes you have taken before? Use the table to make a list of topics with which you need help and a list of topics you need to practice more.

This course focuses on five different **Ways of Thinking**: **justifying**, **generalizing**, **choosing a strategy**, **investigating**, and **reversing**. These are some of the ways in which you think while trying to make sense of a concept or attempting to solve a problem (even outside of math class). During this chapter, you have probably used each Way of Thinking multiple times without even realizing it!

This closure activity will focus on one of these Ways of Thinking: **investigating**. Read the description of this Way of Thinking at right.

Think about the **investigating** that you have done in this chapter. When have you tried something that you weren't specifically asked to do? What did you do when testing your idea did not work as you expected? You may want to flip through the chapter to refresh your memory about the problems that you have worked on. Discuss any of the **investigations** you have made with your team.

Once your discussion is complete, choose one problem you worked on in Chapter 1 in which you **investigated**.

a. Write down the problem and a description of how **investigation** helped you solve the problem or understand the mathematics involved.

b. Could you have **investigated** further? Write two new questions that you could have asked about the problem that may have furthered your **investigation** and helped you to learn more.

Investigating

When you have questions about an idea and design a process to find answers to those questions, you are **investigating**. **Investigating** helps you explore an idea in depth to understand it more thoroughly. Common thoughts you might have when you are **investigating** are: *"What relationships do I see?"* *"I wonder what would happen if I changed…"* *"Can I look at this differently…"* or *"What if I…"* This multi-step process includes asking questions and coming up with answers, summary statements, or more specific questions in response to the original questions you posed.

Answers and Support for Closure Activity #5
What Have I Learned?

Problem	Solutions				Need Help?	More Practice
CL 1-120.	a. 3		b. 2		Lesson 1.1.1	Problems 1-4, 1-5, 1-18, 1-22, and 1-36
	c. $x = 96$		d. $x = -2$ or 3			
CL 1-121.	a. Domain: $-\infty < x < 6$ Range: $-\infty < y \le 6$				Math Notes box in Lesson 1.1.3	Problems 1-21, 1-24, 1-25, 1-28, and 1-35
	b. Domain: all real numbers Range: $-3 \le y \le 3$					
CL 1-122.	a. $(-2, 9)$				Checkpoint 4	Problems 1-94 and 1-97
	b. $(5, 2), (-2, 2)$					

CL 1-123.

Math Notes box in Lesson 1.1.3

Problems 1-21, 1-46, 1-60, 1-81, 1-90, 1-96

Domain: all real numbers;

Range: $y \ge -9$

Intercepts: $(-2, 0), (4, 0),$ and $(0, -8)$

Vertex: $(1, -9)$

Symmetrical about the line $x = 1$

CL 1-124. a.

Math Notes box in Lesson 1.1.2

Problems 1-7, 1-67, 1-74, and 1-105

Intercepts: $(5\frac{1}{3}, 0)$ and $(0, 8)$

b.

Intercepts: $(-3, 0)$ and $(0, 2)$

Problem	Solutions	Need Help?	More Practice
CL 1-125.	a. $y = -5x + 18$ b. $y = -x + 1$ c. $y = -\frac{3}{2}x + 1$	Math Notes box in Lesson 1.1.2	Problem 1-106, Checkpoint 10
CL 1-126.	a. $\frac{44}{13}$ b. $\frac{1}{3}$ c. $\frac{42}{5}$	Checkpoint 14	Problems 1-53, 1-64, 1-65, 1-70, and 1-85
CL 1-127.	a. $\frac{27}{5}$ b. ≈ 5.18	Math Notes box in Lesson 1.2.1	Problems 1-40, 1-61, and 1-68
CL 1-128.	$y = 200 - 15x$, where y represents the total amount of money left and x represents the numbers of weeks that have passed	Lesson 1.1.2	Problems 1-13, 1-20, 1-25, 1-92, and 1-101

Week	$
0	200
1	185
2	170
3	155
4	140
5	125

SEQUENCES AND EQUIVALENCE

2

CHAPTER 2

Sequences and Equivalence

Chapter 2 provides you an opportunity to review and strengthen your algebra skills while you learn about arithmetic and geometric sequences. Early in the chapter, you will find yourself using familiar **strategies** such as looking for patterns, making tables, and guessing and checking to write algebraic rules describing sequences of numbers. Later in the chapter, you will develop shortcuts for writing rules for certain kinds of sequences.

One purpose of this course is to provide you with multiple opportunities to become comfortable representing real-life situations and relationships with variables and equations. Another purpose is to strengthen your algebraic manipulation skills. In the second section of this chapter, you will focus on rewriting expressions and solving equations.

Guiding Questions

Think about these questions throughout this chapter:

How can I represent it?

What are the connections?

How can I rewrite it?

What tools can I use?

In this chapter, you will learn how to:

➢ Understand and recognize growth by multiplication and growth by addition.

➢ Generate multiple representations of arithmetic and geometric sequences.

➢ Understand the connections between sequences and functions.

➢ Represent any term of a sequence with an algebraic expression.

➢ Solve equations by first rewriting them in more convenient forms.

Chapter Outline

Section 2.1 This section begins with lessons that ask you to describe the growth of a rabbit population and the decreasing rebound height of a bouncing ball. You will use tables, graphs, and equations to represent arithmetic and geometric sequences. You will also learn some of the specialized vocabulary used when discussing sequences.

Section 2.2 Here, you will look at the meaning of equivalence. You will develop algebraic **strategies** for rewriting expressions and equations, creating equivalent equations that you already have the tools to solve.

52

Algebra 2 Connections

2.1.1 How does the pattern grow?

. . . .

Representing Exponential Growth

In the last chapter, you began to describe families of functions using multiple representations (especially $x \to y$ tables, graphs, and equations). In this chapter, you will learn about a new family of functions and the type of growth it models.

2-1.   MULTIPLYING LIKE BUNNIES

In the book *Of Mice and Men* by John Steinbeck, two good friends named Lenny and George dream of raising rabbits and living off the land. What if their dream came true?

Suppose Lenny and George started with two rabbits that had two babies after one month, and suppose that every month thereafter, each pair of rabbits had two babies.

Your task: With your team, determine how many rabbits Lenny and George would have after one year. Represent this situation with a diagram, table, and rule. What patterns can you find and how can you **generalize** them?

Discussion Points

What **strategies** could help us keep track of the total number of rabbits?

What patterns can we see in the growth of the rabbit population?

How can we use those patterns to write an equation?

How can we predict the total number of rabbits after many months have passed?

2-2.   How can you determine the number of rabbits that will exist at the end of one year? Consider this as you answer the questions below.

    a.   Draw a diagram to represent how the total number of rabbits is growing each month. How many rabbits will Lenny and George have after three months?

    b.   As the number of rabbits becomes larger, a diagram becomes too cumbersome to be useful. A table might work better. Organize your information in a table showing the total number of rabbits for the first several months (at least 6 months). What patterns can you find in your table? Use those patterns to write a rule for the relationship between the total number of rabbits and the number of months that have passed since Lenny and George obtained the first pair of rabbits.

_____   *Further Guidance*   _____
section ends here.

2-3.   Lenny and George want to raise as many rabbits as possible, so they have a few options to consider. They could start with a larger number of rabbits, or they could raise a breed of rabbits that reproduces faster. How would each of these options change the pattern of growth you observed in the previous problem? Which situation would yield the largest rabbit population after one year?

    a.   To help answer these questions, model each case below with a table. Then use the patterns in each table to write a rule for each case.

        Case 2: Start with 10 rabbits; each pair has 2 babies per month.

        Case 3: Start with 2 rabbits; each pair has 4 babies per month.

        Case 4: Start with 2 rabbits; each pair has 6 babies per month.

    b.   Which case would give Lenny and George the most rabbits after one year? **Justify** your answer using a table or rule from part (a).

    c.   Now make up your own case, stating the initial number of rabbits and the number of babies each pair has per month. Organize your information in a table and write a rule from the pattern you observe in your table. Show how your table is connected to its equation using color-coding, arrows, and any other tools that help you show the connections.

Algebra 2 Connections

2-4.   A NEW FAMILY?

Is the data in "Multiplying Like Bunnies" linear, or is it an example of some other relationship?

a.   Look back at the $x \to y$ tables you created in problem 2-3. What do they all have in common?

b.   Graph all four of the equations from problems 2-1 and 2-3 on your graphing calculator. Adjust the viewing window so that all four graphs show up clearly. Then, on paper, sketch the graphs and label each graph with its equation. How would you describe the graphs?

c.   Now decide whether the data in the rabbit problem is linear. **Justify** your conclusion.

2-5.   LEARNING LOG

To represent the growth in number of rabbits in problems 2-1 and 2-3, you discovered a new family of functions that are not linear. Functions in this new family are called **exponential functions**. Throughout this chapter and the next, you will learn more about this special family of functions.

Write a Learning Log entry to record what you have learned so far about exponential functions. For example, what do their graphs look like? What patterns do you observe in their tables? Title this entry "Exponential Functions, Part 1" and include today's date.

METHODS AND MEANINGS

Solving Systems, Part I: Substitution

MATH NOTES

To solve a system of equations algebraically, it is helpful to reduce the system to a single equation with one variable. One way to do this is by **substitution**.

Consider the system at right.

$$10y - 3x = 14$$
$$2x + 4y = -4$$

First, look for the equation that is easiest to solve for x or y. In this case, the second equation will be solved for x. Be sure you understand each step in the solution shown at right.

$$2x + 4y = -4$$
$$2x = -4 - 4y$$
$$x = -2 - 2y$$

Now replace the x in the *other* equation with $(-2 - 2y)$. This is the **substitution** step. Notice that this creates a new equivalent equation that has only one variable.

$$10y - 3(-2 - 2y) = 14$$
$$10y + 6 + 6y = 14$$
$$16y + 6 = 14$$
$$16y = 8$$

Next, solve for y. Then find x by substituting the value of y (in this case, 0.5) into either original equation and solve for x.

$$y = 0.5$$

$$2x + 4(0.5) = -4$$
$$2x + 2 = -4$$

In this example, the solution is $x = -3$ and $y = 0.5$. This solution can also be written $(-3, 0.5)$.

$$2x = -6$$
$$x = -3$$

Note that you could have solved for x in the other equation or for y in the original equation, and then followed the same process.

2-6.   What if the data for Lenny and George (from problem 2-1) matched the data in each table below? Assuming that the growth of the rabbits multiplies as it did in problem 2-1, complete each of the following tables. Show your thinking or give a brief explanation of how you know what the missing entries are.

a.

Months	Rabbits
0	4
1	12
2	36
3	
4	

b.

Months	Rabbits
0	6
1	
2	24
3	
4	96

2-7.   Solve the following systems of equations algebraically. Then graph each system to confirm your solution. If you need help, refer to the Math Notes box in Lesson 2.1.1.

a. $x + y = 3$
      $x = 3y - 5$

b. $x - y = -5$
      $y = -2x - 4$

2-8.   For the function $f(x) = \frac{6}{2x-3}$, find the value of each expression below.

a. $f(1)$ b. $f(0)$ c. $f(-3)$ d. $f(1.5)$

e.   What value of x would make $f(x) = 4$?

2-9.   Benjamin is taking Algebra 1 and is stuck on the problem shown below. Examine his work so far and help him by showing and explaining the remaining steps.

Original problem: Simplify $(3a^2b)^3$.

He knows that $(3a^2b)^3 = (3a^2b)(3a^2b)(3a^2b)$. Now what?

2-10.   Simplify each expression below. Be sure to show your work. (Hint: Use your understanding of the meaning of exponents to expand each expression and then simplify.) Assume that the denominators in parts (b) and (c) are not equal to zero.

a. $(x^3)(x^2)$ b. $\frac{y^5}{y^2}$ c. $\frac{x^3}{x^7}$ d. $(x^2)^3$

2-11.   The equation of a line describes the relationship between the *x*- and *y*-coordinates of the points on the line.

    a.   Plot the points $(3, -1)$, $(3, 2)$, and $(3, 4)$ and draw the line that passes through them. State the coordinates of two more points on the line. Then answer this question: What will be true of the coordinates of any other point on this line? Now write an equation that says exactly the same thing. (Do not worry if it is very simple! If it accurately describes all the points on this line, it is correct.)

    b.   Plot the points $(5, -1)$, $(1, -1)$, and $(-3, -1)$. What is the equation of the line that goes through these points?

    c.   Choose any three points on the *y*-axis. What must be the equation of the line that goes through those points?

2-12.   Carmel wants to become a "Fraction Master." He has come to you for instruction.

    a.   Help Carmel by demonstrating and explaining every step necessary to simplify the problem at right.
$$\frac{2}{9} - \frac{1}{4}$$

    b.   *"Oh no!"* exclaimed Carmel. *"This one is hard!"* Show him every step he needs to simplify the problem at right. (Note that from this point on in the course, you may assume that all values of a variable that would make a denominator zero are excluded.)
$$\frac{3}{2x} + \frac{4}{xy}$$

2-13.   Jill is studying a strange bacterium. When she first looks at the bacteria, there are 1000 cells in her sample. The next day, there are 2000 cells. Intrigued, she comes back the next day to find that there are 4000 cells! Create multiple representations (table, graph, and rule) of the function. The inputs are the days that have passed after she first began to study the sample, and the outputs are the numbers of cells of bacteria.

2-14.   Write each expression below in a simpler form.

    a. $\dfrac{5^{723}}{5^{721}}$ b. $\dfrac{3^{300}}{3^{249}}$ c. $\dfrac{3.4^{1001}}{7.4^{997}}$ d. $\dfrac{(6^{54})^{11}}{(6^{49})^{10}}$

2-15.   Jackie and Alexandra were working on homework together when Jackie said, *"I got $x = 5$ as the solution, but it looks like you got something different. Which solution is right?"*

$$(x+4)^2 - 2x - 5 = (x-1)^2$$
$$x^2 + 16 - 2x - 5 = x^2 + 1$$
$$16 - 2x - 5 = 1$$
$$11 - 2x = 1$$
$$-2x = -10$$
$$x = 5$$

"I think you made a mistake," said Alexa. Did Jackie make a mistake? Help Jackie figure out whether she made a mistake and, if she did, explain her mistake and show her how to solve the equation correctly. Jackie's work is shown above right.

2-16.   Solve each of the following equations.

   a. $\frac{m}{6} = \frac{15}{18}$

   b. $\frac{\pi}{7} = \frac{a}{4}$

2-17.   Write the equation of each line described below.

   a.   A line with slope –2 and y-intercept 7.

   b.   A line with slope $-\frac{3}{2}$ and x-intercept $(4, 0)$.

2-18.   Perform each operation in part (a) through (d) below.

   a. $\frac{m}{4} + \frac{m}{3}$

   b. $\frac{x}{2} - \frac{x-1}{2}$

   c. $(\frac{8m^2}{x}) \cdot (\frac{y}{mx})$

   d. $(\frac{2}{3}) \div (\frac{5}{3})$

2-19.   The dartboard shown at right is in the shape of an equilateral triangle. It has a smaller equilateral triangle in the center, which was made by joining the midpoints of the three edges. If a dart hits the board at random, what is the probability that:

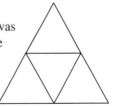

   a.   The dart hits the center triangle?

   b.   The dart misses the center triangle?

2.1.2 How high will it bounce?

Rebound Ratios

In this lesson, you will **investigate** the relationship between the height from which you drop a ball and the height to which it rebounds.

2-20. Many games depend on how a ball bounces. For example, if different basketballs rebounded differently, one basketball would bounce differently off of a backboard than another would, and this could cause basketball players to miss their shots. For this reason, manufacturers have to make balls' bounciness conform to specific standards.

Listed below are "bounciness" standards for different kinds of balls.

- Tennis balls: Must rebound approximately 111 cm when dropped from 200 cm.

- Soccer balls: Must rebound approximately 120 cm when dropped from 200 cm onto a steel plate.

- Basketballs: Must rebound approximately 53.5 inches when dropped from 72 inches onto a wooden floor.

- Squash balls: Must rebound approximately 29.5 inches when dropped from 100 inches onto a steel plate at 70° F.

Discuss with your team how you can measure a ball's bounciness. Which ball listed above is the bounciest? **Justify** your answer.

2-21.   THE BOUNCING BALL, Part One

How can you determine if a ball meets expected standards?

Your task: With your team, find the rebound ratio for a ball. Your teacher will provide you with a ball and a measuring device. You will be using the same ball again later, so make sure you can identify which ball your team is using. Before you start your experiment, discuss the following questions with your team.

What do we need to measure?

How should we organize our data?

How can we be confident that our data is accurate?

You should choose one person in your team to be the recorder, one to be the ball dropper, and two to be the spotters. When you are confident that you have a good plan, ask your teacher to come to your team and approve your plan.

2-22.   GENERALIZING YOUR DATA

Work with your team to **generalize** by considering parts (a) through (d) below.

a.   In problem 2-18, does the height from which the ball is dropped depend on the rebound height, or is it the other way around? With your team, decide which is the independent variable and which is the dependent variable?

b.   Graph your results on a full sheet of graph paper. What pattern or trend do you observe in the graph of your data? Do any of the models you have studied so far (linear or exponential functions) seem to fit? If so, which one? Does this make sense? Why or why not?

c.   Draw a line that best fits your data. Should this line go through the origin? Why or why not? **Justify** your answer in terms of what the origin represents in the context of this problem.

d.   Find an equation for your line.

2-23.   What is the rebound ratio for your team's ball? How is the rebound ratio reflected in the graph of your line of best fit? Where is it reflected in the rule for your data? Where is it reflected in your table?

METHODS AND MEANINGS

Continuous and Discrete Graphs

When the points on a graph are connected, and it *makes sense* to connect them, the graph is said to be **continuous**. If the graph is not continuous, and is just a sequence of separate points, the graph is called **discrete**. For example, the graph below left represents the cost of buying *x* shirts, and it is discrete because you can only buy whole numbers of shirts. The graph furthest right represents the cost of buying *x* gallons of gasoline, and it is continuous because you can buy any non-negative amount of gasoline.

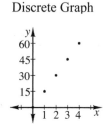

Discrete Graph

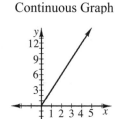

Continuous Graph

2-24. For each table below, find the missing entries and write a rule.

a.

Month (*x*)	0	1	2	3	4	5	6
Population (*y*)	2	8	32				

b.

Year (*x*)	0	1	2	3	4	5	6
Population (*y*)	5	6	7.2				

2-25. Solve each system of equations below. If you remember how to do these problems from another course, go ahead and solve them. If you are not sure how to start, refer to the Math Notes boxes in Lessons 2.1.1 and 2.1.3.

a. $y = 3x + 1$
   $x + 2y = -5$

b. $2x + 3y = 9$
   $x - 2y = 1$
   $-2y = -x + 1$
   $y = .5x + -.5$

Algebra 2 Connections

2-26.   Determine the domain and range of each of the following graphs.

a.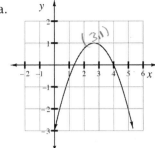

b.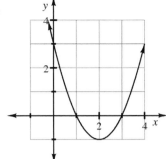

c.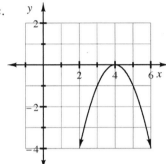

d.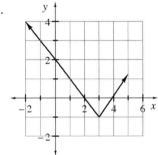

2-27.   Solve each of the following systems of equations algebraically. Then confirm your solutions by graphing.

a. $y = 4x + 5$
      $y = -2x - 13$

b. $2x + y = 9$
      $y = -x + 4$

2-28.   Factor each expression below completely.

a. $x^2 - 2x - 63$

b. $2x^2 - 5x - 12$

2-29.   Simplify each expression below.

a. $\dfrac{6x^2 y^3}{3xy}$

b. $(mn)^3$

c. $(3mn)^3$

d. $\dfrac{(3x^2)^2}{3x}$

2.1.3 What is the pattern?

The Bouncing Ball and Exponential Decay

In Lesson 2.1.2, you found that the relationship between the height from which a ball is dropped and its rebound height is determined by a constant. In this lesson, you will explore the mathematical relationship between how many times a ball has bounced and the height of each bounce.

2-30.   Consider the work you did in Lesson 2.1.2, in which you found a rebound ratio.

     a.   What was the rebound ratio for the ball your team used?

     b.   Did the height you dropped the ball from affect this ratio?

     c.   If you were to use the same ball again and drop it from *any* height, could you predict its rebound height? Explain.

2-31.   THE BOUNCING BALL, Part Two

Imagine that you drop the ball you used in problem 2-21 from a height of 200 cm, but this time you let it bounce repeatedly.

     a.   As a team, discuss this situation. Then sketch a picture showing what this situation would look like. Your sketch should show a minimum of 6 bounces after you release the ball.

     b.   Predict your ball's rebound height after each successive bounce if its starting height is 200 cm. Create a table with these predicted heights.

     c.   What are the independent and dependent variables in this situation?

     d.   Graph your predicted rebound heights.

     e.   Should the points on your graph be connected? How can you tell?

2-32.   THE BOUNCING BALL, Part Three

Now you will test the accuracy of the
predictions you made in problem 2-31.

Your task: Test your predictions by
collecting experimental data. Use the
same team roles as you used in
problem 2-21. Drop your ball, starting
from an initial height of 200 cm, and
record your data in a table. How do your
predicted and measured rebound heights
compare?

These suggestions will help you gather
accurate data:

- Have a spotter catch the ball just as it reaches the top of its first rebound and
  have the spotter "freeze" the ball in place.

- Record the first rebound height and then drop the ball again from that new
  height.

- Catch and "freeze" it again at the second rebound height.

- Repeat this process until you have collected at least six data points (or until the
  height of the bounce is so small that it is not reasonable to continue).

2-33.   What kind of equation is appropriate to model your data? That is, what family of
functions do you think would make the best fit? Discuss this with your team and be
ready to report and **justify** your choice. Then define variables and write an equation
that expresses the rebound height for each bounce.

2-34.   If you continued to let your ball bounce uninterrupted, how high would the ball be
after 12 bounces? Would the ball ever stop bouncing? Explain your answer in terms
of both your experimental data and your equation.

2-35.   Notice that your **investigations** of rebound patterns in Lesson 2.1.2 and 2.1.3 involved
both a linear and an exponential model. Look back over your work and discuss with
your team why each model was appropriate for its specific purpose. Be prepared to
share your ideas with the class.

METHODS AND MEANINGS

Solving Systems, Part 2: Elimination

In some situations, it may be easier to eliminate one of the variables by adding multiples of the two equations. This process is called **elimination**.

$$10y - 3x = 14$$
$$4y + 2x = -4$$

The first step is to rewrite the equations so that the x and y variables are lined up vertically. Next, decide what number to multiply each equation by in order to make the coefficients of either the x-terms or the y-terms add up to zero. Be sure that you can **justify** each step in the solution.

For example, consider the system above right.

You can eliminate the x-terms by multiplying the top equation by 2 and the bottom equation by 3 and then adding the equations, as shown below.

$$(10y - 3x = 14) \cdot 2 \rightarrow 20y - 6x = 28$$
$$(4y + 2x = -4) \cdot 3 \rightarrow \underline{12y + 6x = -12}$$

$$32y = 16 \quad \text{Adding resulting equations}$$
$$y = 0.5 \quad \text{Dividing}$$

Finally, substitute 0.5 for y in either original equation:

Thus, the solution to the original system is $(-3, 0.5)$.

$$10(0.5) - 3x = 14$$
$$5 - 3x = 14$$
$$-3x = 9$$
$$x = -3$$

2-36.   DeShawna and her team gathered data for their ball
        and recorded it in the table shown at right.

        a.   What is the rebound ratio for their ball?

        b.   Predict how high DeShawna's ball will
             rebound if it is dropped from 3 meters.

        c.   Suppose the ball is dropped and you notice that
             its rebound height is 60 cm. From what height
             was the ball dropped?

Drop Height	Rebound Height
150 cm	124 cm
70 cm	58.5 cm
120 cm	99.5 cm
100 cm	82.6 cm
110 cm	92 cm
40 cm	33.4 cm

        d.   Suppose the ball is dropped from a window 200 meters up the Empire State
             Building. What would you predict the rebound height to be after the first
             bounce?

        e.   How high would the ball rebound after the second bounce? After the third
             bounce?

2-37.   Look back at the data given in problem 2-20 that describes the rebound ratio for an
        approved tennis ball. Suppose you drop a tennis ball from an initial height of 10 feet.

        a.   How high would it rebound after the first bounce?

        b.   How high would it rebound after the 12th bounce?

        c.   How high would it rebound after the nth bounce?

2-38.   Solve the following systems of equations algebraically and then confirm your solutions
        by graphing.

        a. $y = 3x - 2$ b. $x = y - 4$
             $4x + 2y = 6$ $2x - y = -5$

2-39.   Lona received a stamp collection from her grandmother. The collection is in a leather book and currently has 120 stamps. Lona joined a stamp club, which sends her 12 new stamps each month. The stamp book holds a maximum of 500 stamps.

a.   Complete the table at right.

b.   How many stamps will Lona have after one year?

c.   Write an equation to represent the total number of stamps that Lona has in her collection after *n* months. Let the total be represented by $t(n)$.

Month	Stamps
0	120
1	132
2	
3	
4	
5	

d.   Solve your equation for *n* when $t(n) = 500$. Will Lona be able to fill her book exactly with no stamps remaining? How do you know? When will the book be filled?

2-40.   Determine whether the points $A(3, 5)$, $B(-2, 6)$, and $C(-5, 7)$ are on the same line. **Justify** your conclusion algebraically.

2-41.   Serena wanted to examine the graphs of the equations below on her graphing calculator. Rewrite each of the equations in **y-form** (when the equation is solved for *y*) so that she can enter them into the calculator.

a. $5 - (y - 2) = 3x$

b. $5(x + y) = -2$

2.1.4   How can I describe a sequence?

Generating and Investigating Sequences

In the bouncy-ball activity from Lesson 2.1.2, you used multiple representations (a table, a rule, and a graph) to represent a discrete situation involving a bouncing ball. Today you will learn about a new way to represent a discrete pattern, called a sequence.

2-42.   Samantha was thinking about George and Lenny and their rabbits. When she listed the number of rabbits George and Lenny could have each month, she ended up with the ordered list below, called a **sequence**.

$$2, 6, 18, 54, \ldots$$

She realized that she could represent this situation using a sequence-generating machine that would generate the number of rabbits each month by doing something to the previous month's number of rabbits. She tested her generator by putting in an **initial value** of 2 (the initial value is the first number of the sequence), and she recorded each output before putting it into the next machine. Below is the diagram she used to explain her idea to her teammates.

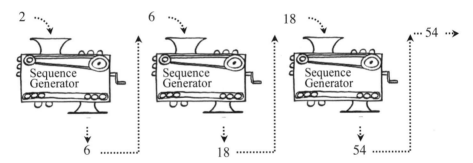

a.   What does Samantha's sequence generator seem to be doing to each input?

b.   What are the next two terms of Samantha's sequence? Show how you got your answer.

c.   Assuming that Samantha's sequence generator can work backwards, what term would come before the 2?

d.   Samantha decided to use the same sequence generator, but this time she started with an initial value of 5. What are the first four terms of this new sequence?

e.   Samantha's teammate, Alex, used the same sequence generator to create a new sequence. *"I won't tell you what I started with, but I will tell you that my third term is 171,"* he said. What was the initial value of Alex's sequence? **Justify** your answer.

2-43.   SEQUENCE FAMILIES

Samantha and her teacher have been busy creating new sequence generators and the sequences they produce. Below are the sequences Samantha and her teacher created.

a. $-4, -1, 2, 5, \dots$ b. $1.5, 3, 6, 12, \dots$

c. $0, 1, 4, 9, \dots$ d. $2, 3.5, 5, 6.5, \dots$

e. $1, 1, 2, 3, 5, 8, \dots$ f. $9, 7, 5, 3, \dots$

g. $48, 24, 12, \dots$ h. $27, 9, 3, 1, \dots$

i. $8, 2, 0, 2, 8, 18, \dots$ j. $\frac{5}{4}, \frac{5}{2}, 5, 10, \dots$

Your teacher will give your team a set of Lesson 2.1.4A Resource Pages with the above sequences on strips so that everyone in your team can see and work with them in the middle of your workspace.

Your task: Working together, organize the sequences into families of similar sequences. Your team will need to decide how many families to make, what common features make the sequences a family, and what characteristics make each family different from the others. Follow the directions below. As you work, use the following questions to help guide your team's discussion.

Discussion Points

How can we describe the pattern?

How does it grow?

What do they have in common?

(1)   As a team, sort the sequence strips into groups based on your first glance at the sequences. Remember that you can sort the sequences into more than two families. Which seem to behave similarly? Record your groupings and what they have in common before proceeding.

(2)   If one exists, find a sequence generator (growth pattern) for each sequence and write it on the strip. You can express the sequence generator either in symbols or in words. Also record the next three terms in each sequence on the strips. Do your sequence families still make sense? If so, what new information do you have about your sequence families? If not, reorganize the strips and explain how you decided to group them.

Problem continues on next page. →

2-43.   *Problem continued from previous page.*

(3)   Get a set of Lesson 2.1.4B Resource Pages for your team. Then record each
sequence in a table. Your table should compare the term number, n, to the value
of each term, $t(n)$. This means that your sequence itself is a list of *outputs* of the
relationship! Write rules for as many of the $n \rightarrow t(n)$ tables as you can. Attach
the table (and rule, if it exists) to the sequence strip it represents. Do your
sequence families still make sense? Record any new information or reorganize
your sequence families if necessary.

(4)   Now graph each sequence on a Lesson 2.1.4C Resource Page. Include as many
terms as will fit on the existing set of axes. Be sure to decide whether your
graphs should be discrete or continuous. Use color to show the growth between
the points on each graph. Attach the graph to the sequence strip it represents. Do
your sequence families still make sense? Record any new information and
reorganize your sequence families if necessary.

2-44.   Choose one of the families of sequences you created in problem 2-43. With your team,
write clear summary statements about this family of sequences. Be sure to use
multiple representations to **justify** each statement. Be prepared to share your summary
statements with the class.

2-45.   Some types of sequences have special names, as you will learn in parts (a) and (b)
below.

a.   When a sequence can be generated by *adding* a constant to each previous term, it
is called an **arithmetic sequence**. Which of your sequences from problem 2-43
fall into this family? Should you include the sequence labeled (f) in this family?
Why or why not?

b.   When a sequence can be generated by *multiplying* a constant times each previous
term, it is called a **geometric sequence**. Which of the sequences from
problem 2-43 are geometric? Should sequence (h) be in this group? Why or why
not?

2-46.   Find the slope of the line you would get if you graphed each sequence listed below and
connected the points.

a.   5, 8, 11, 14, …   b.   3, 9, 15, …

c.   26, 21, 16, …   d.   7, 8.5, 10, …

2-47.   Throughout this book, key problems have been selected as "checkpoints." Each checkpoint problem is marked with an icon like the one at left. These checkpoint problems are provided so that you can check to be sure you are building algebra skills at the expected level. When you have trouble with checkpoint problems, refer to the review materials and practice problems that are available in the "Checkpoint Materials" section at the back of your book.

This problem is a checkpoint for using the slope-intercept form of a line to solve a system of linear equations. It will be referred to as Checkpoint 1.

a.   Solve the system at right by graphing each line and finding the intersection. Then solve the system algebraically to check.

$$x + y = 5$$
$$y = \tfrac{1}{3}x + 1$$

b.   Check your answer to part (a) by referring to the Checkpoint 1 materials located at the back of your book.

If you needed help solving this problem correctly, then you need more practice using the slope-intercept form of a line to solve a system of equations. Review the Checkpoint 1 materials and try the practice problems. Also, consider getting help outside of class time. Be sure you know how to write the equations in y-form and know how use the slope and y-intercept to draw graphs efficiently. From this point on, you will be expected to graph and solve systems like this one quickly and easily.

2-48.   In the diagram at right, $\triangle ABC \sim \triangle AED$.

a.   Solve for x.

b.   Find the perimeter of $\triangle ADE$.

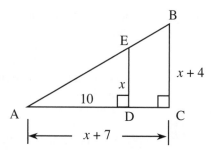

2-49.   Allie is making 8-dozen chocolate-chip muffins for the Food Fair at school. The recipe she is using makes 3-dozen muffins. If the original recipe calls for 16 ounces of chocolate chips, how many ounces of chocolate chips does she need for her new amount? (Allie buys her chocolate chips in bulk and can measure them to the nearest ounce.)

2-50.   Solve each equation below.

a. $2 - (x + 5) = 7 - 2x + 3$ b. $(2x + 4)(x - 3) = 0$

c. $\frac{5x+4}{3} = \frac{2x+1}{5}$

2-51.   The area of a square is 225 square centimeters.

a.   Make a diagram and list any steps that you would need to do to find the length of the diagonal.

b.   What is the length of its diagonal?

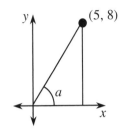

2-52.   Find $m\angle a$ in the diagram at right.

2-53.   Refer to sequences (c) and (i) in problem 2-43. How are these two sequences similar?

a.   Sequences such as those in parts (c) and (i) can be called **quadratic sequences**. Why do you think they are called this?

b.   The numbers in the sequence in part (e) from problem 2-43 are called **Fibonacci numbers**. They are named after an Italian mathematician who discovered the sequence while studying how fast rabbits could breed. What is different about this sequence than the other three you discovered?

2-54.   Chelsea dropped a bouncy ball off the roof while Nery recorded its rebound height. The table at right shows their data. Note that the 0 in the "Bounce" column represents the starting height.

Bounce	Rebound Height
0	800 cm
1	475 cm
2	290 cm
3	175 cm
4	100 cm
5	60 cm

a.   Find a function to model their data. To what family does the function belong? Explain how you know.

b.   Show the data as a sequence. Is the sequence arithmetic, geometric, quadratic, or something else? **Justify** your answer.

2-55.   For the function $f(x) = \sqrt{3x - 2}$, find the value of each expression below.

a. $f(1)$ b. $f(9)$ c. $f(4)$ d. $f(0)$

e.   What value of x makes $f(x) = 6$?

2-56.   When asked to solve $(x - 3)(x - 2) = 0$, Freddie gives the answer "$x = 2$." Samara says the answer is $x = 3$. Who is correct? **Justify** your answer.

2-57.   Find the x- and y-intercepts and the equation of the line of symmetry for the graph of $y = x^2 + 6x + 8$.

2-58.   Simplify each expression below.

a. $y + 0.03y$ b. $z - 0.2z$ c. $x + 0.002x$

2-59.   A dart hits each dartboard below at random. What is the probability that the dart will land in the darkly shaded area?

a.   b.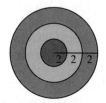

2-60.   A tank contains 8000 liters of water. Each day, half of the water in the tank is removed. How much water will be in the tank at the end of:

a.   The 4th day?   b.   The 8th day?

2.1.5 How do arithmetic sequences work?

Generalizing Arithmetic Sequences

In Lesson 2.1.4, you learned how to identify arithmetic and geometric sequences. Today you will solve problems involving arithmetic sequences. Use the questions below to help your team stay focused and start mathematical conversations.

What type of sequence is this? How do we know?

How can we find the rule?

Is there another way to see it?

2-61.   LEARNING THE LANGUAGE OF SEQUENCES

Sequences have their own notation and special words and phrases that help describe them, such as "term" and "term number." The questions below will help you learn more of this vocabulary and notation.

Consider the sequence $-9, -5, -1, 3, 7, \ldots$ as you complete parts (a) through (f) below.

a.   Is this sequence arithmetic, geometric, or neither? How can you tell?

b.   What are the initial value and the generator for the sequence?

c.   What is the difference between each term and the term before it? How is this related to the generator? For an arithmetic sequence, this is also known as the **common difference**.

d.   Find a rule (beginning $t(n) =$) for the nth term of this sequence. You can assume that for the first term of the sequence, $n = 0$.

e.   Graph your rule. Should the graph be continuous or discrete? Why?

f.   How is the **common difference** related to the graph of your rule? Why does this make sense?

2-62.   Consider the sequence $t(n) = -4, -1, 2, 5, \ldots$

      a.   Write a rule for $t(n)$.

      b.   Is it possible for $t(n)$ to equal 42? **Justify** your answer.

      c.   For the function $f(x) = 3x - 4$, is it possible for $f(x)$ to equal 42? Explain.

      d.   Explain the difference between $t(n)$ and $f(x)$ that makes your answers to parts (b) and (c) different.

2-63.   Trixie wants to create an especially tricky arithmetic sequence. She wants the 5th term of the sequence to equal 11 and the 50th term to equal 371. That is, she wants $t(4) = 11$ and $t(49) = 371$. Is it possible to create an arithmetic sequence to fit her information? If it is possible, find the rule, the initial value $t(0)$, and the common difference for the arithmetic sequence. If it is not possible, explain why not.

2-64.   Seven years ago, Kodi found a box of old baseball cards in the garage. Since then, he has added a consistent number of cards to the collection each year. He had 52 cards in the collection after 3 years and now has 108 cards.

      a.   How many cards were in the original box?

      b.   Kodi plans to keep the collection for a long time. How many cards will the collection contain 10 years from now?

      c.   Write a rule that determines the number of cards in the collection after n years. What does each number in your rule represent?

2-65.   Trixie now wants an arithmetic sequence with a common difference of −17 and a 16th term of 93. (In other words, $t(15) = 93$.) Is it possible to create an arithmetic sequence to fit her information? If it is possible, find the rule. If it is not possible, explain why not.

2-66.   Your favorite radio station, WCPM, is having a
         contest. The DJ poses a question to the listeners.
         If the caller answers correctly, he or she wins the
         prize money. If the caller answers incorrectly,
         $20 is added to the prize money and the next
         caller is eligible to win. The current question is
         difficult, and no one has won for two days.

    a.   Lucky you! Fourteen people already called
         in today with incorrect answers, so when
         you called (with the right answer, of course)
         you won $735! How much was the prize
         worth at the beginning of the day today?

    b.   Suppose the contest always starts
         with $100. How many people would have to guess incorrectly for the winner to
         get $1360?

2-67.   Trixie is at it again. This time she wants an arithmetic sequence that has a graph with a
         slope of 22. She also wants $t(8) = 164$ and the 13th term to have a value of 300. Is it
         possible to create an arithmetic sequence to fit her information? If it is possible, find
         the rule. If it is not possible, explain why not.

2-68.   Find the rule for each arithmetic sequence represented by the $n \rightarrow t(n)$ tables below.

    a.
n	$t(n)$
7	54
3	10
19	186
16	153
40	417

    b.
n	$t(n)$
100	10
20	100

2-69.   Trixie decided to extend her trickiness to tables. Each $n \rightarrow t(n)$ table below represents
         an arithmetic sequence. Find expressions for the missing terms and write a rule.

    a.
n	$t(n)$
0	$t(0)$
1	7
2	
3	
4	

    b.
n	$t(n)$
0	
1	p
2	f

2-70.   Trixie exclaimed, *"Hey! Arithmetic sequences are just another name for linear
         functions."* What do you think? **Justify** your idea based on multiple representations.

2-71.   Determine whether 447 is a term of each sequence below. If so, which term is it?

    a. $t(n) = 5n - 3$ b. $t(n) = 24 - 5n$

    c. $t(n) = -6 + 3(n - 1)$ d. $t(n) = 14 - 3n$

    e. $t(n) = -8 - 7(n - 1)$

2-72.   Choose one of the sequences in problem 2-71 for which you determined that 447 is *not* a term. Write a clear explanation (that an Algebra 1 student would be able to understand) describing how you can be sure that 447 is not a term of the sequence.

2-73.   Find the common difference for each sequence listed below. Write an expression for the nth term in each sequence below, keeping in mind that the first term of each sequence is $t(0)$.

    a.   4, 7, 10, 13, ...   b.   3, 8, 13, ...

    c.   24, 19, 14, ...   d.   7, 9.5, 12, ...

2-74.   Great Amusements Park has been raising its ticket prices every year, as shown in the table at right.

Year	Price
0	$50
1	$55
2	$60.50
3	$66.55

    a.   What will the price of admission be in year 6?

    b.   Describe how the ticket prices are growing.

2-75.   Solve the system at right for m and b.

$$1239 = 94m + b$$
$$810 = 61m + b$$

2-76.   Multiply each expression below.

    a. $(x + 2)(x - 7)$ b. $(3m + 7)(2m - 1)$

    c. $(x - 3)^2$ d. $(2y + 3)(2y - 3)$

2-77.   Simplify each expression.

    a. $(3x)^2$ b. $2(3x)^2$ c. $\dfrac{2(3x)^2}{3x^3}$ d. $\dfrac{2(3x)^2}{(3x)^3}$

2.1.6 How can I use a multiplier?

Using Multipliers to Solve Problems

In the past few lessons, you have **investigated** sequences that grow by adding (arithmetic) and sequences that grow by multiplying (geometric). In today's lesson, you will learn more about growth by multiplication as you use your understanding of geometric sequences and multipliers to solve problems. As you work, use the following questions to move your team's discussion forward:

What type of sequence is this? How do we know?

How can we describe the growth?

How can we be sure that our multiplier is correct?

2-78. Thanks to the millions of teens around the world seeking to be just like their math teachers, industry analysts predict that sales of the new portable MPG (Math Problem Generator) called the πPod will skyrocket!

> **πPODS SWEEP THE NATION**
> *Millions demand one!*
>
> (API) – Teenagers and Hollywood celebrities flocked to an exclusive shop in Beverly Hills, California yesterday, clamoring for the new πPod. The store will have 100 to sell the first week and expects to receive and sell an average of 15% more per week after that.
>
> "I plan to stand in line all night!" said Nelly Hillman. "As soon as I own one, I'll be cooler than everyone else."
>
> Across the globe, millions of fans

a. If sales of πPods continue to increase as described in the article at right, how many πPods will be sold at the store in the 4th week after their release?

b. How many πPods will be sold at the store in the 10th week after their release?

c. If you were to write the number of πPods sold each week as a sequence, would your sequence be arithmetic, geometric, or something else? **Justify** your answer.

d. Write an equation for the number of πPods sold during the nth week, assuming the rate of increase continues. Confirm that your equation is correct by testing it using your results from parts (a) and (b) above.

2-79.   The iNod, a new rival to the πPod, is about to be introduced. It is cheaper than the πPod, so more are expected to sell. The manufacturer plans to sell 10,000 in the first week and expects sales to increase by 7% each week.

   a.   Assuming that the manufacturer's predictions are correct, write an equation for the number of iNods sold during the nth week.

   b.   What if the expected weekly sales increase were 17% instead of 7%? Now what would the equation be?

   c.   Oh no! Thanks to the lower price, 10,000 iNods were sold in the first week, but after that, weekly sales actually decreased by 3%. Find the equation that fits the product's actual weekly sales.

   d.   According to your model, how many weeks will it take for the weekly sales to drop to only one iNod per week?

2-80.   In a geometric sequence, the generator is the number that one term is multiplied by to generate the next term. Another name for this number is the **multiplier**.

   a.   Look back at your work for problem 2-79. What is the multiplier for parts (a), (b), and (c)?

   b.   What is the multiplier for the sequence 8, 8, 8, 8, … ?

   c.   Explain what happens to the terms of the sequence when the multiplier is less than 1, but greater than zero. What happens when the multiplier is greater than 1? Add this description to your Learning Log. Title this entry "Multipliers" and add today's date.

2-81.   Write an equation for each table below.

a.

n	$t(n)$
0	1600
1	2000
2	2500
3	3125
4	3906.25

b.

n	$t(n)$
0	3906.25
1	3125
2	2500
3	2000
4	1600

c.

n	$t(n)$
0	50
1	72
2	103.68
3	149.2992

d.

n	$t(n)$
0	
1	50
2	
3	72
4	
5	103.68
6	
7	149.2992

e.   How are the multipliers for (a) and (b) related, and why?

f.   What **strategies** did you use to find the rule for part (d)?

g.   In part (d), why is term 2 *not* 61?

2-82.   PERCENTS AS MULTIPLIERS

What a deal! Just deShirts is having a 20%-off sale. Trixie rushes to the store and buys 14 shirts. When the clerk rings up her purchases, Trixie sees that the clerk has added the 5% sales tax first, before taking the discount. She wonders whether she got a good deal at the store's expense or whether she should complain to the manager about being ripped off. Without making any calculations, take a guess. Is Trixie getting a good deal? The next few problems will help you figure it out for sure.

2-83.   Karen works for a department store and receives a 20% discount on any purchases that she makes. The department store is having a clearance sale, and every item will be marked 30% off the regular price. Karen has decided to buy the $100 dress she's been wanting. When she includes her employee discount with the sale discount, what is the total discount she will receive? Does it matter what discount she takes first? Use the questions below to help you answer this question.

a.   Use the grids like the ones below to picture another way to think about this situation. Using graph paper, create two 10-by-10 grids (as shown below) to represent the $100 price of the dress.

CASE 1: 20% discount first   CASE 2: 30% discount first

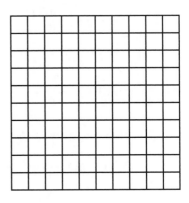

b.   Use the first grid to represent the 20% discount followed by the 30% discount (Case 1). Use one color to shade the number of squares that represent the first 20% discount. For whatever is left (unshaded), find the 30% discount and use another color to shade the corresponding number of squares to represent this second discount. Then repeat the process (using the other grid) for the discounts in **reverse** order (Case 2).

c.   How many squares remain after the first discount in Case 1? In Case 2?

d.   How many squares remain after the second discount in Case 1? In Case 2?

e.   Explain why these results make sense.

2-84.   Suppose that Trixie's shirts cost x dollars in problem 2-82.

    a.   If x represents the cost, how could you represent the tax? How could you represent the cost plus the tax?

    b.   How could you represent the discount? How could you represent the cost of the shirt after the discount?

    c.   Did Trixie get the better deal? **Justify** your reasoning.

2-85.   Remember the "Multiplying Like Bunnies" problem at the beginning of this chapter? Your team found the equation $y = 2 \cdot 2^x$ to represent the number of rabbits, y, after x months.

    a.   Lenny and George now have over 30 million rabbits. How many months have passed?

    b.   With 30 million rabbits, the bunny farm is getting overcrowded and some of the rabbits are dying from a contagious disease. The rabbits have stopped reproducing, and the disease is reducing the total rabbit population at a rate of about 30% each month. If this continues, then in how many months will the population drop below 100 rabbits?

METHODS AND MEANINGS

Arithmetic and Geometric Sequences

MATH NOTES

An **arithmetic sequence** is a sequence with an addition (or subtraction) generator. The number added to each term to get the next term is called the **common difference**.

A **geometric sequence** is a sequence with a multiplication (or division) generator. The number multiplied by each term to get the next term is called the **common ratio** or the **multiplier**.

2-86.   Convert each percent increase or decrease into a multiplier.

    a.   3% increase   b.   25% decrease

    c.   13% decrease   d.   2.08% increase

2-87.   Mr. C is such a mean teacher! The next time Mathias gets in trouble, Mr. C has designed a special detention for him. Mathias will have to go out into the hall and stand exactly 100 meters away from the exit door and pause for a minute. Then he is allowed to walk exactly halfway to the door and pause for another minute. Then he can again walk exactly half the remaining distance to the door and pause again, and so on. Mr. C says that when Mathias reaches the door he can leave, *unless* he breaks the rules and goes more than halfway, even by a tiny amount. When can Mathias leave? Prove your answer using multiple representations.

2-88.   Simplify each expression.

    a. $(2m^3)(4m^2)$ b. $\dfrac{6y^5}{3y^2}$

    c. $\dfrac{-4y^2}{6y^7}$ d. $(-2x^2)^3$

2-89.   *Without a calculator*, perform each operation below.

    a. $\frac{2}{3}+\frac{1}{4}$ b. $\frac{2}{3}+\frac{x}{4}$

    c. $\frac{2}{3}+\frac{1}{x}$ d. $\frac{2}{y}+\frac{3}{x}$

2-90.   Factor each expression below.

    a. $3y^2+6y$ b. w^2-5w+6

    c. x^2-4 d. $9x^2-4$

2-91.   Solve the system of equations at right.

$$y=-x-2$$
$$5x-3y=22$$

2.1.7 Is it a function?

Comparing Sequences and Functions

Throughout this chapter, you have been learning about sequences. In Chapter 1, you started to learn about functions. But what is the difference? In this lesson, you will compare and contrast sequences with functions. By the end of the lesson, you will be able to answer these questions:

Is a sequence different from a function?

What is the difference between a sequence $t(n)$ and the function $f(x)$ with the same rule?

2-92.   Consider sequence $t(n)$ below.

$$-5, -1, 3, 7, \ldots$$

  a. Create multiple representations of the sequence $t(n)$.

  b. Is it possible for the equation representing $t(n)$ to equal 400? **Justify** your answer.

  c. Create multiple representations of the function $f(x) = 4x - 5$. How are $f(x)$ and $t(n)$ different? How can you show their differences in each of the representations?

  d. For the function $f(x) = 4x - 5$, is it possible for $f(x)$ to equal 400? Explain.

2-93.   Let us consider the difference between $t(n) = 2 \cdot 3^n$ and $f(x) = 2 \cdot 3^x$.

  a. Is it possible for $t(n)$ to equal 1400? If so, find the value of n that makes $t(n) = 1400$. If not, **justify** why not.

  b. Is it possible for $f(x)$ to equal 1400? If so, find the value of x that makes $f(x) = 1400$. Be prepared to share your solving **strategy** with the class.

  c. How are the two functions similar? How are they different?

2-94.   LEARNING LOG

  Is a sequence a function? **Justify** your answer completely. If so, what makes it different from the functions that are usually written in the form $f(x) = $ _____ ? If not, why not? Be prepared to share your ideas with the class. After a class discussion about these questions, answer the questions in your Learning Log. Title this entry "Sequences vs. Functions" and label it with today's date.

2-95.   Janine was working on her homework but lost part of it. She knew that one output of $p(r) = 2 \cdot 5^r$ is 78,000, but she could not remember if $p(r)$ is a sequence or if it's a regular function. With your team, help her figure it out. Be sure to **justify** your decision.

2-96.   Solve each of the following equations for x, accurate to the nearest 0.01.

   a. $200(0.5)^x = 3.125$ b. $318 = 6 \cdot 3^x$

2-97.   Khalil is working with a geometric sequence. He knows that $t(0) = 3$ and that the sum of the first three terms ($t(0)$, $t(1)$, and $t(2)$) is 63. Help him figure out the sequence. Be prepared to share your **strategies** with the class.

METHODS AND **M**EANINGS

Exponential Functions and Multipliers

MATH NOTES

An **exponential** function has the general form $y = km^x$, where k is the **initial value** and $m > 0$ is the **multiplier**. The graph of an exponential function is **continuous**. Be careful: The independent variable x has to be in the exponent. For example, $y = x^2$ is *not* an exponential equation, even though it has an exponent.

The number by which you multiply a quantity to increase or decrease it by a given percentage is called the **multiplier** for that percentage. For example, the multiplier for an increase of 7% is 1.07. The multiplier for a decrease of 7% is 0.93.

2-98.   Is it possible for the sequence $t(n) = 5 \cdot 2^n$ to have a term with the value of 200? If so, which term is it? If not, **justify** why not.

2-99.   Is it possible for the function $f(x) = 5 \cdot 2^x$ to have an output of 200? If so, what input gives this output? If not, **justify** why not.

2-100.   Consider the following sequences as you complete parts (a) through (c) below.

Sequence 1	**Sequence 2**	**Sequence 3**
2, 6, ...	24, 12, ...	1, 5, ...

  a.   Assuming that the sequences above are arithmetic with $t(0)$ as the first term, find the next four terms for each sequence. For each sequence, write an explanation of what you did to get the next term and write a formula for $t(n)$.

  b.   Would your terms be different if the sequences were geometric? Find the next four terms for each sequence if they are geometric. For each sequence, write an explanation of what you did to get the next term.

  c.   Create a totally different type of sequence for each pair of values shown above, based on your own rule. Write your rule clearly (using words or algebra) so that someone else will be able to find the next three terms that you want.

2-101.   This problem is a checkpoint for solving systems of linear equations in two variables. It will be referred to as Checkpoint 2.

  a.   Solve the system of linear equations at right.

$$5x - 4y = 7$$
$$6x + 2y = 22$$

  b.   Check your answer to part (a) by referring to the Checkpoint 2 materials located at the back of your book.

  If you needed help solving this system correctly, then you need more practice solving systems of equations in two variables. Review the Checkpoint 2 materials and try the practice problems. Also, consider getting help outside of class time. From this point on, you will be expected to solve systems like this one quickly and easily.

2-102.   For the function $g(x) = x^3 + x^2 - 6x$, find the value of each expression below.

    a. $g(1)$ b. $g(-1)$ c. $g(-2)$ d. $g(10)$

    e.   Find at least one value of x for which $g(x) = 0$?

    f.   If $f(x) = x^2 - x + 3$, find $g(x) - f(x)$.

2-103.   Write equations to solve each of the following problems.

    a.   When the Gleo Retro (a trendy commuter car) is brand new, it costs $23,500. Each year it loses 15% of its value. What will the car be worth when it is 15 years old?

    b.   Each year the population of Algeland increases by 12%. The population is currently 14,365,112. What will the population be 20 years from now?

2-104.   An arithmetic sequence has $t(8) = 1056$ and $t(13) = 116$. What is $t(5)$?

2-105.   Describe the domain of each function or sequence below.

    a.   The function $f(x) = 3x - 5$.

    b.   The sequence $t(n) = 3n - 5$.

    c.   The function $f(x) = \frac{5}{x}$.

    d.   The sequence $t(n) = \frac{5}{n}$.

2.1.8 What is the rule?

Sequences that Begin with $n = 1$

In this lesson, you will continue to develop your understanding of sequences as you learn to write rules for sequences that begin with terms that are different from the initial value, or the 0th term.

2-106. Seven different sequences are represented below. Work with your team to find a possible rule for each sequence.

a.

n	$t(n)$
1	14 ⟍₋₁₂
2	2
3	−10 ⟍₋₁₂

b.

n	$t(n)$
1	6 ⟍ ₁₂
2	18 ⟍
3	54

c.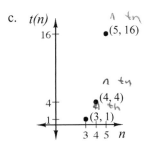

d. $t(n) = $ number of tiles

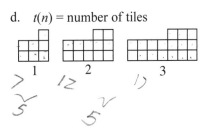

e. $t(n) = $ number of tiles

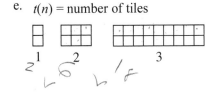

f.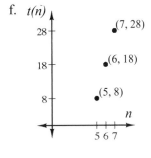

g.

n	$t(n)$
1	17 ⟍₋₅
2	12
3	7 ⟍₋₅

2-107.   Antonio was doing SAT study problems from his review book, but he got stuck. Below is the problem he had questions about.

> 18. Consider the following arithmetic sequence:
>
> $$4, 10, 16, 22, \dots$$
>
> a. Find the rule for the sequence.
>
> b. What would be the value of the 10th term in the sequence?

a.   Antonio likes to find sequence rules by first organizing the sequence into an $n \rightarrow t(n)$ table. Copy and complete his table for the sequence above. Show how to find the rule for the sequence.

n	$t(n)$

b.   Antonio found this rule: $t(n) = 6n + 4$. He used it to determine that $t(10) = 64$. Do you agree?

c.   Wait a minute! When Antonio looked in the back of his review book to check his answers, he saw that both of his answers were *different* than the book's. The book said the rule was $t(n) = 6n - 2$ and that $t(10) = 58$. Why do Antonio and the review book disagree?

2-108.   Antonio's answers disagree with the review book because he and the book made different assumptions. Study the two tables and notes below.

Antonio

	n	$t(n)$
Initial value →	0	4
	1	10
Fourth term	2	16
= $t(3)$ →	3	22
	n	$t(n) = 6n + 4$

Review Book

	n	$t(n)$
First term →	1	4
	2	10
Fourth term	3	16
= $t(4)$ →	4	22
	n	$t(n) = 6n - 2$

a.   With your team, discuss the similarities and differences between the two methods. Be ready to share the advantages and disadvantages of each. Which do you prefer?

Problem continues on next page. →

2-108.   *Problem continued from previous page.*

    b.   Although you might prefer to label sequences starting with term number zero for ease in developing an expression, in fact, the standard way to number sequences is to have the initial value be term number one. With your team, show and explain how to find the rule for an arithmetic sequence when the first term is labeled term one instead of zero. Make up your own example to help you explain. If necessary, look back at your work for problem 2-95.

    c.   Now work with your team to show and explain how to find the rule for a geometric sequence if the first term is labeled term one. Make up your own example to help you explain. Look back at your work for problem 2-95 if necessary.

2-109.   What if you do not know the first term? What **strategies** can help you find rules for these sequences? Use your strategies to find a rule for each sequence.

    a.

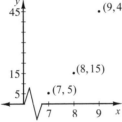

    b.

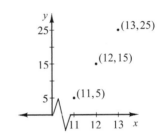

    c.   10, 16, 25.6, ...

    d.

Year	Cost
2000	$100,000
2001	$102,000
2002	$104,000

METHODS AND MEANINGS

MATH NOTES

Sequences

When a **sequence** is written as a list of numbers, the **initial term** is labeled **term number one**, the first term in the sequence. For example, in the sequence below, 3 is term number one, as shown in the $n \rightarrow t(n)$ table that follows.

$$3, 8, 13, 18, 23, 28, \ldots$$

This sequence can be represented by the table at the right.

n	1	2	3	4	5	6
$t(n)$	3	8	13	18	23	28

A sequence can also be defined as a function with its domain being the set of positive integers or counting numbers (1, 2, 3, ...). The variable n is often used to denote the term number (starting with 1), and the corresponding term can be denoted $t(n)$. Note that with this understanding, the rule for the sequence above would be $t(n) = 5n - 2$.

Review & Preview

2-110.   Toss three coins in the air. Make a list of all possible outcomes and find the probability that:

a.   All three coins land "heads" up.

b.   Two of the coins land "tails" up.

2-111.   Kiah and Leah are working on homework problems that involve arithmetic sequences. Kiah wrote down (2, 4) and (3, 5) from one sequence, and Leah had (3, 2) and (0, 3) for a different sequence. Find a rule for each sequence.

2-112. Find a rule for each sequence.

a. $t(n)$=number of tiles

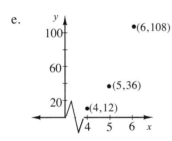

b.

n	$t(n)$
1	7
2	4
3	1

c.

n	$t(n)$
5	−20
6	−10
7	−5

d.

Year	Cost
2	$2000
3	$6000
4	$18000

e.

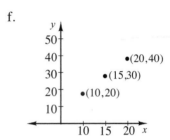

f.

2-113. The right triangle shown below has a height of 8 cm and an area of 60 square cm. Complete parts (a) and (b) below, referring to the Math Notes box in Lesson 1.2.1 for further guidance, if necessary.

a.   Find the measure of $\angle A$ to the nearest tenth.

b.   Find the perimeter of the triangle.

2-114. Find the value of x in the triangle at right. If you need help getting started, refer to the Math Notes box in Lesson 1.2.1.

2-115. Simplify each expression below.

a. $x(x+2)$

b. $\frac{1}{4}(2x^2y)^3$

c. $6(\frac{5b^3}{2c})^3$

d. $5(x^2+2x+1)-3(2x^2-3x+1)$

2-116.   Noah's bowling scores for his last 10 games were 147, 150, 190, 105, 97, 140, 179, 158, 165, and 151. Calculate the mean, median, and mode for Noah's scores. Remember the mean is what people call the average, the median is the middle value (or, if there is an even number of values, it is the number halfway between the two middle values), and the mode is the value that occurs most often.

97, 105, 140, 147, 150, 151, 158, 165, 179

2-117.   Examine the diagram at right. Complete the congruence statement $\triangle MAT \cong \triangle$ ____ and **justify** your answer.

2.2.1   Are they equivalent?

Equivalent Expressions

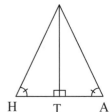

In Chapter 1, you looked at ways to organize your algebraic thinking using multiple representations. In the first part of this chapter, you used multiple representations to analyze arithmetic and geometric sequences. In this section, you will focus on equations and expressions while experimenting with equivalent expressions and rewriting equations to solve them more easily.

2-118.   Kharim is designing a tile border to go around his new square swimming pool. He is not yet sure how big his pool will be, so he is calling the number of tiles that will fit on each side x, as shown in the diagram at right.

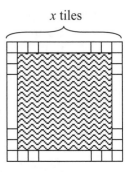

x tiles

a.   How can you write an algebraic expression to represent the total number of tiles Kharim will need for his border? Is there more than one expression you could write? With your team, find as many different expressions as you can to represent the total number of tiles Kharim will need for the border of his pool. Be prepared to share your **strategies** with the class.

b.   Find a way to demonstrate algebraically that all of your expressions are **equivalent**, that is, that they have the same value.

c.   Explain how you used the Distributive, Associative, and Commutative Properties in part (b).

2-119. Jill and Jerrell were looking back at their work on problem 1-54 ("Analyzing Data from a Geometric Relationship") in Lesson 1.2.1. They had come up with two different expressions for the volume of a paper box made from cutting out squares of dimensions x centimeters by x centimeters. Jill's expression was $(15 - 2x)(20 - 2x)x$, and Jerrell's expression was $4x^3 - 70x^2 + 300x$.

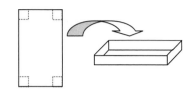

a. Are Jill's and Jerrell's expressions equivalent? **Justify** your answer.

b. If you have not done so already, find an algebraic method to decide whether their expressions are equivalent. What properties did you use? Be ready to share your **strategy**.

c. Jeremy, who was also in their team, joined in on their conversation. He had yet another expression: $(15 - 2x)(10 - x)2x$. Use a **strategy** from part (b) to decide whether his expression is equivalent to Jill's and/or Jerrell's. Be prepared to share your ideas with the class.

d. Would Jeremy's expression represent the dimensions of the same paper box as Jill's and Jerrell's? Explain.

2-120. For each of the following expressions, find at least three equivalent expressions. Be sure to **justify** how you know they are equivalent.

a. $(x + 3)^2 - 4$

b. $(2a^2b^3)^3$

c. $m^2n^5 \cdot mn^4$

d. $(\frac{3p^2q}{q^3})^2$

2-121. LEARNING LOG

What does it mean for two expressions to be equivalent? How can you tell if two expressions are equivalent? Answer these questions in your Learning Log. Be sure to include examples to illustrate your ideas. Title this entry "Equivalent Expressions" and label it with today's date.

2-122. For each of the following expressions, find at least three equivalent expressions. Which do you consider to be the simplest?

a. $(2x-3)^2 + 5$

b. $(\frac{3x^2y}{x^3})^4$

2-123. Match the expressions on the left with their equivalent expressions on the right. Assume that all variables represent positive values. Be sure to **justify** how you know each pair is equivalent.

a. $\sqrt{4x^2y^4}$ 1. $2x\sqrt{y}$

b. $\sqrt{8x^2y}$ 2. $2y\sqrt{2x}$

c. $\sqrt{4x^2y}$ 3. $2xy^2$

d. $\sqrt{16xy^2}$ 4. $2x\sqrt{2y}$

e. $\sqrt{8xy^2}$ 5. $4y\sqrt{x}$

2-124. Donnie and Dylan were both working on simplifying the expression at right. The first step of each of their work is shown below. $(\frac{2x^5y^4}{8xy^3})^3$

Donnie: $\frac{8x^{15}y^{12}}{512x^3y^9}$ Dylan: $(\frac{x^4y}{4})^3$

Each of them is convinced that he has started the problem correctly. Has either of them made an error? If so, explain the error completely. If not, explain how they can both be correct and verify that they will get the same, correct solution. Which student's method do you prefer? Why?

2-125.   While Jenna was solving the equation $150x + 300 = 600$, she wondered if she could first change the equation to $x + 2 = 4$. What do you think?

    a.   Solve both equations and verify that they have the same solution.

    b.   What did Jenna do to the equation $150x + 300 = 600$ to change it to $x + 2 = 4$?

    c.   In the same way, rewrite $60t - 120 = 300$.

2-126.   Solve this system for m and b: $342 = 23m + b$
$$147 = 10m + b$$

2-127.   Tanika made this sequence of triangles:

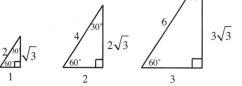

    a.   If the pattern continues, what do you think the next two triangles in the sequence would be?

    b.   Write a sentence to explain how to find the long leg and hypotenuse if you know the short leg (i.e., if the base is n units long).

2-128.   Consider the sequence $3, 9, \ldots$

    a.   Assuming that the sequence is arithmetic with $t(1)$ as the first term, find the next four terms of the sequence and then write a rule for $t(n)$.

    b.   Assuming that the sequence is geometric with $t(1)$ as the first term, find the next four terms of the sequence and then write a rule for $t(n)$.

    c.   Create a sequence that begins with 3 that is neither arithmetic nor geometric. For your sequence, write the next four terms and, if you can, write a rule for $t(n)$.

2-129.   Classify the triangle with vertices $A(3, 2)$, $B(-2, 0)$, and $C(-1, 4)$ by finding the length of each side. Be sure to consider all possible triangle types. Include sufficient evidence to support your conclusion.

2.2.2 Are they equivalent?

Area Models and Equivalent Expressions

In this lesson, you will continue to think about equivalent expressions. You will use an area model to demonstrate that two expressions are equivalent and to find new ways to write expressions. As you work with your team, use the following questions to help focus your discussion.

How can we be sure they are equivalent?

How would this look in a diagram?

Why is this representation convincing?

2-130. Jonah and Graham are working together. Jonah claims that $(x+y)^2 = x^2 + y^2$. Graham is sure Jonah is wrong, but he cannot figure out how to prove it. Help Graham find as many ways as possible to convince Jonah that he is incorrect. How can he rewrite $(x+y)^2$ correctly?

2-131. How can an area model help relate the expressions $(2x-3)(3x+1)$ and $6x^2 - 7x - 3$?

a. Copy the area diagram at right onto your own paper. With your team, discuss how it can be used to show that these expressions are equivalent.

	$2x$	-3
$3x$	$6x^2$	$-9x$
$+1$	$2x$	-3

b. Use an area model to find an expression equivalent to $(5k-3)(2k-1)$.

c. Use an area model to find an expression equivalent to $x^2 - 3x - 4$.

d. How does the area model help use the distributive property?

2-132. Use an area model that shows an equivalent expression for each of the following expressions.

a. $(3m-5)^2$

b. $2x^2 + 5x + 2$

c. $(3x-1)(x+2y-4)$

d. $2x^2 + x - 15$

e. $(x-3)(x+3)$

f. $4x^2 - 49$

2-133.   With your team, decide whether the following expressions can be represented with a model and rewrite each expression. Be prepared to share your **strategies** with the class.

a. $p(p+3)(2p-1)$

b. $x(x+1)+(3x-5)$

2-134.   Copy each area model below and fill in the missing parts. Then write the pairs of equivalent expressions represented by each model. Be prepared to share your reasoning with the class.

a.

b.

c.

d.

$$ \text{Review } \& \text{ Preview} $$

2-135.   Decide whether each of the following pairs of expressions or equations is equivalent for all values of x (or a and b). If they are equivalent, show how you can be sure. If they are not, **justify** your reasoning completely.

a. $(x+3)^2$ and x^2+9

b. $(x+4)^2$ and $x^2+8x+16$

c. $(x+1)(2x-3)$ and $2x^2-x-3$

d. $3(x-4)^2+2$ and $3x^2-24x+50$

e. $(x^3)^4$ and x^7

f. ab^2 and a^2b^2

2-136.   Look back at the expressions in problem 2-135 that are not equivalent. For each pair, are there any values of the variable(s) that would make the two expressions equal? **Justify** your reasoning.

2-137.   Jenna wants to solve the equation $2000x - 4000 = 8000$.

      a.   What easier equation could she solve instead that would give her the same solution? (In other words, what equivalent equation has easier numbers to work with?)

      b.   **Justify** that your equation in part (a) is equivalent to $2000x - 4000 = 8000$ by showing that they have the same solution.

      c.   Now Jenna wants to solve $\frac{3}{50} - \frac{x}{50} = \frac{7}{50}$. Write and solve an equivalent equation with easier numbers that would give her the same answer.

2-138.   Find a rule for each sequence below. Then describe its graph.

      a.

n	$t(n)$
3	8
5	2
7	−4

      b.

n	$t(n)$
1	40
2	32
3	25.6

2-139.   Given that n is the length of the bottom edge of the backward L-shaped figures below, what sequence is generated by the total number of dots in each figure? What is the 46th term, or $t(46)$, of this sequence? The nth term?

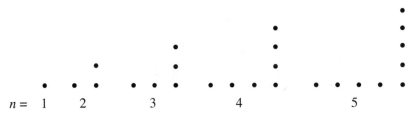

$n =$ 1   2   3   4   5

2-140.   For the function $h(x) = -3x^2 - 11x + 4$, find the value of each expression below.

      a. $h(0)$ b. $h(2)$ c. $h(-1)$ d. $h(\frac{1}{2})$

      e.   For what value(s) of x does $h(x) = 0$?

2-141.   Find the x-intercepts for the graph of $y - x^2 = 6x$.

2-142.   Multiply each pair of functions below to find an expression for $f(x) \cdot g(x)$.

      a. $f(x) = 2x$, $g(x) = (x + 3)$ b. $f(x) = (x + 3)$, $g(x) = (x - 5)$

      c. $f(x) = (2x + 1)$, $g(x) = (x - 3)$ d. $f(x) = (x + 3)$, $g(x) = (x + 3)$

2.2.3 How can I solve it?

Solving by Rewriting

In the past few lessons, you have worked on recognizing and finding equivalent expressions. In this lesson, you will apply these ideas to solve equations. As you work, use the questions below to keep your team's discussion productive and focused.

How can we make it simpler?

Does anyone see another way?

How can we be sure that our answer is correct?

2-143.   Graciella was trying to solve the quadratic equation $x^2 + 2.5x - 1.5 = 0$. *"I think I need to use the Quadratic Formula because of the decimals,"* she told Grover. Grover replied, *"I'm sure there's another way! Can't we rewrite this equation so the decimals are gone?"*

a.   What is Grover talking about? Rewrite the equation so that it has no decimals.

b.   Use your ideas from Lesson 2.2.2 to rewrite your equation again, expressing it as a product.

c.   Now solve your new equation. Be sure to check your solution(s) using Graciella's original equation.

2-144.   SOLVING BY REWRITING

Rewriting $x^2 + 2.5x - 1.5 = 0$ in problem 2-143 gave you a new, equivalent equation that was much easier to solve. How can each equation or system of equations below be rewritten so that it is easier to solve? With your team, find an equivalent equation or system for each part below. Be sure your new equations have no fractions or decimals and have numbers that are reasonably small. Then solve your new equation or system and check your answer(s) using the original equations.

a. $100x^2 + 100x = 2000$

b. $\frac{1}{2}x^2 + \frac{3}{4}x - \frac{1}{2} = 0$

c. $\frac{2x}{5} + \frac{3}{5} = 1$

d. $\frac{x-3}{x} + \frac{2}{x-1} = \frac{5-x}{x}$

e. $15x + 10y = -20$
       $7x - 2y = 24$

f. $\frac{3x+1}{2} + \frac{2y}{3} = -5$
       $\frac{2x}{10} - \frac{4y+3}{5} = -4$

2-145.   Is $6x + 3y = 12$ equivalent to $y = -2x + 4$? How can you tell using each representation (table, graph, equation)?

2-146.   Rewrite each of the following equations so that it is in y-form. Check to be sure your new equation is equivalent to the original equation.

   a. $5x - 2y = 8$

   b. $xy + 3x = 2$

2-147.   Angelica and D'Lee were working on finding roots of two quadratic equations: $y = (x-3)(x-5)$ and $y = 2(x-3)(x-5)$. Angelica made an interesting claim: *"Look,"* she said, *"When I solve each of them for $y = 0$, I get the same solutions. So these equations must be equivalent!"*

   D'Lee is not so sure. *"How can they be equivalent if one of the equations has a factor of 2 that the other equation doesn't?"* she asked.

   a.   Who is correct? Is $y = (x-3)(x-5)$ equivalent to $y = 2(x-3)(x-5)$? How can you **justify** your ideas using tables and graphs?

   b.   Is $0 = (x-3)(x-5)$ equivalent to $0 = 2(x-3)(x-5)$? Again, how can you **justify** your ideas?

2-148.   Consider the tile pattern at right.

   a.   Work with your team to describe what the 100th figure would look like. Then find as many different expressions as you can for the area (the number of tiles) in Figure x. Use algebra to **justify** that all of your expressions are equivalent.

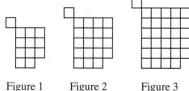

Figure 1   Figure 2   Figure 3

   b.   How can you use your expressions to find out more information about this pattern? Write and solve an equation to determine which figure number has 72 tiles. Do you get different results depending upon which expression you choose to use? Explain.

Algebra 2 Connections

2-149.   Rewrite each equation below. Then solve your new equation. Be sure to check your
          solution using the original equation.

    a. $(n+4)+n(n+2)+n=0$ b. $\frac{4}{x}=x+3$

2-150.   Decide whether each of the following pairs of expressions or equations are equivalent.
          If they are, show how you can be sure. If they are not, **justify** your reasoning
          completely.

    a. $(ab)^2$ and a^2b^2 b. $3x-4y=12$ and $y=\frac{3}{4}x-3$

    c. $y=2(x-1)+3$ and $y=2x+1$ d. $(a+b)^2$ and a^2+b^2

    e. $\frac{x^6}{x^2}$ and x^3 f. $y=3(x-5)+2$ and $y=2x-8$

2-151.   Look back at the expressions in problem 2-150 that are not equivalent. Are there any
          values of the variables that would make them equal? **Justify** your reasoning.

2-152.   This problem is a checkpoint for multiplying polynomials. It will be referred to as
          Checkpoint 3.

          Multiply and simplify each expression below.

    a. $(x+1)(2x^2-3)$ b. $(x+1)(x^2-2x+3)$

    c. $2(x+3)^2$ d. $(x+1)(2x-3)^2$

    e.   Check your answers to parts (a) through (d) by referring to the Checkpoint 3
          materials located at the back of your book.

          If you needed help multiplying and simplifying these expressions correctly, then you
          need more practice with problems like these. Review the Checkpoint 3 materials and
          try the practice problems. Also, consider getting help outside of class time. From this
          point on, you will be expected to multiply expressions like these quickly and easily.

2-153.   Find the formula for $t(n)$ for the arithmetic sequence in which $t(15) = 10$ and $t(63) = 106$.

2-154.   Jillian's parents bought a house for $450,000, and the value of the house has been increasing steadily by 3% each year.

   a.   Find the formula $t(n)$ that represents the value of the house each year.

   b.   If Jillian's parents sell their house 10 years after they bought it, how much profit will they make? (That is, how much more are they selling it for than they bought it for?) Express your answer as both a dollar amount and a percent of the original purchase price.

2-155.   Factor $5x^3y + 35x^2y + 50xy$ completely. Show every step and explain what you did.

2-156.   Consider the sequence $10, 2, \ldots$

   a.   Assuming that the sequence is arithmetic with $t(1)$ as the first term, write the next four terms of the sequence and then write a rule for $t(n)$.

   b.   Assuming that the sequence is geometric with $t(1)$ as the first term, write the next four terms of the sequence and then write a rule for $t(n)$.

   c.   Create a totally different sequence that begins $10, 2, \ldots$ For your sequence, write the next four terms and a rule for $t(n)$.

Chapter 2 Closure What have I learned?

Reflection and Synthesis

The activities below offer you a chance to reflect on what you have learned in this chapter. As you work, look for concepts that you feel very comfortable with, ideas that you would like to learn more about, and topics with which you need more help. Look for connections between ideas as well as connections with material you learned previously.

① TEAM BRAINSTORM

Brainstorm with your team to create a list of words and ideas for each of the following two categories. Be as detailed as you can. How long can you make your lists? Challenge yourselves. Be prepared to share your team's ideas with the class.

Topics: What have you studied in this chapter? What ideas and words were important in what you learned? Remember to be as detailed as you can.

Connections: How are the topics, ideas, and words that you learned in previous courses connected to the new ideas in this chapter? Again, make your list as long as you can.

②   MAKING CONNECTIONS

Below is a list of the vocabulary used in this chapter. Make sure that you are familiar with all of these words and know what they mean. Refer to the glossary or index for any words that you do not yet understand.

arithmetic sequence	common difference	common ratio
equivalent	exponential function	first term
geometric sequence	initial value	linear function
multiplier	quadratic	rewrite
sequence	term	term number
y-intercept		

Make a concept map showing all of the connections you can find among the key words and ideas listed above. To show a connection between two words, draw a line between them and explain the connection, as shown in the example below. A word can be connected to any other word as long as you can **justify** the connection. For each key word or idea, sketch an example.

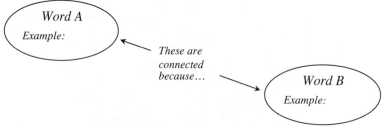

Your teacher may provide you with vocabulary cards to help you get started. If you use the cards to plan your concept map, be sure either to re-draw your concept map on your paper or to attach the vocabulary cards to a poster with all of the connections explained for others to see and understand.

While you are making your map, your team may think of related words or ideas that are not listed above. Be sure to include these ideas on your concept map.

③   GROWTH OVER TIME

This section gives you an opportunity to show growth in your understanding of key mathematical ideas over time as you complete this course. In this section you will complete a problem on its own sheet of paper and will keep it separate from your other work or put it into a portfolio. You will need to refer back to the problem later in the course.

On a separate sheet of paper, explain everything you know about $f(x) = 2^x - 3$.

④ SUMMARIZING MY UNDERSTANDING

This section gives you an opportunity to show what you know about certain math topics or ideas.

With your team, make a list of the *main ideas* of this chapter. Discuss the important ideas of the chapter and try to agree on a short list of no more than five main ideas. Be prepared to share your list in a whole-class discussion. When the class has reached agreement on a list of the main ideas, continue with parts (a) and (b) below.

a. Write your own description of each main idea.

b. For each main idea, provide one or two representative example problems. Solve each problem completely, using multiple representations, if applicable.

Your teacher may give you a "GO" page to work on (or you can download one from www.cpm.org). "GO" stands for "Graphic Organizer," a tool you can use to organize your thoughts and communicate your ideas clearly.

⑤ WHAT HAVE I LEARNED?

This section will help you determine the types of problems with which you feel comfortable and the types of problems with which you need help. This section will appear at the end of every chapter to help you check your understanding. These problems are intended for you to complete independently and outside of class. Even if your teacher does not assign this section, it is a good idea to try these problems and find out for yourself what you know and what you need to work on.

Solve each problem as completely as you can. The table at the end of this closure section has answers to these problems. It also tells you where you can find additional information and practice on similar problems.

CL 2-157. Determine if the following sequences are arithmetic, geometric, or neither:

a. $-7, -3, 1, 5, 9, \ldots$ b. $-64, -16, -4, -1, \ldots$

c. $1, 0, 1, 4, 9, \ldots$ d. $0, 2, 4, \ldots$

CL 2-158. Find an equation to represent each table as a sequence with term 1 as its first term.

a.

n	$t(n)$
2	1
5	-8
10	-23
25	

b.

n	$t(n)$
1	6
2	7.2
3	8.64
4	

CL 2-159. Solve the following systems algebraically. What does each solution reveal about the graph of the equations in the system?

a. $x + 2y = 17$
    $x - y = 2$

b. $4x + 5y = 11$
    $2x + 6y = 16$

c. $4x - 3y = -10$
    $x = \frac{1}{4}y - 1$

d. $2x + y = -2x + 5$
    $3x + 2y = 2x + 3y$

CL 2-160. Solve each equation after first rewriting it in a simpler equivalent form.

a. $3(2x - 1) + 12 = 4x - 3$

b. $\frac{3x}{7} + \frac{2}{7} = 2$

c. $\frac{3}{4}x^2 = \frac{5}{4}x + \frac{1}{2}$

d. $4x(x - 2) = (2x + 1)(2x - 3)$

CL 2-161. The following pairs of equations or expressions are equivalent. Show how to transform the first expression into the second.

a. $2x - 3y = 6$; $y = \frac{2}{3}x - 2$

b. $(2x - 1)^2$; $4x^2 - 4x + 1$

c. $n(2n + 1)(2n - 1)$; $4n^3 - n$

d. $\left(\frac{4x^{12}}{-2x^8}\right)^3$; $-8x^{12}$

e. $10x^2 - 55x - 105$; $5(2x + 3)(x - 7)$

f. $\sqrt{108}$; $6\sqrt{3}$

CL 2-162. Create multiple representations of each line described below.

a. A line with slope 4 and y-intercept –6.

b. A line with slope $\frac{3}{2}$ that passes through the point $(5, 7)$.

CL 2-163. Describe the domain and range of each function or sequence below.

a. The function $f(x) = (x - 2)^2$.

b. The sequence $t(n) = 3n - 5$.

CL 2-164. Find the x- and y-intercepts of $y = x^2 - 3x - 3$.

CL 2-165. Check your answers using the table at the end of this section. Which problems do you feel confident about? Which problems were hard? Have you worked on problems like these in previous math classes? Use the table to make a list of topics you need to learn more about, and a list of topics you just need to practice more.

⑥   HOW AM I THINKING?

This course emphasizes five different **Ways of Thinking**: investigating, generalizing, justifying, choosing a strategy, and reversing. These are some of the ways you might think while trying to make sense of a new concept or attempting to solve a challenging problem (even outside of math class). During this chapter, you have probably used each Way of Thinking more than once without even realizing it!

This closure activity will focus on one of these Ways of Thinking: **justifying**. Read the description of this Way of Thinking at right.

Think about the **justifying** that you did in this chapter. When did you use reasoning to prove or support an idea you had? What previous knowledge did you use to support your claim? You may want to flip through the chapter to refresh your memory about the problems that you have worked on. Discuss any **justifying** you did with your teammates.

Once your discussion is complete, analyze how **justifications** work below.

> ### Justifying
>
> To **justify** means to organize known information with the purpose of making and communicating a convincing argument. **Justifying** an idea or belief is the same as explaining how you know that it is correct. You think this way when you answer questions like "*Is that always true?*" with statements that start, "*Yes, because…*" or "*No, because…*" When you give reasons to support or disprove a statement or idea, you are **justifying** your thinking.
>
>

a.   Four members of a study team were analyzing the sequence 3, 7, 11, … They found the rule for the sequence to be $t(n) = 4n - 1$, and they were trying to figure out if 200 could be a term of their sequence.
They made the following statements. Which students **justified** their statements? Are the **justifications** convincing? Explain why or why not.

Shinna: "I think it's not, because all the terms in the sequence are odd and 200 is an even number."

Aldo: "I think it is, because the equation $200 = 4n - 1$ has a solution."

James: "It can't be, because the solution to $200 = 4n - 1$ is $n = 50.25$, which is not a whole number. There can't be a 50.25th term!"

Leslie: "I think 199 and 203 are terms of the sequence, but not 200."

b.   Your teammate needs help understanding why $(x + y)^2 = x^2 + 2xy + y^2$. She thinks that $(x + y)^2 = x^2 + y^2$. **Justify** why $(x + y)^2 = x^2 + 2xy + y^2$ so that she is convinced that your answer is correct.

Problem continues on next page. →

Problem continued from previous page.

c. Create your own sequence. Then figure out what the 110th term of your sequence would be and whether the number 419 is a term in your sequence. Use multiple representations to **justify** your answers thoroughly.

Answers and Support for Closure Activity #5
What Have I Learned?

Problem	Solutions		Need Help?	More Practice
CL 2-157.	a. arithmetic b. geometric c. neither d. arithmetic		Lesson 2.1.4 Math Notes box in Lesson 2.1.6	Problems 2-43, 2-45, 2-61a, 2-73, 2-92, 2-100, 2-106, 2-107, and 2-109
CL 2-158.	a. $t(n) = -3n + 7$ b. $t(n) = 5(1.2)^n$ or $t(n) = 6(1.2)^{n-1}$		Lessons 2.1.2, 2.1.4, 2.1.6, and 2.1.8 Math Notes box in Lesson 2.1.8	Problems 2-6, 2-24, 2-39, 2-54, 2-68, 2-69, 2-81, 2-106, and 2-109
CL 2-159.	a. $(7, 5)$ b. $(-1, 3)$ c. $(-\frac{1}{4}, 3)$ d. $(1, 1)$		Lesson 1.1.3	Problems 1-31, 2-25, 2-47, 2-75, 2-91, and 2-126
CL 2-160.	a. -6 b. 4 c. $(-\frac{1}{3}, 2)$ d. $\frac{3}{4}$		Lesson 2.2.3	Problems 2-144, 2-145, and 2-149
CL 2-161.	Methods vary. Sample answers below. a. $2x - 3y = 6$, $-3y = -2x + 6$, $y = \frac{2}{3}x - 2$ b. $(2x-1)^2 = (2x-1)(2x-1)$ $= 4x^2 - 2x - 2x + 1 = 4x^2 - 4x + 1$ c. $n(2n+1)(2n-1) = (2n^2 + n)(2n-1)$ $= 4n^3 - 2n^2 + 2n^2 - n = 4n^3 - n$ d. $(\frac{4x^{12}}{-2x^8})^3 = \frac{4^3 x^{36}}{(-2)^3 x^{24}} = \frac{64x^{(36-24)}}{-8}$ $= -8x^{12}$ e. $10x^2 - 55x - 105 = 5(2x^2 - 11x - 21)$ $= 5(2x + 3)(x - 7)$ f. $\sqrt{108} = \sqrt{36 \cdot 3} = \sqrt{6^2 \cdot 3} = 6\sqrt{3}$		Lessons 2.2.1 and 2.2.2	Problems 2-119, 2-120, 2-122, 2-123, 2-132, 2-133, 2-146, and 2-150

Problem	Solutions	Need Help?	More Practice

CL 2-162.   a. $y = 4x - 6$

x	y
-3	-18
-2	-14
-1	-10
0	-6
1	-2
2	2
3	6

Math Notes box in Lesson 1.1.2

Problems 1-20, 1-25, 1-51, 1-92, 2-13, 2-92, and 2-145

b. $y = \frac{3}{2}x - \frac{1}{2}$

x	y
-3	-5
-2	-3.5
-1	-2
0	-0.5
1	1
2	2.5
3	4

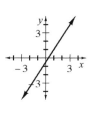

CL 2-163.   a. Domain: all real numbers
Range: $y \geq 0$

b. Domain: all positive whole numbers;
Range: all numbers of the form
$3n - 5$

Lesson 1.1.3

Math Notes boxes in Lessons 1.1.3 and 2.1.8

Problems 1-21, 1-24 part (e), 1-25, 1-32, 1-33, 1-35, 1-36, 1-60, 1-63, 1-86, 1-90, 1-91, 1-110, 2-26, and 2-105

CL 2-164. x-intercepts: $(\frac{3+\sqrt{21}}{2}, 0)$ and $(\frac{3-\sqrt{21}}{2}, 0)$

y-intercept: $(0, -3)$

Math Notes box in Lesson 1.1.4

Problems 1-49 and 1-107

CHAPTER 3   Exponential Functions

Chapter 3 provides an opportunity for you to build your function-**investigation** skills as you learn about families of exponential functions. You will also build more advanced algebra skills, such as solving for an indicated variable, simplifying or rewriting exponential expressions, and finding the linear or exponential function that passes exactly through any pair of given points.

One main focus of this course is the **investigation** of new families of functions. In this chapter, you will **investigate** the family of exponential functions and learn about several important applications of these functions.

In this chapter, you will learn how to:

➢ Recognize exponential growth when given situations, tables, graphs, or equations.

➢ Understand and connect multiple representations of exponential functions.

➢ Represent exponential functions algebraically.

➢ Use exponential functions and equations to solve problems involving growth or decay.

➢ Find equations of linear or exponential functions that pass through two given points.

Guiding Questions

Think about these questions throughout this chapter:

What are the relationships?

What are the connections?

How can I describe them?

What tools can I use?

Chapter Outline

Section 3.1   In Section 3.1, you will **investigate** a family of exponential functions. You will also extend your knowledge of exponents and their properties and learn how to use these properties, along with the algebra skills you already possess, to solve exponential equations. At the end of the section, you will get to apply exponential functions to real-life situations.

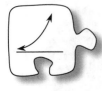

Section 3.2   In Section 3.2, you will learn more about the distinction between a parameter and a variable. You will solve for parameters to find linear and exponential equations that fit given data.

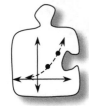

3.1.1 What do exponential graphs look like?

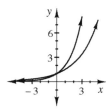

Investigating $y = b^x$

In this lesson you will **investigate** the characteristics of $y = b^x$. As a team, you will generate data, form questions about your data, and answer each of these questions using multiple representations. Your team will show what you have learned on a stand-alone poster.

3-1.   BEGINNING TO INVESTIGATE EXPONENTIALS

In Chapter 2, you graphed several exponential functions. Some graphs, like those that modeled the rabbit populations in problem 2-4, were *increasing* exponential functions and looked similar to the two exponential functions graphed at right.

Other graphs, such as the rebound-height graphs from the bouncy-ball activity (problem 2-23), represented *decreasing* exponential functions and looked similar to the third curve, shown in bold at right.

You already know that equations of the form $y = mx + b$ represent lines, and you know what effect changing the parameters m and b has on the graph. Today you will begin to learn more about exponential functions. In their simplest form, the equations of exponential functions look like $y = b^x$.

Find three equations in $y = b^x$ form that have graphs appearing to match the three graphs shown above. Confirm your results using your graphing calculator.

3-2.   INVESTIGATING $y = b^x$, Part One

What other types of graphs exist for equation of the form $y = b^x$?

Your task: With your team, **investigate** the family of functions of the form $y = b^x$. Decide as a team what different values of b to try so that you find as many different looking graphs as possible. Use the questions listed in the "Discussion Points" section below to help get you started.

Discussion Points

What special values of b should we consider?

Are there any other values of b we should try?

How many different types of graphs can we find?

How do we know we have found all possible graphs?

3-3.   The graph of the function $D(x) = (\frac{1}{2})^x$ is shown at right.

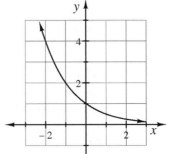

a.   Describe what happens to y as x gets bigger and bigger. For example, what is $D(20)$? $D(100)$? $D(1000)$? D(a very, very larger number)?

b.   Does the graph of $D(x)$ have an x-intercept? Explain how you know.

c.   When x is very large, the graph of $D(x) = (\frac{1}{2})^x$ approaches the x-axis. That is, as x gets bigger and bigger and gets farther to the right along the curve, the closer the curve gets to the x-axis. In this situation, the x-axis is called an **asymptote** of $D(x) = (\frac{1}{2})^x$. You can read more about asymptotes in the Math Notes box at the end of this lesson.

Does $f(x) = (\frac{1}{2})^x$ have a vertical asymptote? In other words, is there a vertical line that the graph above approaches? Why or why not?

d.   Which cases for $y = b^x$ that you found in problem 3-2 have asymptotes? Review your graphs and record any asymptotes you find.

3-4.   INVESTIGATING $y = b^x$, Part Two

Now that you, with your class, have found all of the possible graphs for $y = b^x$, your teacher will assign your team one of the types of graphs to **investigate** further. Use the "Discussion Points" section below in addition to the function-investigation questions your class generated in Chapter 1 to guide your **investigation** of this graph. Look for ways to **justify** your summary statements using more than one representation (equation, table, graph).

As a team, organize your graphs and summary statements into a stand-alone poster that clearly communicates what you learned about your set of graphs. Be sure to include all of your observations along with examples to demonstrate them. Anyone should be able to answer the questions below after examining your poster. Use colors, arrows, labels, and other tools to help explain your ideas.

Discussion Points

For our value(s) of b, what does the graph look like?
Why does the graph look this way?

What values of b generate this type of graph?

What are the special qualities of this graph?

3-5.   Exponential functions have some interesting characteristics. Consider functions of the form $y = b^x$ as you discuss the questions below.

a.   Exponential functions such as $y = b^x$ are defined only for $b > 0$. Why do you think this is? That is, why would you not want to use negative values of b?

b.   Can you consider $y = 1^x$ or $y = 0^x$ to be exponential functions? Why or why not? How are they different from other exponential function?

3-6.   LEARNING LOG

Look over your work from this lesson. What questions did you ask yourself as you were making observations and statements? How does changing the value of b affect a graph? What questions do you still have after this **investigation**? Write a Learning Log entry describing what mathematical ideas you developed during this lesson. Title this entry "Investigating $y = b^x$" and label it with today's date.

METHODS AND MEANINGS

Graphs with Asymptotes

A mathematically clear and complete definition of an asymptote requires some ideas from Calculus, but some examples of **graphs with asymptotes** might help you recognize them when they occur. In the following examples, the dotted lines are the asymptotes, and their equations are given. In the two lower graphs, the y-axis, $x = 0$, is also an asymptote.

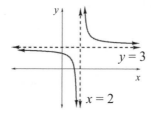

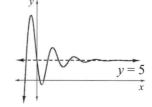

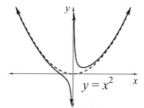

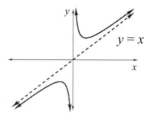

As you can see in the examples above, asymptotes can be diagonal lines or even curves. However, in this course, asymptotes will almost always be horizontal or vertical lines. The graph of a function $y = f(x)$ has a **horizontal asymptote** if, as you trace along the graph out to the left or right (that is, as you choose x-coordinates farther and farther away from zero, either toward infinity or toward negative infinity), the distance between the graph of $f(x)$ and the asymptote gets closer to zero.

A graph has a **vertical asymptote** if, as you choose x-coordinates closer and closer to a certain value, from either the left or right (or both), the y-coordinate gets farther away from zero, either toward infinity or toward negative infinity.

3-7.   Solve each equation below for x.

    a. $2^3 = 2^x$
    b. $x^3 = 5^3$
    c. $3^4 = 3^{2x}$
    d. $2^7 = 2^{(2x+1)}$

3-8.   A grocery store is offering a sale on bread and soup. Khalil buys four cans of soup and three loaves of bread for $11.67. Ronda buys eight cans of soup and one loaf of bread for $12.89.

    a.   Write equations for both Khalil's and Ronda's purchases.

    b.   Solve the system to find the price of one can of soup and the price of one loaf of bread.

3-9.   If two expressions are equivalent, they can form an equation that is considered to be **always true**. For example, since $3(x-5)$ is equivalent to $3x-15$, then the equation $3(x-5) = 3x-15$ is always true, or true for any value of x.

    If two expressions are equal only for certain values of the variable, they can form an equation that is considered to be **sometimes true**. For example, $x+2$ is equal to $3x-8$ only when $x=5$, so the equation $x+2 = 3x-8$ is said to be sometimes true.

    If two expressions are not equal for any value of the variable, they can form an equation that is considered to be **never true**. For example, $x-5$ is not equal to $x+1$ for *any* value of x, so the equation $x-5 = x+1$ is said to be never true.

    Is the equation $(x+3)^2 = x^2+9$ always, sometimes or never true? **Justify** your reasoning completely.

3-10.   Solve $2x^2 - 3x - 7 = 0$ for x. Give your solutions in both radical form and as decimal approximations.

3-11.   Consider the sequence that begins $40, 20, 10, 5, \ldots$

    a.   Based on the information given, can this sequence be arithmetic? Can it be geometric? Why?

    b.   Assume this is a geometric sequence. On graph paper, plot the sequence on a graph up to $n=6$.

    c.   Will the values of the sequence ever become zero or negative? Explain.

3-12.   If a ball is dropped from 160 cm and rebounds to 120 cm on the first bounce, how high will the ball be:

a.   On the 2nd bounce?

b.   On the 5th bounce?

c.   On the nth bounce?

3-13.   Simplify each of the following expressions.

a. $(3x^2yz^4)^2$ b. $\dfrac{2mn^5}{6m^2n}$

c. $(pq^2)(p^3q^5)$ d. $(\dfrac{r^2s}{rs^3t})^3$

3-14.   *Without using a calculator*, perform each operation indicated in the expressions below.

a. $\dfrac{3}{4} - \dfrac{2}{5}$ b. $\dfrac{3}{y} - \dfrac{5}{4}$ c. $(\dfrac{3m}{n}) \cdot (\dfrac{m}{6n})$ d. $(\dfrac{5x^2}{y}) \cdot (\dfrac{10}{x})$

3-15.   Sketch the shape of the graph of the function $y = b^x$ given each of the following values of b.

a. b is a number larger than 1.

b. b is a number between 0 and 1.

c. b is equal to 1.

3-16.   Find rules for each of the following sequences.

a.   108, 120, 132, ...   b. $\dfrac{2}{5}, \dfrac{4}{5}, \dfrac{8}{5}, \ldots$

c.   3741, 3702, 3663, ...   d.   117, 23.4, 4.68, ...

3-17.   Calculate the x-intercepts for the graph of each function below.

a. $y = (x - 2)(x + 1)$ b. $y = 2x^2 + 16x + 30$

3-18.   Write the multiplier for each increase or decrease described below.

   a.   a 25% increase

   b.   a decrease of 18%

   c.   an increase of 39%

   d.   a decrease of 94%

3-19.   Simplify each of the following expressions.

   a. $3x^2yz^3 \cdot 2xyz^4$ b. $\dfrac{21m^5p^4}{3mp^3}$

   c. $(3rs^2t^3)^5$ d. $\dfrac{4a^2}{b} \cdot ab^4$

3-20.   Solve the system of equations at right for m and b. $15 = 5m + b$
$7 = 3m + b$

3-21.   Find the length of the side labeled x in each triangle below.

   a.
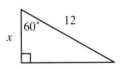

   b.
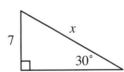

   c.
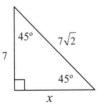

   d.
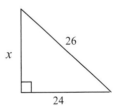

3.1.2 What is the connection?

Multiple Representations

So far, you have used multiple representations (such as a table, graph, rule, or context) to solve problems, **investigate** functions, and **justify** conclusions. But how can the connections between the different representations help you understand more about the family of exponential functions? Today you will **investigate** this question as you develop a deeper understanding of exponential functions.

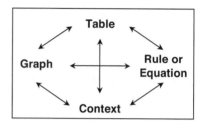

3-22.   What can a graph tell you about a rule? Can you predict the value in a table if you know about the particular situation it represents? Use what you have learned about exponential functions to answer the questions below.

Bounce Number	Height (cm)
0	
1	
2	84.5
3	67.6
4	54.1

a.   Arnold dropped a ball during the bouncy-ball activity and recorded its height in a table. Part of his table is shown at right. What was the rebound ratio of his ball? At what height did he drop the ball? Write a rule that represents his data. Explain your rule.

b.   A major technology company, ExpoGrow, is growing incredibly fast. The latest prospectus (a report on the company) said that so far, the number of employees, y, could be found with the equation $y = 3(4)^x$, where x represents the number of years since the company was founded. How many people founded the company? How can the growth of this company be described?

c.   A computer virus is affecting the technology center in such a way that each day, a certain portion of virus-free computers is infected. The number of virus-free computers is recorded in the table at right. How many computers are in the technology center? What portion of virus-free computers is infected each day? How many computers will remain virus-free at the end of the third day? **Justify** your answer.

Day	Uninfected Computers
0	27
1	18
2	12
3	8

d.   As part of a major scandal, it was discovered that several statements in the prospectus for ExpoGrow were false. If the company actually had five founders and doubles in size each year, what rule should it have printed in its report?

3-23.   Most of the exponential equations you have used in this chapter have been in the form $y = ab^x$.

   a.   What does a represent in this equation? What does b represent?

   b.   How can you identify a by looking at a graph? How can you find it using a table? In a context or situation? Give an example for each representation.

   c.   How can you determine b in each representation? Use arrows or colors to add your ideas about b to the examples you created in part (b).

3-24.   MULTIPLE-REPRESENTATIONS WEB

What connections are you sure you can use in an exponential-functions web? For example, if you have an exponential rule, such as $y = 20(3)^x$, can you complete a table? If so, draw an arrow from the rule and point at the table, as shown at right.

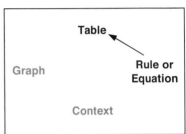

Copy the web into your Learning Log (but do not draw the arrows yet). Discuss with your team the connections you have used so far in this chapter. Use arrows to show which representations you can connect already. Which connections have you not used yet but you are confident that you could? Which connections do you still need to explore? Title this entry "Multiple-Representations Web for Exponential Functions" and label it with today's date. Be ready to share your findings with the rest of the class.

3-25.   RULE → GRAPH

How can you sketch the graph of an exponential function directly from its rule without making a table first? Discuss this with your team. Then make a reasonable sketch of the graph of $y = 7(2)^x$ on your paper.

3-26.   Each table below represents an exponential function of the form $y = ab^x$. Copy and complete each table on your paper and find the corresponding rule.

a.
x	y
0	1.8
1	5.76
2	18.432
3	
4	

b.
x	y
0	5
1	
2	245
3	
4	

3-27.   Brianna is working on her homework. Her assignment is to come up with four representations for an exponential function of her choosing. She decides it is easiest to start by writing an equation, so she chooses $y = 1200(\frac{1}{2})^x$. Help Brianna create the other three components of the web.

3-28.   Sketch the graphs of $y = x^2$, $y = 2x^2$, and $y = \frac{1}{2}x^2$ on the same set of axes. Describe the similarities and differences among the graphs.

3-29.   Factor each expression completely.

   a. $x^2 - 49$ b. $4x^2 - 1$ c. $x^2y^2 - 81z^2$ d. $2x^3 - 8x$

3-30.   Derek and Donovan were trying to solve the equation $4^4 = 16^x$. Derek had an idea.

   "I know," he said. *"Isn't 16 equal to 4^2?"*

   "Yeah, so what?" said Donovan.

   "That means that we can rewrite the equation to look like $4^4 = (4^2)^x$. This is much easier to solve!" replied Derek.

   "Yes," said Donovan. *"That makes sense. Isn't there another way, too? Since 4 is the same as 2^2 and 16 is the same as 2^4, can't we rewrite it as $(2^2)^4 = (2^4)^x$?"*

   a.   What do you think of Derek's and Donovan's methods? Will they both work?

   b.   Use both methods to solve $4^4 = 16^x$.

   c.   Now solve $3^5 = 9^{2x}$.

3-31.   Solve each equation below for x. For parts (c) and (d), use the ideas from problem 3-30 so that you do not have to use Guess and Check.

   a. $2^{(x+3)} = 2^{2x}$ b. $3^{(2x+1)} = 3^3$

   c. $9^x = 3^{40}$ d. $8^{70} = 2^x$

3-32.   The probability of landing on blue using a three-colored spinner is $\frac{2}{5}$. What is the probability of landing on blue on both of the next two spins?

3-33.   Mary has a piece of wood 12 feet long. She needs to cut off a section to use in a project. **Investigate** the function defined by inputs that are the amount of wood she cuts off and outputs that are the amount of wood remaining on the original piece of wood.

3.1.3 How does it grow?

More Applications of Exponential Growth

You may have heard the expression, "Money does not grow on trees." However, money does, in a sense, grow in a savings account. In today's lesson you will apply your understanding of exponential functions to solve problems involving money and interest. As you work, use the questions below to help focus your team's discussions.

How does it grow?

How is the rate written as a percent? As a decimal?

How is it the same (or different)?

3-34.   SAVING FOR COLLEGE

Suppose you have $1000 to invest and know of two investment options. You can invest in bonds (which pay 8% *simple* interest) or put your money in a credit-union account (which pays 8% *compound* interest). Will the option you choose make a difference in the amount of money you earn? Examine these two contexts below.

Bonds with Simple Interest:

a.   If you invest in bonds, your $1000 would grow as shown in the table at right. How does money grow with simple interest?

b.   By what percent would your balance have increased at the end of the 4th year? Show how you know.

VALUE OF BONDS

Number of Years	Amount of Money (in dollars)
0	1000.00 (initial value)
1	1080.00
2	1160.00
3	1240.00
4	

Accounts with Compound Interest:

c.   Instead, if you invest your $1000 in the credit union at 8% compound interest that is compounded once a year, its value would grow as shown in the table at right. Why is there $1166.40 in your account at the end of the second year? Explain how the money grows with compound interest.

VALUE OF CREDIT-UNION ACCOUNT

Number of Years	Amount of Money (in dollars)
0	1000.00 (initial value)
1	1080.00
2	1166.40
3	1259.71
4	

Problem continues on next page →

3-34.   *Problem continued from previous page.*

    d.   What will be the balance of the credit-union account at the end of the 4ᵗʰ year? By what percent would this account balance increase in four years? Show how you know.

    e.   Which type of account—a bond with simple interest or a credit-union account with compound interest—grows most quickly?

    f.   How much would your original $1000 investment be worth at the end of 20 years in this credit union? Show how you got your answer.

3-35.   Examine these two types of investments through other representations below.

    a.   The sequence below represents the value of an investment earning *simple* interest at the beginning of each year.

            1000, 1080, 1160, 1240, …

    Is this sequence arithmetic, geometric, or neither? What calculation is done to each term to get the next term?

    b.   Write a sequence for the value of the investment when $1000 is invested in an account with 8% annually *compounded* interest. Is this sequence arithmetic, geometric, or neither? What calculation is done to each term to get the next term?

    c.   Write an equation for each type of interest (simple and compound), where y represents the value of the investment after x years.

    d.   For each type of investment (simple and compound), draw a graph showing the value of $1000 over the first 8 years. Should these graphs be discrete (points only) or continuous (connected)? Explain.

    e.   What interest rate would the bonds with simple interest need to earn so that you would earn the same amount in both accounts after 6 years? After 20 years? Show how you know.

3-36. A third option for investing money is a money-market account, which offers 8% annual interest *compounded quarterly* (four times per year). This means that the 8% is divided into four parts over the year, so the bank pays 2% every three months.

a. Represent the value (at the end of every three months) of the $1000 investment in this money-market account with a sequence. List at least six terms.

b. Write an equation that determines the value of the investment, y, in the money-market account after x quarters.

c. What will be the value of your $1000 investment at the end of four years? How does this compare with your other investment options?

3-37. You have $500 to invest and have several options available to you.

a. Your banker shows you the graph at right to explain what you can earn if you invest with him. Does this graph represent simple or compound interest? How can you tell? What is the interest rate? Write an equation to represent how much money you would have as time passes. Let x represent time in years.

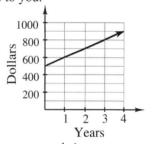

b. Jerry says, *"I've got my money in a great account that compounds interest* **monthly**. *The equation* $y = 388(1.008)^m$ *represents how much money I have at the end of any month."* What is Jerry's annual interest rate? Write an equation to represent *your* total money if you invest your $500 in an account with the same rate of return. Let m represent the number of months the money has been invested.

c. An investment advisor shows you the table of earnings you see at right. Write an equation for the table, letting q represent the number of quarters the money has been invested. What is the annual interest rate?

Quarter	$
0	500
1	515
2	530.45
3	546.36

d. Compare the earning potential of the options described in parts (a), (b), and (c) above. Which account is the best investment if you plan to leave your money in for only one year? Which would grow the most after ten years? Show and explain your work.

3-38. BACK TO THE WEB

Examine your web from problem 3-22. Which connections did you use in this lesson? Did you use any new connections during this lesson that you did not already have represented on your web with arrows? If so, update your web. Which connections do you still need to find?

3-39.   Each table below represents an exponential function in $y = ab^x$ form. Copy and complete each table on your paper and find a corresponding rule.

a.
x	y
−1	3
0	
1	75
2	
3	

b.
x	y
0	
1	
2	96.64
3	77.312
4	

3-40.   Tickets for a concert have been in incredibly high demand, and as the date for the concert draws closer, the price of tickets increases exponentially. The cost of a pair of concert tickets was $150 yesterday, and today it is $162. As you complete parts (a) through (c) below, assume that each day's percent increase from the day before is the same.

a.   What is the daily percent rate of increase? What is the multiplier?

b.   What will be the cost of a pair of concert tickets one week from now?

c.   What was the cost of a pair of tickets two weeks ago?

3-41.   Dusty won $125,000 on the *Who Wants to be a Zillionaire?* game show. He decides to place the money into an account that earns 6.25% interest compounded annually and plans not to use any of it until he retires.

a.   Write an expression that represents how much money Dusty will have in t years.

b.   How much money will be in the account when he retires in 23 years?

3-42.   In 1999, Charlie received the family heirloom marble collection consisting of 1239 marbles. Charlie's great-grandfather had started the original marble collection in 1905. Each year, Charlie's great-grandfather had added the same number of marbles to his collection. When he passed them on to his son, he insisted that each future generation add the same number of marbles per year to the collection. When Charlie's father received the collection in 1966, there were 810 marbles.

a.   By the time Charlie inherited the collection, for how many years had it been in existence?

Problem continues on next page →

3-42.   *Problem continued from previous page.*

  b. How many marbles are added to the collection each year?

  c. Use the information you found in part (b) to figure out how many marbles were in the original collection when Charlie's great-grandfather started it.

  d. **Generalize** this situation by writing a function describing the growth of the marble collection for each year (n) since Charlie's great-grandfather started it.

  e. How old will the marble collection be when Charlie (or one of his children) has more than 2000 marbles? In what year will this occur?

3-43.   Solve the following systems of equations.

  a. $3x - 2y = 14$
   $-2x + 2y = -10$
            b. $y = 5x + 3$
               $-2x - 4y = 10$

  c. Which system above is most efficiently solved by using the Substitution Method? Explain.

  d. Which system above is most efficiently solved by using the Elimination Method? Explain.

3-44.   If $f(x) = \frac{6}{x-1}$, find the value of x that will make $f(x) = 5$.

3-45.   Factor $2x^2 + 3x - 2$ and use an area model to demonstrate the equivalence of your expression to the original.

3-46.   Examine each sequence below. State whether it is arithmetic, geometric, or neither. For the sequences that are arithmetic, find the formula for $t(n)$. For the sequences that are geometric, find the sequence generator for $t(n)$.

  a. $1, 4, 7, 10, 13, \ldots$
            b. $0, 5, 12, 21, 32, \ldots$

  c. $2, 4, 8, 16, 32, \ldots$
            d. $5, 12, 19, 26, \ldots$

  e. $x, x+1, x+2, x+3, \ldots$
            f. $3, 12, 48, 192, \ldots$

3-47.   If you flip a fair coin, what is the probability that it comes up "heads"? "Tails"?

3.1.4 What if it does not grow?

Exponential Decay

To learn more about exponents, today you will study a new context that can be represented with an equation of the form $y = ab^x$.

3-48.   THE PENNY LAB

What about situations that do not grow? In this activity, you will explore a situation that behaves exponentially, but results get smaller. This is an example of **exponential decay**.

Your task: Follow the directions below to model exponential decay using pennies.

Trial #0:   Start with 100 pennies.

Trial #1:   Dump the pennies out on your team's workspace. Remove any pennies that have "tails" side up. Record the number of pennies that *remain* in a table where the input is the trial number and the output is the number of "heads."

Trial #2:   Gather the "heads-up" pennies, shake them up, and dump them on your workspace again. Remove any pennies that have the "tails" side up and count the number of pennies that remain.

Trial #x: Continue this process until the last penny is removed. Be sure to record all of your results in your table and then answer the questions below.

a.   Is it possible that a team conducting this experiment might never remove their last penny? Explain.

b.   Would the results of this experiment have been significantly different if you had removed the "heads" pennies each time?

c.   If you had started with 200 pennies, how would this have affected the results?

3-49.   Decide what your dependent and independent variables are for "The Penny Lab" data, clearly label them, and graph your data on your own graph paper. Then graph your data carefully on a team Lesson 3.1.4 Resource Page transparency obtained from your teacher.

   a.   Stack your team's transparency with of those from other teams on an overhead projector so that the axes are aligned. Then examine and describe the resulting scatter plot. Where does the graph cross the y-axis? Does the graph have any asymptotes? Should the graph be continuous or discrete?

   b.   Write an equation for an exponential function that approximates the data.

   c.   What output does your function give for $x = 0$? What could this mean in relation to the situation?

   d.   Could there be an output value for $x = -1$? If so, what might it mean?

3-50.   HALF-LIFE

   Carbon-14 dating is used to approximate the age of ancient discoveries and to learn more about things like dinosaur fossils. Scientists have studied the rate of decay of carbon-14 and have learned that no matter how much of this element they start with, only half of it will remain after about 5730 years (which is called its **half-life**).

   All living things on this planet contain the same proportion of this carbon-14 relative to overall carbon in their bodies. Knowing how much carbon-14 to expect, scientists can then measure how much carbon-14 is left in ancient items to figure out how much time has passed since the object was living.

   a.   If a living object is supposed to contain 100 grams of carbon-14, how much would be expected to remain after one half-life (5730 years)? After two half-lives (11,460 years)?

   b.   Draw a graph showing the expected amount, y, of carbon-14 (in grams) remaining after x half-lives.

   c.   Write an equation for a function that represents the amount of carbon-14 that will remain after x half-lives.

   d.   What output does your function give for $x = 0$? Does this make sense? **Justify** why or why not.

   e.   What output would the function give for $x = -1$?

3-51.   In addition to helping you learn about exponential decay, half-life can also provide insight into some special exponent properties.

   a.   For example, in part (d) of problem 3-50, you determined that $100(\frac{1}{2})^0 = 100$. So what must $(\frac{1}{2})^0$ equal? What do you think 3^0 or $(-5)^0$ equals? How do your graphs from Lesson 3.1.1 help you predict this? Use your calculator to check your predictions. Then write a conjecture about the value of x^0 (when $x \neq 0$).

   b.   What if $x = -1$? According to your graph, how much carbon-14 should there be when $x = -1$? Use this information to make sense of the value of $(\frac{1}{2})^{-1}$. Confirm your conclusion with your calculator.

   c.   Now find the value of your equation when $x = -2$. Use this information to make sense of the value of $(\frac{1}{2})^{-2}$. Then, as a team, write a conjecture about the value of x^{-2} when $x \neq 0$. Test your conjecture by predicting the value of 3^{-2} and $(\frac{2}{3})^{-2}$. Be sure to test your predictions with your calculator.

3-52.   Use the graphing calculator to compare the graphs of $y = (\frac{1}{2})^x$ and $y = 2^{-x}$.

   a.   What do you notice? How does a negative exponent affect the base number?

   b.   Use this idea to rewrite each of the following expressions in a different form. If you and your team members disagree, check your results with the calculator.

   i. $(\frac{1}{5})^{-1}$ ii. 100^{-1} iii. $(\frac{5}{8})^{-1}$ iv. $(\frac{1}{3})^{-2}$

   v. $(\frac{2}{3})^{-3}$ vi. 6^{-3} vii. $(\frac{3}{2})^{-1}$ viii. 2^{-5}

METHODS AND MEANINGS

Basic Laws of Exponents

The following laws of exponents follow logically from the basic definition $x^n = \underbrace{x \cdot x \cdot x \cdot ... \cdot x}_{n \text{ times}}$, where n is a positive integer or counting number.

If $x > 0$ and $y > 0$, the following equations are always true.

$$x^m \cdot x^n = x^{m+n} \qquad (xy)^k = x^k y^k \qquad \frac{x^m}{x^n} = x^{m-n}$$

$$(\frac{x}{y})^k = \frac{x^k}{y^k} \qquad (x^m)^n = x^{mn}$$

MATH NOTES

3-53.   Assume that a DVD loses 60% of its value every year it is in a video store. Suppose the initial value of the DVD was $80.

    a.   What multiplier would you use to calculate the video's new values?

    b.   What is the value of the DVD after one year? After four years?

    c.   Write a function $V(t) = ?$ to represent the value in t years.

    d.   When does the video have no value?

    e.   Sketch a graph of this function. Be sure to scale and label the axes.

3-54.   Use the basic definition of exponents to show an example that demonstrates each of the laws of exponents listed in the Math Notes box in this lesson. An example demonstrating $x^m \cdot x^n = x^{m+n}$ is shown at right.

$$x^3 \cdot x^2 = (x \cdot x \cdot x)(x \cdot x)$$
$$= x \cdot x \cdot x \cdot x \cdot x$$
$$= x^5$$
$$= x^{3+2}$$

3-55.   This problem is a checkpoint for simplifying expressions with positive integral exponents. It will be referred to as Checkpoint 4.

    Simplify each expression.

    a. $(2x^2y)^4$ b. $\dfrac{-3x^2y^3}{(-6)^2}$

    c. $\dfrac{(2x^2y)^4}{3xy^5}$ d. $5(5xy)^2(x^3y)$

    e.   Check your answers to parts (a) through (d) by referring to the Checkpoint 4 materials located at the back of your book.

    If you needed help simplifying these expressions correctly, then you need more practice. Review the Checkpoint 4 materials and try the practice problems. Also, consider getting help outside of class time. From this point on, you will be expected to simplify expressions like these quickly and easily.

3-56.   Consider the pattern at right.

$$\frac{1}{2^3} = \frac{1}{8}$$

a.   Continue the pattern to find $\frac{1}{2^{-1}}$, $\frac{1}{2^{-2}}$, $\frac{1}{2^{-3}}$, and $\frac{1}{2^{-4}}$.

$$\frac{1}{2^2} = \frac{1}{4}$$

b.   What is the value of $\frac{1}{2^{-n}}$?

$$\frac{1}{2^1} = \frac{1}{2}$$

c.   Write a conjecture about how to rewrite $\frac{1}{a^{-n}}$ without a negative exponent.

$$\frac{1}{2^0} = 1$$

3-57.   Solve each equation below for x. Refer back to problem 3-30 for examples, if necessary.

a. $2^{(x+3)} = 64$ b. $8^x = 4^6$

c. $9^x = \frac{1}{27}$

3-58.   Dr. Sanchez asked her class to simplify the expression $x + 0.6x$, but some students disagree on how to simplify it. Terry says that $x + 0.6x = 1.6x$, but Jo says that $x + 0.6x = 0.7x$. Who is correct? **Justify** your conclusion.

3-59.   Use your exponent patterns to rewrite each of the expressions below. For example, if the original expression has a negative exponent, then rewrite the expression so that it has no negative exponents, and vice versa. Also, if you can simplify the expression, go ahead and do so. Note: In part (b), assume that $m \neq 0$.

a. k^{-5} b. m^0 c. $x^{-2} \cdot x^5$ d. $\frac{1}{p^2}$

e. $\frac{y^{-2}}{y^{-3}}$ f. $(x^{-2})^3$ g. $(a^2b)^{-1}$ h. $\frac{1}{x^{-1}}$

3-60.   Factor each expression below.

a. $x^2 + 8x$ b. $6x^2 + 48x$

c. $2x^2 + 14x - 16$ d. $2x^3 - 128x$

3-61.   Multiply and simplify each expression below.

a. $(x-3)^2$ b. $(2m+1)^2$

c. $x(x-3)(x+1)$ d. $(2y-1)(y^2+7)$

3.1.5 What are the connections?

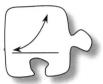

Graph → Rule

In Lesson 3.1.2, you started an exponential multiple-representations web. Today your team will develop methods for finding a rule from a graph. As you find ways to write rules based on a graph, you will build deeper understanding of exponential functions.

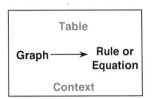

What information do we have?

Can we use other representations to help us think about our rule?

How can we be sure that our rule works?

3-62.   GRAPH → RULE

Use the clues provided in each graph below to find a possible corresponding rule in $y = ab^x$ form. Assume that if the graph has an asymptote, it is located on the x-axis.

a.

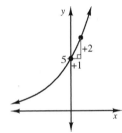

b.

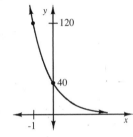

c.

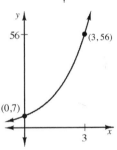

d.

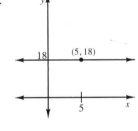

e.

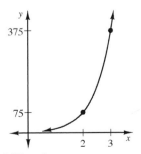

f.

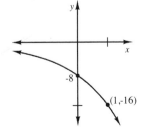

3-63.   **LEARNING LOG**

Create a Learning Log entry in which you describe methods
for creating an exponential rule given a graph. Be sure to
include examples to illustrate your reasoning. Title this entry
"Graph → Rule for Exponential Functions" and label it with
today's date.

3-64.   Use the clues in the graph at right to find a possible
corresponding rule in $y = ab^x$ form. Assume the graph has an
asymptote at the x-axis.

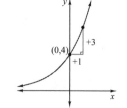

3-65.   Kristin's grandparents started a savings account for her when she was born. They
invested $500 in an account that pays 8% interest compounded annually.

a.   Write an equation to express the amount of money in the account on Kristin's
x^{th} birthday.

b.   How much money is in the account on Kristin's 16th birthday?

c.   What are the domain and range of the equation that you wrote in part (a)?

3-66.   Jack and Jill were working on simplifying the expression at right, but they
were having some trouble. Then Jill had an idea. $\dfrac{3x^2 y^{-3}}{x^{-1} y^2}$

"Can't we separate the parts?" she said. *"That way, it might
be easier to tell what we can simplify."* She rewrote the
expression as shown at right. $3 \cdot x^2 \cdot \dfrac{1}{x^{-1}} \cdot y^{-3} \cdot \dfrac{1}{y^2}$

"Okay," said Jack. *"Now we can rewrite each of the parts with negative exponents
and simplify."*

a.   Help Jack and Jill finish simplifying their expression.

b.   Use their idea to rewrite and simplify $\dfrac{m^2 pq^{-1}}{4m^{-2} pq^3}$.

3-67.   Consider the sequence $2, 8, 3y + 5, \ldots$

    a.   Find the value of y if the sequence is arithmetic.

    b.   Find the value of y if the sequence is geometric.

3-68.   The solution to the equation $x^3 = 64$ is called the **cube root** of 64. The idea is similar to the idea of a square root, except that the value must be cubed (multiplied by itself three times) to become 64. One way to write the cube root of 64 is using the notation $\sqrt[3]{64}$. Use this information to evaluate each of the following expressions.

    a. $\sqrt[3]{64}$ b. $\sqrt[4]{16}$ c. $\sqrt[3]{-8}$ d. $\sqrt[3]{125}$

3-69.   Determine which of the following equations are true for all values (always true). For those that are not, decide whether they are true for certain values (sometimes true) or not true for any values (never true). **Justify** your decisions clearly.

    a. $(x - 5)^2 = x^2 + 25$ b. $(2x - 1)(x + 4) = 2x^2 + 7x - 4$

    c. $\dfrac{2x^2 y^3}{y^2} = 2x^2 y$ d. $(3x - 2)(2x + 1) = 6x^2 - x - 5$

3-70.   Graph $y = x^2 + 3$ and $y = (x + 3)^2$. What are the similarities and differences between the graphs? How do these graphs compare to the graph of $y = x^2$?

3-71.   Find the domain and range for each of the relations graphed below.

    a.

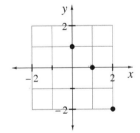

    b.

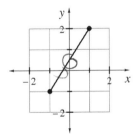

    c.

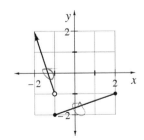

    d.

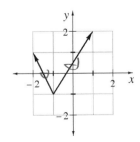

3.1.6 What's the connection?

Completing the Web

Review the exponential multiple-representations web that you created in Lesson 3.1.2. Are there any connections you have made since Lesson 3.1.2 that you need to add to your web? What connections between representations do you still need to explore?

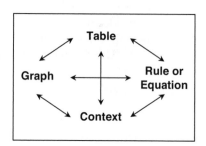

In today's lesson, design your own teamwork based on the connections that are incomplete in your web. Plan to begin your teamwork today with the problems that appear to your team to be the most challenging. The goal is for your team to complete the web by the end of this lesson.

3-72.   **WRITING A CONTEXT**

Each representation below represents a different set of data. For each part, brainstorm a context that could fit the data. Provide enough information in your "problem" description so that someone else could generate the graph, table, or rule for the data. Be creative! Your team's context may be selected for a future assessment!

a.

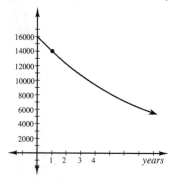

b. $B(t) = 180(1.22)^t$

c.

Year	Amount
1980	226 million
1981	_____
1982	_____
.	
.	
.	
1990	_____
.	
.	
.	
_____	1,000,000,000

x 1.02
x 1.02

3-73.   CONTEXT → GRAPH

A virus has invaded Leticia's favorite mountain fishing lake. Currently there are an estimated 1800 trout in the lake, and the Fish and Game Department has determined that the rate of fish deaths will be one-third of the population per week if left untreated.

    a.   Sketch a graph showing how many fish are left in Leticia's favorite lake over several weeks.

    b.   Theoretically, will the trout ever completely disappear from the lake? Use the graph to **justify** your answer.

3-74.   GRAPH → EQUATION

Suppose the annual fees for attending a public university were $1200 in 1986 and the annual cost increase is shown in the graph at right. Note that x represents the number of years after 1986.

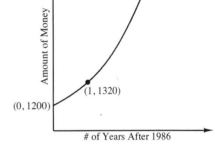

    a.   Write an equation to describe this situation.

    b.   Use this model to predict the cost of attending a public university in the first year you would be eligible to enroll.

    c.   What was the cost in 1980, assuming the 10% increase still applied?

    d.   By 1993 the annual cost was actually $3276. How accurate was the model? What actually happened?

3-75.   EQUATION → GRAPH

For each equation below, make a reasonable sketch of the graph without making a table first. Discuss your **strategy** with your team before you begin.

    a. $y = 5(3)^x$ b. $y = 10(\frac{1}{2})^x$ c. $y = \frac{1}{10}(5)^x$

3-76.   CONTEXT → ?

Use each of the situations below to complete missing pieces of the web or to practice moving from a context directly to a specific representation. For each part, decide which representation you will generate from the context description based on where your team needs to work.

   a.   A 100-gram sample of a radioactive isotope decays at a rate of 6% every week. How big will the sample be one year from now?

   b.   The math club is fast becoming one of the most popular clubs on campus because of the fabulous activities it sponsors annually for Pi Day on March 14. Each year, the club's enrollment increases by 30%. If the club has 45 members this year, how many members should it expect to enroll 5 years from now?

   c.   Barbara made a bad investment. Rather than earning interest, her money is decreasing in value by 11% each week! After just one week, she is down to just $142.40. How much money did she start with? If she does not withdraw her money, how long will it be before she has less than half of what she originally invested?

   d.   Larry loves music. He bought $285 worth of MP3 files on his credit card, and now he cannot afford to pay off his debt. If the credit-card company charges him 18% annual interest compounded monthly, how does Larry's debt grow as time passes? How much would he owe at the end of the year if he had a "no payments for 12 months" feature for his credit card?

3-77.   LEARNING LOG

Consider all of the things you have learned so far in this chapter. If you were creating a presentation for families for Back to School Night and wanted to teach them the main ideas about exponential functions, what would they be? Write a Learning Log entry describing the main ideas and why they are important. Title this entry "Important Ideas about Exponential Functions" and include today's date.

3-78.   According to the U.S. Census Bureau, the population of the United States has been growing at an average rate of approximately 2% per year. The census is taken every 10 years, and the population in 1980 was estimated at 226 million people.

   a.   How many people would the Census Bureau have expected to count in the 1990 census?

   b.   How many people should the Census Bureau have expected to count in the 2000 census?

   c.   How does your answer compare with the actual 2000 census population data of 281.4 million? What does this mean?

   d.   If the rate of population growth in the U.S. had continued at about 2%, in about what year would the population in the United States reach and surpass one billion?

3-79.   Solve each equation below.

   a. $2^{(x-1)} = 64$

   b. $4.7 = x^{1/3}$

   c. $8^{(x+3)} = 16^x$

   d. $9^3 = 27^{(2x-1)}$

   e. $x^6 = 29$

   f. $25^x = 125$

3-80.   Solve each equation below for x.

   a. $5^x = 5^{-3}$

   b. $6^x = 216$

   c. $7^x = \frac{1}{49}$

   d. $10^x = 0.001$

3-81.   Find values of a and b that make each system of equations true (i.e., solve each system). Be sure to show your work or explain your thinking clearly.

   a. $6 = a \cdot b^0$
        $24 = a \cdot b^2$

   b. $32 = a \cdot b^2$
        $128 = a \cdot b^3$

3-82.　Determine whether each of the following sequences is arithmetic, geometric, or neither. Then find a rule for the sequence, if possible.

　　a.　12.2, 13, 13.8, ...　　　　　　　b.　90, 81, 72.9, ...

　　c.　1, 1, 1, ...　　　　　　　　　　d.　2, 4, 16, ...

3-83.　A particular sequence can be represented by $t(n) = 2(3)^n$.

　　a.　What are $t(0)$, $t(1)$, $t(2)$, and $t(3)$?

　　b.　Graph this sequence. What is the domain?

　　c.　On the same set of axes, graph the function $f(x) = 2(3)^x$.

　　d.　How are the two graphs similar? How are they different?

3-84.　Solve the system of equations at right algebraically.　　$2x - 3y = 12$
　　　　　　　　　　　　　　　　　　　　　　　　　　　　　　　　　$y + x = -9$

3-85.　An integer between 10 and 20 is selected at random. What is the probability that 2 is a factor of that integer?

3-86.　Place the triangle at right on a set of x and y axes so that B is located at the origin.

　　a.　Find the coordinates of A and C.

　　b.　Find the area and perimeter of triangle ABC.

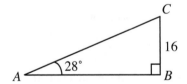

3.2.1 How can I find the equation?

Curve Fitting and Fractional Exponents

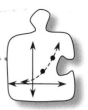

In this section, you will use your knowledge of linear equations to help develop algebraic **strategies** for finding linear and exponential functions. You will also learn more about working with roots and exponents.

3-87. How can finding linear equations help you form **strategies** for finding exponential equations? Parts (a) and (b) below will help you answer that question.

    a. In the equation $y = mx + b$, which letters represent variables? Which represent parameters? Briefly describe the difference between a variable and a parameter.

    b. Find the equation of the line with slope 3 that passes through the point (5, 19). Take careful note of the method that you use.

3-88. Can you use similar ideas to find an exponential equation?

    a. In the equation $y = ab^x$, which letters represent variables? Which represent parameters?

    b. While trying to find the equation for the graph in part (c) of problem 3-62 (shown again at right), Errol stated, *"I think 'a' must be 7 because the y-intercept is at (0, 7)."* Do you agree? **Justify** your answer.

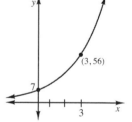

    c. *"But we still don't know what 'b' is,"* Errol noticed. His teammate, Sandy, had an idea. *"I think that* $56 = 7(b)^3$ *."* How did she get this equation? Is it valid? Explain.

    d. If you have not done so already, solve $56 = 7(b)^3$ for b. Explain how you solved this equation.

    e. Use a and b to write the equation for this graph. Does it agree with the equation you found in part (c) of problem 3-62?

3-89.   Use Errol's and Sandy's method from problem 3-88 to find the equation of an
         exponential function with an asymptote at $y = 0$ that passes through the points $(0, 5)$
         and $(3, 320)$.

3-90.   NEW NOTATION FOR ROOTS

The solution of the equation $b^3 = 8$ is called the **cube
root** of 8. The idea of a cube root is similar to the idea of
a square root, except that the cube root of 8 must be cubed
(multiplied by itself three times) to become 8. One way to
write the cube root of 8 is using the notation $\sqrt[3]{8}$.

a.   How can this notation be used to write the solution
      of $t^3 = 11$?

b.   Addison wondered how to find $\sqrt[3]{17}$ with her graphing calculator. *"If we could
      write $\sqrt[3]{17}$ in an exponent form instead of with a root symbol, we could use the
      graphing calculator to find it."* She showed her team this equation: $17^x = \sqrt[3]{17}$.
      Do you have any guesses about what the exponent might be? Discuss this with
      your team.

c.   *"But we also know that $(\sqrt[3]{17})^3 = 17$, and we want to write $\sqrt[3]{17}$ with an
      exponent instead, like 17^x . So why don't we combine these and write
      $(17^x)^3 = 17$?"* Addison asked. What do you think?

d.   Addison continued, *"Oh, so $(17^x)^3 = 17^{3x}$?"* Is she correct? Is it true that
      $(17^x)^3 = 17^{3x}$? Be ready to share your reasoning with the class.

e.   Addison wrote: $17^{3x} = 17^1$. Complete Addison's work to find the value of x in
      this equation. What does this tell you about another way to write $\sqrt[3]{17}$?

f.   Use similar logic to find exponential expressions for $\sqrt{5}$ and $\sqrt[5]{11}$. Show your
      reasoning. Then use your graphing calculator to find their decimal equivalents,
      rounded to the nearest 0.01.

3-91.   REWRITING EXPRESSIONS

The property $(k^m)^n = k^{mn}$ can help you rewrite expressions with roots and fractional
exponents, as it helped you in part (e) of problem 3-90.

For example, since $16^{3/2} = (16^3)^{1/2}$, $16^{3/2}$ can be rewritten as $\sqrt{16^3}$. However, since
$16^{3/2} = (16^{1/2})^3$, $16^{3/2}$ can also be rewritten as $(\sqrt{16})^3$ or 4^3.

With your team, find ways to rewrite the expressions below *two different ways*. Be
ready to **justify** your answers.

a. $10^{2/3}$ b. $(\sqrt[3]{9})^4$ c. $\sqrt[5]{x^3}$

d. $(\sqrt{2})^5$ e. $5^{7/2}$ f. $y^{3/3}$

3-92.   Fractional powers can give surprising results when used with negative bases. Answer the following questions using what you now know about how to rewrite fractional powers and your mental math skills. Avoid using your calculator.

    a.   Show or explain why $(-27)^{1/2}$ has no real solution but $(-27)^{1/3} = -3$.

    b.   Given that $(-27)^{1/3} = -3$, is $(-27)^{2/3}$ positive or negative, or does it have no real solution? What about $(-27)^{1/4}$? And $(-27)^{1/5}$? **Justify** your answers.

    c.   Mischa was working with her team on the idea of negative bases, but she got confused. Consider her thinking below.

        i.   *"Wait,"* she said. *"Isn't it true that* $(-100)^{1/2}$ *has no real solution?"* What does Mischa mean? Is she right?

        ii.   *"But,"* she continued, *"I can figure out that* $(-100)^{2/4} = 10$.*"* Check her calculation. Is she correct?

        iii.   *"That doesn't make any sense, since* $\frac{2}{4}$ *can be reduced to* $\frac{1}{2}$ *!"* What do you think?

3-93.   Recall that when you **investigated** $y = b^x$ in problem 3-2, the graphing calculator produced graphs like the one at right for negative values of b when you used the "zoom decimal" option. Use what you have learned about the meaning of fractional exponents to explain why $y = (-2)^x$ is impossible to graph accurately.

3-94.   You have now worked with exponents that have been zero, exponents that have been negative numbers, and exponents that have been fractions. In your Learning Log, explain everything you know about these kinds of exponents. Show equivalent ways to write expressions with zero, negative, and fractional exponents. What does each kind of exponent mean? Explain using both words and examples. Title this entry "Zero, Negative, and Fractional Exponents" and label it with today's date.

3-95.   Find a possible exponential function in $y = a \cdot b^x$ form that represents each situation described below.

a.   Has an initial value of 2 and passes through the point (3, 128).

b.   Passes through the points (0, 4) and (2, 1).

3-96.   Solve the following systems of equations. In other words, find values of a and b that make each system true. Be sure to show your work or explain your thinking clearly.

a. $3 = a \cdot b^0$
     $75 = a \cdot b^2$

b. $18 = a \cdot b^2$
     $54 = a \cdot b^3$

3-97.   Evaluate each expression below.

a. $\sqrt[3]{-64}$ b. $\sqrt[5]{32}$ c. $\sqrt[3]{27}$ d. $\sqrt[4]{10000}$

3-98.   Rewrite $16^{3/4}$ in as many different ways as you can.

3-99.   Show two steps to simplify each of the following expressions, and then calculate the value of each expression.

a. $64^{2/3}$ b. $25^{5/2}$ c. $81^{7/4}$

3-100.   Solve each of the following equations for x.

a. $2^{1.4} = 2^{2x}$ b. $8^x = 4$ c. $3^{5x} = 9^2$

3-101.   For each of the problems below, find the initial value.

a.   Five years from now, a bond that appreciates at 4% per year will be worth $146.

b.   Seventeen years from now, Ms. Speedi's car, which is depreciating at 20% per year, will be worth $500.

3-102.   In the diagram at right, the area of square A is 121 square units and the perimeter of square B is 80 units. Find the area of square C.

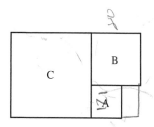

3-103.   Solve each system of equations below.

a. $2x + y = -7y$
      $y = x + 10$

b. $3x = -5y$
      $6x - 7y = 17$

3-104.   Find the equation of the line passing through the points $(7, 16)$ and $(2, -4)$. Then state the slope and x- and y-intercepts. Explain how you found them.

3.2.2   How can I find the equation?

. . . .

More Curve Fitting

In this lesson, you will continue your work from Lesson 3.2.1 as you develop a new method to find linear and exponential equations given two points.

3-105.   Mitchell was working on his Algebra 2 homework, when suddenly he had an idea about finding linear equations. He was trying to find the equation of the line that passes through the points $(5, 15)$ and $(3, 7)$. *"Look!"* he exclaimed. *"We know that the line can be written in the form $y = mx + b$, and we also know that the points $(5, 15)$ and $(3, 7)$ have to make the equation true. So we can substitute in these two points to create a system of equations. When we solve that, we'll know the values of m and b, and we'll have our equation!"*

a.   What is Mitchell talking about? Use his method to find the equation of the line through the points $(5, 15)$ and $(3, 7)$.

b.   Will Mitchell's method work to find the equation of a line through any two points? **Justify** your answer.

3-106.   Use Mitchell's method from problem 3-105 to find the equation of the line that passes through the points $(2, 3)$ and $(5, -6)$.

3-107.   Can Mitchell's method from problem 3-105 be used to find the *exponential* function that passes through the points $(2,16)$ and $(6,256)$? Consider this as you answer the questions below.

    a.   What is the general form for an exponential function that has an asymptote at $y = 0$?

    b.   Use the two points that you know to create a system of equations.

    c.   Solve your system of equations to find the values of a and b. What is the equation? Be prepared to share your method with the class.

3-108.   Find an exponential function that passes through each pair of points.

    a. $(-1, -2)$ and $(3, -162)$ b. $(2, 1.75)$ and $(-2, 28)$

METHODS AND MEANINGS

Summary of Exponents

For all x not equal to zero:
$$x^0 = 1$$
Examples: $2^0 = 1$, $(-3)^0 = 1$, $(\tfrac{1}{4})^0 = 1$

For positive values of x:

$$x^{-n} = \frac{1}{x^n}$$
Examples: $x^{-3} = \frac{1}{x^3}$, $y^{-4} = \frac{1}{y^4}$, $4^{-2} = \frac{1}{4^2} = \frac{1}{16}$

$$\frac{1}{x^{-n}} = x^n$$
Examples: $\frac{1}{x^{-5}} = x^5$, $\frac{1}{x^{-2}} = x^2$, $\frac{1}{3^{-2}} = 3^2 = 9$

$$x^{a/b} = (x^a)^{1/b} = \sqrt[b]{x^a} \quad \text{or} \quad x^{a/b} = (x^{1/b})^a = (\sqrt[b]{x})^a$$

Examples: $5^{1/2} = \sqrt{5}$, $32^{2/3} = \sqrt[3]{3^2} = \sqrt[3]{9}$,

                $16^{3/4} = (16^{1/4})^3 = (\sqrt[4]{16})^3 = 2^3 = 8$

MATH NOTES

Algebra 2 Connections

3-109. Find an exponential function that passes through each pair of points.

    a. $(1, 7.5)$ and $(3, 16.875)$ b. $(-1, 1.25)$ and $(3, 0.032)$

3-110. Solve the following equations for x, if possible. Some you can solve exactly, others approximately. If a solution is not possible, explain how you know.

    a. $1^x = 5$ b. $\sqrt{27^x} = 81$

    c. $2^x = 9$ d. $25^{(x+1)} = 125^x$

    e. $8^x = 2^5 \cdot 4^4$

3-111. This problem is a checkpoint for factoring quadratic expressions. It will be referred to as Checkpoint 5.

    Factor each expression below.

    a. $4x^2 - 1$ b. $4x^2 + 4x + 1$

    c. $2y^2 + 5y + 2$ d. $3m^2 - 5m - 2$

    e.   Check your answers to parts (a) through (d) by referring to the Checkpoint 5 materials located at the back of your book.

    If you needed help factoring these expressions correctly, then you need more practice. Review the Checkpoint 5 materials and try the practice problems. Also, consider getting help outside of class time. From this point on, you will be expected to factor expressions like these quickly and easily.

3-112. To what power do you have to raise:

    a.   3 to get 27?   b   2 to get 32?

    c.   5 to get 625?   d.   64 to get 8?

    e.   81 to get 3?   f.   64 to get 2?

    g. (x^2) to get x^1?   h. (x^3) to get x^{12}?

    i. x to get x^a?

3-113.   Simplify each expression below.

   a. $\frac{x}{3} - \frac{x+1}{5}$ b. $\frac{5}{x} + \frac{3}{x^2}$ c. $(\frac{7x^2}{m}) \cdot (\frac{m}{x^2})$ d. $\frac{1}{3} \div m^2$

3-114.   Find the length of $\overline{AC}$ in the diagram at right.

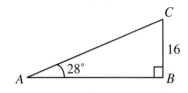

3-115.   If $f(x) = 3(2)^x$, find the value of the expressions in parts (a) through (c) below. Then complete parts (d) through (f).

   a. $f(-1)$ b. $f(0)$ c. $f(1)$

   d.   What value of x gives $f(x) = 12$?

   e.   Where does the graph of this function cross the x-axis? The y-axis?

   f.   If $g(x) = \frac{1}{3x}$, find $f(x) \cdot g(x)$.

3-116.   On the spinner at right, each "slice" is the same size. What is the probability that when you spin you will get:

   a.   The number 1?

   b.   The number 2?

   c.   The number 3?

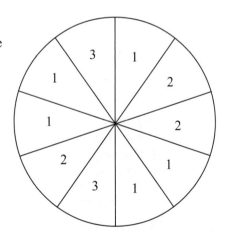

3.2.3 How can I use exponential functions?

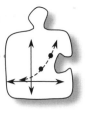

Solving a System of Exponential Functions Graphically

In this lesson, you will apply your skills with exponential functions to a system of equations as you explore the value of cars in an **investigation** called "Fast Cars."

3-117. FAST CARS

The moment you drive a new car off the dealer's lot, the car is worth less than what you paid for it. This phenomenon is called *depreciation*, which means you will sell the car for less than the price that you paid for it. Some cars depreciate more than others (that is, they depreciate at different rates), but most cars depreciate over time. On the other hand, some older cars actually increase in value. This is called *appreciation*. Let's suppose that in 2008, Jeralyn had a choice between buying a 2006 Fonda Concord EX for $21,000, which depreciates at 6% per year; a 2006 Padillac Escalate for $33,000, which depreciates at 22.5% per year; or a 1967 Fyord Rustang for $15,000 that is appreciating at 10% per year.

Your task: Investigate the value of each of the three cars over time.

- Generate multiple representations of the value of each car over time.

- For each of the new cars, determine how much value they lost (in dollars) from the time they were new in 2006 until 2008.

- Decide which car Jeralyn should buy and defend your choice in as many ways as you can.

Discussion Points

What is the multiplier?

How can we represent this situation in a table? a graph? an equation?

What should we consider when deciding which car to buy?

3-118.   **Investigate** the changing values of each of the cars by addressing the questions below.

    a.   What is the multiplier for the Concord? For the Escalate? For the Rustang?

    b.   Make a table like the one below and calculate the value for each car for each year shown.

Year	Concord	Escalate	Rustang
0	$21,000	$33,000	$15,000
1	$19,740	$25,575	
2			
3			
4			
5			
...			
10			
...			
n			

    c.   On your own graph paper, graph the data for all three cars on the same set of axes. Are the graphs linear? How are they similar? How are they different? You may want to use a different color for each car.

    d.   Write a function to represent the value of each car.

    e.   What were the values of the Concord and the Escalate when they were new? How much value (in dollars) did each car lose from 2006 to 2008?

    f.   Using the graph, which of the three cars is worth the most after one year? After 3 years? After 10 years? In how many years will the values of the Concord and Escalate be the same?

    g.   Pick one of the three cars and explain why Jeralyn should buy it. Has this problem changed your view of buying cars?

―――――   *Further Guidance*   ―――――
                     section ends here.

3-119. As you saw in "The Penny Lab," half-life applies to situations other than radioactive decay. In fact, the idea can be applied to anything that is depreciating or decaying exponentially.

  a. From the values in problem 3-117, Fast Cars, estimate the half-life of the value of the Concord and the Escalate.

  b. According to the mathematical model (not necessarily corresponding to reality), when will each car have no value?

  c. Why do you think some cars depreciate so much more quickly than others?

3-120. In 2004, a brand new SUV cost $26,000 to drive off the lot. In 2007 that same SUV was valued at $18,000. Write an exponential equation to represent this information. Then find the rate of depreciation for the SUV.

3-121. **Investigate** the function $y = 2 \cdot 4^x$. What would be the effect of replacing the 2 with a 5? What would be the effect of adding +1 to the end of the equation, making it $y = 2 \cdot 4^x + 1$? Include sketches as a part of your **investigation**.

3-122. Find the equation of an exponential function that passes through the points $(2, 48)$ and $(5, 750)$.

3-123. Billy Rich and Michael Million are two *very* wealthy, elderly men. Since neither of them have any heirs, they decide to give away all but $1 of their fortune before they die. Billy Rich has $1,340,000 and is giving $\frac{1}{3}$ of his remaining money away each year. Michael Million has $980,000 and is giving away $\frac{1}{4}$ of his money away each year. Who will get down to their final dollar first: Billy or Michael? How many years will it take each of them to give away their fortune? **Justify** your answer.

3-124. Factor each expression below.

  a. $x^2 - x - 72$

  b. $9x^2 - 100$

  c. $2x^2 - 8$

  d. $3x^2 - 11x - 4$

3-125. Decide whether each sequence below is arithmetic, geometric, or neither. Then find equations to represent each sequence, if possible.

    a. $10.3, 11.5, 12.7, \ldots$

    b. $\frac{1}{2}, \frac{1}{4}, \frac{1}{8}, \ldots$

    c. $1, 4, 9, \ldots$

    d. $1.1, 1.21, 1.331, \ldots$

3-126. Find x and $m\angle A$ in the triangle at right.

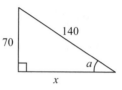

3-127. Decide which of the following pairs of expressions are equivalent. For those that are not equivalent, determine if there are any values of the variables that would make them equal (in other words, determine if they are *sometimes* equal). **Justify** each of your decisions thoroughly.

    a. $(3x^2y)^3$ and $3x^6y^3$

    b. $(3x^2y)^3$ and $27x^6y^3$

    c. $(3x^2y)^3$ and $27x^5y^4$

    d. $(3x^2y)^3$ and $27x^5y^3$

3-128. When data is arranged from least to greatest, the middle number (or the number between the two middle numbers, in the case of an even number of data pieces) is the median. The median of the lower half of data determines the boundary of the **first** and **second quartiles**. The median of the upper half of data determines the boundary of the **third** and **fourth quartiles**. The scores for 12 golfers were as follows: $68, 73, 80, 95, 86, 68, 74, 72, 90, 85, 70,$ and 82. Find the scores in the third quartile.

3-129. Solve $2x = \sqrt{8x + 12}$ for x by first rewriting the equation as an equivalent equation without the square-root sign. After solving the new equation, answer these questions: Do both answers make the original equation true? Was the equation that led to the two solutions equivalent to the original equation? Why or why not?

3-130. Examine the diagram below. Complete the congruence statement and **justify** your answer.

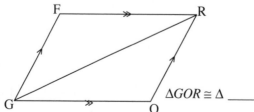

$\Delta GOR \cong \Delta$ _____

Chapter 3 Closure What have I learned?

Reflection and Synthesis

The activities below offer you a chance to reflect on what you have learned in this chapter. As you work, look for concepts that you feel very comfortable with, ideas that you would like to learn more about, and topics with which you need more help. Look for connections between ideas as well as connections with material you have learned previously.

①   TEAM BRAINSTORM

Brainstorm with your team to create a list of words and ideas for each of the following two categories. Be as detailed as you can. How long can you make your lists? Challenge yourselves. Be prepared to share your team's ideas with the class.

Topics: What have you studied in this chapter? What ideas and words were important in what you learned? Remember to be as detailed as you can.

Connections: How are the topics, ideas, and words that you learned in previous chapters and courses connected to the new ideas in this chapter? Again, make your list as long as you can.

②   MAKING CONNECTIONS

Below is a list of the vocabulary used in this chapter. Make sure that you are familiar with all of these words and know what they mean. Refer to the glossary or index for any words that you do not yet understand.

appreciation	asymptotes	depreciation
exponential function	half-life	initial value
multiplier	parameter	roots

Make a concept map showing all of the connections you can find among the key words and ideas listed above. To show a connection between two words, draw a line between them and explain the connection, as shown in the example below. A word can be connected to any other word as long as you can **justify** the connection. For each key word or idea, sketch an example.

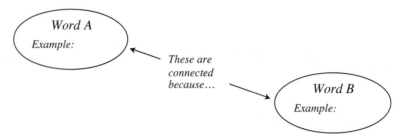

Your teacher may provide you with vocabulary cards to help you get started. If you use the cards to plan your concept map, be sure either to re-draw your concept map on your paper or to attach the vocabulary cards to a poster with all of the connections explained for others to see and understand.

While you are making your map, your team may think of related words or ideas that are not listed above. Be sure to include these ideas on your concept map.

③   GROWTH OVER TIME

This section gives you an opportunity to show growth in your understanding of key mathematical ideas over time as you progress through this course.

Answer the following question on its own sheet of paper. (You will keep this problem separate from your other work or put it into a portfolio.) You will see this problem again at the end of Chapter 6 and at the end of Chapter 9, when you should expect to have some new graphs to add to your list of examples.

How many different kinds of graphs can you create that have:

a.   No x-intercepts?   b.   One x-intercept?

c.   Two x-intercepts?   d.   Three or more x-intercepts?

For each type of graph, show a sketch, label the key points, and give its equation. Make sure that each graph you give as an example represents a different family, and describe the family in words or with a general equation. Show how to calculate the x-intercepts of each of your sample graphs.

④   SUMMARIZING MY UNDERSTANDING

This section gives you an opportunity to show what you know about certain math topics or ideas.

With your team, make a list of the **big ideas** of this chapter. Discuss the important ideas of the chapter and try to agree on a short list of no more than five big ideas. Be prepared to share your list in a whole-class discussion. When the class has reached agreement on a list, continue with parts (a) and (b) below.

a.   Write your own description of each big idea.

b.   For each big idea, provide one or two representative example problems. Solve each problem completely, using multiple representations, if applicable.

Your teacher may give you a "GO" page to work on (or you can download one from www.cpm.org). "GO" stands for "Graphic Organizer," a tool you can use to organize your thoughts and communicate your ideas clearly.

⑤   CLEANING UP MY LEARNING LOG

Read through all of the Learning Log entries you have made so far in this course. Do any of them need to be revised? Do you see mistakes you made that you can now correct? Is there any new information you can add? Do any of your entries need to be rewritten to be easier to understand? Work on cleaning up your Learning Log. As you work, be sure to ask your teammates for any thoughts or ideas they might have that could help you.

⑥   WHAT HAVE I LEARNED?

This section will help you recognize the types of problems you feel comfortable with and those with which you need more help. This section will appear at the end of every chapter to help you check your understanding. Even if your teacher does not assign this section, it is a good idea to try these problems and find out for yourself what you know and what you need to work on.

Solve each problem as completely as you can. The table at the end of this closure section has answers to these problems. It also tells you where you can find additional help and practice with similar problems.

CL 3-131. Find an exponential function in $y = ab^x$ form that satisfies each of the following sets of conditions.

    a.   Has a y-intercept of $(0, 2)$ and a multiplier of 0.8.

    b.   Passes through the points $(0, 3.5)$ and $(2, 31.5)$.

    c.   Passes through the points $(2, 20)$ and $(7, 640)$.

CL 3-132. Sam wants to create an arithmetic sequence and a geometric sequence, both of which have $t(1) = 8$ and $t(7) = 512$. Is this possible? If it is, help Sam create his sequences. If not, **justify** why not.

CL 3-133. Write each expression below as an equivalent expression without negative exponents.

    a. 3^{-2} b. m^{-4} c. $(\frac{1}{2})^{-3}$ d. $(\frac{3}{5x})^{-1}$

CL 3-134. Write each expression below in radical form and compute the value without using a calculator.

    a. $8^{1/3}$ b. $16^{3/4}$ c. $125^{-4/3}$

CL 3-135. Rewrite the following expressions using fractional exponents.

    a. $(\sqrt{3x})^3$ b. $\sqrt[x]{81}$ c. $(\sqrt[3]{17})^x$

CL 3-136. Solve each equation.

    a. $8^{x+3} = 16^x$ b. $y^{1/3} = 9$ c. $x^6 = 35$

CL 3-137. Find the annual multiplier and the percent decrease if a share of CPM stock was worth $60 in 2000 and only worth $45 in 2005.

CL 3-138. On January 17, 2005, the average price of a gallon of gasoline in the United States was $1.84 per gallon. Nineteen months later, on July 17, 2006, the average price per gallon had risen to $2.99, an average monthly growth of about 2.6%. At this rate, what will be the average price of a gallon of gas the summer after you graduate from high school?

CL 3-139. Simplify each expression.

a. $\dfrac{-8x^6y^2}{-4xy}$

b. $x^2y^3 \cdot x^3y^5z$

c. $(3x^2)^2 \div (6x^4)$

d. $\dfrac{(3x^2y)^2}{2z^2y^3} \cdot \dfrac{4x(y^2z^3)^3}{3x^2(z^2)^2}$

CL 3-140. Below are several situations that can be described using exponential functions. They represent a small sampling of the situations where quantities grow or decay by a constant percentage over equal periods of time. For each situation (a) through (d):

- Find an appropriate unit of time (such as days, weeks, years).

- Find the multiplier that should be used.

- Identify the initial value.

- Write an exponential equation in the form $f(x) = ab^x$ that represents the growth or decay.

a. A house purchased for $120,000 has an annual appreciation of 6%.

b. The number of bacteria present in a colony is 180 at noon, and it increases at a rate of 22% per hour.

c. The value of a car with an initial purchase price of $12,250 depreciates by 11% per year.

d. An investment of $1000 earns 6% annual interest, compounded monthly.

CL 3-141. Write an equation for the line that passes through the points $(-5,4)$ and $(3,-2)$.

CL 3-142. Add the fractions in part (a) and show two ways to solve the equation in part (b).

a. $\frac{x}{3} + \frac{2}{5}$

b. $\frac{x}{3} + \frac{2}{5} = x + 1$

CL 3-143. Check your answers using the table at the end of this section. Which problems do you feel confident about? Which problems were hard? Have you worked on problems like these in previous math classes? Use the table to make a list of topics you need help on, and a list of topics you need to practice more.

⑦ HOW AM I THINKING?

This course focuses on five different **Ways of Thinking**: reversing thinking, justifying, generalizing, investigating, and choosing a strategy. These are some of the ways in which you think while trying to make sense of a concept or to solve a problem (even outside of math class). During this chapter, you have probably used each Way of Thinking multiple times without even realizing it!

This closure activity will focus on one of these Ways of Thinking: **reversing thinking**. Read the description of this Way of Thinking at right.

Think about the topics that you have learned during this chapter. When did you undo a process? When did you try to go backward in your problem-

Reversing Thinking

To **reverse your thinking** can be described as "thinking backward." You think this way when you want to understand a concept in a new direction. Often, it requires you to try to undo a process. When you catch yourself thinking, "*What if I try to go backwards?*", you are **reversing your thinking**.

solving process? You may want to flip through the chapter to refresh your memory about the problems that you have worked on. Discuss any ideas you have with the rest of the class. Once your discussion is complete, examine some of the ways you have **reversed your thinking** as you answer the questions below.

a. If you know how to go from one representation to another, then there is a way to **reverse the process**. Consider the web connection graph ↔ rule.

  i. On graph paper, graph the equation $y = 2(4)^x$.

  ii. Now **reverse the process**. Find the equation of the exponential function graphed at right.

  iii. Explore another connection in the web where you **reversed your thinking** about exponential functions. Find or create a problem that represents one direction of solving. Then write and solve another problem that requires you to **reverse the process**.

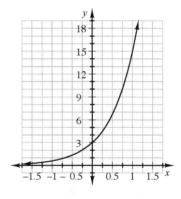

Problem continues on next page →

Problem continued from previous page.

b. Usually, if you change an expression into an equivalent expression, there is way to **reverse the process** to return to the original expression. Consider this as you answer the questions below.

    i. Show how to rewrite the expression $(9x^4y^3)^{\frac{1}{2}}$ in at least three different simpler forms.

    ii. Now, for each form, **reverse your thinking** to complicate it again three times. In other words, write three new expressions that are equivalent to your simplified ones. In each case, show how you know your new expression is equivalent to the original.

Answers and Support for Closure Activity #6:
What Have I Learned?

Problem	Solutions		Need Help?	More Practice
CL 3-131.	a. $y = 2(0.8)^x$ c. $y = 5 \cdot 2^x$	b. $y = 3.5(3)^x$	Lessons 3.2.1 and 3.2.2	Problems 3-22 through 3-26, 3-39, 3-62, 3-95, 3-107, 3-108, 3-109, and 3-122
CL 3-132.	Arithmetic: $t(n) = 84n - 76$ Geometric: $t(n) = 4(2)^n$		Lessons 2.1.5, 2.1.6, and 2.1.8 Math Notes box in Lesson 2.1.6	Problems 2-106, 2-109, 2-112, 2-128, 2-138, 2-153, 2-156, 3-16, 3-35, 3-46, 3-82, and 3-125
CL 3-133.	a. $\frac{1}{9}$ c. 8	b. $\frac{1}{m^4}$ d. $\frac{5x}{3}$	Lesson 3.1.4 Math Notes box in Lesson 3.2.2	Problem 3-52, 3-56, 3-59, and 3-66
CL 3-134.	a. $\sqrt[3]{8} = 2$ c. $\frac{1}{(\sqrt[3]{125})^4} = \frac{1}{625}$	b. $(\sqrt[4]{16})^3 = 8$	Lesson 3.2.1 Math Notes box in Lesson 3.2.2	Problems 3-91 and 3-99
CL 3-135.	a. $(3x)^{3/2}$ c. $17^{x/3}$	b. $81^{1/x}$ or $3^{4/x}$	Lesson 3.2.1 Math Notes box in Lesson 3.2.2	Problems 3-91 and 3-99

Problem	Solutions	Need Help?	More Practice
CL 3-136.	a. 9 b. 729 c. $\sqrt[6]{35} \approx 1.81$	Lessons 3.1.1, 3.1.3, and 3.2.1 Math Notes box in Lesson 3.2.2 Problem 3-30	Problems 3-31, 3-57, 3-79, 3-80, 3-100, and 3-110
CL 3-137.	a. ≈ 0.944 b. $\approx 5.6\%$ decrease	Lessons 2.1.6 and 3.2.2	Problem 2-103, 2-154, 3-18, 3-40, and 3-120
CL 3-138.	If \$1.84 is chosen as the initial value, the equation is $y = 1.84(1.026)^x$. If \$2.99 is chosen as the initial value, the equation is $y = 2.99(1.026)^x$. Answers vary depending upon students' year of graduation.	Lessons 2.1.6, 3.1.3, 3.2.2, and 3.2.3	Problems 3-40, 3-41, 3-78, and 3-120
CL 3-139.	a. $2x^5y$ b. x^5y^8z c. $\frac{3}{2}$ d. $6x^3y^5z^3$	Checkpoint 4	Problems 3-13, 3-19, and 3-55
CL 3-140.	a. years; 1.06; 120,000; $f(x) = 120000(1.06)^x$ b. hours; 1.22; 180; $f(x) = 180(1.22)^x$ c. years; 0.89; 12250; $f(x) = 12250(0.89)^x$ d. months; 1.005; 1000; $f(x) = 1000(1.005)^x$	Lessons 2.1.6 and 3.1.3	Problems 3-22, 3-34, 3-35, 3-36, 3-53, and 3-76
CL 3-141.	$y = -\frac{3}{4}x + \frac{1}{4}$	Math Notes box in Lesson 1.1.2 Checkpoint 6 Problem 3-105	Problems 1-106, 3-104, and 3-106
CL 3-142.	a. $\frac{5x+6}{15}$ b. $-\frac{9}{10}$	Checkpoint 13	Problems 2-89, 3-14, and 3-113

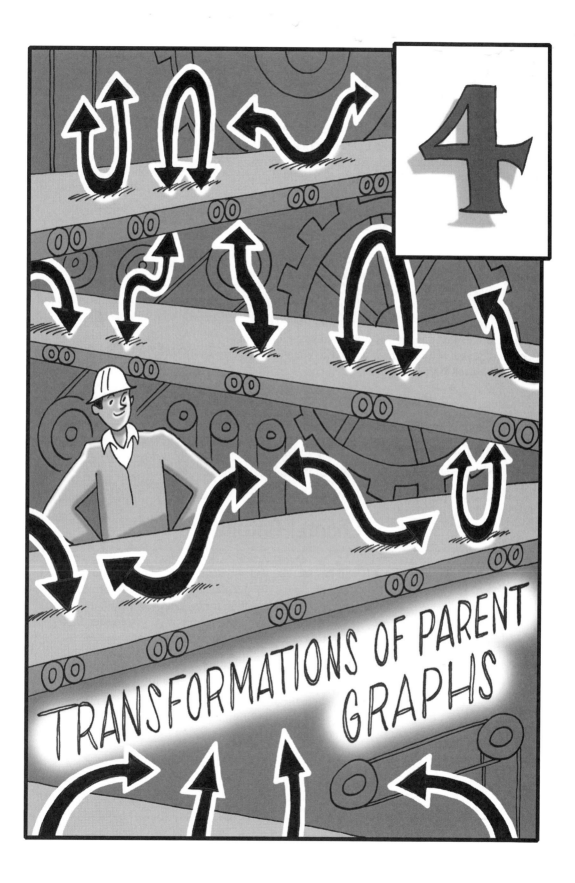

4

TRANSFORMATIONS OF PARENT GRAPHS

CHAPTER 4   Transformations of Parent Graphs

In the first section of Chapter 4, you will learn how to change the equation of a parabola to make it fit a set of nonlinear data. After you learn how to stretch, compress, reflect, and shift the graph of $f(x) = x^2$, you will be able to create a variety of parabolic shapes and sizes. You will use this family of functions to model physical situations, such as the arc of a jumping rabbit and the path of a soccer ball.

In Section 4.2, you will apply the same kinds of transformations to other parent relations. You will also learn what makes a relation a function.

You will learn that a graph's transformations are clearly recognizable when its equation is written in graphing form. In Section 4.3, you will learn how to rewrite equations so that they are easier to graph.

In this chapter, you will learn how to:

➤ Transform a graph by stretching or compressing it, shifting it left or right, or flipping it.

➤ Write a general equation for a family of functions.

➤ Model physical situations with quadratic functions.

➤ Write equations in graphing form.

Guiding Questions

Think about these questions throughout this chapter:

How can I transform this graph?

How can I **generalize**?

How are the members of a family of functions related?

How can I recognize transformations?

Chapter Outline

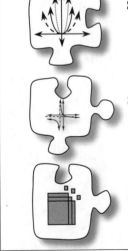

Section 4.1   In this section, you will learn how to shift, stretch, compress, and flip the graph of $f(x) = x^2$, and you will write a general equation for the family of quadratic functions. Then you will learn how to graph a quadratic function quickly when it is written in graphing form.

Section 4.2   You will apply the concepts of transformation to other parent functions, and you will learn about a new parent function, the absolute value function $f(x) = |x|$. You will also learn that transforming each parent function creates a whole family of functions.

Section 4.3   You will learn how to complete the square to rewrite a quadratic function $f(x) = ax^2 + bx + c$ in graphing form. You will apply the same method to the equations of circles.

4.1.1 How can an equation help me predict?

Modeling Non-Linear Data

This chapter will help you develop the power to manipulate functions to that are useful in a wide variety of situations. Today's lesson focuses on collecting data and finding a function to model the trend. You will then **generalize** your results and make predictions beyond the range of data you can measure. Discuss the following focus questions while you work:

What will the graph look like?

Should I connect the data points?

How can I find an equation that fits the data?

4-1. SHRINKING TARGETS LAB

What is the relationship between the radius of a disk and its mass? If you double the radius of the disk, does the mass also double?

To answer these questions, your team will use scissors, a scale, and a Lesson 4.1.1A Resource Page as you measure the weight of at least 8 different circular disks of varying radii (the plural of "radius"). Find your first data point by cutting out the large circle, measuring its radius, and using the scale to weigh it carefully. Repeat this process for circles of different radii.

After your team has collected its data, answer the questions below.

a. Look at your data with your team and predict what you think the graph will look like. **Justify** your prediction.

b. Enter your data in the graphing calculator and plot it. Graph your data on your paper.

c. What kind of equation do you think will model your data?

d. Work with your team to find an equation that fits your data. Test the accuracy of your team's equation by entering it into your graphing calculator. If necessary, adjust your equation to make its graph fit your data better. Once you are satisfied with your model, sketch the graph of your equation on your graph from part (b).

e. What would be the mass of a target with a radius twice as large as the largest one you measured? How do you know?

4-2.   What more can be said about the equation you used to model your data from the Shrinking Targets Lab? Consider this as you answer the questions below.

    a.   What are all of the acceptable input and output values (domain and range) for the activity in Shrinking Targets Lab? Do they match the domain and range of the function you used to model your data? If not, why are they different?

    b.   In part (a), you may have noticed that your equation only makes sense as a model for your data for part of its domain. Therefore, to accurately describe your model, you can add a condition to your equation, such as, "This equation is a good model when _____."

    What condition can you add to describe when your model is valid?

4-3.   According to the scenario described in the Shrinking Targets Lab, should your scatter plot from problem 4-1 have any x- or y-intercepts? If so, what are they and what do they represent? Does the graph of your equation have the same intercept(s)? If not, explain completely why not.

4-4.   Look back at the adjustments you made to your equation in problem 4-1 in order to make it fit your data. What did you change in your equation, and what effects did your changes have on its graph? Discuss these questions with your team and be prepared to share your ideas with the class.

4-5.   For each equation in parts (a) through (d) below, find the input value that gives the *smallest* possible output. In other words, find the x-value of the *lowest* point on the graph. Then find the input value that gives the *largest* possible output (or the x-value of the *highest* point on the graph).

    a. $y = (x - 2)^2$ b. $y = x^2 + 2$ c. $y = (x + 3)^2$ d. $y = -x^2 + 5$

    e.   Where on the graphs of each of the above equations would you find the points with the smallest or largest y-values?

4-6.   Sketch $y = x^2$, $y = -3x^2$, and $y = -0.25x^2$ on the same set of axes. What does a negative coefficient do to the graph?

4-7.   Your results from this problem will be useful in the parabola **investigation** that you will do in Lesson 4.1.2.

    a.   Draw the graph of $y = (x - 3)^2$. If you are drawing the graph by hand be sure to use the domain $0 \le x \le 6$.

    b.   How is this graph different from the graph of $y = x^2$?

4-8.   Consider the sequence with the initial value 256, followed by 64, 16, ...

   a.   Write the next three terms of this sequence, then find a rule for the sequence.

   b.   If you were to keep writing out more and more terms of the sequence, what would happen to the terms?

   c.   Sketch a graph of the sequence. What happens to the points as you go farther to the right?

4-9.   If $\frac{2}{3}$ of A is $\frac{5}{12}$, and $\frac{4}{3}$ of B is $\frac{8}{9}$, which is larger, A or B?

4-10.   Write the equation for each graph.

   a.

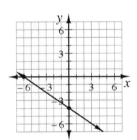

   b.

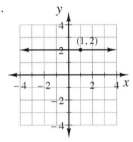

   c.

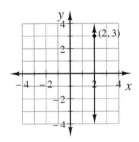

   d.

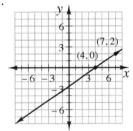

4-11.   Examine the diagram at right. Imagine spinning the rectangle around the y-axis. Think of a rectangular flap attached to the y-axis so that the rectangle will revolve around the y-axis.

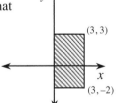

   a.   Draw the resulting shape.

   b.   Find the volume of this shape.

4-12.   What is a line of symmetry?

   a.   Draw a figure that has a line of symmetry.

   b.   Draw a figure that has *two* lines of symmetry.

   c.   Can you find a basic geometric shape that has an infinite number of lines of symmetry?

4.1.2 How can I shift a parabola?

Parabola Investigation

In Algebra 1 you learned about slope and *y*-intercept, ideas that allow you to write equations and sketch graphs of any line. During this lesson you will work on developing similar tools for parabolas.

4-13.   PARABOLA LAB, Part One

What happens to a parabola's graph when you change the numbers in the equation? To get a better sense of the different ways to transform the graph of a parabola, complete the lab outlined below as a team. As you work, be sure to sketch the graphs you see in your graphing calculator carefully and record the equations you enter.

a. On graph paper, graph the equation $y = (x-2)(x-2)$.
Be sure to label any important points on your graph, including the lowest point on the graph, called the **vertex**. (If the graph were to open downward, the vertex would be the highest point on the graph.) Also, sketch and write the equation of the line of symmetry of your graph.

b. Use your graphing calculator to find the equations of two parabolas with *different* graphs that also open upward and still have a vertex at $(2, 0)$. Add sketches of these two new graphs to your graph from part (a), along with their equations. As you work, keep track of any ideas you try along with their results, even if they do not answer this question, as they may help you later.

c. Use your graphing calculator to find the equations of two different parabolas that open *downward*, each with its vertex on the *x*-axis at $x = 2$. How did you change the equation so that the parabola would open downward? Add sketches of these graphs and their equations to your axes. What are their lines of symmetry?

d. Use your graphing calculator to find the equation of a parabola that opens downward with a vertex at $(-4, 0)$. What is the equation of your parabola's line of symmetry?

e. Choose a new point on the *x*-axis and find at least three equations of parabolas that touch the *x*-axis only at that one point.

4-14.   PARABOLA LAB, Part Two

Polly Parabola had been the manager of the parabola department of Functions of America, but she has decided to branch off and start her own company called "Professional Parabola Productions." She needs your help. See her memo below.

MEMO

To: *Your Study Team*
From: *Ms. Polly Parabola, CEO*
Re: *New Parabola Possibilities*

I am starting a new company specializing only in parabolas. To win over new customers, I need to be able to show them that we know more about parabolas than any of the other function factories around, since every company sells $y = x^2$ already.

My customers will need all sorts of parabolas, and we will need to have the knowledge to make them happy. I would love to offer parabolas that are completely new to them.

Please investigate all different kinds of parabolas. Determine all the ways that you can change the equation $y = x^2$ to change the shape, direction, and location of a parabola on a graph.

Remember that I'm counting on you! I need you to uncover the parabola secrets that our competitors do not know.

Sincerely,
Ms. Polly Parabola

Your task: Work with your team to determine all of the ways you can change the graph of a parabola by changing its equation. Be prepared to share your ideas with the class. As other teams contribute ideas to a class discussion, write down any new ideas.

Start by choosing one transformation from the list generated by the class; then find a way to change the equation $y = x^2$ to create this transformation of the parent graph. Whenever you figure out a new transformation, record a clear summary statement before moving on to the next transformation. Be prepared to explain your summary statement to Ms. Polly Parabola.

Discussion Points

What changes can we make to a parabola's graph?

What changes can we make to the equation $y = x^2$?

How do changes in the equation relate to changes in the graph?

4-15.   Graph the parabola $y = x^2$. Be sure to label any important points. When you are sure that your graph is complete and accurate, trace over it in colored pencil.

    a.   Find a way to change the equation to make the $y = x^2$ parabola *stretch vertically* (to make the graph look narrower, so the points in the parabola seem to rise away from the vertex more quickly). The new parabola should have the same vertex and orientation (i.e., open up) as $y = x^2$. Record the equations you try, along with their results. Write down the results even when they are wrong – they may come in handy below.

    b.   Find a way to change the equation to make the $y = x^2$ parabola *compress vertically* (to make the graph look flatter, so that the points seem to rise away from the vertex less quickly). Record the equations you try, along with their results and your observations.

    c.   Find a way to change the equation to make the same parabola *open downward*. The new parabola should be congruent (the same shape and size) to $y = x^2$, with the same vertex, except it should open downward so its vertex will be its highest point. Record the equations you try, their results, and your observations.

    d.   Find a way to change the equation to make the $y = x^2$ parabola *move 5 units down*. Your new parabola should look exactly like $y = x^2$, but the vertex should be at $(0,-5)$. Record the equations you try, along with their results. Include a comment about moving the graph up as well as down.

    e.   Find a way to change the equation to make the $y = x^2$ parabola *move 3 units to the right*. Your new parabola should look exactly like $y = x^2$, except that the vertex should be at the point $(3,0)$. If you need an idea to get started, review your work on problem 4-13. Record the equations you try, along with their results. Include a comment about how to move the parabola to the left as well as how to move it to the right.

    f.   Find a way to change the equation to make the $y = x^2$ parabola *move 3 units to the left* and *stretch vertically*, as in part (a). Record the equations you try, along with their results.

═════   *Further Guidance*   ═════
section ends here.

4-16.   Find a way to change the equation to make the $y = x^2$ parabola *vertically compressed, open down, move six units up, and move two units to the left*. Where is the vertex of your new parabola?

4-17.   Now that you are a parabola expert, you can impress Ms. Polly Parabola!

    a.   Make up your own fancy transformation and show her how you can change your equation to create it.

    b.   Write a **general equation for a parabola** that could be shifted or stretched in any direction by any amount. Be prepared to share your ideas with the class.

4-18.   Explain what the differences are between an *accurate sketch* and a *careful graph*.

4-19.   If $p(x) = x^2 + 5x - 6$, find:

    a.   Where $p(x)$ intersects the y-axis.

    b.   Where $p(x)$ intersects the x-axis.

    c.   If $q(x) = x^2 + 5x$.

        i.   Find the intercepts of $q(x)$ and compare the graphs of $p(x)$ and $q(x)$.

        ii. Find $p(x) - q(x)$.

4-20.   Find the point where $y = 3x - 1$ intersects $2y + 5x = 53$.

4-21.   Solve for z in each equation below.

    a. $4^z = 8$ b. $4^{2z/3} = 8^{(z+2)}$

    c. $3^z = 81^2$ d. $5^{(z+1)/3} = 25^{1/z}$

4-22.   Simplify each of the following expressions. Be sure that your answer has no negative or fractional exponents.

    a. $\left(\frac{1}{81}\right)^{-1/4}$ b. $x^{-2}y^{-4}$ c. $(2x)^{-2}(16x^2y)^{1/2}$

4-23.   Daniela, Kieu, and Duyen decide to go to the
         movies one hot summer afternoon. The theater
         is having a summer special: Three Go Free (if
         they each buy a large popcorn and a large soft
         drink). They take the deal and end up spending
         $22.50. The next week, they go back again, only
         this time, they each pay $8.00 to get in, they each
         get a large soft drink, and they share one large
         bucket of popcorn. This return trip costs them a
         total of $37.50.

a.   Find the price of a large soft drink and the
      price of a large bucket of popcorn.

b.   Did you write two equations or did you use another method? If you used another
      method, write two equations now and solve them. If you already used a system
      of equations, skip this part.

4-24.   The season free throw percentage for the Pi State Trigonometers basketball team was
         the following: 68, 69, 75, 80, 82, 85, 55, 67, 70, 70, 84, 83. Find the percentages above
         the third quartile. If you need help with quartiles, refer to problem 3-128.

4-25.   Lettie just got her driver's license. Her friends soon nicknamed her "Leadfoot"
         because she is always going 80 mph on the freeway even though the speed limit is
         65 mph.

a.   At this speed, how long will it take her to travel 50 miles?

b.   How long would it take her if she drove the 50 miles at 65 mph?

c.   Speeding tickets carry fines of about $200 and usually increase the cost of
      insurance. If Lettie gets a ticket on this trip, then what would be her cost per
      minute of time saved?

4-26.   Your friend is taking an algebra class at a different school where she is not allowed to
         use a graphing calculator. Explain to her how she can get a good sketch of the graph of
         the function $y = 2(x+3)^2 - 8$ without using a calculator *and* without having to make
         an $x \rightarrow y$ table.

a.   Be sure to explain how to locate the vertex, whether the parabola
      should open up or down, and how its shape is related to the shape
      of the graph of $y = x^2$.

b.   Your friend also needs to know the x- and y-intercepts. Show her
      how to find them without having to draw an accurate graph or use a graphing
      calculator.

4-27.   Consider the equations $y = 3(x-1)^2 - 5$ and $y = 3x^2 - 6x - 2$.

   a.   Verify that they are equivalent by creating a table or graph for each equation.

   b.   Show algebraically that these two equations are equivalent by starting with one form and showing how to get the other.

   c.   Notice that the value for a is 3 in both forms of the equation, but that the numbers for b and c are different from the numbers for h and k. Why do you think the value for a would be the same number in both forms of the equation?

4-28.   Use what you learned in the parabola investigation to write an equation for each of the parabolas described below.

   a.   A parabola just like $y = x^2$ but shifted 8 units right and 5 units down.

   b.   A parabola with a stretch factor of 10, sitting with its vertex on the x-axis at $(-6,0)$.

   c.   A downward-opening parabola with vertex $(-7,-2)$ and a vertical compression of 0.6.

4-29.   This is a Checkpoint for writing the equation of a line given two points.

Write the linear equation for each line described in parts (a) and (b) below.

   a.   The line that goes through the points $(-1, 4)$ and $(2, 1)$.

   b.   The line that goes through the points $(-8, 18)$ and $(4, 9)$.

   c.   The line that passes through the points $(-1, -2)$ and $(11, 2)$.

   d.   Check your answers by referring to the Checkpoint 6 materials located at the back of your book.

   If you needed help to solve these problems correctly, then you need more practice writing the equation of a line through two given points. Review the Checkpoint 6 materials and try the practice problems. Also, consider getting help outside of class time. From this point on, you will be expected to find equations of lines such as these quickly and easily.

4-30.   Solve for the indicated value. Leave your answer in exact form.

a. $x =$ _____

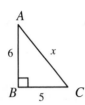

b. $m\angle C =$ _____

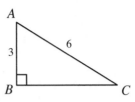

c. $m\angle B =$ _____

d. $a =$ _____

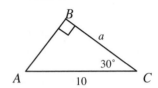

4-31.   Simplify each expression without using a calculator. Remember that to simplify expressions with radicals, you can remove perfect square factors. Part (a) below is provided as an example.

a. $\sqrt{18} = \sqrt{9 \cdot 2} = \sqrt{9} \cdot \sqrt{2} = 3\sqrt{2}$

b. $\sqrt{50}$

c. $\sqrt{72}$

d. $\sqrt{45}$

4-32.   Find the value of x.

a.

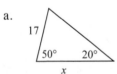

b.

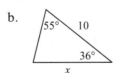

4-33.   Suppose your parents spend an average of $300 each month for your food.

a.   In five years, when you are living on your own, how much will you be spending on food each month if you are eating about the same amount and inflation averages about 4% per year?

b.   Write an equation that represents your monthly food bill x years from now if both the rate of inflation and your eating habits stay the same.

4.1.3 How can I graph it quickly?

Graphing a Parabola Without a Table

You have developed several tools that enable you to transform graphs of parabolas by altering their equations. In the next few lessons, you will use this power to do more with equations and graphs of parabolic functions than ever before. In this lesson, you will figure out how to use your growing knowledge of transforming graphs to make a quick and fairly accurate graph of any parabolic function.

4-34. TRANSFORMING GRAPHS

Use your dynamic graphing tool to support a class discussion about the equation $y = a(x - h)^2 + k$. Refer to the bulleted points below.

- Identify which **parameter** (a, h, or k) affects the orientation, vertical shift, horizontal shift, vertical stretch, and vertical compression of the graph compared to the graph of the parent function $y = x^2$.

- What values stretch the graph vertically? Compress the graph horizontally? Why do those values have these impacts?

- What values cause the graph to flip vertically?

- What values cause the graph to shift to the left? To the right? Why?

- What values cause the graph to shift up or down? Why?

- Are there points on your graph that connect to specific parameters in the equation? Explain.

4-35. For each equation below, predict the coordinates of the vertex, the orientation (opens up or down?), and whether the graph will be a vertical stretch or a compression of $y = x^2$. (Do not use a graphing calculator.) Quickly make a graph based on your predictions. How can you make the shape of your graph accurate without using a table? Be prepared to share your **strategies** with the class.

a. $y = (x + 9)^2$

b. $y = x^2 + 7$

c. $y = 3x^2$

d. $y = \frac{1}{3}(x - 1)^2$

e. $y = -(x - 7)^2 + 6$

f. $y = 2(x + 3)^2 - 8$

g. Now take out your graphing calculator and check your predictions for the equations in parts (a) through (f). Did you make any mistakes? If so, describe the mistake and what you need to do in order to correct it.

4-36.   Graph each equation below without making a table or using your graphing calculator. Look for ways to go directly from the rule to the graph. What information did you need to make a graph without using a table? How did you find that information from the equation? Be ready to share your **strategies** with the class.

a. $y = (x - 7)^2 - 2$

b. $y = 0.5(x + 3)^2 + 1$

4-37.   In problem 4-36, you figured out that having an equation for a parabola in **graphing form** ($y = a(x - h)^2 + k$) allows you to know the vertex, the orientation, and the stretch factor, and that knowing these attributes allows you to graph without having to make a table. How can you make a graph without a table when the equation is given in **standard form** ($y = ax^2 + bx + c$)? Consider the equation $y = 2x^2 + 4x - 30$.

a.   What is the orientation of $y = 2x^2 + 4x - 30$? That is, does it open upward or open downward? How could you change the equation to make the graph open the opposite way?

b.   What is the stretch factor of $y = 2x^2 + 4x - 30$? **Justify** your answer.

c.   Can you identify the vertex of $y = 2x^2 + 4x - 30$ by looking at the equation? If not, talk with your team about **strategies** you could use to find the vertex without using a table or graphing calculator and then apply your new **strategy** to the problem. If your team is stuck consider parts (*i*) through (*iii*) below.

   i.   What are the *x*-intercepts of the parabola?

   ii.   Where is the vertex located in relation to the *x*-intercepts? Can you use this relationship to find the *x* coordinate of the vertex?

   iii. Use the *x*-coordinate of the vertex to find its *y*-coordinate.

d.   Make a quick graph of $y = 2x^2 + 4x - 30$ and write its equation in graphing form.

4-38.   Rewrite each equation in graphing form and then sketch a graph. Label each sketch so that it is possible to connect it to the equation.

a. $p(x) = x^2 - 10x + 16$

b. $f(x) = x^2 + 3x - 10$

c. $g(x) = x^2 - 4x - 2$

d. $h(x) = -4x^2 + 4x + 8$

METHODS AND MEANINGS

Graphing and Standard Form of Parabolas

As you have worked with quadratic functions, equations, and expressions in your previous math courses as well as this course, you have regularly seen two forms of quadratic equations.

One is known as **graphing form** (or **vertex form**), and it looks like $y = a(x - h)^2 + k$. For example, the equation $y = 3(x - 1)^2 - 5$ is in graphing form where $a = 3$, $h = 1$, and $k = -5$.

The other form is known as **standard form** and looks like $y = ax^2 + bx + c$. For example, if $y = 3x^2 - 6x - 2$, then $a = 3$, $b = -6$, and $c = -2$.

4-39.   Solve each of the following equations *without using the Quadratic Formula*.

a. $y^2 - 6y = 0$

b. $n^2 + 5n + 7 = 7$

c. $2t^2 - 14t + 3 = 3$

d. $\frac{1}{3}x^2 + 3x - 4 = -4$

e.   Zero is one of the solutions of each of the above equations. What do all of the above equations have in common that causes them to have zero as a solution?

4-40.   Find the vertex of each of the following parabolas by averaging the *x*-intercepts. Then write each equation in graphing form.

a. $y = (x - 3)(x - 11)$

b. $y = (x + 2)(x - 6)$

c. $y = x^2 - 14x + 40$

d. $y = (x - 2)^2 - 1$

4-41. Did you need to average the x-intercepts to find the vertex in part (d) of the preceding problem?

    a. What are the coordinates of the vertex for part (d)?

    b. How do these coordinates relate to the equation?

4-42. Scientists can estimate the increase in carbon dioxide in the atmosphere by measuring increases in carbon emissions. In 1998 the annual carbon emission was about eight gigatons (a gigaton is a billion metric tons). Over the last several years, annual carbon emission has been increasing by about one percent.

    a. At this rate, how much carbon will be emitted in 2010?

    b. Write a function, $C(x)$, to represent the amount of carbon emitted in any year starting with the year 2000.

4-43. Make predictions about how many places the graph of each equation below will touch the x-axis. You may first want to rewrite some of the equations in a more useful form.

    a. $y = (x-2)(x-3)$ b. $y = (x+1)^2$

    c. $y = x^2 + 6x + 9$ d. $y = x^2 + 7x + 10$

    e. $y = x^2 + 6x + 8$ f. $y = -x^2 - 4x - 4$

    g. Check your predictions with your calculator.

    h. Write a clear explanation describing how you can tell whether the equation of a parabola will touch the x-axis at only one point.

4-44. Simplify each of the following expressions. Be sure that your answer has no negative or fractional exponents.

    a. $64^{1/3}$ b. $(4x^2y^5)^{-2}$ c. $(2x^2 \cdot y^{-3})(3x^{-1}y^5)$

4-45. Suppose you have a 3 by 3 by 3 cube. It is painted on all six faces and then cut apart into 27 pieces, each a 1 by 1 by 1 cube. If one of the cubes is chosen at random, what is the probability that:

    a. Three sides are painted?   b. Two sides are painted?

    c. One side is painted?   d. No sides are painted?

4.1.4 How can I model the data?

Mathematical Modeling with Parabolas

In the past few lessons, you have determined how to move graphs of parabolas around on a set of axes. In this lesson you will put these new skills to work as you use parabolas and their equations to model situations.

4-46. JUMPING JACKRABBITS

The diagram at right shows a jackrabbit jumping over a three-foot-high fence. To clear the fence, the rabbit must start its jump at a point four feet from the fence.

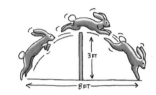

Sketch the situation and write an equation that models the path of the jackrabbit. Show or explain how you know your sketch and equation fit the situation.

Discussion Points

How can we make a graph fit this situation?

What information do we need in order to find an equation?

How can we be sure that our equation fits the situation?

Further Guidance

4-47. What is the shape of the path of the jackrabbit? What kind of equation would best model this situation?

a. Sketch the path of the jackrabbit on your own paper. Choose where to place the *x*- and *y*-axes in your diagram. Label as many points as you can on your sketch.

b. What point on your graph can tell you about the values of *h* and *k* in the equation? Write the values for *h* and *k* into the general equation. Is your equation finished?

c. With your team, find a **strategy** to find the exact value of *a*. Will any of the points on your diagram help? Be prepared to share your **strategy** with the class.

d. What are the domain and range for your model?

e. Did any team in your class get a different equation? If so, write down their equation and show how it can also model the path of the jackrabbit. What choices did that team make differently that resulted in the different equation?

———————— *Further Guidance section ends here.* ————————

4-48.   When Ms. Bibbi kicked a soccer ball, it traveled a horizontal distance of 150 feet and reached a height of 100 feet at its highest point. Sketch the path of the soccer ball and find the equation of the parabola that models it.

4-49.   At the skateboard park, the hot new attraction is the *U-Dip*, a cement structure embedded into the ground. The cross-sectional view of the *U-Dip* is a parabola that dips 15 feet below the ground. The width at ground level, its widest part, is 40 feet across. Sketch the cross sectional view of the *U-Dip*, and find the equation of the parabola that models it.

4-50.   LEARNING LOG

With your team, discuss all the different forms you know for the equation of a parabola. In your Learning Log, write down each form, along with a brief explanation of how that form is useful. Title this entry, "Forms of a Quadratic Function" and label it with today's date.

Review & Preview

4-51.   FIRE! CALL 9-1-1!

A fireboat in the harbor is helping put out a fire in a warehouse along the pier. The distance from the barrel of the water cannon to the roof of the warehouse is 120 feet, and the water shoots up 50 feet above the barrel of the water cannon.

Sketch a graph and find the equation of the parabola that models the path of the water from the fireboat to the fire. Give the domain and range for which the function makes sense in relation to the fireboat.

4-52.   Draw accurate graphs of $y = 2x + 5$, $y = 2x^2 + 5$, and $y = \frac{1}{2}x^2 + 5$ on the same set of axes. Label the intercepts.

a.   In the equation $y = 2x + 5$, what does the 2 tell you about the graph?

b.   Is the 2 in $y = 2x^2 + 5$ also the slope? Explain.

Algebra 2 Connections

4-53.   Do the sides of a parabola ever curve back in like the figure at right? Explain your reasoning.

4-54.   Do the sides of the parabola approach straight vertical lines as shown in the figure at right? (In other words, do parabolas have asymptotes?) Give a reason for your answer.

4-55.   Find the x- and y-intercepts of the graphs of the two equations below.

a. $y = 2x^2 + 3x - 5$ b. $y = \sqrt{2x - 4}$

4-56.   The vertex of a parabola (point (h, k)) locates its position on the axes. The vertex serves as a **Locator Point** for a parabola. The other shapes you will be **investigating** in this course also have locator points. These points have different names but the same purpose for each different type of graph.

Sketch graphs for each of the following equations. On each sketch, label the locator point.

a. $y = 3x^2 + 5$ b. $f(x) = -(x - 3)^2 - 7$

4-57.   If $g(x) = x^2 - 5$, find:

a. $g(\frac{1}{2})$ b. $g(h + 1)$

4-58.   If $g(x) = x^2 - 5$, find the value(s) of x so that:

a. $g(x) = 20$ b. $g(x) = 6$

4.2.1 How can I transform any graph?

· ·

Transforming Other Parent Graphs

You have been learning how to move a parabola around a set of axes, write equations, sketch graphs, and model situations. The graph of $y = x^2$ is called the **parent graph** for the family of parabolas because every other parabola can be seen as a transformation of that one graph.

4-59.   In this **investigation** you will use what you have learned about transforming the graph of $y = x^2$ to transform four new parent graphs. In fact, your team will figure out how to use what you have learned to transform the graph of *any* function!

Your task: As a team, determine how you can make the graph of any function move left, right, up, and down and how you can stretch it vertically, compress it vertically, and flip it. Each team member should choose one of the following parent functions to **investigate**: $y = x^3$, $y = \frac{1}{x}$, $y = \sqrt{x}$, and $y = b^x$. Remember that to **investigate** completely, you should sketch graphs, identify the domain and range, and label any important points or asymptotes. Then graph and write an equation to demonstrate each transformation you find. Finally, you will find a general equation for your family of graphs. (If you are **investigating** $y = b^x$, your teacher will give you a value to use for b.)

Discussion Points

How can we move a parabola?

How can we use our ideas about moving parabolas to move other functions?

What changes can we make to the equation?

4-60.   **Investigate** your parent graph.

          a.   Graph your equation on a full sheet of graph paper.

          b.   As a team, place your parent graphs into the middle of your workspace. For each graph, identify the domain and range and label any important points or asymptotes.

4-61.   For your parent graph:

          a.   Find and graph an equation that will shift your parent graph left or right.

          b.   Find and graph an equation that will shift your parent graph up or down.

          c.   Find and graph an equation that will stretch or compress your parent graph vertically.

          d.   Find and graph an equation that will flip your parent graph upside-down.

4-62.   One way of writing a general equation for a parabola is $y = a(x - h)^2 + k$. This equation tells you how to start with the parent graph $y = x^2$ and shift or stretch it to get any other parabola.

          a.   Explain what each parameter (a, h, and k) represents in the graph of a parabola.

          b.   As a team, write general equations for each given parent equation. Be ready to explain how your general equations work; that is, tell what effect each part has on the orientation (right-side-up or upside-down), relative size (stretched or compressed), horizontal location (left or right shift), and vertical location (up or down shift).

═══════   *Further Guidance*   ═══════
                section ends here.

4-63.   As a team, organize your work into a large poster that shows clearly:

          • Each parent graph you worked with,

          • Examples of each transformation you found, and

          • Each general equation.

          Use tools such as colors, arrows, and shading to show all of the connections you can find. Then add the following problems for other teams to solve:

          • Show the graph of a function in your family for which other teams need to find the equation.

          • Give an equation of a function in your family that other teams will graph.

4-64.   While watering her outdoor plants,
          Maura noticed that the water coming
          out of her garden hose followed a
          parabolic path. Thinking that she
          might be able to model the path of
          the water with an equation, she
          quickly took some measurements.
          The highest point the water reached
          was 8 feet, and it landed on the plants
          10 feet from where she was standing.
          Both the nozzle of the hose and the
          top of the flowers were 4 feet above
          the ground. Help Maura write an
          equation that describes the path of the water from the hose to the top of her plants.
          What domain and range make sense for the model?

4-65.   Draw the graph of $y = 2x^2 + 3x + 1$.

          a.   Find the x- and y-intercepts.

          b.   Where is the line of symmetry of this parabola? Write its equation.

          c.   Find the coordinates of the vertex.

4-66.   Change the equation in the previous problem so that the parabola has only one
          x-intercept.

4-67.   Simplify each expression. Remember you can simplify radicals by removing perfect
          square factors (e.g. $\sqrt{12} = \sqrt{4 \cdot 3} = 2\sqrt{3}$).

          a. $\sqrt{24}$ b. $\sqrt{18}$ c. $\sqrt{3} + \sqrt{3}$ d. $\sqrt{27} + \sqrt{12}$

4-68. Rewrite each of the following expressions so that your answer has no negative or fractional exponents.

a. $16^{5/4}$ b. $(x^5y^4)^{1/2}$ c. $(x^2y^{-1})(x^{-3}y)^0$

4-69. Harvey's Expresso Express, a drive-through coffee stop, is famous for its great house coffee, a blend of Colombian and Mocha Java beans. Their archrival, Jojo's Java, sent a spy to steal their ratio for blending beans. The spy returned with a torn part of an old receipt that showed only the total number of pounds and the total cost, 18 pounds for $92.07. At first Jojo was angry, but then he realized that he knew the price per pound of each kind of coffee ($4.89 for Colombian and $5.43 for Mocha Java). Show how he could use equations to figure out how many pounds of each type of beans Harvey's used.

4-70. Lilia wants to have a circular pool put in her backyard. She wants the rest of the yard to be paved with concrete.

a. If her yard is a 50 ft. by 30 ft. rectangle, what is the largest radius pool that can fit in her yard?

b. If the concrete is to be 8 inches thick, and costs $2.39 per cubic foot, what is the cost of putting in the concrete? No concrete will be used in the pool. (Reminder: Volume = (Base Area) · Depth).

4-71. Write the equation $y = x^2 + 7x - 8$ in graphing form. Use what you learned about finding the vertex in Lesson 4.1.3 to help you.

4-72. Consider a line with a slope of 3 and a y-intercept at $(0, 2)$.

a. Sketch the graph of this line.

b. Write the equation of the line.

c. Find the initial term and the next three terms of the sequence $t(n) = 3n - 1$. Plot the terms on a new set of axes next to your graph from part (a) above.

d. Explain the similarities and differences between the graphs and equations in parts (a) through (c). Are both continuous?

4-73.   The gross national product (GNP) was $1.665 \cdot 10^{12}$ dollars in 1960 and it increased at the rate of 3.17% per year until 1989. Use this information to answer each of the questions below. (The number $1.665 \cdot 10^{12}$ is expressed in scientific notation. Written in standard notation, the number is 1,665,000,000,000.)

   a.   What was the GNP in 1989?

   b.   Write an equation to represent the GNP t years after 1960, assuming that the rate of growth remained constant.

   c.   Do you think the rate of growth really remains constant? Explain.

4-74.   Write each expression in simpler radical form.

   a. $\sqrt{x} + \sqrt{y} + 5\sqrt{x} + 2\sqrt{y}$ b. $(2\sqrt{8})^2$

   c. $\dfrac{\sqrt{50}}{\sqrt{2}}$ d. $\sqrt{\dfrac{3}{4}}$

4-75.   Multiply each of the following expressions.

   a. $2x^2(3x + 4x^2 y)$ b. $(x^3 y^2)^4 (x^2 y)$

4-76.   Sketch a graph and draw the line of symmetry for the equation $y = 2(x - 4)^2 - 3$. What is the equation of the line of symmetry?

4-77.   People who live in isolated or rural areas often have their own tanks that hold gas to run appliances like stoves, washers, and water heaters. Some of these tanks are made in the shape of a cylinder with two hemispheres on the ends, as shown in the picture at right. (A hemisphere is half of a sphere, and the volume of a sphere is found by using $V = \frac{4}{3}\pi r^3$.)

   The Inland Propane Gas Tank Company wants to make tanks with this shape, but offer different models in different sizes. The cylindrical portion of each of the tanks will be 4 meters long. However, the radius r will vary among the different models.

   a.   One of their tanks has a radius of 1 meter. What is its volume?

   b.   When the radius doubles (to 2 meters), will the volume double? Explain. Then figure out the volume of the larger tank with $r = 2$ m.

   c.   Write an equation that will let Inland Propane Gas Tank Company determine the volume of a tank with any size radius.

4-78.   Write a possible equation for each of these graphs. Assume that one mark on each axis is one unit. When you are in class, check your equations on a graphing calculator and compare your results with your teammates.

a.
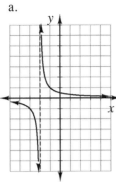

b.
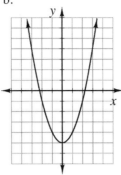

c.
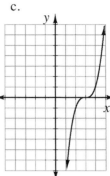

d.
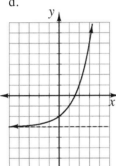

e.
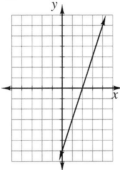

f.
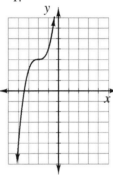

g.
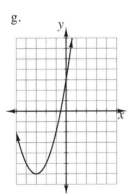

h.
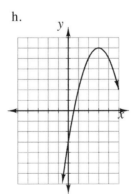

i.
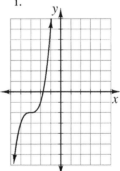

4-79.   By mistake, Jim graphed $y = x^3 - 4x$ instead of $y = x^3 - 4x + 6$. What should he do to his graph to get the correct one?

4-80. This is a Checkpoint for solving quadratic equations and for finding the x- and y-intercepts of the graph of a quadratic function.

   a. Find the x- and y-intercepts for the graph of $y = x^2 + 4x - 17$ without using a graphing calculator.

   b. Check your answers by referring to the Checkpoint 7 materials located at the back of your book.

   If you needed help to solve this problem correctly, then you need more practice in solving quadratic equations and finding the intercepts of a quadratic function. Review the Checkpoint 7 materials and try the practice problems. Also, consider getting help outside of class time. From this point on, you will be expected to find intercepts of quadratic functions easily and accurately.

4-81. Simplify each radical expression.

   a. $(3\sqrt{2})^2$ b. $\sqrt{\frac{9}{4}}$ c. $\sqrt{\frac{1}{3}}$ d. $(3 + \sqrt{2})^2$

4-82. Factor each of the following expressions. Look for the difference of squares and common factors.

   a. $4x^2 - 9y^2$ b. $8x^3 - 2x^7$ c. $x^4 - 81y^4$ d. $8x^3 + 2x^7$

   e. Did you use a shortcut to factor the expressions in parts (a) through (c)? If so, describe it. If not, what pattern do you see in these expressions? How can you use that pattern to factor quickly?

4-83. Solve for x: $ax + by^3 = c + 7$.

4-84. The slope of $\overline{AB}$ is 5, with points $A(-3,-1)$ and $B(2, n)$. Find the value of n and the distance between points A and B.

4-85. Given $f(x) = x^3 + 1$ and $g(x) = (x + 1)^2$:

   a. Sketch the graphs of the two functions.

   b. Solve $f(x) = 9$.   c. Solve $g(x) = 0$.

   d. Solve $f(x) = -12$.   e. Solve $g(x) = -12$.

   f. For how many values of x does $f(x)$ equal $g(x)$? Explain.

   g. Find and simplify an expression for $f(x) - g(x)$.

4.2.2 What is the significance of (h, k)?

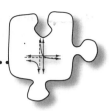

Describing (h, k) for Each Family of Functions

In Lesson 4.2.1, you learned that you can apply your knowledge of transforming parabolas to transform many other parent functions. In this lesson, you will consolidate your knowledge of each of the parent functions that you know and you will identify the importance of the point (h, k) for each parent function and its family.

4-86. Think about the parent graph for parabolas, $y = x^2$.

   a. Write the equation of a parabola that will be the same as the parent graph, but shifted four units to the right.

   b. Does the **strategy** you used to move parabolas horizontally also work for other parent graphs? **Justify** your answer.

   c. You have learned that the general equation for a parabola is $y = a(x - h)^2 + k$. To move the graph of $y = x^2$ h units to the *right*, you replaced x^2 with $(x - h)^2$. Work with your team to **justify** *why* replacing x with $(x - h)$ moves a graph to the right. Think about multiple representations as you discuss this and be prepared to share your ideas with the class.

4-87. With your team, brainstorm a list of all of the families of functions that you have learned about so far in your study of algebra.

4-88. Obtain copies of the Parent Graph Tool Kit (Lesson 4.2.2 Resource Page) from your teacher. Work with your team to complete a Tool Kit entry for each of the parent graphs you have studied so far in this course. For each parent graph, complete each of the following.

   • Name the family of functions.

   • Write the equation of the parent function.

   • Create a table and graph of the parent function.

   • Write the general equation of the family in graphing form.

   • Describe the properties of that family of functions.

   • State the domain and range of the parent function.

   • Describe the significance of the point (h, k) for the family.

4-89.　What is the equation of the parent graph of a line? Use what you have learned about transforming parent graphs to write the general equation of a transformed line.

a.　Use this general equation of a line to write the equation of a line with slope $\frac{4}{5}$ that passes through the point $(3, 9)$.

b.　A line passes through the points $(-1, 5)$ and $(8, -2)$. Substitute each of these into the general equation to create a system of equations. Now solve this system to find the slope. Is this how you have found slope in the past?

4-90.　LEARNING LOG

How can the point (h, k) help you to graph a function from its equation? How can it help you write the equation for a function given its graph? Discuss these questions with your team and then answer them in a Learning Log entry. Be sure to include examples to help you illustrate your ideas. Title this entry "How to use (h, k)" and label it with today's date.

MᴇᴛHODS AND Mᴇᴀɴɪɴɢs

Point-Slope Equations for Lines

MATH NOTES

If you think of $y = x$ as a parent equation, then the general equation for the family of lines can be written as

$$y = a(x - h) + k .$$

When this equation is rewritten as $y - k = a(x - h)$ it is often called the **point-slope** form of the equation for a line that contains the point (h, k) and has slope a.

For example, if you know a line contains the point $(7, -8)$ and has slope -4 then the equation can be written $y - (-8) = -4(x - 7)$ or $y + 8 = -4(x - 7)$.

4-91.   Use the point (h, k) to help you write a possible equation for each graph shown below.

a   b.   c.

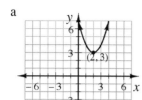 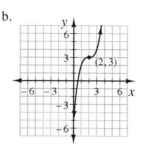 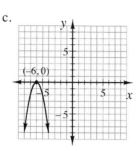

4-92.   Find the domain and range for each of the graphs in the previous problem.

4-93.   For each of the following equations, describe how d transforms the parent graph.

   a. $y = dx^3$ b. $y = 3x^2 - d$

   c. $y = (x - d)^2 + 7$ d. $y = \frac{1}{x} + d$

4-94.   Plot each pair of points and find the distance between them. Give answers in both square-root form and as decimal approximations.

   a. $(3, -6)$ and $(-2, 5)$ b. $(5, -8)$ and $(-3, 1)$

   c. $(0, 5)$ and $(5, 0)$

   d.   Write the distance you found in part (c) in simplified square-root form.

4-95.   Rewrite each of the following expressions so that your answers have no negative or fractional exponents.

   a. $5^{-2} \cdot 4^{1/2}$ b. $\frac{3xy^2z^{-2}}{(xy)^{-1}z^2}$

   c. $(3m^2)^3(2mn)^{-1}(8n^3)^{2/3}$ d. $(5x^2y^3z)^{1/3}$

4-96.   Solve each equation for x (that is, put it in $x = \_\_\_$ form).

   a. $y = 2(x-17)^2$

   b. $y + 7 = \sqrt[3]{x+5}$

4-97.   Where do the following pairs of lines intersect?

   a. $y = 5x - 2$
         $y = 3x + 18$

   b. $y = x - 4$
         $2x + 3y = 17$

4-98.   Graph these two lines on the same set of axes: $y = 2x$ and $y = -\frac{1}{2}x + 6$.

   a.   Find the x- and y-intercepts for each equation.

   b.   Shade the region bounded by the two lines and the x-axis.

   c.   What are the domain and range of the region? How did you find these values?

   d.   Find the area of this region. Round your answer to the nearest tenth.

4.2.3 Can I transform a new function?

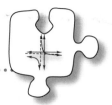

Transforming the Absolute Value Parent Graph

Today you will use what you have learned about shifting graphs to find the general equation for a new parent function, $f(x) = |x|$. (This reads, "f of x is equal to the absolute value of x.")

4-99. **LEARNING A FUNCTION**

Consider the function machines below for the function $f(x) = |x|$.

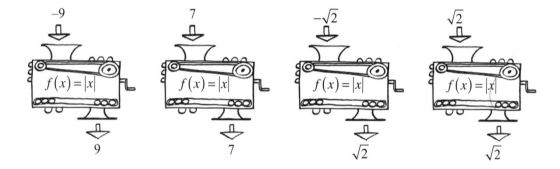

a.   Describe what $f(x) = |x|$ does to each input.

b.   Find the missing inputs and outputs below. Make sure you find all of the possibilities.

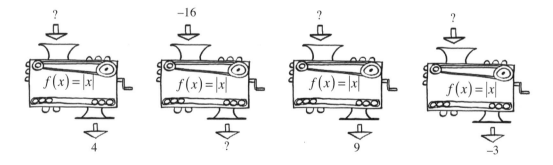

c.   If you are given an output for this machine, how can you figure out the input?

4-100.   TRANSFORMATION TEAM CHALLENGE

Find all of the possible types of transformations of the graph of $f(x) = |x|$. For each transformation you find, show the graph and its equation. Then find the general equation (in graphing form) for the family of absolute value graphs. When you have finished, add absolute value functions to your Parent Graph Tool Kit. Be prepared to explain your reasoning to the class.

4-101.   Use your knowledge of absolute value functions to find the equation of the graph at right. Be prepared to share your **strategies** with the class.

4-102.   LEARNING LOG

In the last few lessons, you have developed the ability to create a family of functions by transforming *any* parent function. Does the function you start with (the parent) affect how you will transform it? If so, how? If not, why not? Are there any parent graphs that are hard for you to transform? Why or why not? Write a Learning Log entry answering these questions. Title it "Give me any Function" and label it with today's date.

4-103.   Another way to look at absolute value is to think of the absolute value of a number as its distance from zero on a number line. For example, $|6| = 6$ and $|-6| = 6$ because both 6 and –6 are exactly 6 units from zero on the number line. You can, therefore, think of the equation such as $|x| = 5$ as the question, *"What numbers are exactly five units from zero on the number line?"* Thus, the solutions are 5 and –5. Draw a number line to show the solutions to the following equations.

   a. $|x| = 3$ b. $|x| = 0$ c. $|x| + 2 = 6$

   d. $3|x| = 15$ e. $|x - 5| = 2$ f. $|x + 3| = 7$

4-104.   Compare the two expressions $|11 - 5|$ and $|5 - 11|$.

   a.   How would you simplify each of them?

   b.   Explain why you get the same answer.

4-105.   Think of absolute value as a statement about distance as you answer the questions below. What values of x in parts (a) through (d) make each equation true?

   a. $|x - 7| = 50$ b. $|x + 7| = 50$

   c. $|10 - x| = 12$ d. $|2x + 1| = -3$

   e.   What mathematical operation is best used for finding the distance between two numbers? In other words, if you wanted to know the distance from 42 to 117, what arithmetic expression would represent that distance?

   f.   Suppose you wanted to write an equation to represent the statement, "The distance between a number and 47 is 21." You would not know whether to write $x - 47 = 21$ or $47 - x = 21$. Absolute value equations can allow you to write a correct expression without knowing which value is larger. Write two absolute value equations that mean "the distance between a number and 47 is 21."

   g.   Write and solve an absolute value equation that says each of the following:

      i.   *"The distance between x and 4 is 12."*

      ii.   *"The distance between x and –9 is 15."*

4-106.   What difference is there between $f(x) = |x|$ and $y = |x|$, in relation to their graphs or tables? What conclusions can you draw from your answer?

4-107.   The graph of $y = x^2$ is shown as a dashed curve to the right. Estimate the equations of the two other parabolas.

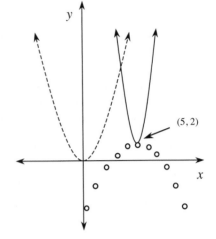

(5, 2)

4-108.   Find the x- and y-intercepts and the vertex of $y = x^2 + 2x - 80$, sketch the graph, and write the equation in graphing form.

4-109.   You are standing outside the school, waiting to cross the street, when you hear a booming car stereo approaching.

   a.   Sketch a graph that shows the relationship between how far away from you the car is and the loudness of the music.

   b.   Which is the dependent variable and which is the independent variable?

4-110.   Write each expression below in simplest radical form.

   a. $\sqrt{75} + \sqrt{27}$ b. $\sqrt{x} + 2\sqrt{x}$ c. $(\sqrt{12})^2$ d. $(3\sqrt{12})^2$

4-111.   Is -578 a term in the sequence defined by $t(n) = -5n + 7$? **Justify** your answer.

4.2.4 How can I transform relations?

Transforming Non-Functions

In this lesson, you consider two new parent equations that are different from the ones you have seen in the past. You will **investigate** them and apply the knowledge you have gained in this chapter to transform them. You will identify ways in which these new equations are different from the functions you have been working with.

4-112.   Begin by **investigating** $x = y^2$ and $x^2 + y^2 = 25$.

      a.   Without using your graphing calculator, make a table and a graph for each equation.

      b.   Marabel and Melissa were working on this problem at home. Marabel was making a table for $x = y^2$. For an x-value of 4, she found a y-value of 2. Melissa was watching and said, *"Wait! When x is 4, there is also another possible value for y."* What did Melissa mean? Look back at your tables, and decide if there are more points you could add.

      c.   Now describe $x = y^2$ and $x^2 + y^2 = 25$ completely. This includes finding the domain and range of each relation, the important points, and describing what happens to y as x increases.

      d.   How are these relations different from others you have been working with?

      e.   All of the parent equations you have been working with before this lesson are **functions**, but $x = y^2$ and $x^2 + y^2 = 25$ are not. Read the Math Notes box about functions at the end of this lesson. With your team, find another equation of a relation that is not a function.

4-113.   How can you rewrite $x = y^2$ and $x^2 + y^2 = 25$ so that you can graph them with your graphing calculator? When you have rewritten both equations, try graphing them using your calculator. Do they look like they should?

4-114.   TRANSFORMATIONS OF NON-FUNCTIONS

In order to enter non-functions into the graphing calculator, you had to express each non-function as two functions. How can you apply your knowledge of transforming functions to create general equations for your non-functions?

Your task: As a team, transform the graphs of $x = y^2$ and $x^2 + y^2 = 25$ in as many ways as you can. Then find a general equation (or combination of equations) for both families of graphs. Be prepared to share your findings and your **strategies** with the class.

Discussion Points

How can we change the equation so that the graph moves horizontally? Vertically?

How can the graph be stretched? Flipped?

4-115.   How can you rewrite your equations for the sleeping parabola and the circle into more useful forms?

a.   Work with your team to **reverse your thinking** and solve $y = \pm a\sqrt{x - h} + k$ for x to get a more useful form of the general equation for a sleeping parabola. What information does each of the parameters in the equation give about the graph of the sleeping parabola?

b.   Now rewrite $y = \pm\sqrt{-(x - h)^2 + 25} + k$ to isolate 25 on one side of the equation and leave all the variables and parameters on the other, in order to get a more useful form of the general equation for a circle. What information does each of the parameters in the equation give about the graph of the circle?

4-116.   A circle has a special characteristic, its radius, which defines its shape.

a.   Refer back to the graph of $x^2 + y^2 = 25$. What is the radius? How is the radius of the circle related to the equation?

b.   What would be the equation of a circle that has its center at $(5, -7)$ with radius 10? With radius 12?

c.   **Generalize** the connection of the radius to the equation of a circle by writing a general equation for a circle with any center (h, k) and radius r.

d.   Given the equation $(x - 3)^2 + (y + 7)^2 = 169$, how can you find the radius of the circle?

4-117. Consider the equation $(x-4)^2 + (y+1)^2 = 16$.

    a. What is the shape of the graph? How can you tell?

    b. What information can you learn about the graph just by looking at the equation?

    c. Sketch a graph of $(x-4)^2 + (y+1)^2 = 16$.

4-118. Make a personal poster that shows and explains how moving the graph of each non-function is related to its general equation. Use math, color-coding, arrows, labels, etc., to make your ideas and ways of thinking clear.

METHODS AND MEANINGS

MATH NOTES

Relations and Functions

    A **relation** establishes a correspondence between its x- and y-values. Some relations can be represented by equations of two variables. Some examples of relations are:

$$x = y^2 \qquad y = \frac{x}{x+3} \qquad y = -2x+5$$

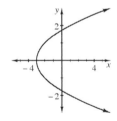

The set of possible inputs of a relation is called the **domain**, while the set of all possible outputs of a relation is called the **range**. For example, notice that all the points on the graph at right have x-values that are greater than or equal to -3. The arrows on the graph indicate that the graph will continue to extend to the right. Thus, the domain is the entire set of numbers that are greater than or equal to -3. Likewise, since each y-value has a corresponding point on the graph, the range is the set of all real numbers.

A **relation** is called a **function** if there is *no more than one* output for each input. If a relation has two or more outputs for a single input value, it is not a function. For example, the relation graphed above is not a function because there are two y-values for each x-value greater than -3.

For functions, the value of y usually depends on x, and y is often referred to as the **dependent variable**, while x is called the **independent variable**.

4-119.   A parabola has vertex $(2, 3)$ and contains the point $(0, 0)$.

     a.   If this parabola is a function, find its equation.

     b.   Suppose this parabola is not a function, but is a "sleeping" parabola. Find its equation.

4-120.   The quadratic formula can be used to help solve $4x^3 + 23x^2 - 2x = 0$. Show or explain how.

4-121.   For each equation below, find the x- and y-intercepts and the locator point (h, k), then write the equations in graphing form.

     a. $y = 7 + 2x^2 + 4x - 5$ b. $x^2 = 2x + x(2x - 4) + y$

4-122.   This is a Checkpoint for finding the slope of a line that passes through two points and for finding the distance between the points.

Find the slope of a line that passes through each of the pairs of points given below and then find the distance between the two points.

     a. $(0, 0)$ and $(4, 4)$ b. $(-2, 4)$ and $(4, 7)$

     c. $(12, 18)$ and $(-16, -19)$ d. $(0, 0)$ and $(25, 25)$

     e.   Check your answers by referring to the Checkpoint 8 materials located at the back of your book.

If you needed help to find the slope or distance correctly, then you need more practice. Review the Checkpoint 8 materials and try the practice problems. Also, consider getting help outside of class time. From this point on, you will be expected to find slope and distance given two points easily and accurately.

4-123.   Consider the system of equations at right:

                                                      $3y - 4x = -1$

     a.   What is the parent of each equation? $9y + 2x = 4$

     b.   Solve this system algebraically.

     c.   Find where the two graphs intersect.

     d.   Explain the relationship between parts (b) and (c) above.

4-124. Find the intercepts, the locator point (h, k), the domain, and the range for each of the following functions.

    a. $y = |x - 4| - 2$ b. $y = -|x + 1| + 3$

4-125. A line passes through the points $(0, 2)$ and $(1, 0)$.

    a.   Find the slope of the line.

    b.   Find the slope of a line parallel to the given line.

    c.   Find the slope of a line perpendicular to the given line.

    d.   Find the product of the slopes.

    e.   Make a conjecture about the product of the slopes of any two perpendicular lines. Test your conjecture by creating more examples.

4-126. Find the value of x.

    a.

    b.

    c.
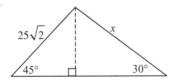

4-127. A dart hits each of these dart boards at random. What is the probability that the dart will not land in the shaded area?

    a.

    b.

4.3.1 How can I write it in graphing form?

Completing the Square

In Lesson 4.1.3, you found that one way to change the equation of a parabola from the standard form $f(x) = ax^2 + bx + c$ to the graphing form $f(x) = a(x - h)^2 + k$ is to find the vertex and then substitute the coordinates of the vertex for h and k. But how can you find the graphing form for an equation like $x^2 + 4x + y^2 + 2y = 11$? In this lesson and the next, you will learn a new method called **completing the square**.

4-128.   With your team, decide on a **strategy** to find the vertex of the parabola
$y = x^2 - 2x - 15$. Then write the equation of the parabola in graphing form.

    a.   Write the equation of the parabola in graphing form.

    b.   Now consider $y = x^2 + 8x + 10$. Does your team's **strategy** work for this parabola?

4-129.   A NEW METHOD

Jessica was at home struggling with her Algebra 2 homework. She had missed class and did not understand the new method called **completing the square**. She was supposed to use it to change $f(x) = x^2 + 8x + 10$ to graphing form without figuring out the vertex first. Then her precocious younger sister, who was playing with algebra tiles, said, "*Hey, I bet I know what they mean.*" Anita's Algebra 1 class had been using tiles to multiply and factor binomials. Anita explained:

x^2 represents the area of a square tile with dimensions x by x,

x represents the area of a rectangle with dimensions x by 1, and

1 represents the area of a square with dimensions 1 by 1.

"*Yes,*" said Jessica, "*I took Algebra 1 too, remember?*" Then Anita said, "*Good, so $f(x) = x^2 + 8x + 10$ would look like this:*"

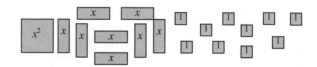

and you need to make it into a square!"

Problem continues on next page →

Problem continued from previous page.

"*OK,*" said Jessica, and she arranged her tiles as shown in the picture below.

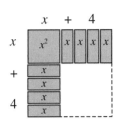

"*Oh,*" said Jessica. "*So with the 8 x's, I just need 16 small unit tiles to fill in the corner.*"

"*But you only have 10,*" Anita reminded her.

"*Right, I only have ten,*" Jessica replied. She put in the 10 small square tiles then drew the outline of the whole square and said:

"*Oh, I get it! The* **complete square** *is* $(x+4)^2$*, but I have six fewer tiles than that, so what I have is* $(x+4)^2$*, minus 6.*"

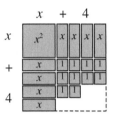

"*Oh, I see,*" said Anita. "*You started with* $x^2 + 8x + 10$*, but now you can rewrite it as* $x^2 + 8x + 10 = (x+4)^2 - 6$*.*"

a. How can you prove that $x^2 + 8x + 10$ and $(x+4)^2 - 6$ are equivalent expressions?

b. Where is the vertex of the parabola $f(x) = (x+4)^2 - 6$?

c. Sketch a quick graph of $f(x) = (x+4)^2 - 6$.

4-130. Help Jessica with a new problem. She needs to complete the square to write $y = x^2 + 4x + 9$ in graphing form. Draw tiles to help her figure out how to make this expression into a square. Does she have too few or too many unit squares this time? Write her equation in graphing form, name the vertex, and sketch the graph.

4-131.   How could you complete the square to change $f(x) = x^2 + 5x + 2$ into graphing form? How would you split the five x-tiles into two equal parts?

Jessica decided to use force! She cut one tile in half, as shown below. Then she added her two small unit tiles.

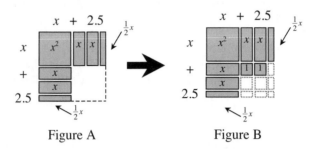

Figure A   Figure B

a.   How many small unit tiles are missing from Jessica's square?

b.   Write the graphing form of the function, name the vertex, and sketch the graph.

4-132.   Write each function in graphing form, then state the vertex of each parabola.

a. $f(x) = x^2 + 6x + 7$ b. $f(x) = x^2 + 4x + 11$

c. $f(x) = x^2 + 10x$ d. $f(x) = x^2 + 7x + 2$

4-133.   Oscar was working with his team on solving the equation $x^2 + 6x + 7 = 23$, when he had an idea. *"Can't we use completing the square to rewrite the left side of the equation?"* he said. *"Then we would get $(x + 3)^2 - 2 = 23$, which we can solve without factoring or using the quadratic formula!"* Work with your team to finish solving Oscar's equation. Then complete the square to solve each of the equations below.

a. $x^2 - 4x + 8 = 20$ b. $x^2 + 2x - 5 = 30$

4-134.   **GENERALIZATION** CHALLENGE

Work with your team to write the graphing form for $f(x) = x^2 + bx + c$. Be prepared to share your **strategies** with the class.

Review & Preview

4-135.   For each quadratic function below, use the idea of completing the square to write it in graphing form. Then state the vertex of each parabola.

a. $f(x) = x^2 + 6x + 15$ b. $y = x^2 - 4x + 9$

c. $f(x) = x^2 + 8x$ d. $y = x^2 + 5x - 2$

Algebra 2 Connections

4-136.   Represent the number of small squares you would have to add to an expression of the form $x^2 + bx$ to make a complete square. Use drawings and examples if they help to clarify.

4-137.   Consider the equation $(x-2)^2 + (y+7)^2 = 81$.

    a.   What is the shape of the graph? How can you tell?

    b.   What other information can you get about the graph by looking at the equation?

    c.   Graph the equation without a table. Is the relation a function? Why or why not?

4-138.   Explain the difference between the graphs of $y = \frac{1}{x}$ and $y = 4(\frac{1}{x+5}) + 7$.

4-139.   How is $y = 2^x$ different from $y = -(2^x)$? Sketch the graph of $y = -(2^x)$.

4-140.   Sketch the graph of $y = 2(x-1)^2 + 4$.

    a.   Now rewrite the equation $y = 2(x-1)^2 + 4$ without parentheses. Remember the order of operations!

    b.   What would the difference be between the graphs of the two equations above? This is sort of a trick question, but explain your reasoning.

    c.   What is the parent of $y = 2(x-1)^2 + 4$?

    d.   What is the parent of $y = 2x^2 - 4x + 6$?

4-141.   Find the coordinates of the intercepts for each of the following functions:

    a. $g(x) = (x+3)^3$ b. $y - 1 = 3^x$

4-142.   If $h(x) = (x+2)^{-1}$, find:

    a. $h(3)$ b. $h(-3)$ c. $h(a-2)$

4-143.   The point $(3, -7)$ is on a line with a slope of $\frac{2}{3}$. Find another point on the line.

4.3.2 How can I find the center of a circle?

More Completing the Square

Completing the square is a convenient method to change equations of parabolas into graphing form, but it is not the only method you know. You can also find the *x*-intercepts (if there are any) of the graph and use them to find the vertex. But how can you put the equation of a circle into graphing form?

Perfect squares are also convenient for graphing circles, as the general equation in graphing form for a circle $(x-h)^2 + (y-k)^2 = r^2$ shows.

4-144.   Consider the equation $(x-4)^2 + (y+1)^2 = 9$.

   a.   What is the shape of the graph? How can you tell?

   b.   What can you learn from the equation that can help you make a quick graph?

   c.   Sketch a quick graph of $(x-4)^2 + (y+1)^2 = 9$.

4-145.   Jessica is back at home, stuck on another homework problem, and needs your team's help again. She is supposed to sketch a quick graph of $x^2 + 4x + y^2 + 2y = 11$. She is pretty sure that it is a circle, but she does not know how to get it into graphing form. She is pretty sure she can use algebra tiles to figure it out, only this time she will need more shapes. She collected the tiles shown in the picture below.

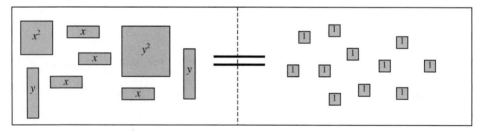

   a.   With your team, figure out how to arrange the tiles to form the shape of two squares on the left side of the diagram.

   b.   How many unit tiles are needed to complete the two squares?

   c.   How can you complete the squares and keep the equation balanced?

   d.   Write the equation in graphing form and sketch a quick graph.

4-146. Change $x^2 + y^2 - 4x + 6y - 3 = 0$ to graphing form and sketch a quick graph.

4-147. Jessica's older sister Tisha is in math analysis and is stuck on a homework problem that asks her to find the points of intersection between the two circles at right.

$$x^2 + 4x + y^2 - 6y - 12 = 0$$
$$x^2 - 8x + y^2 - 6y = 0$$

a. Tisha thinks she can find the intersection by solving the system of equations. If she tries to do this, what will she find?

b. Jessica thinks that she will figure out the intersections by using her knowledge of completing the square. Put the two equations into graphing form and then sketch the graphs. Use Jessica's method to find the points of intersection.

 METHODS AND MEANINGS

General Equations for Families

If $y = f(x)$ is a parent equation, then the general equation for the family of functions with similar characteristics as $f(x)$ can be written as:

$$y = af(x - h) + k$$

Where (h, k) is the point corresponding to $(0, 0)$ in the parent graph and, relative to the parent graph, the function has been:

- Vertically stretched if the absolute value of a is greater than 1.
- Vertically compressed if the absolute value of a is less than 1.
- Reflected across the x-axis if a is less than 0.

So far in this chapter you have worked with the following families:

Parent	Family	General Equation
$y = x^2$	Parabola	$y = a(x - h)^2 + k$
$y = x^3$	Cubic	$y = a(x - h)^3 + k$
$y = \frac{1}{x}$	Hyperbola	$y = a(\frac{1}{x-h}) + k$
$y = \sqrt{x}$	Square Root	$y = a\sqrt{x - h} + k$
$y = b^x$	Exponential	$y = ab^{(x-h)} + k$

4-148.   Jessica's new dilemma is the following problem:

Use the idea of completing the square to write the following quadratic function in graphing form:

$$y = x^2 - 6x - 2.$$

As usual, Anita was looking over Jessica's shoulder as she read the problem. *"You can't do that one with the tiles,"* she announced.

"Why not?" asked Jessica.

"Because it has negatives in it, and our teacher said the tiles are only a good model for positive numbers, but not negatives," Anita assured her.

"Who needs the tiles?" said Jessica. *"I can use the idea of completing the square algebraically. See, the complete square for $x^2 - 6x$ is $(x-3)^2 = x^2 - 6x + 9$. So I just have to subtract 11 to get that expression to equal $x^2 - 6x - 2$."*

a.   Based on Jessica's method above, what is the graphing form of this equation? State the vertex and sketch the graph.

b.   Use the idea of completing the square to write the function $f(x) = x^2 - 4x - 5$ in graphing form. State the vertex and sketch the graph.

4-149.   Use the technique of completing the square to express $y = x^2 - 5x + 7$ in graphing form and state the vertex.

4-150.   The amount of profit (in millions) made by Scandal Math, a company that writes math problems based on tabloid articles, can be found by the equation $P(n) = -n^2 + 10n$, where n is the number of textbooks sold (also in millions). Find the maximum profit and the number of textbooks that Scandal Math must sell to attain this maximum profit.

4-151.   Shortcut Shuneel claims he has a short cut for finding the vertex of a parabola. While using his short cut on $y = 2x^2 + 3x + 1$, he ended up with $y = 2(x + \frac{3}{4})^2 - \frac{7}{2}$. Is Shuneel correct? Why or why not?

4-152.   Remember function machines? Each of the following pictures shows how the same machine changes the given x-value into a corresponding $f(x)$ value. Find the rule for this machine.

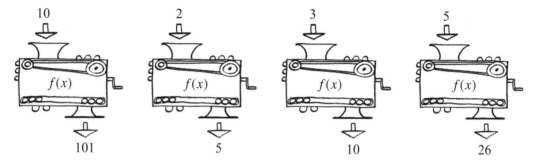

4-153.   If $x^2 + kx + 18$ is factorable, what are the possible values of k?

4-154.   Give the equations of two functions, $f(x)$ and $g(x)$, so that $f(x)$ and $g(x)$ cross at exactly:

    a.   One point.   b.   Two points.   c.   No points.

4-155.   Multiply the expressions in parts (a) through (c) to remove the parentheses.

    a. $(x - 1)(x + 1)$ b. $2x(x + 1)(x + 1)$

    c. $(x - 1)(x + 1)(x - 2)$

    d.   Find the x- and y-intercepts of $y = x^3 - 2x^2 - x + 2$. The factors in part (c) should be useful.

Chapter 4 Closure What have I learned?

Reflection and Synthesis

The activities below offer you a chance to reflect on what you have learned in this chapter. As you work, look for concepts that you feel very comfortable with, ideas that you would like to learn more about, and topics you need more help with. Look for connections between ideas as well as connections with material you learned previously.

①   TEAM BRAINSTORM

With your team, brainstorm a list for each of the following three categories. Be as detailed as you can. How long can you make your lists? Challenge yourselves. Be prepared to share your team's ideas with the class.

Topics: What have you studied in this chapter? What ideas and words were important in what you learned? Remember to be as detailed as you can.

Investigations: You know a lot more now about what to look for when you **investigate** mathematical relationships. What new questions did you ask yourself? List as many aspects, new and old, of **investigations** as you can.

Connections: How are the topics, ideas, and words that you learned in previous courses connected to the new ideas in this chapter? Again, make your list as long as you can.

②   MAKING CONNECTIONS

Below is a list of the vocabulary used in this chapter. Make sure that you are familiar with all of these words and know what they mean. Refer to the glossary or index for any words that you do not yet understand.

absolute value	asymptote	completing the square
compress	domain	function
general equation	graphing form	horizontal shift
non-function	parameter	parent graph
range	relation	standard form
stretch	transformation	variable
vertex	vertical shift	(h, k)

Continues on next page. →

Algebra 2 Connections

② *Continued from previous page.*

Make a concept map showing all of the connections you can find among the key words and ideas listed above. To show a connection between two words, draw a line between them and explain the connection, as shown in the example below. A word can be connected to any other word as long as you can **justify** the connection. For each key word or idea, provide a sketch of an example.

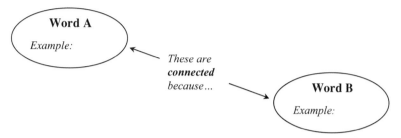

Your teacher may provide you with vocabulary cards to help you get started. If you use the cards to plan your concept map, be sure either to re-draw your concept map on your paper or to glue the vocabulary cards to a poster with all of the connections explained for others to see and understand.

While you are making your map, your team may think of related words or ideas that are not listed above. Be sure to include these ideas on your concept map.

③   GROWTH OVER TIME

This section gives you an opportunity to show growth in your understanding of key mathematical ideas over time as you complete this course.

On its own sheet of paper (you will keep this problem separate from your other work or put it into a portfolio), explain everything that you know about $y = x^2 - 4$ and $y = \sqrt{x+4}$.

④ SUMMARIZING MY UNDERSTANDING

This section gives you an opportunity to show what you know about certain math topics or ideas.

With your team, make a list of the **big ideas** of this chapter. Discuss the important ideas of the chapter and try to agree on a short list of no more than five big ideas. Be prepared to share your list in a whole class discussion. When the class has reached agreement on a list, continue with parts (a) and (b) below.

a. Write your own description of each big idea.

b. For each big idea, provide one or two representative example problems. Solve each problem completely, using multiple representations, if applicable.

Your teacher may give you a "GO" page to work on (or you can download this from www.cpm.org). "GO" stands for "Graphic Organizer," a tool you can use to organize your thoughts and communicate your ideas clearly.

⑤ WHAT HAVE I LEARNED?

This section will help you evaluate which types of problems you feel comfortable with and which you need more help with. This section will appear at the end of every chapter to help you check your understanding. Even if your teacher does not assign this section, it is a good idea to try these problems and find out for yourself what you know and what you need to work on.

Solve each problem as completely as you can. The table at the end of this closure section has answers to these problems. It also tells you where you can find additional help and practice with similar problems.

CL 4-156. Chucky and Angelica were reviewing equations of parabolas for their upcoming math test. They disagreed on what the equation would look like for a parabola whose vertex was at $(-4, 3)$.

a. Help them write an equation for a parabola that opens upward from its vertex at $(-4, 3)$. What is the equation of its line of symmetry?

b. Chucky wants the same parabola to open down and Angelica wants it to be compressed. Show them how to change your original equation to meet their desires. Does the line of symmetry change?

c. Move your parabola from part (b) 7 units to the right and 8 units down and stretch it vertically so that it is thinner than the original parabola. What is the equation of the parabola? What is the equation of its line of symmetry?

CL 4-157. For each equation, give the locator point (h, k), the equations of any asymptotes, and draw the graph.

    a. $f(x) = -|x+2| - 1$ b. $y = \frac{1}{x} + 2$

    c. $(x-1)^2 + (y+2)^2 = 9$ d. $x = (y-1)^2$

CL 4-158. Gloria the grasshopper is working on her hops. She is trying to jump as high and as far as she can. Her best jump so far was 28 cm long and she reached a height of 20 cm. Sketch a graph and write an equation of the parabola that describes the path of her jump.

CL 4-159. Find the equation of the exponential functions with a horizontal asymptote at $y = 0$ through the following pairs of points.

    a. $(2, 99)$ and $(6, 8019)$ b. $(-1, 50)$ and $(2, 25.6)$

CL 4-160. Create multiple representations of each of the following sequences.

    a. $10, 7, 4, \ldots$ b. $-2, -8, -32, \ldots$

CL 4-161. For each of the equations below, complete the following:
- Find the x- and y-intercepts.
- Find the vertex.
- Sketch a graph of each parabola on its own set of axes.
- Write the equation in graphing form.

    a. $y = x^2 + 8x + 12$ b. $y = (x-4)(x+2)$

    c. $y = x^2 - 6x - 9$ d. $y = x^2 + 5x + 1$

CL 4-162. Factor each of the following expressions.

    a. $2x^2 + 7x - 4$ b. $8x^2 + 24x + 10$

CL 4-163. Dinner at David's costs $8.95 today and has been increasing an average of 7% per year.

    a.   What will it cost in 10 years?   b.   What did it cost 10 years ago?

CL 4-164. If $g(x) = (x+1)^2$, find each of the following.

    a. $g(5)$ b. $g(2m+4)$ c. x if $g(x) = 9$

CL 4-165. Solve each equation for y.

    a. $4 - 2(x + y) = 9$ b. $x = 2(y - 1)^2 + 2$

CL 4-166. Check your answers using the table at the end of this section. Which problems do you feel confident about? Which problems were hard? Have you worked on problems like these in math classes you have taken before? Use the table to make a list of topics you need help on and a list of topics you need to practice more.

⑥   HOW AM I THINKING?

This course focuses on five different **Ways of Thinking**: reversing thinking, justifying, generalizing, choosing a strategy, and investigating. These are some of the ways in which you think while trying to make sense of a concept or to solve a problem (even outside of math class). During this chapter, you have probably used each Way of Thinking multiple times without even realizing it!

This closure activity will focus on one of these Ways of Thinking: **generalizing**. Read the description of this Way of Thinking at right.

Think about the topics that you have learned during this chapter. When did you need to describe patterns? When did you draw a conclusion or make a **general** statement? You may want to flip through the chapter to refresh your memory about the problems that you have worked on. Discuss any ideas you have with your team.

Once your discussion is complete, examine some of the ways you have generalized as you answer the following questions.

Generalizing

To **generalize** means to make a general statement or conclusion about something from partial evidence. You think this way when you describe patterns, because you are looking for a general statement that describes each term in the pattern. Often, a generalization is the answer to the question, "What is in common?" When you catch yourself thinking, "*I think this is always true…*", or " I could represent this generically as…" you are **generalizing**.

Continues on next page $\rightarrow$

a. In this chapter, you learned about transforming many types of parent graphs. Think about what the general equations had in common to help you **generalize** for any function $f(x)$, as you answer the questions below.

   i. How can you represent the new function you get by shifting the graph of $f(x)$ up 3 units? –5 units? k units?

   ii. How can you represent the new function you get by shifting the graph of $f(x)$ to the right 2 units? –4 units? h units?

   iii. How can you represent the new function you get by stretching the graph of $f(x)$ vertically by a factor of 2? Of 5? Of a?

   iv. Write a **general expression** for the family of functions created by any transformation to the function $f(x)$.

b. The function $g(x)$ is graphed at right. Graph each of the following functions.

   i. $y = 2g(x) + 3$

   ii. $y = -g(x - 1)$

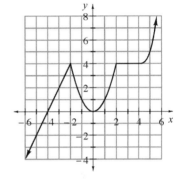

c. During Section 4.3, you probably **generalized** about how to write equations in graphing form by completing the square. For example, you started to learn completing the square by analyzing actual squares that represented the algebraic quantities you were working with, such as the expression represented by the tiles at right. Then you **generalized the process** to complete the square for expressions involving negative and fractional terms, which are not easy to represent with tiles. Consider this as you answer the questions below.

   i. In general, what can you do to complete the square for a quadratic function, no matter what the x term is?

   ii. Use the **general strategy** you described in part (*i*) above to complete the square for the quadratic equation below.

   $$f(x) = x^2 - 4.5x + 17$$

Answers and Support for Closure Activity #5
What Have I Learned?

Problem	Solution	Need Help?	More Practice
CL 4-156.	a. Answers may vary but should be in the form of $y = a(x+4)^2 + 3$, where a is any positive number. $x = -4$	Lessons 4.1.2, and 4.1.3	Problems 4-28, 4-35, 4-36, and 4-56
	b. $y = a(x+4)^2 + 3$, where a is between 0 and -1; Line of symmetry does not change.		
	c. $y = a(x-3)^2 - 5$, where a is less than -1. $x = 3$		
CL 4-157.	a. $(-2, -1)$	Lessons 4.2.1, 4.2.2, 4.2.3 and 4.2.4	Problems 4-91, 4-93, 4-101, 4-117, and 4-124
	b. $(0, 2)$ $x = 0; y = 2$	Problem 4-56	
	c. $(1, -2)$		
	d. $(0, 1)$		
CL 4-158.	$y = -\frac{5}{49} x(x - 28) = -\frac{5}{49} x^2 + \frac{20}{7} x$	Lesson 4.1.4	Problems 4-46, 4-48, 4-49, 4-51, and 4-64
CL 4-159.	a. $y = 11 \cdot 3^x$	Lesson 3.2.2	Problems 3-22, 3-39, 3-62, 3-95, 3-107, 3-108, 3-109, and 3-122
	b. $y = 40(0.8)^x$		
CL 4-160.	a. $t(n) = -3n + 13$	Lessons 2.1.5, 2.1.6, 2.1.7, 3.1.2, and 3.1.6	Problems 2-106, 2-107, 2-109, 2-112, 2-138, 2-156, 3-16, and 3-46
	b. $t(n) = -\frac{1}{2}(4)^n$ or $-2(4)^{n-1}$ Both using $t(1)$ as the first term.	Math Notes box in Lesson 2.1.6	

Problem	Solution	Need Help?	More Practice
CL 4-161.	a. x-int: $(-6,0), (-2,0)$; y-int: $(0, 12)$; vertex: $(-4,-4)$ $y = (x+4)^2 - 4$	Lessons 4.1.2, 4.1.3, 4.3.1, and 4.3.2 Checkpoint 7 Math Notes box in Lesson 4.1.3 Problem 4-37	Problems 4-19, 4-38, 4-55, 4-65, 4-71, 4-80, 4-108, 4-135, and 4-149
	b. x-int: $(-2,0), (4,0)$; y-int: $(0, -8)$; vertex: $(1,-9)$; $y = (x-1)^2 - 9$		
	c. x-int: $(3 \pm \sqrt{18}, 0)$; y-int: $(0, -9)$; vertex: $(3, -18)$; $y = (x-3)^2 - 18$		
	d. x-int: $(\frac{-5 \pm \sqrt{21}}{2}, 0)$; y-int: $(0, 1)$; vertex: $(-2.5, -5.25)$; $y = (x+2.5)^2 - 5.25$		
CL 4-162.	a. $(2x-1)(x+4)$ b. $2(2x+5)(2x+1)$	Lesson 2.2.2 Checkpoint 5	Problems 2-28, 2-90, 2-155, 3-29, 3-60, 3-111, 3-124, and 4-82
CL 4-163.	a. $17.61 b. $4.55	Lesson 2.1.6	Problems 2-79, 2-87, 2-103, 2-154, 3-18, 3-40, 4-33, and 4-73
CL 4-164.	a. 36 b. $4m^2 + 20m + 25$ c. $2, -4$	Math Notes box in Lesson 1.1.1 Problem 1-4 Checkpoint 9	Problems 1-22, 1-36, 1-87, 2-8, 2-55, 2-102, 3-115, 4-57, and 4-58
CL 4-165.	a. $y = -x - \frac{5}{2}$ b. $y = \pm\sqrt{\frac{x-2}{2}} + 1$	Checkpoint 10	Problems 1-74 part (b), 1-88, 2-41, 2-146, and 4-96

SOLVING AND INTERSECTIONS

5

CHAPTER 5   Solving and Intersections

This chapter begins with a focus on two ways of solving equations and systems of equations: algebraically and graphically. You will build on your understanding from previous courses to gain a broad and strong understanding of the meaning of solutions.

In Section 5.2, you will expand your understanding of solving and solutions to include inequalities. You will solve problems designed to illustrate how inequalities might be used for more complicated applications.

Guiding Questions

Think about these questions throughout this chapter:

How can I solve it?

What is the meaning of solutions?

Can I see it another way?

How can I visualize it?

In this chapter, you will learn:

➢ How to solve equations and systems of equations algebraically and graphically.

➢ Multiple ways to understand the meaning of solutions.

➢ How to use equations, inequalities, and systems to solve problems.

Chapter Outline

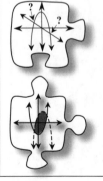

Section 5.1   In this section, you will write and solve equations and systems of equations. You will develop algebraic and graphical methods for solving and you will gain a broader understanding of the meaning of solutions.

Section 5.2   Here you will extend your understanding of solving and solutions to include inequalities and systems of inequalities.

5.1.1 How can I solve?

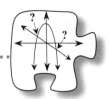

Strategies for Solving Equations

Today you will have the opportunity to solve challenging equations. As you work with your team, you will be challenged to solve equations using multiple approaches and to write clear explanations to show your understanding. The goal today is for you to examine all of the ways you already know to solve equations and to learn how to use these methods to solve other types of equations.

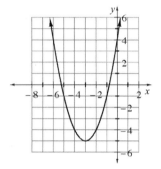

5-1.   SOLVING GRAPHICALLY

One of the big questions of Chapter 4 was how to find special points of a function. For example, you now have the skills to look at an equation of a parabola in graphing form and name its vertex quickly. But what about the locations of other points on the parabola? Consider the graph of $y = (x + 3)^2 - 5$ at right.

a.   Use the graph to solve the equation $(x + 3)^2 - 5 = 4$. How did the graph help you solve the equation?

b.   How can you use the equation $y = (x + 3)^2 - 5$ to verify that your solutions from part (a) are correct? Discuss this with your team.

5-2.   ALGEBRAIC STRATEGIES

The graph in problem 5-1 was useful to solve an equation like $(x + 3)^2 - 5 = 4$. But what if you do not have an accurate graph? And what can you do when the solution is not on a grid point or is off your graph?

Your task: Solve the equation below algebraically (that is, using the equation without a graph) at least three different ways. The "Discussion Points" below are provided to help you get started. Be ready to share your **strategies** with the class.

$$(x + 3)^2 - 5 = 4$$

Discussion Points

What algebraic **strategies** might be useful?

What makes this equation look challenging? How can we make the equation simpler?

How can we be sure that our **strategy** helps us find *all* possible solutions?

5-3.   Three **strategies** you may have used in problem 5-2 are **rewriting** (using algebra to write a new equivalent equation that is easier to solve), **looking inside** (reasoning out the value of the expression inside the function or parentheses), and **undoing** (**reversing** or doing the opposite of an operation; for example, taking the square root to eliminate the squaring). These **strategies** and others will be useful throughout the rest of this course. Examine how these **strategies** can be used to solve the equation below.

$$\frac{x-5}{4} + \frac{1}{3} = \frac{5}{6}$$

a.   Ernie decided to multiply both sides of the equation by 24 so that his equation becomes $6(x-5)+8 = 20$. Which **strategy** did Ernie use? How can you tell?

b.   Elle took Ernie's equation and decided to subtract 8 from both sides to get $6(x-5) = 12$. Which **strategy** did Elle use?

c.   Eric looked at Elle's equation and said, "I can tell that $(x-5)$ must equal 2 because $6 \cdot 2 = 12$. Therefore, if $x - 5 = 2$, then x must be 7." What **strategy** did Eric use?

d.   Verify that Eric's solution in part (c) is correct. Then use the **strategies** from parts (a) through (c) in a different way to solve $\frac{x-5}{4} + \frac{1}{3} = \frac{5}{6}$. Did you get the same result?

5-4.   Solve each equation below, if possible, using any **strategy**. Check with your teammates to see what strategies they chose. Be sure to check your solutions.

a. $4|8x - 2| = 8$ b. $3\sqrt{4x - 8} + 9 = 15$

c. $(x - 3)^2 - 2 = -5$ d. $(2y - 3)(y - 2) = -12y + 18$

e. $\frac{5}{x} + \frac{1}{3x} = \frac{4x}{3}$ f. $|3 - 7x| = -6$

g. $\frac{6w-1}{5} - 3w = \frac{12w-16}{15}$ h. $(x + 2)^2 + 4(x + 2) - 5 = 0$

5-5.   Create a Learning Log entry about all of the solving **strategies** you saw today. For each **strategy**, show an example and explain which types of equations work best with that **strategy**. Title this entry "**Strategies** for Solving Equations" and label it with today's date.

5-6.   Solve $(x - 2)^2 - 3 = 1$ graphically. That is, graph $y = (x - 2)^2 - 3$ and $y = 1$ on the same set of axes and find the x-value(s) of any points of intersection. Then use algebraic **strategies** to solve the equation and verify that your graphical solutions are correct.

5-7.   Solve each equation below. Think about rewriting, looking inside, or undoing to simplify the process.

  a. $2(x-1)^2 + 7 = 39$

  b. $7(\sqrt{m+1} - 3) = 21$

  c. $\frac{x}{2} + \frac{x}{3} = \frac{5x+2}{6}$

  d. $-7 + (\frac{4x+2}{2}) = 8$

5-8.   Describe the graphs of the equations given in parts (a) and (b) below. What are their domains and ranges?

  a. $y = 3$ b. $x = -2$ c.   Where do the two graphs cross?

5-9.   Find the equation of the line that passes through $(0, 2)$ and $(5, 2)$. Then complete parts (a) and (b) below.

  a.   What would be the equation of the x-axis?

  b.   What would be the equation of the y-axis?

5-10.   Solve the system of equations shown at right.

$$2x + 6y = 10$$
$$x = 8 - 3y$$

  a.   Describe what happened when you tried to solve the system.

  b.   Draw the graph of the system.

  c.   How does the graph of the system explain what happened with the equations? Make your answer as clear and thorough as possible.

5-11.   Rewrite each radical below as an equivalent expression using fractional exponents.

  a. $\sqrt[2]{5}$ b. $\sqrt[3]{9}$ c. $\sqrt[8]{17^x}$ d. $7\sqrt[4]{x^3}$

5-12.   The graph of a line and an exponential can intersect twice, once, or not at all. Describe the possible number of intersections for each of the following pairs of graphs. Your solution to each part should include all of the possibilities and a quickly sketched example of each one.

  a.   A line and a parabola

  b.   Two different parabolas

  c.   A parabola and a circle

  d.   A parabola and the hyperbola $y = \frac{1}{x}$

5.1.2 How can I use a graph to solve?

Solving Equations and Systems Graphically

In the previous lesson, you used and named three algebraic methods to solve different kinds of equations. In today's lesson, you will solve different equations again, but this time you will use your understanding of graphs, as well as your algebra skills, to solve the equations and to verify your algebraic results.

5-13.   In problem 5-1, you used a graph to solve an equation. In what other ways can a graph be a useful solution tool? Consider this question as you solve the equation $\sqrt{2x+3} = x$.

   a.   Use algebraic **strategies** to solve $\sqrt{2x+3} = x$. How many solutions did you find? Which **strategies** did you use?

   b.   Miranda graphed the functions $y = \sqrt{2x+3}$ and $y = x$ to test the solutions from part (a). *"I think something is wrong,"* she said. Graph the system on your graphing calculator and find the intersection(s) of the functions. What happened? How many solutions must there be to this equation?

   c.   When a result from a solution process does not make the original equation true, it is called an **extraneous solution**. It is not a solution of the equation, even though it is a result from solving algebraically. For example, since $\sqrt{2(-1)+3} \neq -1$, then $x = -1$ is not a solution of the equation $\sqrt{2x+3} = x$. The fact that extraneous solutions can arise after following straightforward solving techniques makes it especially important to check your solutions!

   But why did the extraneous solution appear in this problem? Examine the graph of the system of equations $y = \sqrt{2x+3}$ and $y = x$, shown at right. Where would an extraneous solution $x = -1$ appear on the graph? And why do the graphs not intersect there? Explain.

5-14.   After solving the equation $2x^2 + 5x - 3 = x^2 + 4x + 3$, Gustav got called to the office and left his team. When his teammates examined his graphing calculator to try to find out how he found his solution, they only saw the graph of $y = x^2 + x - 6$. Consider this situation as you answer the questions below.

   a.   Solve $2x^2 + 5x - 3 = x^2 + 4x + 3$ algebraically.

   b.   Where did Gustav get the equation $y = x^2 + x - 6$?

Problem continues on next page →

5-14.   *Problem continued from previous page.*

    c.   How can you see the solutions to $2x^2 + 5x - 3 = x^2 + 4x + 3$ in the graph of $y = x^2 + x - 6$? Explain why this makes sense.

    d.   Grieta solved $2x^2 + 5x - 3 = x^2 + 4x + 3$ by graphing a system of equations and looking for the points of intersection. What equations do you think she used? Graph these equations on your graphing calculator and explain where the solutions to the equation exist on the graph.

5-15.   Karen could not figure out how to solve $20x + 1 = 3^x$ algebraically, so she decided to use her graphing calculator. However, after she finished entering the equations $y = 20x + 1$ and $y = 3^x$, she got the graph shown at right. After studying the graph, Karen suspects there are no solutions to $20x + 1 = 3^x$.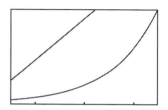

    a.   What do you think? If there are solutions, find them and prove that they are solutions. If there are no solutions, demonstrate that there cannot be a solution.

    b.   What should solutions to the equation, $20x + 1 = 3^x$, look like? In other words, will solutions be a single number, or should they be the coordinates of a point? Explain.

    c.   Elana started to solve first by subtracting 1 from both sides of her equation. So when she graphed her system later, she used the equations $y = 20x$ and $y = 3^x - 1$. Should she get the same solutions? Test your conclusion with your graphing calculator.

    d.   Discuss with your team why Karen could not solve the system algebraically. What do you think?

5-16.   Jack was working on solving an equation and he graphed the functions $f(x) = \frac{12}{x}$ and $g(x) = -(x - 3)^2 + 4$, as shown at right.

    a.   What equation was Jack solving?

    b.   Use points A and B to solve the equation you wrote in part (a).

    c.   Are there any other solutions to this same equation that are represented by neither point A nor point B? If so, show that these other solutions make your equation true.

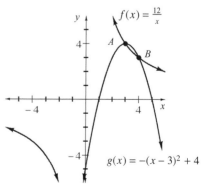

5-17.   What does the solution to an equation mean? Do you have any new ideas about solutions that you did not have before? Create a Learning Log entry that explains the meaning of a solution in as many ways as possible. Title this entry "The Meaning of Solution, Part 1" (Parts 2 and 3 will be coming later) and label it with today's date.

5-18.   Solve $(x-3)^2 - 2 = x+1$ graphically. Is there more than one way to do this? Explain.

5-19.   Graph a system of equations to solve $2|x-4| - 3 = \frac{2}{3}x - 3$. Show your solutions clearly on your graph.

5-20.   Solve each of the following equations using any method. Be sure to check your solutions.

   a. $-3\sqrt{2x-5} + 7 = -8$ b. $2|3x+4| - 10 = 12$

5-21.   Ted needs to find the point of intersection for the lines $y = 18x - 30$ and $y = -22x + 50$. He takes out a piece of graph paper and then realizes that he can solve this problem without graphing. Explain how Ted is going to accomplish this, and then find the point of intersection.

5-22.   Your family plans to buy a new air conditioner. They can buy the Super Cool X1400 for $800, or they can buy the Efficient Energy X2000 for $1200. Both models will cool your home equally well, but the Efficient Energy model is less expensive to operate. The Super Cool X1400 will cost $60 a month to operate, while the Efficient Energy X2000 costs only $40 a month to operate.

   a.   Write an equation to represent the cost of buying and operating the Super Cool X1400 where C = cost and m = months.

   b.   Write an equation to represent the cost of buying and operating the Efficient Energy X2000.

   c.   How many months would your family have to use the Efficient Energy model to compensate for the additional cost of the original purchase?

   d.   Figuring your family will only use the air conditioner for 4 months each year, how many years will you have to wait to start saving money overall?

5-23.   Find the x- and y-intercepts.

   a. $2x - 3y = 9$ b. $3y = 2x + 12$

5-24.   Find the value of x.

   a.   b.

5-25.   Solve $3x - 1 = 2^x$ graphically. Could you solve this equation algebraically? Explain.

5-26.   Consider the graphs of $f(x) = \frac{1}{2}(x-2)^3 + 1$ and
         $g(x) = 2x^2 - 6x - 3$ at right.

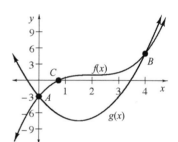

   a.   Write an equation that you could solve using
         points A and B. What are the solutions to your
         equation? Substitute them into your equation to
         show that they work.

   b.   Are there any solutions to the equation in part
         (a) that do not appear on the graph? Explain.

   c.   Write an equation that you could solve using point C. What does the solution to
         your equation appear to be? Again, substitute your solution into the equation.
         How close was your estimate?

   d.   What are the domains and ranges of $f(x)$ and $g(x)$?

5-27.   Solve each of the following equations using any method.

   a. $2(x+3)^2 - 5 = -5$ b. $3(x-2)^2 + 6 = 9$

   c. $|2x - 5| - 6 = 15$ d. $3\sqrt{5x-2} + 1 = 7$

5-28.   Given the parabola $f(x) = x^2 - 2x - 3$, complete parts (a) through (c) below.

   a.   Find the vertex by averaging the x-intercepts.

   b.   Find the vertex by completing the square.

   c.   Find the vertex of $f(x) = x^2 + 5x + 2$ using your method of choice.

   d.   What are the domain and range for $f(x) = x^2 + 5x + 2$?

5-29.   Solve each of the following equations for the indicated variable.

   a. $5x - 3y = 12$ for y b. $F = \frac{Gm_1m_2}{r^2}$ for m_2

   c. $E = \frac{1}{2}mv^2$ for m d. $(x - 4)^2 + (y - 1)^2 = 10$ for y

5-30.   Paul states that $(a + b)^2$ is equivalent to $a^2 + b^2$. Joyce thinks that something is missing. Help Joyce show Paul that the two expressions are not equivalent. Explain using at least two different approaches: diagrams, algebra, numbers, or words.

5-31.   Graph each of the following equations. (Keep the graphs handy, because you will need them later.)

   a. $y = |x|$ b. $|y| = x$

   c.   How are the two graphs similar? How are they different?

   d.   What are the domain and range of each relation?

5-32.   Find the value of x.

   a.   b.

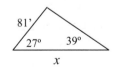

5.1.3 How many solutions are there?

Finding Multiple Solutions to Systems of Equations

You have used many different solving **strategies** to find solutions of equations with one variable both algebraically and graphically. You have also worked with systems of two equations with two variables. In this lesson, you will use your algebraic and graphing tools to determine the number of solutions that various systems have and to determine the meaning of those solutions.

5-33. Solve each system of equations below without graphing. For each one, explain what the solution (or lack thereof) tells you about the graph of the system.

a. $y = -3x + 5$
   $y = -3x - 1$

b. $y = \frac{1}{2}x^2 + 1$
   $y = 2x - 1$

c. $y^2 = x$
   $y = x - 2$

d. $4x - 2y = 10$
   $y = 2x - 5$

5-34. Now consider the system shown at right.

$x^2 + y^2 = 25$
$y = x^2 - 13$

a. How many solutions do you expect this system to have? Explain how you made your prediction.

b. Solve this system by graphing. How many solutions did you find? Was your prediction in part (a) correct?

c. Find a way to combine these equations to create a new equation so that the only variable is x. Then find another way to combine $x^2 + y^2 = 25$ and $y = x^2 - 13$ to form a different equation that contains only the variable y. Which of these equations would be easier to solve? Why?

d. If you have not already done so, solve one of the combined equations from part (c). If solving becomes too difficult, you may want to switch to the other combined equation.

When you have solutions for one variable, solve for the other variable by substituting each solution into one of the original equations and solving for the remaining variable. Then locate each solution on the graph from part (b).

5-35.   In problem 5-34, you analyzed the system shown at right.

$$x^2 + y^2 = 25$$

$$y = x^2 - 13$$

a.   What minor adjustments can you make to an equation (or both equations) in this system so that the new system has no solutions? Have each member of your team find a different way to alter the system. **Justify** that your system has no solution algebraically. Also, be ready to share your **strategies** for changing the system along with your **justification** with the class.

b.   Now work with your team to alter the system three more times so that the new systems have 3, 2, or 1 solution. For each new system that your team creates, solve the system algebraically to study how the algebraic solution helps indicate how many solutions will be possible. Be prepared to explain what different situations occur during solving that result in a different number of solutions.

5-36.   Look over your work from today. Name all of the **strategies** you used to solve systems of equations. Which **strategies** were most useful for solving linear systems? What about non-linear systems? Write a Learning Log entry describing your ideas you about solving systems. Title this entry "Finding Solutions to Systems" and label it with today's date.

5-37.   Solve each of the following systems algebraically. What do the solutions tell you about each system? Visualizing the graphs may help with your description.

a. $y = 3x - 5$
      $y = -2x - 15$

b. $y - 7 = -2x$
      $4x + 2y = 14$

c. $y = 2(x + 3)^2 - 5$
      $y = 14x + 17$

d. $y = 3(x - 2)^2 + 3$
      $y = 6x - 12$

5-38.   Solve each equation below. Think about rewriting, looking inside, or undoing to simplify the process.

a. $3(y + 1)^2 - 5 = 43$

b. $\sqrt{1 - 4x} = 10$

c. $\frac{6y-1}{y} - 3 = 2$

d. $\sqrt[3]{1 - 2x} = 3$

5-39.   This is a Checkpoint for use of function notation and describing domains and ranges.

    Find the domain and range of $g(x) = 2(x + 3)^2$. Then answer the questions below.

    a.   Find $g(-5)$.   b.   Find $g(a+1)$.

    c.   If $g(x) = 32$, figure out what number x can be.

    d.   If $g(x) = 0$, figure out what number x can be.

    e.   Check your answers by referring to the Checkpoint 9 materials located at the back of your book.

    If you needed help to solve these problems correctly, then you need more practice using function notation and describing domains and ranges. Review the Checkpoint 9 materials and try the practice problems. Also, consider getting help outside of class time. From this point on, you will be expected to solve problems like these easily and accurately.

5-40.   Wet World has an 18-foot-long water slide. The angle of elevation of the slide (the angle it forms with a horizontal line) is 50°. At the end of the slide, there is a 6-foot drop into a pool. After you climb the ladder to the top of the slide, how many feet above the water level are you? Draw a diagram.

5-41.   Describe how the graph of $y + 3 = -2(x + 1)^2$ is different from $y = x^2$.

5-42.   Solve the system of equations at right.

$$2^{(x+y)} = 16$$
$$2^{(2x+y)} = \frac{1}{8}$$

5-43.   The price of a movie ticket averages $10.25 and is increasing by 3% per year. Use that information to complete parts (a) through (c) below.

    a.   What is the multiplier in this situation?

    b.   Write a function that represents the cost of a movie ticket n years from now.

    c.   If tickets continue to increase at the same rate, what will they cost 10 years from now?

5.1.4 How can I use systems?

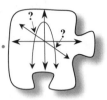

Using Systems of Equations to Solve Problems

You have developed several **strategies** for solving equations and systems of equations. You have also focused on the meaning of a solution. In this lesson, you will have the opportunity to see how your **strategies** can be used in real-life contexts. You will expand your understanding of solutions by applying them to these situations. As you work today, use the questions below to help stimulate mathematical conversations:

How can we make this situation into equations?

What does this solution tell us?

How can we solve it?

Are there any other **strategies** that could be useful?

5-44. HOW TALL IS HAROLD?

Jamal and Dinah were still eating as they came into Algebra 2 class from lunch. Someone had left a book on the floor and they tripped. As they each hit the floor, the food they were carrying went flying across the room directly toward Harold, who was showing off his latest dance moves.

As Jamal and Dinah watched in horror, Jamal's cupcake and Dinah's sandwich splattered Harold right on the top of his head! Jamal's cupcake flew on a path that would have landed on the floor 20 feet away from him if it had not hit Harold. Dinah's sandwich flew on a path that would have landed on the floor 24 feet away from her if it had not hit Harold. Jamal's cupcake got up to 9 feet high, and Dinah's sandwich reached a height of 6 feet, before hitting Harold.

How tall is Harold? Show your solution in as many ways as you can.

5-45.   Write a system of equations to fit
the situation below. Then solve
the system using as many
strategies as you can. How many
solutions are possible?

Your math class wants to collect
money for a field trip, so it
decides to sell two kinds of candy
bags. The Chocolate Lovers Bag
costs $4.25 for five chocolate
truffles and two caramel turtle candies. The Combusting Caramel Bag costs $3.50 for
eight caramel turtle candies and two chocolate truffles. How much does each
chocolate truffle and caramel turtle candy cost?

5-46.   Lucky you! You are a new college graduate and have already been offered two jobs.
Each job involves exactly the same tasks, but the salary plans differ, as shown below.

Job A offers a starting salary of $52,000 per year with an annual increase of $3,000.

Job B starts at $36,000 per year with a raise of 11% each year.

a.   Under what conditions would Job A be a better choice? When would Job B be a
better choice? Use graphs, tables, and equations to help you **justify** your answer.

b.   How could you change this problem slightly so that Job B is always a better
choice? How could you change it so that Job A is always better? If it is not
possible for Job A or Job B always to be a better choice, explain why not.

5-47.   What does the solution to a system of equations mean? Can you find
more than one way to answer that question? Create a Learning Log
entry that expands on your thinking about the meaning of a solution.
Title this entry "The Meaning of Solution, Part 2" and label it with
today's date.

5-48.   Gloria is weighing combinations of geometric solids. She found that 4 cylinders and 5 prisms weigh 32 ounces and that 1 cylinder and 8 prisms weigh 35 ounces. Write and solve a system of equations to determine the weight of each cylinder and prism.

5-49.   Is $x = -1$ a solution to the inequality $2x^2 + 5x - 3 \le x^2 + 4x + 3$? What about $x = 5$? Show how you know. Then find three more solutions.

5-50.   Solve each equation below algebraically. Think about rewriting, looking inside, or undoing to simplify the process.

    a. $5 - 3(\frac{1}{2}x + 2) = -7$ b. $5(\sqrt{x - 2} + 1) = 15$

    c. $12 - (\frac{2x}{3} + x) = 2$ d. $-3(2x + 1)^3 = -192$

5-51.   Given the parabola $y = x^2 - 8x + 10$, complete parts (a) through (c) below.

    a.   Find the vertex by averaging the x-intercepts.

    b.   Find the vertex by completing the square.

    c.   Find the vertex of $y = x^2 - 3x$ using your method of choice.

5-52.   Refer back to the graphs you made for problem 5-31. (It was a homework problem from Lesson 5.1.2.) Use those graphs to help you to graph each of the following inequalities.

    a. $y \le |x|$ b. $|y| \ge x$

5-53.   For the equation $y = -(x + 1)^3 + 2$:

    a.   Draw a graph.

    b.   Use your graph to estimate the solution to $-3 = -(x + 1)^3 + 2$.

5.2.1 How can I solve inequalities?

Solving Inequalities with One or Two Variables

In Section 5.1, you developed many **strategies** for solving equations with one variable and systems of equations with two variables. But what if you want to solve an inequality or system of inequalities instead? Today you will explore how to use familiar **strategies** to find solutions for an inequality.

As you work, the questions below can help focus team discussions:

What strategy should we use?

How can we know if this solution is correct?

How can we be sure we found all solutions?

5-54. In Lessons 5.1.1 and 5.1.2, you learned how to use the graph of a system to solve an equation. How can the graphs of $y = 2x^2 + 5x - 3$ and $y = x^2 + 4x + 3$ (shown at right) help you solve an *inequality*? Consider this as you answer the questions below.

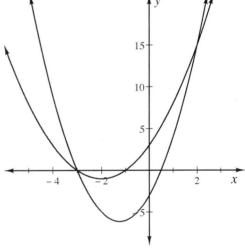

a. How are the solutions of $2x^2 + 5x - 3 = x^2 + 4x + 3$ represented on this graph? What are the solutions?

b. Obtain a Lesson 5.2.1 Resource Page from your teacher. On the resource page, label each graph with its equation and highlight each function with a different color. How did you decide which graph matches which function?

c. On the graph, identify the *x*-values for which $2x^2 + 5x - 3 \le x^2 + 4x + 3$. How did you locate the solutions? How many solutions are there? Find a way to describe all of the solutions.

d. How can these solutions be represented on a number line? Locate the number line labeled with $2x^2 + 5x - 3 \le x^2 + 4x + 3$ below the graph on your resource page. Use a colored marker to highlight the solutions to the inequality on the number line.

e. What about the inequality $2x^2 + 5x - 3 > x^2 + 4x + 3$? What are the solutions to this inequality? Represent your solutions algebraically and on a number line.

5-55.   Now consider the inequality $2x - 5 > 1$.

   a.   List at least three solutions of this inequality.

   b.   What is the smallest number that will make this inequality true? If you cannot find the smallest number, which number is the largest that makes it *not* true? This number is a **boundary** .

   c.   Draw a number line like the one at right on your paper and mark the boundary point for $2x - 5 > 1$. Is the point part of the solution of the inequality? If yes, fill in a point on the line; if not draw an open circle. On which side of the boundary do the solutions lie? Indicate the solutions by "bolding" the appropriate portion of the number line and representing the graph algebraically.

5-56.   Consider the inequality $4|x + 1| - 2 > 6$.

   a.   How many boundary points are there? What are they? Should they be marked with filled or unfilled circles? Make the appropriate markings on a number line.

   b.   Which portions of the number line contain the solutions? How many regions do you need to test? Represent the solutions algebraically and on a number line.

5-57.   Burt and Ernie were solving the inequality $2x^2 + 5x - 3 < x^2 + 4x + 3$. They were looking at the graph in problem 5-54 when Burt had an idea. *"Can't we change this into one parabola and solve our inequality that way?"* he said.

   Ernie asked, *"What do you mean?"*

   "Can't we find the solutions by looking at the graph of $f(x) = x^2 + x - 6$?" Burt replied.

   a.   Where did Burt get the equation $y = x^2 + x - 6$?

   b.   Try Burt's idea. Graph the parabola and show how it can be used to solve the original inequality.

   c.   *"Just a minute!"* mumbled Ernie, *"I think I have a short cut. Instead of graphing the parabola, can't we just rewrite the original inequality as $x^2 + x - 6 < 0$ and then solve the equation $x^2 + x - 6 = 0$? This would give us the boundary points and then we could test numbers to find the regions that contain the solutions."* Check Ernie's short cut. Does it give the same solution?

   d.   Use any method to solve the inequality $x^2 - 3x - 10 \geq 0$.

5-58.   Next, Burt and Ernie were working on solving the inequality $4|x+1|-2>6$ from problem 5-56. This time, Ernie had an idea. *"Why don't we find the solutions to this by graphing a system of equations like we did in problem 5-54?"*

     a.   What system of equations should they graph?

     b.   Graph the system and explain how you can use it to find the solutions to $4|x+1|-2>6$.

5-59.   In problem 5-54 you looked at solutions to an inequality with one variable (x). Now consider the system of inequalities with two variables (x and y) below.

$$y \geq 2x^2 + 5x - 3$$
$$y < x^2 + 4x + 3$$

     a.   Which points make both inequalities true? For example, does the point $(-3,0)$ make both inequalities true? What about $(-1,1)$? $(1,5)$? Refer back to your Lesson 5.2.1A Resource Page to help you think about these questions.

     b.   What is the difference between a solution to the *system* of inequalities above and a solution to the inequality found in problem 5-54?

     c.   How are the graphs of the equations $y = 2x^2 + 5x - 3$ and $y = x^2 + 4x + 3$ related to the graph of the system of inequalities?

     d.   With your team, find a way to represent all of the solutions to the system of inequalities on the Lesson 5.2.1A Resource Page graph.

5-60.   For each of the following graphs, find an equation, inequality, or system that could have the solution shown. Note that the equations for the line and the parabola are given.

     a.

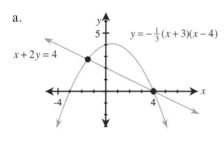

     b.

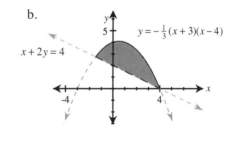

     c.

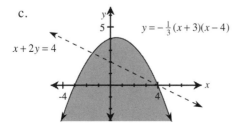

     d.

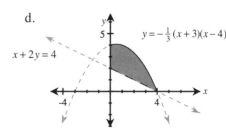

5-61.   What does the solution to an inequality or a system of inequalities
         mean? Does it matter if the inequality has one variable or two?
         Create a Learning Log entry that expands on your thinking about the
         meaning of a solution. Title this entry "The Meaning of Solution,
         Part 3" and label it with today's date.

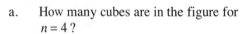

5-62.   Find boundary points for each of the following inequalities. Draw the boundaries on a
         number line and shade the solution regions.

         a. $3x + 2 \geq x - 6$ b. $2x^2 - 5x < 12$

5-63.   Solve the following inequalities and draw a number line graph to represent each
         solution.

         a. $|2x + 3| < 5$ b. $|2x + 3| \geq 5$

         c. $|2x - 3| < 5$ d. $|2x - 3| \geq 5$

         e. $|3 - 2x| < 5$ f. $|3 - 2x| \geq 5$

         g.   Describe any relationships you see among these six problems.

5-64.   Examine the figures at right, and then visualize
         the figure for $n = 4$.

         a.   How many cubes are in the figure for
               $n = 4$?

         b.   How many cubes are in the figure for
               $n = 1$?

         c.   Find the general equation for the number
               of cubes for any n. Verify your formula
               with the cases of $n = 1$ and $n = 5$.

         d.   Is the sequence arithmetic, geometric or neither? Explain your reasoning.

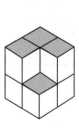
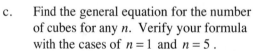

$n = 2$ $n = 3$

5-65.   Lexington High School has an annual growth rate of 4.7%. Three years ago there were 1500 students at the school.

   a.   How many students are there now?

   b.   How many students were there 5 years ago?

   c.   How many students will there be n years from now?

5-66.   Complete the square to rewrite the equation below, changing it to graphing form. Then graph it.

$$x^2 + y^2 - 2y - 8 = 0$$

5-67.   Factor each expression in parts (a) and (b). Then, in parts (c) and (d), factor *and reduce* each expression.

   a. $bx + ax$ b. $x + ax$ c. $\dfrac{ax+a}{x^2+2x+1}$ d. $\dfrac{x^2-b^2}{ax+ab}$

5-68.   Graph the four inequalities below on the same set of axes.

   i. $2y \geq x - 3$ ii. $x - 2y \geq -7$

   iii. $y \leq -2x + 6$ iv. $-9 \leq 2x + y$

   a.   What type of polygon is formed by the solution of this set of inequalities? Write a convincing argument to **justify** your answer.

   b.   Find the vertices of the polygon. If your graph is very accurately drawn you will be able to determine the points from the graph. If it is not, you will need to solve the systems (pairs) of equations that represent the corners of your graphs.

5-69.   Solve the following absolute value inequalities.

   a. $|x - 4| < 9$ b. $\left|\frac{1}{2}x - 45\right| \geq 80$

   c. $|2x - 5| \leq 2$

5-70. Consider the arithmetic sequence 2, $a - b$, $a + b$, 35 , ... Find a and b.

5-71. MARVELOUS MARK'S FUNCTION MACHINES

Mark has set up a series of three function machines that he claims will surprise you.

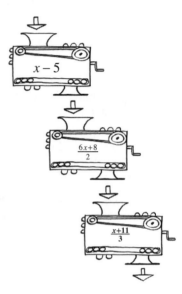

a. Try a few numbers. Are you surprised by your results?

b. Carrie claims that she was not surprised by her results. She also says that she can show why the sequence of machines does what it does by simply dropping in a variable and writing out step-by-step what happens inside each machine. Try it. (Use something like c or m.) Be sure to show all of the steps.

5-72. Give the equation of each circle below in graphing form.

a. A circle with center $(0, 0)$ and radius 6.

b. A circle with center $(2, -3)$ and radius 6.

c. A circle with equation $x^2 + y^2 - 8x + 10y + 5 = 0$.

5-73. Find the equation (in $y = mx + b$ form) of each line described below.

a. A line with slope $\frac{1}{2}$ passing through the point $(6, 1)$.

b. The line $y = 2x + b$ passing through the point $(1, 4)$.

5-74. Sketch the graph of the function $f(x) = 3 \cdot 5^x$.

a. What is the domain of $f(x)$?

b. Sketch the graph of the geometric sequence $t(n) = 3 \cdot 5^n$.

c. What is the difference between $f(x)$ and $t(n)$? Explain completely.

5.2.2 How can I organize the possibilities?

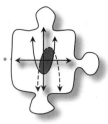

· ·

Using Systems to Solve a Problem

The system of linear equalities and inequalities are used by businesses and manufacturers to make service and production decisions. They use linear programming for this application. Today you will get to sample this technique.

5-75.   THE TOY FACTORY

Otto Toyom builds toy cars and trucks. To make each car, he needs 4 wheels, 2 seats, and 1 gas tank. To make each truck, he needs 6 wheels, 1 seat, and 3 gas tanks. His storeroom has 36 wheels, 14 seats, and 15 gas tanks. He is trying to decide how many cars and trucks to build so he can make the largest possible amount of money when he sells them. Help Otto figure out what his options are. What are all of the choices he could make about how many cars and how many trucks he will build? Make a list of all possible combinations. Then plot the number of possible cars and trucks in the first quadrant of a graph.

5-76.   Otto wants to make as much profit as possible. Use your list to find which combination of cars and trucks will make the most profit based on the information below.

a.   Which of Otto's options gives him the greatest profit if he makes $1 on each car and $1 on each truck he sells? How do you know?

b.   The market has just changed, and Otto can now make $2 for each truck but only $1 for each car. What is his best choice for the number of cars and the number of trucks to make now? How can you be sure? Explain.

5-77.   In problem 5-76, you probably had to show many calculations to convince Otto that your recommendation was a good one. Now you will take another look at Otto's business using algebra and graphing tools.

a.   Write three inequalities to represent the relationship between the number of cars (x), the number of trucks (y), and the number of:

   i. wheels   ii. seats   iii. gas tanks

b.   Graph this system of inequalities on the same set of axes you used for problem 5-75. Shade the solution region lightly. Why is it okay to assume that $x \geq 0$ and $y \geq 0$?

c.   What are the vertices of the pentagon that outlines your region? Explain how you could find the exact coordinates of those points if you could not read them easily from the graph.

d.   Are there any points in the solution region that represent choices that seem more likely to give Otto the maximum profit? Where are they? Why do you think they show the best choices?

e.   Write an equation to represent Otto's total profit (P) if he makes $1 on each car and $2 on each truck. What if Otto ended up with a profit of only $8? Show how to use the graph of the profit equation when $P = 8$ to figure out how many cars and trucks he made.

f.   Which points do you need to test in the profit equation to get the maximum profit? Is it necessary to try all of the points? Why or why not?

g.   What if Otto got greedy and wanted to make a profit of $14? How could you use a profit line to show Otto that this would be impossible based on his current pricing?

5-78.   Find Otto's highest possible profit if he gets $3 per car and $2 per truck. Find the profit expression and find the best combinations of cars and trucks to maximize the profit.

MᴇᴛHODS AND Mᴇᴀɴɪɴɢs

Inequalities with Absolute Value

MATH NOTES

If k is any positive number, an inequality of the form $|f(x)| > k$ is equivalent to the statement $f(x) > k$ **or** $f(x) < -k$.

For example, $|2x - 17| > 9$ is equivalent to $2x - 17 > 9$ or $2x - 17 < -9$. Solving yields $x > 13$ or $x < 4$.

$|f(x)| < k$ is equivalent to the statement $-k < f(x) < k$. Another way to write this is $f(x) > -k$ and $f(x) < k$. For example, $|x + 4| < 9$ is equivalent to $-9 < x + 4 < 9$. Solving yields $-13 < x < 5$, that is, $x > -13$ and $x < 5$.

Review & Preview

5-79.   Solve the system of equations at right. What subproblems did you need to solve?

$$x + 2y = 4$$
$$2x - y = -7$$
$$x + y + z = -4$$

5-80.   Solve each of the following inequalities. Express the solutions algebraically and on a number line.

a. $3x - 5 \le 7$ b. $x^2 + 6 > 42$

5-81.   Three red rods are 2 cm longer than two blue rods. Three blue rods are 2 cm longer than four red rods. How long is each rod?

5-82.   Simone has been absent and does not know the difference between the graph of $y \le 2x - 2$ and the graph of $y < 2x - 2$. Explain thoroughly so that she completely understands what points are excluded from the second graph and why.

5-83.   Graph the solutions to each of the following inequalities on a different set of axes (but you should be able to fit all four on one side of the graph paper). Label each graph with the inequality as given and with its y-form. Choose a test point and show that it gives the same result in both forms of your inequality.

    a. $3x - 3 < y$ b. $3 > y$

    c. $3x - 2y \le 6$ d. $x^2 - y \le 9$

5-84.   This is a Checkpoint for solving for one variable in an equation with two or more variables.

Rewrite the following equations so that you could enter them into the graphing calculator. In other words, solve for y.

    a. $x - 3(y + 2) = 6$ b. $\frac{6x-1}{y} - 3 = 2$

    c. $\sqrt{y - 4} = x + 1$ d. $\sqrt{y + 4} = x + 2$

    e.   Check your answers by referring to the Checkpoint 10 materials located at the back of your book.

If you needed help to solve these equations correctly, then you need more practice in solving for one variable in an equation involving two or more variables. Review Checkpoint 10 materials and try the practice problems. Also, consider getting help outside of class time. From this point on, you will be expected to solve equations such as these easily and accurately.

5-85.   Think about the axis system in the two-dimensional coordinate plane. What is the equation of the x-axis? What is the equation of the y-axis?

5-86.   Samy has a 10-foot wooden ladder, which he needs to climb to reach the roof of his house. The roof is 12 feet above the ground. The base of the ladder must be at least 1.5 feet from the base of the house. How far is it from the top step of the ladder to the edge of the roof? Draw a sketch.

Algebra 2 Connections

5.2.3 How can I find the best combination?

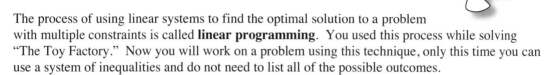

Application of Systems of Linear Inequalities

The process of using linear systems to find the optimal solution to a problem with multiple constraints is called **linear programming**. You used this process while solving "The Toy Factory." Now you will work on a problem using this technique, only this time you can use a system of inequalities and do not need to list all of the possible outcomes.

5-87. SANDY DANDY DUNE BUGGIES

Jacklyn Toyom, CEO of the Sandy Dandy Dune Buggy Company and sister of Otto, has discovered that your team has found a way to optimize the profit for the Toy Factory. She would like to hire your team to help her company. Here is her letter:

> Dear Study Team,
>
> I was so impressed to hear about how you helped Otto maximize his profits at his Toy Factory! I think your team could help my company as well.
>
> Here at the Sandy Dandy Dune Buggy Company we make two popular models of off-road vehicles: the Crawler and the Rover. Each week, we receive enough parts to build at most 15 Crawlers and 12 Rovers. The only exceptions to the supply of parts are the colored night lamps and high-definition speakers, which have to be specially manufactured for our off-road vehicles. Each of the Crawlers requires 5 of the lamps and 2 of the speakers. The Rover requires 3 lamps and 6 speakers. Our supplier is a small company and can only manufacture 81 of the lamps and 78 of the speakers for us each week.
>
> Since we are also a small company, we have only 12 employees. By contract, the maximum number of hours each employee can work is 37.5 hours per week. It takes our employees 20 hours to assemble one Crawler and 30 hours to assemble one Rover.
>
> Each Crawler sold brings in a profit of $500. The Rover is less expensive to manufacture than the Crawler but is very popular and can be sold at a profit of $1000 each.
>
> I need a detailed proposal of how to maximize our profit that I can submit to our Board of Trustees. I look forward to a profitable business relationship!
>
> Sincerely,
> *Ms. Jacklyn Toyom*
> CEO, Sandy Dandy Dune Buggy Company

Problem continues on next page →

5-87.   *Problem continued from previous page.*

Your task: Find the best combination of Crawlers and Rovers to produce each week to maximize the company's profit. Create a detailed proposal to submit to Ms. Toyom that includes:

- The number of Crawlers and Rovers to manufacture each week.

- The maximum profit the company can expect to make.

- Calculations and graphs to **justify** your recommendation.

Constraints to keep in mind are the number of:

(1)   speakers available
(2)   lamps available
(3)   total employee hours each week

Discussion Points

How does this problem compare to "The Toy Factory" from the previous lesson?

What is the maximum number of hours for all of the employees that can be worked in one week?

How can we **justify** that we have found the most profitable combination of each vehicle to manufacture?

Further Guidance

5-88.   After emailing a few questions to Ms. Toyom, your team received the following email:

From: "Ms. Toyom" <toyom@welovemath.com>
To: <studyteam@thinkingisgood.net>
Subject: Clarifications to your Questions

Dear Study Team,

Thank you for your questions. I am happy to clarify them. Our Board of Trustees requires the following information in your proposal:

1. A list of all of the constraints (to make sure you took them into consideration).
2. An inequality for each of the constraints.
3. A full-page graph showing all inequalities and the resulting solution region (use a different color for each inequality).
4. Calculations for each of the vertices on your solution region. List these points at their vertex.
5. Profit calculations, with maximum profit included on your graph.

Please make sure to include a cover letter summarizing your proposal. Also include a brief explanation for each of the items listed above.

Sincerely, Ms. Toyom

Further Guidance
section ends here.

METHODS AND MEANINGS

MATH NOTES

Graphing Inequalities with Two Variables

To graph an inequality with two variables, first graph the boundary line or curve. If the inequality does not include equality (that is, if it is > or < rather than ≥ or ≤), then the graph of the boundary is dashed to indicate that it is not included in the solution. Otherwise, the boundary is a solid line or curve.

Once the boundary is graphed, choose a point that does not lie on the boundary to test in the inequality. If that point makes the inequality true, then the entire region in which that point lies is a solution. If that point makes the inequality false, then the entire region in which the point lies is not a solution. Examine the two examples below.

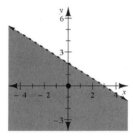

Test $(0,0)$:

$0 \overset{?}{<} -\frac{2}{3}(0) + 2$

$0 \overset{?}{<} 2$

True, so shade below the line.

$y < -\frac{2}{3}x + 2$

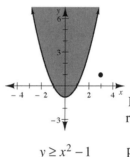

Test $(3,1)$:

$1 \overset{?}{\geq} 3^2 - 1$

$1 \overset{?}{\geq} 8$

False, so shade the region that does not contain the test point, that is, shade above the parabola.

$y \geq x^2 - 1$

Review & Preview

5-89. Solve the system of equations at right algebraically and explain what the solution tells you about the graphs of the two equations.

$3x + 2 = y$

$-9x + 3y = 11$

5-90. Draw the graph of the system of inequalities at right.

a. What polygon does the intersection form? **Justify** your answer.

b. What are its vertices?

c. Find the area of the intersection.

$y \geq |x| - 3$

$y \leq -|x| + 5$

5-91.   Solve each of the following inequalities. Express the solutions algebraically and on a number line.

a. $3(x+2) > 4x - 7$

b. $3x^2 - 4x + 2 \leq x^2 + x + 6$

5-92.   Solve each equation for y so that it could be entered into a graphing calculator.

a. $5 - (y - 3) = 3x$

b. $4(x + y) = -2$

5-93.   Janelle conducted an experiment by mistake by leaving her bologna sandwich at school over winter break. When she got back, her sandwich was much larger than it was when she left it. Her science teacher explained that the sandwich had produced large quantities of a rare bacterium, bolognicus sandwichae. Based on a sample taken from the sandwich, Janelle determined that there were approximately 72 million bacteria present. Her science teacher explained that this is not very surprising, since the number of this bacteria triples every 24 hours.

Since the sandwich had been made only 15 days ago, Janelle is sure that she can sue the meat company; the food-industry standard for the most bacteria a sandwich-sized portion can have at the time of production is 100. Find out how many of the bacteria were present when the sandwich was made to determine if Janelle has a case.

5-94.   Solve the system of equations at right.

$$x + 3y = 16$$
$$x - 2y = 31$$

a.   Now rewrite the system and replace x with x^2.

b.   What effect will this have on the solution to the system? Solve the new system.

5-95.   A line intersects the graph of $y = x^2$ twice. One point has an x-coordinate of -4, and the other point has an x-coordinate of 2.

a.   Draw a sketch of both graphs, and find the equation of the line.

b.   Find the measure of the angle that the line makes with the x-axis.

5.2.4 What can I learn from a graph?

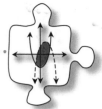

Using Graphs to Find Solutions

You have seen that you can find solutions to problems, equations, inequalities and systems using graphs. In this lesson, you will apply this knowledge to a math competition challenge.

5-96.   MATH TEAM CHALLENGE

At the annual two-day Math Challenge, teams from various high schools get together for a sometimes not-too-friendly math competition. Your school's biggest rival, Silicon Mountain High School, has won the competition the last five years and is already bragging that they will take first place again. However, your team has worked exceptionally hard this year to understand the Algebra 2 curriculum and its challenging concepts. Everyone on your team feels confident that they can beat Silicon Mountain High.

At the end of the first day of competition, scores for each school are posted and WOW! Your team and Silicon Mountain's team are tied for first place! Before the teams leave for the day, they are handed a copy of the final problem in the competition (shown below). At first your team is excited, but when your team reads the "Final Challenge," you all realize that everyone has a lot of work to do before tomorrow's event.

Final Challenge

The three math judges will ask your team five questions that can be answered by looking at the graph of the functions at right. Your score for each answer will depend on its accuracy and completeness.

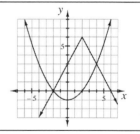

Your task: Obtain a Lesson 5.2.4 Resource page from your teacher, which contains the graph in the "Final Challenge." With your team, discuss the graph and decide what questions the judges might ask about it. For each question, form a complete response so that your team is prepared for the "Final Challenge."

Discussion Points

What can a graph tell us about equations? About inequalities?

Can we use the graph to get information about equations and inequalities in one variable and in two variables?

METHODS AND MEANINGS

Solutions to One-Variable and Two-Variable Equations

When an equation has one variable, solutions are single numbers. When an equation contains two variables, solutions are ordered pairs.

For example, the solutions for the system of equations shown at right are the ordered pairs of numbers $(4, 44)$ and $(-1, -11)$ because these are the (x, y) pairs that make both equations true. They are also the points at which the graphs of the two equations intersect.

$$y = x^2 + 8x - 4$$
$$y = 2x^2 + 5x - 8$$

The solutions for the equation $2x^2 + 5x - 8 = x^2 + 8x - 4$ (notice that it has only one variable) are the numbers 4 and -1, because they are the two x-values that make the equation true.

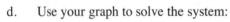

Review & Preview

5-97.   Consider the graph at right as you answer the following questions.

a.   Find the equation of the parabola.

b.   Find the equation of the line.

c.   Use your graph to solve $x + 5 = \frac{1}{2}(x + 3)^2 - 2$.

d.   Use your graph to solve the system:

$$y = \frac{1}{2}(x + 3)^2 - 2$$
$$y = x + 5$$

e.   Use your graph to solve the inequality $x + 5 < \frac{1}{2}(x + 3)^2 - 2$.

f.   Use your graph to solve $\frac{1}{2}(x + 3)^2 - 2 = 0$.

g.   Use your graph to solve $x + 5 = 4$.

h.   How could you change the equation of the parabola so that the parabola and the line do not intersect? Is there more than one way?

5-98.   Write the three inequalities that form the triangle shown at right.

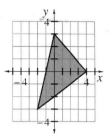

5-99.   Solve eqach of the following inequalities. Represent the solutions algebraically and on a number line.

a. $2|3x-5| \geq 4$

b. $\frac{1}{3}(3x-6)^3 + 4 < 13$

5-100.   On separate pairs of axes, sketch the graph of each equation or inequality below.

a. $y+5 = (x-2)^2$ b. $y \leq (x+3)^3$

c. $y = 4 + \frac{1}{x-3}$

5-101.   Find the measure of $\angle CPM$ in the diagram at right.

List any subproblems that were necessary to solve this problem.

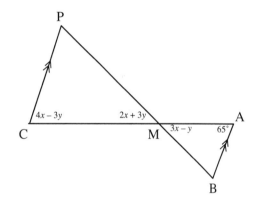

5-102.   Solve for w in each equation below.

a. $w^2 + 4w = 0$ b. $5w^2 - 2w = 0$

c. $w^2 = 6w$

Chapter 5 Closure What have I learned?

Reflection and Synthesis

The activities below offer you a chance to reflect on what you have learned in this chapter. As you work, look for concepts that you feel very comfortable with, ideas that you would like to learn more about, and topics you need more help with. Look for connections between ideas as well as connections with material you learned previously.

①　　TEAM BRAINSTORM

With your team, brainstorm a list for each of the following categories. Be as detailed as you can. How long can you make your lists? Challenge yourselves. Be prepared to share your team's ideas with the class.

Topics:　　What have you studied in this chapter? What ideas and words were important in what you learned? Remember to be as detailed as you can.

Connections:　How are the topics, ideas, and words that you learned in previous courses connected to the new ideas in this chapter? Again, make your list as long as you can.

②   MAKING CONNECTIONS

Below is a list of the vocabulary used in this chapter. Make sure that you are familiar with all of these words and know what they mean. Refer to the glossary or index for any words that you do not yet understand.

algebraic strategies	boundary curve	boundary line
boundary point	equation	extraneous
inequality	intersection	intercept
linear programming	looking inside	maximize
profit	region	rewriting
solution	system of equations	undoing

Make a concept map showing all of the connections you can find among the key words and ideas listed above. To show a connection between two words, draw a line between them and explain the connection, as shown in the example below. A word can be connected to any other word as long as you can **justify** the connection. For each key word or idea, provide a sketch of an example.

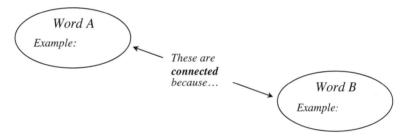

Your teacher may provide you with vocabulary cards to help you get started. If you use the cards to plan your concept map, be sure either to re-draw your concept map on your paper or to glue the vocabulary cards to a poster with all of the connections explained for others to see and understand.

While you are making your map, your team may think of related words or ideas that are not listed above. Be sure to include these ideas on your concept map.

③   GROWTH OVER TIME

This section gives you an opportunity to show growth in understanding of key mathematical ideas over time as you complete this course.

On its own sheet of paper (you will keep this problem separate from your other work or put it into a portfolio), explain everything that you know about $f(x) = 2^x - 3$.

④   SUMMARIZING MY UNDERSTANDING

This section gives you an opportunity to show what you know about certain math topics or ideas.

With your team, make a list of the **big ideas** of this chapter. Discuss the important ideas of the chapter and try to agree on a short list of no more than five big ideas. Be prepared to share your list in a whole class discussion. When the class has reached agreement on a list, continue with parts (a) and (b) below.

a.   Write your own description of each big idea.

b.   For each big idea, provide one or two representative example problems. Solve each problem completely, using multiple representations, if applicable.

Your teacher may give you a "GO" page to work on (or you can download this from www.cpm.org). "GO" stands for "Graphic Organizer," a tool you can use to organize your thoughts and communicate your ideas clearly.

⑤   WHAT HAVE I LEARNED?

This section will help you evaluate which types of problems you feel comfortable with and which you need more help with. This section will appear at the end of every chapter to help you check your understanding. Even if your teacher does not assign this section, it is a good idea to try these problems and find out for yourself what you know and what you need to work on.

Solve each problem as completely as you can. The table at the end of this closure section has answers to these problems. It also tells you where you can find additional help and practice on similar problems.

CL 5-103. Look inside, rewrite, or undo to solve each equation.

a. $3(y+1)^2 - 5 = 43$

b. $\sqrt{1-2x} = 10$

c. $\frac{6y-1}{y} - 2 = 3$

d. $|2x+1| = 5$

CL 5-104. Solve each system of equations without graphing. For each case, explain what the solution tells you about the graph of the system.

a. $y = \frac{1}{3}x^2 + 1$
   $y = 2x - 2$

b. $x = y^2$
   $x - y = 6$

c. $6x - 2y = -4$
   $y = 3x + 2$

CL 5-105. Estelle and Carlos will be hosting a party and will buy 6 pies for their guests. Two lemon meringue pies cost $3 less than 4 blueberry pies. Three lemon meringue pies cost $9 more than 3 blueberry pies. How much does each type of pie cost?

CL 5-106. Graph the following inequality or systems of inequalities.

a. $y \le 4x + 16$
   $y > -\frac{4}{3}x - 4$

b. $y < x^2 - 2x - 3$
   $y \le \frac{3}{4}x + 2$

c. $y \ge |x + 2| - 3$

d. $y \le \frac{1}{2}x + 3$
   $y \ge (x + 1)^2 - 2$

CL 5-107. Solve each inequality and graph the solution on a number line.

a. $x^2 - 2x - 15 < 0$

b. $|3x - 2| \ge 10$

CL 5-108. Find the equation of each of the lines described below.

a. The line that passes through $(6, 1)$ and $(-10, -7)$.

b. The line that is perpendicular to $y = \frac{2}{3}x + 1$ and passes through $(0, 5)$.

CL 5-109. Solve each equation for y.

a. $2y^2 + 3y = 7$

b. $3(2x - y) + 12 = 4x - 3$

c. $y(2y + 1) + 3(2y + 1) = 0$

d. $-4y - 1 = 4y(y - 2)$

CL 5-110. Complete the square and state the center and radius of the circle.

$$x^2 + y^2 - 4x + 6y - 3 = 0$$

CL 5-111. Evan spent the summer earning
money so he could buy the
classic car of his dreams. He
purchased the car for $2,295
from Fast Deal Freddie, the
local used car salesman.
Freddie told Evan that the car
would increase by half its
value after five years. Evan
knows that this model
appreciates 8% annually. Did
Freddie try to trick Evan, or
was his claim accurate?

CL 5-112. Check your answers using the table at the end of this section. Which problems do you
feel confident about? Which problems were hard? Have you worked on problems like
these in math classes you have taken before? Use the table to make a list of topics you
need help on and a list of topics you need to practice more.

This course focuses on five different **Ways of Thinking**: reversing thinking, justifying, generalizing, choosing a strategy, and investigating. These are some of the ways in which you think while trying to make sense of a concept or to solve a problem (even outside of math class). During this chapter, you have probably used each Way of Thinking multiple times without even realizing it!

This closure activity will focus on one of these Ways of Thinking: **choosing a strategy**. Read the description of this Way of Thinking at right.

Think about the problems you have worked on in this chapter. When did you need to think about what method you would use to solve a problem? What helped you decide how to approach a problem? Were there times when more than one **strategy** seemed useful? You may want to flip through the chapter to refresh your memory about the problems that you have worked on. Discuss these ideas with the class.

Once your discussion is complete, think about the way you think as you answer the questions below.

> ### Choosing a Strategy
>
> To **choose a strategy** means to think about what you know about a problem and match that information with methods and processes for solving problems. As you develop this way of thinking you will learn how to choose ways of solving problems based in given information. You think this way when you ask/answer questions like *"What strategy might work for...?"* or, *"How can I use this information to answer...?"* When you catch yourself looking for a method to answer a problem, you are **choosing a strategy**.
>
>
>
> *Which method should I use?*

a.   Sometimes, the key to being able to **choose a strategy or tool** is to recognize that different tools can be used on the same problem, but that sometimes some tools are more efficient than others.

   For example, consider the system below. Describe all of the **strategies** you can think of to solve this system of equations. Of all of these **strategies**, which would you choose to use to solve this system? Solve the system using the **strategy you have chosen** and explain why that choice is best for you.

$$y = 2x - 1 \qquad y = -\tfrac{1}{3}x + 6$$

b.   Find a problem from this chapter that can be solved using more than one **strategy**. Why did you choose to solve it the way you did? Now solve the problem again, this time using a different **strategy**?

Answers and Support for Closure Activity #5
What Have I Learned?

Problem	Solutions	Need Help?	More Practice
CL 5-103.	a. $y = 7$ or $y = -5$ b. $x = -\frac{99}{2}$ c. $y = 1$ d. $x = 2$ or $x = -3$	Lesson 5.1.1	Problems 5-3, 5-4, 5-7, 5-20, 5-27, 5-38, and 5-50
CL 5-104.	a. (3, 4)—a line tangent to parabola b. (9, 3); (4, –2)—a line intersecting a parabola twice c. infinite solution—lines are equivalent	Lessons 5.1.2 and 5.1.3 Math Notes boxes in Lessons 2.1.1, 2.1.3, and 5.2.4 Checkpoint 1 Checkpoint 2	Problems 2-7, 2-25, 2-27, 2-38, 2-91, 3-43, 3-84, 3-103, 4-123, 5-10, 5-33, 5-37, 5-89, and 5-94
CL 5-105.	$2L = 4B - 3$ $3L = 3B + 9$ Lemon meringue pies cost $7.50 each and blueberry pies cost $4.50 each.	Lessons 5.1.3 and 5.1.4 Math Notes boxes in Lessons 2.1.1 and 2.1.3 Checkpoint 2	Problems 3-8, 4-23, 4-69, 5-46, 5-48, 5-48, and 5-81
CL 5-106.	a. b. c. d.	Lesson 5.2.1 Math Notes box in Lesson 5.2.3 Checkpoint 12	Problems 5-59, 5-60, 5-68, 5-83, 5-90, and 5-98

Problem	Solutions	Need Help?	More Practice
CL 5-107.	a. $-3 < x < 5$ b. $x \le -\frac{8}{3}$ or $x \ge 4$	Lesson 5.2.1 Math Notes box in Lesson 5.2.2 Checkpoint 16	Problems 5-56, 5-62, 5-63, 5-69, 5-91, and 5-99
CL 5-108.	a. $y = \frac{1}{2}x - 2$ b. $y = -\frac{3}{2}x + 5$	Checkpoint 6 Problem 3-105	Problems 1-106, 3-104, 3-106, and 5-73
CL 5-109	a. $y = \frac{-3 \pm \sqrt{65}}{4}$ b. $y = \frac{2}{3}x + 5$ c. $y = -\frac{1}{2}, -3$ d. $y = \frac{1}{2}$	Math Notes box in Lesson 1.1.4 Checkpoint 7	Problems 1-14, 1-49, 1-88, 4-39, 4-80, 4-96, 5-29, 5-84, and 5-92
CL 5-110.	$(x - 2)^2 + (y + 3)^2 = 16$ center $(2, -3)$, radius: 4	Lesson 4.3.2 Problem 4-131	Problems 4-137, 4-144, 4-145, 4-146, 5-66, and 5-72
CL 5-111.	$y = (1.08)^t$ so when $t = 5$, $y \approx 1.46$ which is about 1.5, so Freddie's claim was fairly accurate.	Lessons 2.1.6 and 3.2.3	Problems 2-78, 2-79, 2-103, 2-154, 3-40, 3-53, 3-78, 3-117, 3-118, 3-119, 3-120, 4-42, 4-73, 5-43, and 5-65

INVERSES
AND
LOGARITHMS

CHAPTER 6   Inverses and Logarithms

Throughout this course, one of the Ways of Thinking you have considered as you solved problems is **reversing**. In this chapter you will focus on using ideas about **reversing** to **investigate** functions that "undo" each other. You will learn about inverse relations and **investigate** the relationships between functions and their inverses. You will also learn about compositions of functions.

In Section 6.2, you will find the inverses of many parent graphs and add them to the tools you have for working with parent graphs. You will find inverses for exponential functions and learn that these are called logarithmic functions. You will then **investigate** this family of functions and transform its graphs.

Guiding Questions

Think about these questions throughout this chapter:

How can I **reverse** the process?

How can I do this in another way?

How are these different ideas connected?

In this chapter, you will learn:

➢ How to undo functions.

➢ How to form compositions of functions.

➢ Different ways to express the relationship between a function and its inverse.

➢ What logarithms are and how to transform their graphs.

Chapter Outline

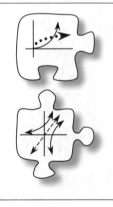

Section 6.1   You will examine relations, called inverses, that "undo" the actions of functions. You will also learn how to create composite functions by "stacking" function machines, and you will **investigate** what happens when you compose functions and their inverses.

Section 6.2   You will be introduced to an important new family of functions, called logarithms, which are the inverses of exponential functions. You will **investigate** this family and learn to transform its graphs.

6.1.1 How can I "undo" a function?

"Undo" Rules

Have you ever heard the expression, "She knows it forward and backward," to describe someone who understands an idea deeply? Often, being able to **reverse** a process is a way to show how thoroughly you understand it. Today you will **reverse** mathematical processes, including functions. As you work today, keep these questions in mind:

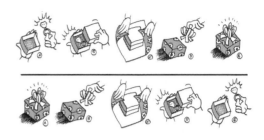

How can I "undo" it?

How can I **justify** each step?

6-1. GUESS MY NUMBER

Today you will play the "Guess My Number" game. Your teacher will think of a number and tell you some information about that number. You will try to figure out what your teacher's number is. (You can use your calculator or paper if it helps.) When you think you know the number, sit silently and do not tell anyone! Be sure to give others a chance to figure it out!

For example your teacher might say: *"When I add 4 to my number and then multiply the sum by 10, I get –70. What is my number?"*

Your task will be to find the number and explain your reasoning.

6-2. A picture of Anita's function machine is shown at right. When she put 3 into the machine, 7 came out. When she put in 4, 9 came out, and when she put in –3, –5 came out.

a. Make a table to organize the inputs and outputs from Anita's function machine. Explain in words what this machine is doing to the input to generate an output.

b. Anita's function machine suddenly starts working backwards: it is pulling outputs back up into the machine, **reversing** the machine's process, and returning the original input. If 7 is being pulled back into this machine, what value do you think will come out of the top? Anita sets up her new backwards function machine and enters the other ouputs. What would you expect to come out the top if 9 is entered? If –5 is entered? Explain.

Problem continues on next page. →

6-2.   *Problem continued from previous page.*

      c.   Record the inputs and outputs of the backwards function machine in a table. Record the numbers going in as x, and the numbers coming out as y. Explain in words what Anita's backwards function machine is doing.

      d.   Write rules for Anita's original function machine and for her backwards machine. How are the two rules related?

6-3.   The function machine at right follows the rule $f(x) = 5x + 2$.

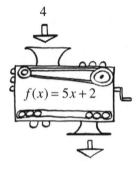

      a.   If the crank is turned backwards, what number should be pulled up into the machine in order to have a 4 come out of the top?

      b.   Keiko wants to build a new machine that will **undo** what $f(x)$ does to an input. What must Keiko's machine do to 17 to undo it and return a value of 3? Write your undo rule in function notation and call it $g(x)$.

      c.   Choose a value for x. Then find a **strategy** to show that your rule, $g(x)$, undoes the effects of the function machine $f(x)$.

6-4.   Find the undo rules for each of the functions below. Use function notation and give the undo rule a name different from the original function's. **Justify** that each undo rule works for its function.

      a. $f(x) = 3x - 6$ b. $h(x) = x^3 - 5$

      c. $p(x) = 2(x + 3)^3$ d. $t(x) = \frac{10(x-4)}{3}$

6-5.   Each team member should choose one function and its undo rule from the previous problem, and create multiple representations of each pair. Be sure to graph the function and its undo rule on the same set of axes.

      When each person in your team has finished, put everyone's work into the middle of the workspace. Describe what relationships you see between the representations of a function and its undo rule.

6-6.   What **strategies** did your team use to find undo rules? How can you
        be sure that the undo rules you found are correct? Discuss this idea
        and then write a Learning Log entry about the **strategies** you have for
        finding undo rules and checking that they work. Title this entry
        "Finding and Checking Undo Rules" and label it with today's date.

6-7.   Graph $y = \frac{1}{2}x - 3$ and its undoing function on the same set of axes.

   a.   What is the equation of the undoing function?

   b.   Does this graph, including both lines, have a line of symmetry? If so, what is the
         equation of the line of symmetry?

6-8.   Antonio's function machine is shown at right.

   a.   What is $A(2)$?

   b.   If 81 came out, what was dropped in?

   c.   If 8 came out, what was dropped in? Be
         accurate to two decimal places.

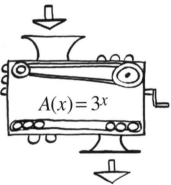

$A(x) = 3^x$

6-9.   Nossis has been working on his geometry
        homework and he is almost finished. His last task is to find a solution
        of $\sin(x) = 0.75$. Nossis cannot figure out what x could be! Explain how he can find
        a value for x and show that it works.

6-10.   If $10^x = 10^y$, what is true about x and y? **Justify** your answer.

6-11.   Solve each of the following equations for x.

   a. $\frac{x}{3} = \frac{4}{5}$ b. $\frac{x}{x+1} = \frac{5}{7}$

   c. $\frac{6}{15} = 2 - \frac{x}{5}$ d. $\frac{2}{3} + \frac{x}{5} = 6$

6-12. Sketch the solution of this system of inequalities.

$$y \geq x^2 - 5$$
$$y \leq -(x-1)^2 + 7$$

6-13. Gary has his function $g(x) = 10^x$ and Amy has her function $a(m) = 10^m$.

a. Each person is going to choose a whole number at random from the numbers $1, 2, 3 \ldots 10$, and substitute it into his or her respective function. After they do this, what is the probability that $g(x) = a(m)$?

b. Find and simplify an expression for $g(x) \cdot a(m)$.

6-14. Jamilla collected data comparing the weight and cost of pieces of sterling silver jewelry. Her data is listed as (weight in ounces, cost in dollars): $(5, 44.00)$, $(8.5, 78.50)$, $(12, 112.00)$, $(10, 93.00)$, $(7, 63.50)$, $(9, 83.20)$.

a. Plot the data on a set of axes.

b. Use a ruler to draw a line that best approximates the data.

c. Determine the equation of the line of best fit drawn in (b).

d. Use your equation to predict the cost of a 50-ounce silver bracelet.

6-15. The angle of elevation of the sun (the angle the rays of sunlight make with the flat ground) at 10:00 a.m. is 29°. At that point, a tree's shadow is 32 feet long. How tall is the tree?

6.1.2 How can I find the inverse?

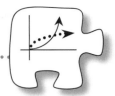

Using a Graph to Find an Inverse

What factors would you consider if you were thinking about buying a car? The first things that come to mind might be color or cost, but increasingly people are considering fuel efficiency (the number of miles a car can drive on a gallon of gas). You can think of the average number of miles per gallon that a car gets as a function that has *gallons* as the input and *miles traveled* as the output. A graph of this function would allow you to use what you know about the number of gallons in your tank to predict how far you could travel.

What would happen if you wanted to look at this situation differently? Imagine you regularly travel a route where there are many miles between gas stations. In this scenario, you would start with the information of the number of miles to the next filling station, and want to determine how many gallons of gas you would need to get there. In this case, you would start with the number of miles and work backwards to find gallons. Your new function would **reverse** the process.

6-16. In Lesson 6.1.1 you started with functions and worked backwards to find their undo rules. These undo rules are also called **inverses** of their related functions. Now you will focus on functions and their inverses represented as graphs. Use what you discovered yesterday as a basis for answering the questions below.

$y = 0.5x + 3$

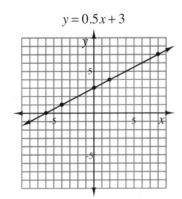

$y = 3(x+2)^2 - 6$

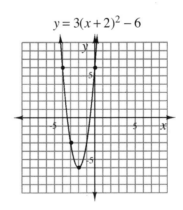

$y = \frac{1}{6}x^3 - \frac{13}{6}x + 2$

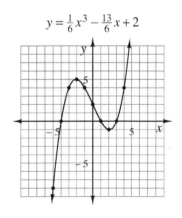

a. Obtain a Lesson 6.1.2 Resource Page from your teacher and make a careful graph of each undo rule on the same set of axes as its corresponding function. Look for a way to make the graph without finding the undo rule first. Be prepared to share your **strategy** with the class.

b. Make statements about the relationship between the coordinates of a function and the coordinates of its inverse. Use $x \to y$ tables of the function and its inverse to show what you mean.

6-17.   When you look at the graph of a function and its inverse, you can see a symmetrical relationship between the two graphs demonstrated by a line of symmetry.

   a.   Draw the line of symmetry for each pair of graphs in problem 6-16.

   b.   Find the equations of the lines of symmetry.

   c.   Why do you think these lines make sense as the lines of symmetry between the graphs of a function and its inverse relation?

6-18.   The line of symmetry you identified in problem 6-17 can be used to help graph the inverse of a function without creating an $x \rightarrow y$ table.

   a.   Graph $y = (\frac{x}{2})^2$ carefully on a full sheet of graph paper. Scale the x- and y-axes the same way on your graph.

   b.   On the same set of axes, graph the line of symmetry $y = x$.

   c.   With a pencil or crayon, trace over the curve $y = (\frac{x}{2})^2$ until the curve is heavy and dark. Then fold your paper along the line $y = x$, with the graphs on the inside of the fold. Rub the graph to make a "carbon copy" of the parabola.

   d.   When you open the paper you should see the graph of the inverse. Fill in any pieces of the new graph that did not copy completely. **Justify** that the graphs you see are inverses of each other.

6-19.   Your graphing calculator can also help you to graph the inverse of a function. Check your inverse graph from problem 6-18 by following your teacher's instructions to use the "DrawInv" feature of your graphing calculator. Was the inverse graph that you drew correct?

6-20.   Find the equation of the inverse of $y = (\frac{x}{2})^2$. Is there another way you could write it? If so, show how the two equations are the same. **Justify** that your inverse equation undoes the original function and use a graphing calculator to check the graphs.

6-21.   Consider your equation for the inverse of $y = (\frac{x}{2})^2$.

   a.   Is the inverse a function? How can you tell?

   b.   Use color to trace over the portion of your graph of $y = (\frac{x}{2})^2$ for which $x \geq 0$. Then use another color to trace the inverse of *only this part* of $y = (\frac{x}{2})^2$. Is the inverse of this part of $y = (\frac{x}{2})^2$ a function?

   c.   Find a rule for the inverse of the restricted graph of $y = (\frac{x}{2})^2$. How is this rule different from the one you found in problem 6-20?

6-22.   Consider the function $f(x) = (x-3)^2$.

    a.   How could you restrict the domain of $f(x)$ so that its inverse will be a function?

    b.   Graph $f(x)$ with its restricted domain and then graph its inverse on the same set of axes.

    c.   Find the equation of the inverse of $f(x)$ with its restricted domain.

6-23.   Is there a way to look at any graph to determine if its inverse will be a function? Explain. Find examples of other functions whose inverses are not functions.

6-24.   Use graphs to find the inverses for the following functions. Label the graph of each function and its inverse with its equation.

    a. $y = 5(x-2)$

    b. $y = 1 + \frac{2}{x}$

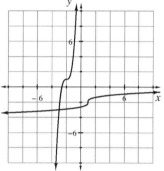

6-25.   Look at the graph at right of a function and its inverse. If $p(x)$ is a function and $q(x)$ is its inverse, can you tell which is which? Why or why not?

MⒺTHODS AND MⒺANINGS

Notation for Inverses

    When given a function $f(x)$, the notation for the inverse of the function is $f^{-1}(x)$. For example, if $f(x) = x^3 - 1$ then $f^{-1}(x) = \sqrt[3]{x+1}$.

Many calculators use this notation to identify the inverse of trigonometric functions. For example the inverse of $\sin(x)$ is written $\sin^{-1}(x)$.

6-26. Make a graph of $f(x) = \frac{1}{2}(x-1)^3$ and then graph its inverse on the same set of axes.

6-27. Solve the system of equations at right.

$$x + y = -3$$
$$2x - y = -6$$
$$3x - 2y + 5z = 16$$

6-28. Solve the equation $3 = 8^x$ for x, accurate to the nearest hundredth (two decimal places).

6-29. Write the equation of a circle with a center at $(-3, 5)$ that is tangent to the y-axis (in other words, it touches the y-axis at only one point). Sketching a picture will help.

6-30. Perform the indicated operation to simplify each of the following expressions. In some cases, factoring may help you simplify.

a. $\dfrac{(x+2)(x-3)}{(x+1)(x-4)} \cdot \dfrac{(x+1)}{x(x+2)}$

b. $\dfrac{x^2+5x+6}{x^2-4} \cdot \dfrac{4}{x+3}$

c. $\dfrac{2x}{x+4} + \dfrac{8}{x+4}$

d. $\dfrac{x}{x+1} - \dfrac{1}{x+1}$

6-31. Barnaby's grandfather is always complaining that back when he was a teenager, he used to be able to buy his girlfriend dinner for only $1.50.

a. If that same dinner that Barnaby's grandfather purchased for $1.50 sixty years ago now costs $25.25, and the price has increased exponentially, write an equation that will give you the costs at different times.

b. How much would you expect the same dinner to cost in 60 years?

6-32. Ever eat a maggot? Guess again! The FDA publishes a list, the Food Defect Action Levels list, which indicates limits for "natural or unavoidable" substances in processed food (*Time*, October 1990). So in 100 g of mushrooms, for instance, the government allows 20 maggots! The average batch of rich and chunky spaghetti sauce has 350 grams of mushrooms. How many maggots does the government allow in a batch?

Algebra 2 Connections

6-33.   Lacey and Richens each have their own personal
         function machines. Lacey's, $L(x)$, squares the
         input and then subtracts one. Richen's function,
         $R(x)$, adds 2 to the input and then multiplies the
         result by three.

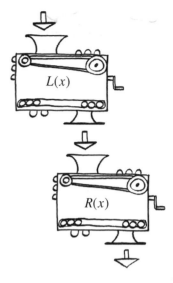

   a.   Write the equations that represent $L(x)$
         and $R(x)$.

   b.   Lacey and Richens decide to connect their two
         machines, so that Lacey's output becomes
         Richens' input. Eventually, what is the output
         if 3 is the initial input?

   c.   What if the order of the machines was
         changed? Would it change the output?
         Justify your answer.

6-34.   Solve the system of equations at right. $x - 2y = 7$

   a.   What happened? What does this mean? $6y - 3x = 33$

   b.   What does the solution tell you about the graphs?

6-35.   Dana's mother gave her $175 on her sixteenth birthday. *"But you must put it in the
         bank and leave it there until your eighteenth birthday,"* she told Dana. Dana already
         had $237.54 in her account, which pays 3.25% annual interest, compounded quarterly.
         What is the minimum amount of money she will have on her eighteenth birthday if she
         makes *no* withdrawals before then? **Justify** your answer.

6-36.   Consider the function $f(x) = \frac{2}{7-x}$.

   a.   What is $f(7)$?

   b.   What is the domain of $f(x)$?

   c.   If $g(x) = 2x + 5$, what is $g(3)$?

   d.   Now use the output of $g(3)$ as the input for f to calculate $f(g(3))$.

6-37.   If $2^{x+4} = 2^{3x-1}$, what is the value of x?

6.1.3 What can I do with inverses?

Finding Inverses and Justifying Algebraically

In this chapter you first learned how to find an inverse by undoing a function, and then you learned how to find an inverse graphically. You and your team may also have developed other **strategies**. In this lesson you will determine how to find an inverse by putting the ideas together and rewriting the equation. You will also learn a new way to combine functions that you can use to decide whether they have an inverse relationship.

6-38. Consider the table at right.

x	y
1	−5
3	7
5	19
7	31

    a.   Write an equation for the relationship represented in the table.

    b.   Make a table for the inverse.

    c.   How are these two tables related to each other?

    d.   Use the relationship between the tables to find a shortcut for changing the equation of the original function into its inverse.

    e.   Now solve this new equation for y.

    f.   **Justify** that the equations are inverses of each other.

6-39. Find the inverse function of the following functions using your new algebraic method, clearly showing all your steps.

    a. $y = 2(x-1)^3$

    b. $y = \sqrt{x-2} + 3$

    c. $y = 3(\frac{x-9}{2}) + 20$

    d. $y = \frac{4}{3}(x-1)^3 + 6$

6-40.   Adriena's **strategy** for checking that the functions $f(x)$ and $g(x)$ are inverses is to think of them as stacked function machines. She starts by choosing an input to drop into $f(x)$. Then she drops the output from $f(x)$ into $g(x)$. If she gets her original number, she is pretty sure that the two equations are inverses.

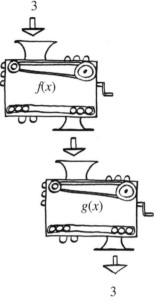

a.   Is Adriena's **strategy** sufficient? Is there anything else she should test to be sure?

b.   With your team, select a pair of inverse equations from problem 6-39, name them $f(x)$ and $g(x)$, then use Adriena's ideas to test them.

c.   Adriena wants to find a shortcut to show her work. She knows that if she chooses her input for $f(x)$ to be 3, she can write the output as $f(3)$. Next, $f(3)$ becomes the input for $g(x)$, and her output is 3. Since $f(3)$ is the new input for $g(x)$, she thinks that she can write this process as $g(f(3)) = 3$. Does her idea make sense? Why or why not?

d.   Her friend, Cemetra thinks she could also write $f(g(3))$. Is Cemetra correct? Why or why not.

e.   Will this **strategy** for testing inverses work with any input? Choose a variable to use as an input to test with your team's functions, $f(x)$ and $g(x)$.

6-41.   Christian, Adriena's teammate, is always looking for shortcuts. He thinks he has a way to adapt Adriena's **strategy**, but wants to check with his team before he tries it. *"If I use her strategy but instead of using a number, I skip a step and put the expression $f(x)$ directly into $g(x)$ to create $g(f(x))$, will I still be able to show that the equations are inverses?"*

a.   What do you think about Christian's changes? What can you expect to get out?

b.   Try Christian's idea on your team's equations, $f(x)$ and $g(x)$.

c.   Describe your results.

d.   Does Christian's **strategy** show that the two equations are inverses? How?

6-42.　Adriena was finding inverses of some equations. Use Christian's **strategy** from Problem 6-41 to check Adriena's work and test if each pair of equations are inverses of each other. If they are not, explain what went wrong and show how to get the inverse correctly.

a.　$f(x) = \frac{3}{5}x - 15$

　　$g(x) = \frac{5}{3}x + 25$

b.　$f(x) = \frac{2(x+6)}{3} + 10$

　　$g(x) = \frac{3}{2}x - 21$

c.　$e(x) = \frac{(x-10)^2}{4}$

　　$d(x) = 4\sqrt{x} + 10$

6-43.　Make a personal poster that shows what you have learned about inverses so far. Choose an equation and its inverse then **justify** that your equations are inverses of each other using several representations.

METHODS AND **M**EANINGS

Composition of Functions

MATH NOTES

When we stack one function machine on top of another so that the output of the first machine becomes the input of the second, we create a new function, which is a **composition** of the two functions. If the first function is $g(x)$ and the second is $f(x)$, the composition of f and g can be written $f(g(x))$. (Note that the notations $f \circ g$ or $f \circ g(x)$ are used in some texts to denote the same composition.)

Note that the order of the composition matters. In general, the compositions $g(f(x))$ and $f(g(x))$ will be different functions.

Review & Preview

6-44.　Trejo says that if you know the x-intercepts, y-intercepts, domain, and range of an equation then you automatically know the x-intercepts, y-intercepts, domain, and range for the inverse. Hilary disagrees. She says you know the intercepts but that is all you know for sure. Who is correct? **Justify** your answer.

6-45.   The function $f(x)$ is represented in the graph at right. Draw a graph of its inverse function. Be sure to state the domain and range for both $f(x)$ and $f^{-1}(x)$.

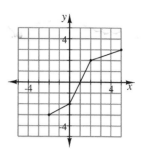

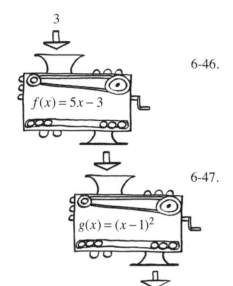

6-46.   Two function machines, $f(x) = 5x - 3$ and $g(x) = (x-1)^2$, are shown at left. Suppose $f(3)$, (*not* $x = 3$), is dropped into the $g(x)$ machine. This is written as $g(f(3))$. What is this output?

6-47.   Using the same function machines as in the previous problem, what is $f(g(3))$? Be careful! The result is different from the last one because the *order* in which you use the machines has been switched! With $f(g(3))$, first you find $g(3)$, then you substitute that answer into the machine named f.

6-48.   This is a Checkpoint for working with integral and rational exponents.

Use integer or rational exponents to write each of the following expressions as an exponential expression with a base of x.

a. $\sqrt[5]{x}$ b. $\frac{1}{x^3}$ c. $\sqrt[3]{x^2}$ d. $\frac{1}{\sqrt{x}}$

e.   Check your answers by referring to the Checkpoint 11 materials located at the back of your book.

If you needed help to rewrite these expressions correctly, then you need more practice in simplifying expressions with integral or rational exponents. Review Checkpoint 11 materials and try the practice problems. Also, consider getting help outside of class time. From this point on, you will be expected to simplify expressions such as these easily and accurately.

6-49.   Solve each of the following equations.

a. $\frac{3x}{5} = \frac{x-2}{4}$ b. $\frac{4x-1}{x} = 3x$

c. $\frac{2x}{5} - \frac{1}{3} = \frac{137}{3}$ d. $\frac{4x-1}{x+1} = x - 1$

6-50. Rebecca thinks that she has found a quick way to graph an inverse of a function. She figures that if you can interchange x and y to find the inverse, she will interchange the x- and y-axes by flipping the paper over so that when she looks through the back the x-axis is vertical and the y-axis is horizontal as shown in the pair of graphs below left. Copy the graph on the right onto your paper and try her technique. Does it work? If so, do you like this method? Why or why not?

 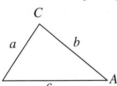 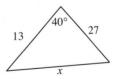

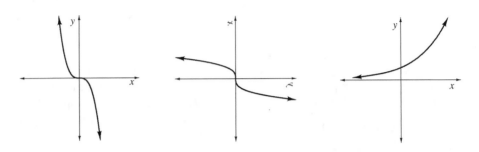

METHODS AND MEANINGS

Laws of Sines and Cosines

MATH NOTES

For any uniquely determined triangle, missing sides and angles can be determined by using the **Law of Sines** or the **Law of Cosines**.

Law of Sines: $\dfrac{\sin A}{a} = \dfrac{\sin B}{b} = \dfrac{\sin C}{c}$

Law of Cosines: $c^2 = a^2 + b^2 - 2ab \cos C$

6-51. Find the value of x. Refer to the Math Notes box above, for a reminder of the Laws of Sines and Cosines. **Justify** how you know your answer is reasonable.

6-52. Complete the square to write $x^2 + y^2 - 4x - 16 = 0$ in graphing form and sketch the graph.

6-53.   Perform each operation below and simplify your results.

a. $\dfrac{x^2+4x+3}{x^2+3x} \cdot \dfrac{3x}{x+1}$

b. $\dfrac{y^2}{y+4} - \dfrac{16}{y+4}$

c. $\dfrac{x^2+x}{x^2-4x-5} \div \dfrac{3x^2}{x-5}$

d. $\dfrac{x^2-6x}{x^2-4x+4} + \dfrac{4x}{x^2-4x+4}$

$6.2.1$ How can I undo an exponential function?

Finding the Inverse of an Exponential Function

When you first began **investigating** exponential functions you looked at how their different representations were interconnected, as in the web at right. So far in this chapter you have considered how functions and their inverses are related in different representations including rules, $x \rightarrow y$ tables, and graphs. What would the inverse relation for each of the parent functions you worked with in Chapter 4 look like in each representation?

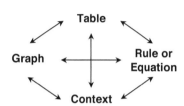

As you work with your team today, ask each other these questions:

> What does the parent function look like in this representation?
> How can that help us see the inverse relation?
>
> Would another representation be more helpful?
>
> How can we describe the relationship in words?

6-54.   So far, you have learned a lot about eight different parent graphs:

i. $y = x^2$ ii. $y = x^3$ iii. $y = x$ iv. $y = |x|$

v. $y = \sqrt{x}$ vi. $y = \frac{1}{x}$ vii. $y = b^x$ viii. $x^2 + y^2 = 1$

a.   For each parent, find the inverse. Be sure to write the equation of the inverse in y-form, if possible. Include a sketch of each parent graph and its inverse. Remember that you can use DrawInv on your graphing calculator to help test your ideas.

b.   Are any parent functions their own inverses? Explain how you know.

c.   Do any parent functions have inverses that are not functions? If so, which ones?

6-55.   THE INVERSE EXPONENTIAL FUNCTION

There are two parent functions, $y = |x|$ and $y = b^x$, that have inverses that you do not yet know how to write in y-form. You will come back to $y = |x|$ later. Since exponential functions are so useful for modeling situations in the world, the inverse of an exponential function is also important. Use $y = 3^x$ as an example. Even though you may not know how to write the inverse of $y = 3^x$ in y-form, you know a lot about it.

a.   You know how to make an $x \rightarrow y$ table for the inverse of $y = 3^x$. Make the table.

b.   You also know what the graph of the inverse looks like. Sketch the graph.

c.   You also have one way to write the equation based on your algebraic shortcut from problem 6-38 (d). Write an equation for the inverse, even though it may not be in y-form.

d.   If the input for the inverse function is 81, what is the output? If you could write an equation for this function in y-form, or as a function $g(x) =$, and you put in any number for x, how would you describe the outcome?

6-56.   AN ANCIENT PUZZLE

Parts (a) – (f) below are similar to a puzzle that is more than 2100 years old. Mathematicians first created the puzzle in ancient India in the 2nd century BC. More recently, about 700 years ago, Muslim mathematicians created the first tables allowing them to find answers to this type of puzzle quickly. Tables similar to them appeared in school math books until recently.

Here are some clues to help you figure out how the puzzle works:

$$\log_2 8 = 3 \qquad\qquad \log_3 27 = 3$$

$$\log_5 25 = 2 \qquad\qquad \log_{10} 10{,}000 = 4$$

Use the clues to find the missing pieces of the puzzles below:

a. $\log_2 8 = ?$ b. $\log_2 32 = ?$

c. $\log_? 100 = 2$ d. $\log_5 ? = 3$

e. $\log_? 81 = 4$ f. $\log_{100} 10 = ?$

6-57.   How is the Ancient Puzzle related to the problem of the inverse function for $y = 3^x$ in problem 6-55? Show how you can use the idea in the Ancient Puzzle to write an equation in y-form or as $g(x) =$ for the inverse function in problem 6-55.

6-58.   THE INVERSE OF ABSOLUTE VALUE

a.   Find the inverse equation and graph of $y = 2|x+1|$.

b.   Although you know how to find the table, graph, and equation for the inverse of absolute value, this is another function whose inverse equation cannot easily be written in y-form. In fact, there is no standard notation for the inverse of the absolute value function. With your team, invent a symbol to represent the inverse, and give examples to show how your symbol works. Be sure to explain how your symbol handles that fact that the inverse of $y = |x|$ is not a function or explain why it is difficult to come up with a reasonable notation.

6-59.   In problem 6-55, you looked at the inverse of $y = 3^x$. Finish **investigating** this function.

6-60.   Amanda wants to showcase her favorite function: $f(x) = 1 + \sqrt{x+5}$. She has built a function machine that performs these operations on the input values. Her brother Eric is always trying to mess up Amanda's stuff, so he created the inverse of $f(x)$, called it $e(x)$, and programmed it into a machine.

a.   What is Eric's equation for his function $e(x)$?

b.   What happens if the two machines are pushed together? What is $e(f(-4))$? Explain why this happens.

c.   If $f(x)$ and $e(x)$ are graphed on the same set of axes, what would be true about the two graphs?

d.   Draw the two graphs on the same set of axes. Be sure to show clearly the restricted domain and range of Amanda's function.

6-61.   Sketch the graph of $y + 3 = 2^x$.

a.   What are the domain and range of this function?

b.   Does this function have a line of symmetry? If so, what is it?

c.   What are the x- and y-intercepts?

d.   Change the equation so that the graph of the new equation has no x-intercepts.

6-62.   Solve for x in the following diagrams.

a.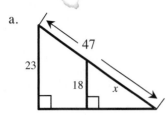

b.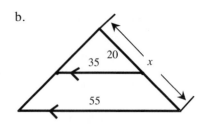

6-63.   Sketch square $ABCD$ on your paper, then randomly choose a point on $\overline{AB}$ and label it X. Draw $\overline{XC}$ and $\overline{XD}$ to form $\triangle XCD$. If a dart is thrown and lands inside the square, what is the probability that it landed inside $\triangle XCD$? Does it matter where you place X on $\overline{AB}$?

6-64.   A woman plans to invest x dollars. Her investment counselor advises her that a safe plan is to invest 30% of that money in bonds and 70% in low risk stocks. The bonds currently have a simple interest rate of 7% and the stock has a dividend rate (like simple interest) of 9%.

   a.   Write an expression for the annual income that will come from the bond investment.

   b.   Write an expression for the annual income that will come from the stock investment.

   c.   Write an equation and solve it to find out how much the client needs to invest to have an annual income of $5,000.

6-65.   Some of the following algebraic fractions have common denominators and some do not. Add or subtract the expressions and simplify, if possible.

   a. $\dfrac{3}{(x-4)(x+1)} + \dfrac{6}{x+1}$

   b. $\dfrac{5}{2(x-5)} + \dfrac{3x}{x-5}$

   c. $\dfrac{x}{x^2-x-2} - \dfrac{2}{x^2-x-2}$

   d. $\dfrac{x+2}{x^2-9} - \dfrac{1}{x+3}$

6-66.   Sketch the solution to this system of inequalities.

$$y \geq (x+5)^2 - 6$$
$$y \leq -(x+4)^2 - 1$$

$6.2.2$ What is a logarithm?

Defining the Inverse of an Exponential Function

So far, you have learned how to "undo" many different functions. However, the exponential function has posed more difficulty. In this lesson, you will learn more about the inverse exponential function. In particular, you will learn how to write an inverse exponential function in y-form.

6-67. SILENT BOARD GAME

Your teacher will put an $x \rightarrow y$ table on the board or overhead that the whole class will work together to complete. The table will be like the one below. See which values you can fill in.

x	8	32	$\frac{1}{2}$	1	16	4	3	64	2	0	0.25	-1	$\sqrt{2}$	0.2	$\frac{1}{8}$
$g(x)$	3		-1					6					$\frac{1}{2}$		

a. Describe a rule that relates x and $g(x)$.

b. Look back to the Ancient Puzzle in problem 6-55. If you haven't already, use the idea of the Ancient Puzzle to write an equation for $g(x)$.

c. Why was it difficult to think of an output for the input of 0 or -1?

d. Find an output for $x = 25$ to the nearest hundredth.

6-68. ANOTHER LOGARITHM TABLE

Lynn was supposed to fill in this table for $g(x) = \log_5 x$. She thought she could use the log button on her calculator, but when she tried to enter $5, 25,$ and 125, she did not get the ouputs the table below displays. She was fuming over how long it was going to take to guess and check each one when her sister suggested that she did not have to do that for all of them. She could fill in a few more and then use what she knew about exponents to figure out some of the others.

x	$\frac{1}{25}$	$\frac{1}{5}$	$\frac{1}{2}$	1	2	3	4	5	6	7	8	10	25	100	125	625
$g(x)$		-1		0				1					2		3	

a. Discuss with your team which outputs can be filled in without a calculator. Fill those in and explain how you found these entries.

Problem continues on next page $\rightarrow$

6-68.   *Continued from previous page.*

    b.   With your team, use your calculator to estimate the remaining values of $g(x)$ to the nearest hundredth. Once you have entered several, use your knowledge of exponent rules to see if you can find any shortcuts.

    c.   What do you notice about the results for $g(x)$ as x increases?

    d.   Use your table to draw the graph of $y = \log_5 x$. How does your graph compare to the graph of $y = 5^x$?

6-69.   Find each of the values below, and then **justify** your answers by writing the equivalent exponential form.

    a. $\log_2(32) = ?$ b. $\log_2(\tfrac{1}{2}) = ?$

    c. $\log_2(4) = ?$ d. $\log_2(0) = ?$

    e. $\log_2(?) = 3$ f. $\log_2(?) = \tfrac{1}{2}$

    g. $\log_2(\tfrac{1}{16}) = ?$ h. $\log_2(?) = 0$

6-70.   While the idea behind the Ancient Puzzle is more than 2100 years old, the symbol **log** is more recent. It was created by John Napier, a Scottish mathematician in the 1600's. "Log" is short for **logarithm**, and represents the function that is the **inverse of an exponential function**. You can use this idea to find the inverse equations of each of the following functions. Find the inverses and write your answers in y-form.

    a. $y = \log_9(x)$ b. $y = 10^x$

    c. $y = \log_6(x + 1)$ d. $y = 5^{2x}$

6-71.   Practice your logarithm fluency by calculating each of the following, *without changing the expressions to exponential form*. Be ready to explain your thinking.

    a. $\log_7 49 =$ ___   b. $\log_3 81 =$ ___

    c. $\log_5 5^7 =$ ___   d. $\log_{10} 10^{1.2} =$ ___

    e. $\log_2 2^{w+3} =$ ___

METHODS AND MEANINGS

Logarithms and Their Notation

MATH NOTES

A **logarithm** (called a "log" for short) is an exponent. An expression in logarithmic form, such as $\log_2(32)$, is read, *"the log, base 2, of 32."* To evaluate log expressions, think of the exponent: $\log_2(32) = 5$, because the exponent needed for base 2 to become 32 is 5.

An equation in logarithmic form is equivalent to another equation in exponential form, as shown at right. This conversion helps show why (based on an $x \rightarrow y$ interchange) $y = \log_b(x)$ and $y = b^x$ are inverse functions.

$$y = \log_b(x)$$
$$b^y = x$$

Review & Preview

6-72. Let $y = \log_2(x)$. Rewrite the equation so that it begins with $x =$. Think about how you defined $y = \log_2(x)$ if you get stuck. Put a large box around both equations. Do the two equations look the same? Do the two equations mean the same thing? Are they equivalent? How do you know? This is very important. Think about it, and write a clear explanation.

6-73. Every exponential equation has an equivalent logarithmic form and every logarithmic equation has an equivalent exponential form. For example,

exponent
$$4^3 = 64 \quad \text{is equivalent to} \quad 3 = \log_4 64$$
base · · · exponent · base

Copy the table shown below and fill in the missing form in each row.

	Exponential Form	Logarithmic Form
a.	$y = 5^x$	
b.		$y = \log_7(x)$
c.	$8^x = y$	
d.	$A^K = C$	
e.		$K = \log_A(C)$
f.		$\log_{1/2}(K) = N$

6-74.　If $x = 7^y$, how would you write this equation in y-form? Explain.

6-75.　Find the value of x in the equation $2^x = 3$. Be accurate to three decimal places.

6-76.　Although the quadratic formula always works as a **strategy** to solve quadratic equations, for many problems it is not the most efficient method. Sometimes it is faster to factor or complete the square or even just "out-think" the problem. For each equation below, choose the method you think is most efficient to solve the equation and explain your reason. **Note that you do *not* actually need to solve the equation.**

　　a.　$x^2 + 7x - 8 = 0$ 　　　　　　　　b.　$(x + 2)^2 = 49$

　　c.　$5x^2 - x - 7 = 0$ 　　　　　　　　d.　$x^2 + 4x = -1$

6-77.　If $10^{3x} = 10^{(x-8)}$, solve for x. Show that your solution works by checking your answer.

6-78.　Find the value of x in each diagram below.

　　a.
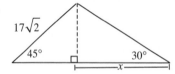

　　b.

6-79.　Consider the function defined by inputs that are the length of the radii of a circle, and the outputs are the areas of those circles. Write the rule for this function and **investigate** it completely.

6-80.　Consider the equation $y = (x + 6)^2 - 7$.

　　a.　Explain completely how to get a good sketch of the graph of $y = (x + 6)^2 - 7$.

　　b.　Explain how to change the original graph to represent the graph of $y = (x + 6)^2 + 2$.

　　c.　Given the original graph, how can you get the graph of $y = |(x + 6)^2 - 7|$?

　　d.　Restrict the domain of the original parabola to $x \geq -6$ and graph its inverse function.

　　e.　What would be the equation for the inverse function if you restricted the domain to $x \geq -6$?

6.2.3 What can I learn about logs?

Investigating the Family of Logarithmic Functions

In the last two lessons you have learned what a log is and how to convert an equation in log form to exponential form (and back again). In this lesson, you will explore logs as a family of functions.

6-81.   INVESTIGATING THE FAMILY OF LOGARITHMIC FUNCTIONS

You have learned that a logarithm is the inverse of an exponential function. Since exponential functions can have different bases, so can logarithms. **Investigate** the family of logarithmic functions $y = \log_b(x)$. The questions below will help you **investigate**.

Your task: Generate data with your team and use it to write summary statements about this family of functions. For each summary statement you find, prepare a transparency that shows and explains the summary statement and be prepared to present it to the class. Remember that summary statements should always include thorough **justification**.

Discussion Points

How can we collect data for this family? How much data is enough?

What have we learned about logs and inverses that can help us work with this family? How can "DrawInv" help?

What patterns can we find in our data? Why do they happen?

What are all the possible inputs for our function? Are there some *x*-values that do not make sense? Why or why not?
How do these results appear in different mathematical representations?

What are some characteristics that all logarithmic functions have in common?

What happens as the value of *b* changes? What values of *b* make sense?

6-82.   As a team, begin your **investigation** of $y = \log_b x$ by choosing a positive value for b and work together to generate a table and a graph. Then, have each member of your team choose a different value for b. Since there is no key for a log of base b on your calculator, you will need to find another method to generate data for a table. Several **strategies** are suggested below.

- While it may still be hard to make a table for your equation, your knowledge of inverses will help you. Write the inverse of your equation and make an $x \to y$ table for it. Use this table to help you make a table for your original function.

- Use the calculator to guess and check possible outcomes.

- Rewrite your log equation as an equivalent exponential equation and **reverse your thinking**.

_____   *Further Guidance*   _____
              section ends here.

6-83.   Write a Learning Log entry about the family of functions $y = \log_b x$. Include the summary statements your team came up with and any others that you think should be added from the class discuission. As you write, think about which statements are very clear to you and which need further clarification. Title this entry "The Family of Logarithmic Functions" and label it with today's date.

6-84.   Write the equation of an increasing exponential function that has a horizontal asymptote at $y = 15$.

6-85.   If a point inside the figure at right is chosen at random, what is the probability that it is in the shaded region?

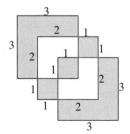

6-86.   Solve for n: $n^3 = 49$.

6-87.   A circle has the equation $x^2 + (y+2)^2 = r^2$. If the circle is shifted 2 units to the left, 5 units up, and the radius is doubled, what will its new equation be?

6-88.   On Wednesdays at Tara's Taqueria four tacos are the same price as three burritos. Last Wednesday the Lunch Bunch ordered five tacos and six burritos, and their total bill was $8.58 (with no tax or drinks included). Nobody in the Lunch Bunch can remember the cost of one of Tara's tacos. Help them figure it out.

6-89.   Graph the two functions at right on the same set of axes. $y = 3(2^x)$

         $y = 3(2^x) + 10$

         a.   How do the two graphs compare?

         b.   Suppose the first equation is $y = km^x$ and the graph is shifted up b units. What is the new equation?

6-90.   Solve each equation or inequality.

         a. $|x-1| = 9$ b. $2|x+1| + 3 = 9$

         c. $|x-1| < 3$ d. $|x+5| \geq 8$

6-91.   For each of the following rational expressions, add or subtract, then simplify.

         a. $\frac{2-x}{x+4} + \frac{3x+6}{x+4}$ b. $\frac{3}{(x+2)(x+3)} + \frac{x}{(x+2)(x+3)}$

         c. $\frac{3}{x-1} - \frac{2}{x-2}$ d. $\frac{8}{x} - \frac{4}{x+2}$

6-92.   Each step of a simplification process must be **justifiable** using the properties of algebra.

         a.   Examine the **justification** for each step in the simplification below.

               Given expression: $2(x + \frac{3}{x}) - \frac{4}{x}$

               Step 1: $2x + \frac{6}{x} - \frac{4}{x}$ Distributive Property

               Step 2: $\frac{2x^2}{x} + \frac{6}{x} - \frac{4}{x}$ Multiplicative Identity ($1 \cdot a = a$)

               Step 3: $\frac{1}{x}(2x^2 + 6 - 4)$ Distributive Property

               Step 4: $\frac{2x^2 + 6 - 4}{x}$ Definition of Division ($a \div b = a(\frac{1}{b})$)

               Step 5: $\frac{2x^2 + 2}{x}$ Associative Property of Addition

         b.   Use the properties of algebra to **justify** each step in simplifying the expression in part (d) of problem 6-91.

6.2.4 How can I transform log functions?

Transformations of Logarithmic Functions

In Lesson 6.2.3, you **investigated** logarithmic functions with different bases. To do this, you had to convert a log equation into its corresponding exponential form. In this lesson, you will figure out what a graphing calculator can and cannot do with logs. This will help you write a general equation for a log function. As you work with your team, use the following questions to help focus your discussions.

What is a log?

How are logarithms and exponential equations related to each other?

How can we find an equivalent exponential equation for an equation that is in log form?

How can we transform the graphs of log functions?

6-93.   SOLVE THE LOG MYSTERY!

Have you noticed the $\boxed{\text{LOG}}$ key on your calculator? Clearly it is a logarithm, but what is its base? It would have been nice if the designers of your graphing calculator had allowed the $\boxed{\text{LOG}}$ key to work with any base, but they did not!

Your task: Find the base of the $\boxed{\text{LOG}}$ key on your calculator. With your team, start by gathering some data and making a table for $y = \log x$. Analyze your data, and when you are sure you have figured out the base, write a clear summary statement **justifying** your conclusion.

Discussion Points

What input values give whole number outputs?
What do those values tell us?

How can we rewrite $y = \log_? x$?

6-94.   Now that you know the base of $f(x) = \log x$, you are ready to use your transformation skills to write a general equation.

a.   Copy and complete the following table for $f(x) = \log x$.

x								1	2	3	4	5	6
y	−6	−5	−4	−3	−2	−1	0						

b.   Using a full sheet of graph paper, make an accurate graph of $f(x) = \log(x)$. Remember that, just like the graphs of exponential functions, the graphs of log functions have asymptotes, so make sure any asymptotes on your graph are clearly shown.

c.   Find all of the possible types of transformations of the graph of $f(x) = \log x$. For each transformation you find, show the graph and its equation. Then, find the general form for this family of logarithm graphs. Be prepared to explain your reasoning to the class.

6-95.   You have learned a lot about logs in a short time. Use what you have learned so far to answer the questions below.

a.   Why does your calculator say that $\log(6) \approx 0.778$?

b.   **Justify** why $\log(6)$ must have a value less than 1 but greater than 0.

c.   Create a Learning Log entry that includes your answers to the focus questions from today's lesson, reprinted below. Show examples and use color or arrows to help explain your ideas. Title this entry "Working with Logs" and label it with today's date.

What is a log?

How are logarithms and exponential equations related to each other?

How can you find an equivalent exponential equation for an equation that is in log form?

How can you transform log functions?

6-96. Last night, while on patrol, Agent 008 came upon a spaceship! He hid behind a tree and watched a group of little space creatures carry all sorts of equipment out of the ship. But suddenly, he sneezed. The creatures jumped back into their ship and sped off into the night. 008 noticed that they had dropped something so he went to pick it up. It was  a calculator! What a great find. He noticed that it had a LOG button, but he noticed something interesting: log 10 did not equal 1! With this calculator, $\log 10 \approx 0.926628408$. He tried some more: $\log 100 \approx 1.853256816$ and $\log 1000 \approx 2.779885224$.

    a.   What base do the space creatures work in? Explain how you can tell.

    b.   How many fingers do you think the space creatures have?

6-97. Copy these equations and solve for x. You should be able to do all these problems without a calculator.

    a. $\log_x(25) = 1$ b. $x = \log_3(9)$

    c. $3 = \log_7(x)$ d. $\log_3(x) = \frac{1}{2}$

    e. $3 = \log_x(27)$ f. $\log_{10}(10000) = x$

6-98. Is $\log(0.3)$ greater than or less than one? **Justify** your anwer.

6-99. Solve $1.04^x = 2$. Your answer should be accurate to three decimal places.

6-100.   Perform each operation below and simplify your results.

a. $\dfrac{x^2+5x+6}{x^2-4x} \cdot \dfrac{4x}{x+2}$

b. $\dfrac{x^2-2x}{x^2-4x+4} \div \dfrac{4x^2}{x-2}$

6-101.   Solve the following inequalities.

a. $x^2-2x<3$

b. $3x-x^2\leq 2$

6-102.   Solve for m: $m^5=50$.

6-103.   Is it true that $\log_3(2)=\log_2(3)$? **Justify** your answer.

6-104.   Consider the general form of an exponential function: $y=ab^x$.

a.   Solve for a.

b.   Solve for b.

6-105.   Make a sketch of a graph that is a decreasing exponential function with the x-axis as the horizontal asymptote. Then make a similar sketch, but this time with the line $y=5$ as the horizontal asymptote.

6.2.5 How can I build a new function?

Investigating Compositions of Functions

Today you will work with your team to create and analyze new, interesting functions that are compositions of functions with which you are already familiar.

6-106. Polly Parabola's first corporate venture, Professional Parabola Productions, was so successful that Felix's Famous Functions bought her out in a corporate takeover. With all of the money she made from the transaction, she has decided to start a new company, Creative Compositions. Creative Compositions plans to develop a line of composite functions designed to appeal to the imagination of the next generation of function groupies. She wants to market three new functions and is offering huge contracts to the winners of the competition. Your boss wants your company to enter this competition and has assigned your team to do the development.

CREATIVE COMPOSITIONS
Call for new and visually interesting
Compositions of functions

The Creative Composition Corporation announces an open competition for contracts to design new products. The products must be a composition of two or more functions whose parent functions are listed below:

$$f(x) = x^2 \quad g(x) = x^3 \quad h(x) = b^x \quad i(x) = \frac{1}{x} \quad j(x) = \sqrt{x} \quad k(x) = |x| \quad l(x) = \log_b x$$

Competing teams will prepare a poster to display their composite function and respond to questions from a panel of judges. Three contracts will be awarded based on the evaluation of the judges.

The judges will base their review on the following:

Is the graph of the composition a new and interesting shape?

Are multiple representations used effectively to show key features of the new function?

Does the selection of examples show off a variety of ways the function will appear when it is transformed?

Problem continues on next page →

6-106.   *Problem continued from previous page.*

Your task: With your team, try out different ways to write compositions involving two or more of the given functions and check their graphs. Record everything you try as documentation for the report you will need to give your boss. When your team agrees on a function they like, **investigate** it thoroughly and prepare a poster for the competition.

Discussion Points

What does the graph of each function look like separately?

How does making the output of one function the input of the other change the original graph?

How do we have to adjust the domains and ranges?

Is the inverse a function?

Further Guidance

6-107.   Consider $f(x) = 2^x$ and $k(x) = |x|$. Write the rule for each composite function $k(f(x))$ and $f(k(x))$. Discuss what each graph will look like and then sketch it. For each graph, explain the effect of one parent function on the other.

6-108.   Choose other pairs of parent functions from the list. Then write the composite functions in both directions. In other words, use one function as the input for the other and then switch. Check the graphs and decide whether either is a good candidate for the competition. Try out at least five different pairs and record your equations and sketches of their graphs.

6-109.   As a team, decide which of the functions you created that you want to enter in the competition. Now do a thorough **investigation** of that function.

6-110.   Prepare a poster to show off your new function. Be sure to include all of the important details from your **investigation** on your poster and be prepared to respond to the judges with your arguments for why this function should be selected as one of the new products of Creative Compositions.

—————   *Further Guidance*   —————
section ends here.

6-111. Consider the functions $f(x)$ in parts (a) and (b) below. For each $f(x)$, find two functions $h(x)$ and $g(x)$, so that $h(g(x)) = f(x)$. Use numerical examples to demonstrate that your functions $h(x)$ and $g(x)$ work.

a. $f(x) = \sqrt{3x + 6}$

b. $f(x) = \frac{5}{\sqrt{x}}$

c. **Challenge:** Work with your team to find another possibility for $h(x)$ and $g(x)$ such that $h(g(x)) = f(x)$ for each function given in parts (a) and (b). Be prepared to share your ideas with the class.

6-112. Create a Learning Log entry explaining what you have learned about compositions of functions. Use examples to illustrate your ideas. Title this entry "Compositions of Functions" and label it with today's date.

6-113. If $f(x) = \sqrt{7 - x} - 6$ and $g(x) = -(x + 6)^2 + 7$, find $f(g(x))$ and $g(f(x))$. What do the results tell you about $f(x)$ and $g(x)$?

6-114. For functions of the form $f(x) = mx$, it is true that $f(a) + f(b) = f(a + b)$? For example, when $f(x) = 5x$, $f(a) + f(b) = 5a + 5b = 5(a + b)$ and $f(a + b) = 5(a + b)$. Is $f(a) + f(b) = f(a + b)$ true for all linear functions? Explain why or show why not.

6-115. Consider the following three sequences:

$t(n) = 50 - 7n$ $\qquad$ $h(n) = 4 \cdot 3^n$ $\qquad$ $q(n) = n^2 - 6n + 17$

a. Which, if any, is arithmetic? Geometric? Neither?

b. Are there any terms that all three sequences have in common? **Justify** how you know for sure.

c. Are there any terms that two of them share? **Justify** how you know for sure.

6-116.   Using the sequences in the previous problem, suppose we define a new sequence, $s(n)$, defined as $s(n) = q(t(n))$, a compostion of two sequences. Do you think the new sequence will be arithmetic? Geometric? Neither? Explain. Make a table of values. Does the table support your hypothesis, or do you want to change your guess? Explain.

6-117.   Sketch the graph of $y = 3\log(x+4)-1$.

6-118.   Consider two functions $f(x) = \log x$ and $g(x) = |x|$.

   a.   Use these two functions to write an equation for a composite function and sketch its graph.

   b.   Use these two functions to write a different composite function and sketch its graph.

   c.   What makes the two composite functions so different from each other?

   d.   **Challenge:** Now try graphing $g(f(g(x)))$.

6-119.   Solve $5^x = 15$ for x. Be accurate to two decimal places.

6-120.   Simplify each of the expressions in parts (a) through (c) below.

   a. $ab(\frac{1}{a}+\frac{1}{b})$ b. $cd(\frac{3}{c}+\frac{2c}{d})$ c. $x(1-\frac{1}{x})$

   d.   What expression would go in the box in order to make the equation $\Box\left(\frac{5}{x}+\frac{8}{y}\right) = 5y + 8x$ true?

Chapter 6 Closure What have I learned?

Reflection and Synthesis

The activities below offer you a chance to reflect on what you have learned in this chapter. As you work, look for concepts that you feel very comfortable with, ideas that you would like to learn more about, and topics with wich you need more help. Look for connections between ideas as well as connections with material you learned previously.

①   TEAM BRAINSTORM

Brainstorm with your team to create a list of words and ideas for each of the following two categories. Be as detailed as you can. How long can you make your lists? Challenge yourselves. Be prepared to share your team's ideas with the class.

Topics: What have you studied in this chapter? What ideas and words were important in what you learned? Remember to be as detailed as you can.

Connections: How are the topics, ideas, and words that you learned in previous chapters or courses connected to the new ideas in this chapter? Again, make your list as long as you can.

②   MAKING CONNECTIONS

Below is a list of the vocabulary used in this chapter. Make sure that you are familiar with all of these words and know what they mean. Refer to the glossary or index for any words that you do not yet understand.

asymptote	composite function	domain
exponential equation	$f^{-1}(x)$	inverse function
inverse relation	line of symmetry	logarithm
range	reversing	undo
$y = x$		

Make a concept map showing all of the connections you can find among the key words and ideas listed above. To show a connection between two words, draw a line between them and explain the connection, as shown in the example below. A word can be connected to any other word as long as you can **justifiy** the connection. For each key word or idea, provide a sketch of an example.

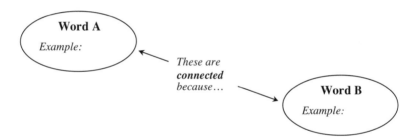

Your teacher may provide you with vocabulary cards to help you get started. If you use the cards to plan your concept map, be sure either to re-draw your concept map on your paper or to glue the vocabulary cards to a poster with all of the connections explained for others to see and understand.

While you are making your map, your team may think of related words or ideas that are not listed above. Be sure to include these ideas on your concept map.

③　　　GROWTH OVER TIME

This section gives you an opportunity to show growth in understanding of key mathematical ideas as you progress through this course.

Answer the following question on its own sheet of paper. (You will keep this problem separate from your other work or put it into a portfolio.) You saw this problem already at the end of Chapter 3. Now you should have new graphs to add to your list of examples. You should expect to be able to add even more when you revisit this problem again at the end of Chapter 9.

How many different kinds of graphs can you create that have:

a.　　No x-intercepts?

b.　　One x-intercept?

c.　　Two x-intercepts?

d.　　Three or more x-intercepts?

For each type of graph, show a sketch, label the key points, and give its equation. Make sure that each graph you give as an example represents a different family and describe the family in words or with a general equation. Show how to calculate the x-intercepts of each of your sample graphs.

④　　　SUMMARIZING MY UNDERSTANDING

This section gives you an opportunity to show what you know about certain math topics or ideas.

With your team, make a list of the *main ideas* of this chapter. Discuss the important ideas of the chapter and try to agree on a short list of no more than five main ideas. Be prepared to share your list in a whole class discussion. When the class has reached agreement on a list, continue with parts (a) and (b) below.

a.　　Write your own description of each main idea.

b.　　For each main idea, provide one or two representative example problems. Solve each problem completely, using multiple representations, if applicable.

Your teacher may give you a "GO" page to work on (or you can download this from www.cpm.org). "GO" stands for "Graphic Organizer," a tool you can use to organize your thoughts and communicate your ideas clearly.

⑤   WHAT HAVE I LEARNED?

This section will help you determine the types of problems with which you feel comfortable and the types of problems with which you need help. This section will appear at the end of every chapter to help you check your understanding. These problems are intended for you to complete independently and outside of class. Even if your teacher does not assign this section, it is a good idea to try these problems and find out for yourself what you know and what you need to work on.

Solve each problem as completely as you can. The table at the end of this closure section has answers to these problems. It also tells you where you can find additional help and practice with similar problems.

CL 6-121. Quinten and his sister Kelsey always make a habit of undoing each other's work. If Kelsey folds the laundry, Quinten unfolds it. If Quinten rakes the leaves in the yard, Kelsey "unrakes" them! While working on her math homework, Kelsey wrote the following equations. Help Quinten undo these equations by finding their inverse equations.

a. $y = 3x - 2$

b. $y = \frac{x+1}{4}$

c. $y = x^3 + 1$

d. $y = 1 + \sqrt{x+5}$

CL 6-122. Given the function $f(x) = 2 + \sqrt{x-1}$:

a.   Graph $f(x)$ and state the domain and range.

b.   Determine the equation for $f^{-1}(x)$, that is, the inverse of $f(x)$.

c.   Graph $f^{-1}(x)$ using the appropriate new domain and range.

d.   Compute $f^{-1}(f(5))$ and $f(f^{-1}(5))$ to show that your answer is correct.

CL 6-123. Use the definition of logarithms to compute each of the following *without a calculator*.

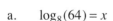

a. $\log_8(64) = x$

b. $\log_9(x) = \frac{1}{2}$

c. $\log_3(3^4) = x$

d. $10^{\log_{10}(4)} = x$

e.   What do the answers to (c) and (d) demonstrate about logs and exponents with the same base?

CL 6-124. Use your Parent Graph Tool Kit or make a table to graph $y = \log_2(x)$.

CL 6-125. Use your answer to the previous problem to graph $y = 1 + \log_2(x - 3)$. State the equation of the new asymptote and the new x-intercept.

CL 6-126. Use the graph at right to help answer the questions below.

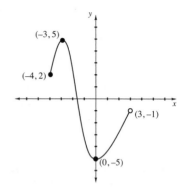

a. State the domain and range of the graph. Is this graph a function?

b. Draw the inverse of the graph. Is the inverse a function? Explain your answer.

c. State the domain and range of the inverse.

CL 6-127. A gallon of milk costs $3.89. Inflation has steadily increased 4% per year.

a. What did a gallon of milk cost ten years ago?

b. How much longer will it be until it costs $10?

CL 6-128. Write possible equations for the graphs shown below.

a.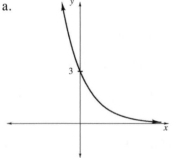

b.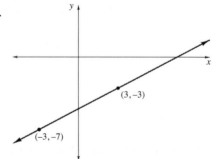

c.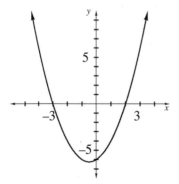

d.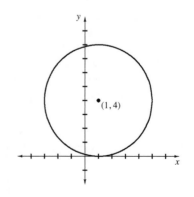

CL 6-129. Factor the expressions in parts (a) through (d) below.

    a. $3x^2 + 11x + 10$

    b. $6x^3 - 31x^2 + 5x$

    c. $6ab^2 + 15ab - 21a$

    d. $y^2 + 5y - 24$

CL 6-130. Check your answers using the table at the end of this section. Which problems do you feel confident about? Which problems were hard? Have you worked on problems like these in previous math classes? Use the table to make a list of topics you need to learn more about, and a list of topics you just need to practice more.

⑥   HOW AM I THINKING?

This course emphasizes five different **Ways of Thinking**: investigating, reversing thinking, justifying, generalizing, and choosing a strategy. These are some of the ways you might think while trying to make sense of a new concept or attempting to solve a challenging problem (even outside of math class). During this chapter, you have probably used each Way of Thinking multiple times without even realizing it!

Review each of the five Ways of Thinking described in the closure sections of Chapters 1 through 5. Then choose three of these Ways of Thinking that you remember using while working on this chapter. Show and explain where and how you used each one. Describe why thinking in this way helped you solve a particular problem or understand something new. Be sure to include examples to demonstrate your ideas.

Answers and Support for Closure Activity #5
What Have I Learned?

Problem	Solutions	Need Help?	More Practice
CL 6-121.	a. $y = \frac{x+2}{3}$ b. $y = 4x - 1$ c. $y = \sqrt[3]{x-1}$ d. $y = (x-1)^2 - 5$	Lessons 6.1.1 and 6.1.3	Problems 6-2, 6-3, 6-4, 6-38, and 6-39
CL 6-122.	a. domain $x \geq 1$; range $y \geq 2$ b. $f^{-1}(x) = (x-2)^2 + 1$ c. domain $x \geq 2$; range $y \geq 1$ d. $f^{-1}(f(5)) = f(f^{-1}(5)) = 5$	Lessons 6.1.2 and 6.1.3 Math Notes box in Lesson 6.1.2 Problems 6-40 and 6-41	Problems 6-21, 6-22, 6-24, 6-26, 6-39, 6-42, 6-44, 6-45, 6-60, and 6-113
CL 6-123.	a. 2 b. 3 c. 4 d. 4	Lesson 6.2.2 Math Notes box in Lesson 6.2.2	Problems 6-69, 6-71, 6-73, and 6-97
CL 6-124.		Lessons 6.2.2 and 6.2.3 Problem 6-69	Problems 6-67, 6-68, and 6-94
CL 6-125.	Asymptote $x = 3$ Intercept $(3.5, 0)$	Lesson 6.2.4	Problems 6-94 and 6-117

Problem	Solutions	Need Help?	More Practice

CL 6-126.

a. domain: $-4 \leq x < 3$

range: $-5 \leq y \leq 5$

b. No, there are 2 outputs when $-5 < x < -1$ and $2 < x \leq 5$

c. domain: $-5 \leq x \leq 5$

range: $-4 \leq y < 3$

Need Help? Lesson 6.1.2

More Practice Problems 6-16, 6-21, 6-24, 6-44, 6-45, and 6-50

CL 6-127.

a. $2.63

b. ≈ 24 years (by guess and check)

Need Help? Lessons 2.1.6 and 3.2.3

More Practice Problems 2-78, 2-79, 2-103, 2-154, 3-40, 3-53, 3-78, 3-117, 3-118, 3-119, 3-120, 4-42, 4-73, 5-43, 5-65

CL 6-128. Possibilities include:

a. $y = 3(\frac{1}{2})^x$ or $y = 3(2)^{-x}$

b. $y = \frac{2}{3}x - 5$

c. $y = (x-2)(x+3)$ or $y = x^2 + x - 6$

d. $(x-1)^2 + (y-4)^2 = 16$

Need Help? Lessons 3.1.5, 4.1.3, 4.2.1, 4.2.2, and 4.2.4

Math Notes boxes in Lessons 1.1.2, 4.1.3, 4.2.2, 4.3.2

Checkpoint 6

Problem 3-105

More Practice Problems 1-106, 3-62, 3-64, 3-104, 3-106, 4-78, 4-91, 4-138, and 5-72

CL 6-129.

a. $(3x+5)(x+2)$

b. $x(6x-1)(x-5)$

c. $3a(2b+7)(b-1)$

d. $(y-3)(y+8)$

Need Help? Lesson 2.2.2

Checkpoint 5

More Practice Problems 2-28, 2-90, 2-155, 3-29, 3-60, 3-111, 3-124, and 4-82

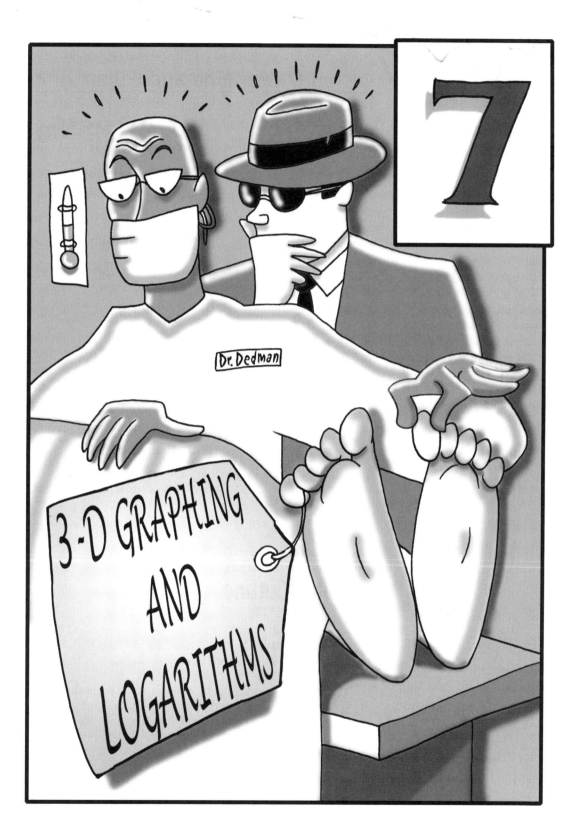

CHAPTER 7   3-D Graphing and Logarithms

In this chapter, you will learn to extend your mathematical thinking to three dimensions and you will further your understanding of logarithms, which will give you the tools to solve a murder mystery.

In the first section, you will expand your understanding of graphing equations and systems of equations to three dimensions and you will broaden your understanding of solutions to include solutions to systems in three dimensions. In Section 7.2, you will return to logarithms to learn more about their properties and why they are useful. You will construct an exponential function to model a situation, and you will use logarithms to solve a mathematical murder mystery. In Section 7.3, you will learn what a matrix is and how matrices, along with your graphing calculator, can be useful tools for solving complicated systems of equations.

Guiding Questions

Think about these questions throughout this chapter:

How can I visualize this?

How are these different ideas connected?

How can I model this situation?

How can I solve it?

In this chapter, you will learn:

➤ How to graph points, equations, and system of equations in three dimensions.

➤ How to solve systems of 3-D equations algebraically and how to interpret the meaning of the solution graphically.

➤ How to use systems of three equations in three variables to solve problems, including finding the equation of a parabola passing through any three points.

➤ Some useful properties of logarithms.

➤ How to use logarithms to solve exponential equations.

Chapter Outline

Section 7.1 In this section, you will learn how to graph points and equations in three dimensions, and you will solve three-dimensional systems of equations.

Section 7.2 You will learn some important properties of logarithms that will enable you to solve equations and will solve a murder mystery, "The Mystery of the Cooling Corpse."

Section 7.3 In this final section, you will learn what matrices are and how to perform simple operations on matrices. You will also learn how they can be useful for solving complicated systems of equations.

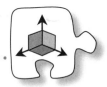

Creating a Three-Dimensional Model

In geometry, you worked with objects that existed in different dimensions. You considered lines and line segments, which have only one dimension: length. You also looked at flat shapes like circles, rectangles, and trapezoids that have two dimensions: length and width. Prisms, cones, and most objects that we encounter in the world have volume, and therefore have three dimensions: length, width and height.

When you worked with graphs in Algebra 1, you represented points, the number line, and curves on a **two-dimensional** (flat) surface called the xy-plane. So far, you have only been able to represent relationships with at most two unknowns, usually the variables x and y. However, many problems have more than two unknowns. Today, you and your team will build a model that will help you graph in three dimensions. As you work on this lesson, consider the following questions with your team:

How can we plot a point in three dimensions?

How can we write the coordinates of a point in three dimensions?

How can we show three dimensions on flat paper?

7-1. The following questions ask you to consider when it is appropriate to graph a situation in one, two, and/or three dimensions. It may be helpful to think about your experience representing numbers and relationships on a number line or an xy-plane, and how that could be adapted to work in three dimensions. Discuss each question with your team before writing your response.

a. How can you represent the solution to $x = 5$ graphically? Can you think of more than one way?

b. How can you represent the solutions to $x + 2y = 5$ graphically?

c. How could you represent the solutions to $x + 2y + z = 5$? What would the solutions look like? Discuss these questions with your team and write down any ideas that you have.

7-2. To graph solutions to equations with three variables, you need to use a three-dimensional coordinate system. Obtain a Lesson 7.1.1A or 7.1.1B Resource Page from your teacher. Use scissors to cut out the region indicated on the page. Then fold along each of the axes and use tape to attach the dashed edge to the z-axis. Be sure that the grid ends up on the *inside* of your model (rather than the outside). The result should look similar to the diagram at right.

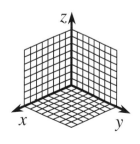

7-3.　Place a dime (or other marker) on the bottom surface of your model at the point where $x = 4$ and $y = 2$. Now lift your dime straight up so that it you are holding it 3 units above the bottom of the model.

    a.　With your team, find a way to write the coordinates of this point.

    b.　In your model, find the point where $x = 3$, $y = 4$, and $z = 2$. Use your team's method to write the coordinates for this point.

    c.　The model you have created is only a portion of the entire coordinate system used to represent three dimensions mathematically. How many of these models would you have to put together to create a model that represents the entire three-dimensional coordinate system? Think about the regions you would need to graph points like $(5, -2, -7)$ or $(-1, -2, -4)$.

7-4.　Use cubes to build each shape described below inside your three-dimensional model. Make sure that one corner of each shape you build lies at the **origin** (at the point $(0, 0, 0)$).

    a.　Build a $2 \times 2 \times 2$ cube. Use coordinates to name the vertex that is farthest from the origin.

    b.　Build a rectangular prism that is 2 units in length along the x-axis, 1 unit in length along the y-axis, and 3 units in length along the z-axis. Use coordinates to name the vertex that is farthest from the origin.

    c.　Draw and label a three-dimensional coordinate system on isometric dot paper like the one shown at right. Now add the prism from part (b) to the drawing. On your dot paper, label the coordinates of *all* of the vertices.

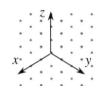

7-5.　Build a rectangular prism that will have vertices in your model at $(1, 0, 0)$, $(0, 0, 4)$, and $(0, 3, 0)$.

    a.　Find the coordinates of the other five vertices.

    b.　Move the rectangular prism so that three vertices are at $(-1, 0, 0)$, $(0, 0, 4)$, and $(0, 3, 0)$. Now where are the other vertices?

    c.　Is it possible to build another rectangular prism that has the same coordinates for the vertex farthest from the origin as the prism in part (b)? Be sure to **justify** your conclusion.

7-6.   On isometric dot paper, draw a three-dimensional coordinate system and plot the following points: $(0, 1, -1)$, $(1, 2, 0)$, and $(2, 3, 1)$.

   a.   What do you notice about the three points?

   b.   With your team, find a **strategy** to make each point clearly different from the others. Be prepared to share your **strategy** with the class.

   c.   Identify the coordinates of two points that appear to be the same as $(-2, 0, 0)$.

7-7.   In your Learning Log, show and explain how to graph points in three dimensions. Include clear pictures to illustrate your method. Title this entry "Plotting Points in *xyz*-Space" and label it with today's date.

7-8.   Make a table like the one below. Choose points in each of the locations listed at the top of the table and write in the coordinates of the points you have chosen.

	Points on the x-axis	Points on the y-axis	Points on the z-axis	Points not on the x-, y-, or z-axes
1st point	(, ,)	(, ,)	(, ,)	(, ,)
2nd point	(, ,)	(, ,)	(, ,)	(, ,)
3rd point	(, ,)	(, ,)	(, ,)	(, ,)
4th point	(, ,)	(, ,)	(, ,)	(, ,)

   a.   What do you notice about the coordinates of the points on the *x*-axis?

   b.   Make a conjecture about the coordinates of points that lie on any of the coordinate axes.

7-9.   Solve the system of equations at right.

$$3x + 8 = 2$$
$$7x + 3y = 1$$

7-10. Each cube below is 1 cm on a side.

(I)   (II)   (III) ?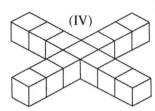
(IV)

a. Based on the pattern, find the volume of Figure III.

b. If the pattern continues, write an expression to represent the volume of figure N. What kind of sequence is this?

7-11. Solve each exponential equation for x.

a. $10^x = 16$ b. $10^x = 41$ c. $3^x = 729$ d. $10^x = 101$

7-12. Rewrite each expression below as an equivalent expression without negative exponents.

a. 5^{-2} b. xy^{-2} c. $(xy)^{-2}$ d. $a^3b^4a^{-4}b^6$

7-13. Graph the system of $y \geq x^2$ and $y \geq (x-4)^2 + 2$ and shade their overlapping region. How is the graph of $y \geq (x-4)^2 + 2$ positioned in relation to the graph of $y \geq x^2$?

7-14. Given the two points (–2, 0) and (0, 1), complete parts (a) through (c) below.

a. Find the slope of the line that passes through these two points.

b. Find the slope of the line perpendicular to the line that passes through these two points.

c. Describe the relationship between the slopes of perpendicular lines.

7-15. The cost of food has been increasing by 4% per year for many years. To find the cost of an item 15 years ago, Heather said, "*Take the current price and divide it by* $(1.04)^{15}$."

Her friend Elissa said, "*No, you should take the current price and multiply it by* $(0.96)^{15}$ *!*"

Explain who is correct and why.

7.1.2 How can I graph a rule in three dimensions?

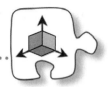

Graphing Equations in Three Dimensions

In the past, you have used the two-dimensional Cartesian coordinate system (*x*- and *y*-axes) to graph equations involving two variables. In the previous lesson, you used a three-dimensional coordinate system to plot points. Today you will use the three-dimensional coordinate system to graph rules that have three variables. As you are working through the lesson, use the following questions to help focus your discussion:

> How can we use what we know about graphing in two dimensions
> to help us graph in three dimensions?

> What does a solution to a three-variable equation represent?

7-16. Consider the 3-D equation $5x + 8y + 10z = 40$.

    a. Discuss with your team what you think the shape of the graph would be. Explain how you decided.

    b. Is the point (4, 5, –2) a solution to the equation $5x + 8y + 10z = 40$? **Justify** your answer.

    c. Your team will be given a list of points to test in the equation. Plot each point that makes the equation true on the three-dimensional grapher your teacher has set up.

    d. Now examine the solutions displayed on the grapher. With your team, discuss the questions below. Be ready to share your discoveries with the class.

        (*i*) Are there any points that you suspect are solutions, but do not have a point showing on the graph?

        (*ii*) How many solutions do you think there are?

        (*iii*) Are there any points showing that you think are not solutions? Explain.

        (*iv*) What shape is formed by all of the solutions? That is, what is the shape of the graph of $5x + 8y + 10z = 40$?

7-17. How can you graph an equation like $12x + 4y + 5z = 60$ in three dimensions? To come up with a **strategy** to graph a three-variable equation, look at the **strategies** you can use to graph a two-variable equation in two dimensions. For example, consider $5x + 8y = 40$.

    a. What is the shape of the graph of $5x + 8y = 40$? How can you tell?

    b. With your team, brainstorm all of the **strategies** you could use to graph $5x + 8y = 40$. Which **strategy** do you prefer? Why?

7-18.   Now you will work with your team to graph $12x + 4y + 5z = 60$.

   a.   What do you think it will look like?

   b.   Which of the **strategies** you used to graph a two-variable equation in
         problem 7-17 can be used to graph this three-variable equation? Work with your
         team to find a **strategy** and then graph $12x + 4y + 5z = 60$ on your isometric dot
         paper. Be prepared to share your **strategy** with the class.

7-19.   Use your new **strategy** to graph each of the following equations in three dimensions.

   a. $13x + 4y + 5z = 260$ b. $12x - 9y + 108 = 0$

7-20.   Consider the graph of $x = 4$ for each of the following problems.

   a.   Graph the solution to $x = 4$ in one dimension (on a number line).

   b.   Graph the solutions to $x = 4$ in two dimensions (on the xy-plane).

   c.   Graph the solutions to $x = 4$ in three dimensions (in the xyz-space).

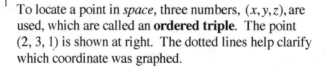
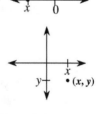

7-21.   For each of the following equations, find every point where its *three-dimensional* graph intersects one of the coordinate axes. That is, find the x-, y- and z-intercepts. Express your answer in (x, y, z) form.

   a. $6y + 15z = 60$ b. $3x + 4y + 2z = 24$

   c. $(x + 3)^2 + z^2 = 25$ d. $z = 6$

7-22.   Answer each of the following questions. Illustrate your answers with a sketch.

   a.   What do you think the intersection of two planes looks like?

   b.   What do you think it means for two planes to be parallel?

   c.   What do you think it means for a line and a plane to be parallel?

7-23.   Find an equation that will generate each graph.

   a.   b.   c.

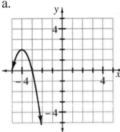   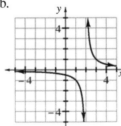   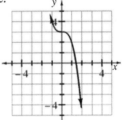

7-24.   Is $y = \frac{1}{x}$ the parent of $y = \frac{1}{x^2+7}$? Explain your reasoning.

7-25.   Solve each equation below for x.

   a. $2x + x = b$ b. $2ax + 3ax = b$

   c. $x + ax = b$

7-26.   Mark claims to have created a sequence of three
         function machines that always gives him the same
         number he started with.

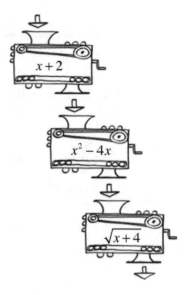

    a.   Test his machines. Do you think he is right?

    b.   Be sure to test negative numbers. What
        happens for negative numbers?

    c.   Mark wants to get his machines patented but
        has to prove that the set of machines will
        always do what he says it will, at least for
        positive numbers. Show Mark how to prove
        that his machines work for positive numbers
        by dropping in a variable (for example, n) and
        writing out each step the machines must take.

    d.   Why do the negative numbers come out
        positive?

7-27.   Flipping a penny and a nickel can be shown in a **tree diagram**.
         Use the tree diagram at right to calculate the following
         probabilities.

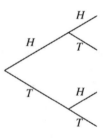

    a. $P(H,T)$
        (Note: This means the probability of getting one head and
        then one tail.)

    b. $P(T,H)$

    c. $P(H,H)$ or $P(T,T)$

7-28.   Given $f(x) = -2x^2 - 4$ and $g(x) = 5x + 3$, calculate:

    a. $g(-2)$ b. $f(-7)$

    c. $f(g(-2))$ d. $f(g(1))$

7.1.3 What can I discover about 3-D systems?

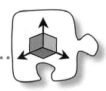

Systems of Three-Variable Equations

You know a lot about systems of two-variable equations, their solutions, and their graphs. Today you will **investigate** systems of three-variable equations.

7-29.   THREE-DIMENSIONAL SYSTEM INVESTIGATION

Consider the following systems of equations:

System I	*System II*
$20x + 12y + 15z = 60$	$20x + 15y + 12z = 60$
$20x + 12y + 15z = 120$	$10x + 30y + 12z = 60$

Your task: With your team, find out as much as you can about each of these systems of equations, their graphs, and their solutions. Be sure to record all of your work carefully and be prepared to share your summary statements with the class.

Discussion Points

What does the graph of a three-variable equation look like?

What does it mean to be a solution to a system of equations?

What does a solution to a three-variable system of equations look like on a graph?

Is there always a solution to a system of equations?

7-30.   Using isometric dot paper, graph both equations in *System I* from problem 7-29 on a single three-dimensional coordinate system. Use different colors to help identify each graph.

   a.   Describe the graph of the system in as much detail as you can.

   b.   Looking at the graph, can you tell what the solution to this system is? Explain.

7-31.   Using isometric dot paper, graph both equations in *System II* from problem 7-29 on a single three-dimensional coordinate system. Use different colors to help identify each graph.

   a.   Describe the graph of the system in as much detail as you can.

   b.   Looking at the graph, can you tell what the solution to this system is? Explain.

7-32.   Now compare the graphs of the two systems. How are they similar? How are they different?

Further Guidance
section ends here.

7-33.   Look closely at your graph of *System II*. Can you see the intersection of the two planes clearly? If not, make a new set of axes and graph the systems carefully.

   a.   What does the intersection of two planes look like?

   b.   Work with your team to find the coordinates of as many points as you can that lie in both planes. Show your work and describe your **strategies**. Be prepared to share your ideas with the class.

   c.   Can you add a third equation to the system that will share the same intersection with the original two graphs?

Algebra 2 Connections

7-34.   On isometric dot paper, graph the system of equations at right. What shape is the intersection? Use color to show the intersection clearly on your graph.

$$10x + 6y + 5z = 30$$
$$6x + 15y + 5z = 30$$

7-35.   Verify that $2^7 = 128$. Is it true that $\log 2^7 = \log 128$?

7-36.   If $24 = y$, is it true that $\log 24 = \log y$? **Justify** your answer.

7-37.   Write the system of inequalities that would give the graph at right.

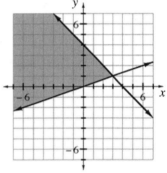

7-38.   Solve $1 - \frac{b}{x} = a$ for x.

7-39.   Cheri has forgotten how to change a quadratic equation from standard form to graphing form. She remembers *some* things about averaging intercepts and completing the square, but she is really confused. Clearly show Cheri *both* methods to change $y = x^2 + 4x - 7$ into graphing form.

7-40.   Solve $\sqrt{x+2} = 8$ and check your solution.

7-41.   Factor each expression completely.

a. $25x^2 - 1$

b. $5x^3 - 125x$

c. $x^2 + x - 72$

d. $x^3 - 3x^2 - 18x$

7-42.   Solve for x, y, and z: $(2^x)(3^y)(5^z) = (2^3)(3^{x-2})(5^{2x-3y})$.

7.1.4 What is a solution in three dimensions?

Solving Systems of Three Equations with Three Unknowns

Today you will extend what you know about systems of equations to examine how to solve systems of equations with three variables. As you work with your team, look for connections to previous work. The focus questions below can help generate mathematical discussion.

What does a solution to a system in three variables mean?

What **strategies** can we use?

What does the intersection look like?

7-43. Review the **strategies** for solving systems that you already have as you solve the following two-variable system of equations. Use any method. Do not hesitate to change **strategies** if your first **strategy** seems cumbersome. If there is no solution, explain what that indicates about the graph of this system. Leave your solution in (x, y) form.

$$12x - 2y = 16$$
$$30x + 2y = 68$$

7-44. Solve the following three-variable system of equations by graphing it with your graphing tool or on isometric dot paper. Give your solution in (x, y, z) form. Then test your solution in the equations and describe your results.

$$2x + 3y + 3z = 6$$
$$6x - 3y + 4z = 12$$
$$2x - 3y + 2z = 6$$

7-45. FINDING AN EASIER WAY

As you saw in problem 7-44, using a graph to solve a system of three equations with three variables can lead to inconclusive results. What other **strategies** should be considered? Discuss this with your team and be prepared to share your ideas with the class.

7-46.   Looking at the equations in problem 7-44, Elissa wanted to see if she could apply some of her solving techniques from two-variable equations to this 3-D system.

a.   Elissa noticed that the first two equations could be combined to form the new equation $8x + 7z = 18$. How did she accomplish this? Explain.

b.   Now that Elissa has an equation with only x and z, she needs to find another equation with only x and z to be able to solve the system. Choose a different pair of equations to combine and find a way to eliminate y so that the new equation only has x and z. Then solve the system to find x and z.

c.   For which variable do you still need to solve? Work with your team to solve for this variable. Then write the solution as a point in (x, y, z) form.

d.   Is your solution reasonable? Does it make sense? Does it agree with your graph?

7-47.   Practice using your algebraic **strategies** by solving the systems below, if possible. If there is no solution or if the solution is different than you expected, use the graphing tool to help you figure out why.

a. $x + y + 3z = 3$
       $2x + y + 6z = 2$
       $2x - y + 3z = -7$

b. $20x + 12y + 15z = 60$
       $20x + 12y + 15z = 120$
       $10x + 20z = 30$

c. $5x - 4y - 6z = -19$
       $-2x + 2y + z = 5$
       $3x - 6y - 5z = -16$

d. $6x + 4y + z = 12$
       $6x + 4y + 2z = 12$
       $6x + 4y + 3z = 12$

7-48.   Today you developed a way to solve a system of three equations with three variables. But what does the solution of a system like those provided in problem 7-47 represent? Consider this as you answer the questions below with your graphing tool.

a.   One of the systems in problem 7-47 should have had no solution. Graph this system with your graphing tool. Describe how the planes are positioned and why there is no common point on all three planes.

b.   In what other ways could three planes be positioned so that there is no solution? Use paper or cardboard to help you communicate your ideas with others.

c.   Graph the system in part (d) of problem 7-47 with your graphing tool and examine the result. How can you describe the intersection of these planes?

7-49.   LEARNING LOG

In your Learning Log, describe your algebraic **strategy** to solve a
system of three equations with three variables. Give enough details
to help you later when you need to refer to it. Title this entry
"Systems of Three Equations with Three Variables" and include today's date.

METHODS AND **M**EANINGS

Graphing Planes in Three Dimensions

To graph a plane, it is easiest to use the intercepts to draw the trace
lines (the intersections of the plane with the xy-, xz-, and yz-planes)
that will represent the plane.

To find the intercepts, let two of the variables equal zero. Then solve to find
the intercept corresponding to the remaining variable.

For example, for $2x + 3y + 4z = 12$, the x-intercept is found by letting y and z
equal zero, which gives $2x = 12$. Therefore the x-intercept is $(6, 0, 0)$.
Similarly, the y-intercept is $(0, 4, 0)$, and the z-intercept is $(0, 0, 3)$.

Drawing the line between two intercepts gives the trace
line for the plane. For example, connecting the x- and
y-intercepts, you would get the equation $2x + 3y = 12$,
which is the trace line in the xy-plane when $z = 0$ in the
equation $2x + 3y + 4z = 12$. Connecting the x- and
z-intercepts gives the trace line in the xz-plane.

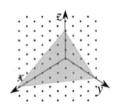

Review & Preview

7-50.   Use the algebraic **strategies** you developed in today's lesson to
solve the system of equations at right. Be sure to check your
solution.

$$2x + y - 3z = -12$$
$$5x - y + z = 11$$
$$x + 3y - 2z = -13$$

7-51.   Use each pair of points given below to write a system of equations in $y = mx + b$ form
to find the equation of a line that passes through the points.

a. $(20, 2)$ and $(32, -4)$ b. $(-3, -17)$ and $(12, -7)$

7-52.   Write a system of inequalities that could be represented by the graph at right.

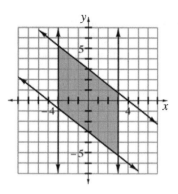

7-53.   Solve $\sqrt{5x-1} = \sqrt{6+4x}$ and check your solution.

7-54.   If two quantities are equal, are their logarithms also equal? Consider the questions below.

   a.   Is it true that 4^2 is equal to 2^4? Is this a special case, or is a^b equal to b^a for any values of a and b?

   b.   Is $\log 4^2$ equal to $\log 2^4$? How can you be sure?

   c.   Are the equations $x = 5$ and $\log x = \log 5$ equivalent? **Justify** your answer.

   d.   Is the equation $\log 7 = \log x^2$ equivalent to the equation $7 = x^2$? How can you be sure?

7-55.   Use the ideas from problem 7-54 to help you solve the following equations.

   a. $\log 10 = \log(2x-3)$ b. $\log 25 = \log(4x^2 - 5x - 50)$

7-56.   Find an equation for each of the lines described below.

   a.   The line with slope $\frac{1}{3}$ that goes through the point $(0, 5)$.

   b.   The line parallel to $y = 2x - 5$ that goes through the point $(1, 7)$.

   c.   The line perpendicular to $y = 2x - 5$ that goes through the point $(1, 7)$.

   d.   The line that goes through the point $(0, 0)$ so that the tangent of the angle it makes with the x-axis is 2.

7-57.   Solve each equation below for y so that it could be entered in the graphing calculator.

   a. $x^2 = x(2x - 4) + y$ b. $x = 3 + (y - 5)^2$

7-58.   Sketch the graph of each equation or inequality below.

   a. $(x-2)^2 + (y+3)^2 = 9$

   b. $(x-2)^2 + (y+3)^2 \geq 9$

7-59.   You are standing 60 feet away from a
         five-story building in Los Angeles, looking
         up at its rooftop. In the distance you can
         see the billboard on top of your hotel,
         but the building is completely obscured by
         the one in front of you. If your hotel is
         32 stories tall and the average story is
         10 feet high, how far away from your hotel
         are you?

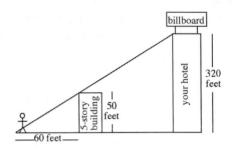

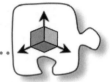

$7.1.5$ How can I apply systems of equations?

Using Systems of Three Equations for Curve Fitting

In this lesson you will work with your team to find the equation of a quadratic function that passes through three specific points. You will be challenged to extend what you know about writing and solving a system of equations in *two variables* to solving a system of equations in *three variables*.

7-60.   In your work with parabolas, you have developed two forms for the general equation of
         a quadratic function: $y = ax^2 + bx + c$ and $y = a(x-h)^2 + k$. What information does
         each equation give you about the graph of a parabola? Be as detailed in your
         explanation as possible. When is each form most useful?

7-61.   Suppose the graph of a quadratic function passes through the points $(1, 0)$, $(2, 5)$, and
         $(3, 12)$. Sketch its graph. Then work with your team to develop an algebraic method
         to find the equation $y = ax^2 + bx + c$ of this specific quadratic function.

Discussion Points

What does the graph of any quadratic function look like?

What does it mean for the graph of $y = ax^2 + bx + c$ to pass
through the point $(3, 12)$?

What solving method can we use to find a, b, and c?

How can we check our equation?

Would this method allow us to find the equation of a quadratic
using *any* three points?

Would this method work if we only had two points?

7-62.   How many points does it take to determine the equation of a linear function $y = ax + b$? Discuss this with your team and include at least one sketch to support your answer.

Now think about the graph of a quadratic function $y = ax^2 + bx + c$. How many points do you think it would take to determine this graph? Why? Does there need to be any restrictions on the points you use? Discuss these questions with your team and **justify** your answers before moving on to part (a).

a.   Suppose you wanted the graph of a quadratic function $y = ax^2 + bx + c$ to pass through the points $(1, 0)$, $(2, 5)$, and $(3, 12)$. How would these points be useful in finding the specific equation of this function? If your team has not already done so, include a sketch of the parabola going through these points to support your answer.

b.   It is often useful to label points with the variable they represent. For instance, for the point $(3, 12)$, which variable does the 3 represent? Which variable does the 12 represent?

c.   Using the general equation of a quadratic, $y = ax^2 + bx + c$, substitute the x- and y-values from your first point into the equation. Then do the same for the other two points to create three equations where the unknowns are a, b, and c.

d.   Now use the **strategies** you developed in Lesson 7.1.4 to solve the system of equations for a, b, and c.

e.   Use your results to write the equation of the quadratic function that passes through the points $(1, 0)$, $(2, 5)$, and $(3, 12)$. How can you check your answer? That is, how can you make sure your equation would actually go through the three points? Using the method your team decides on, check your equation.

—————   *Further Guidance*   —————
           section ends here.

7-63.   LEARNING LOG

In your Learning Log, summarize the method you used in problem 7-61 (or problem 7-62) to find the equation $y = ax^2 + bx + c$ of the quadratic function whose graph passes through three given points. Title this entry "Finding the Equation of a Parabola Given Three Points" and label it with today's date.

7-64.   Find the equation $y = ax^2 + bx + c$ of the function that passes through the three points given in parts (a) and (b) below. Be sure to check your answers.

a. $(3, 10)$, $(5, 36)$, and $(-2, 15)$ b. $(2, 2)$, $(-4, 5)$, and $(6, 0)$

7-65.   What happened in part (b) of problem 7-64? Why did this occur? (If you are not sure, plot the points on graph paper.)

7-66.   Space Shuttle CPM is approaching a star and is caught in its gravitational pull. When the shuttle's engines are fired, the shuttle will slow down, stop momentarily, and then pick up speed and move away from the star, avoiding its gravitational field. Space Shuttle CPM engaged its engines when it was 750 thousand miles from the star. After one full minute, the shuttle was 635 thousand miles from the star. After two minutes, the ship was 530 thousand miles from the star.

a.   Name the three points given in the information above if $x =$ the time since the engines were engaged and $y =$ the distance (in thousands of miles) from the star.

b.   Based on the points in part (a), make a rough sketch of a graph that shows the distance reaching a minimum and then increasing again, over time. What kind of function could follow this pattern?

c.   Find the equation of a graph that fits the three points you found in part (a).

d.   If the ship comes within 50 thousand miles of the star, the shields will fail and the ship will burn up. Use your equation to determine whether the space ship has failed to escape the gravity of the star.

7-67.   Sickly Sid has contracted a serious infection and has gone to the doctor for help. The doctor takes a blood sample and finds 900 bacteria per cc (cubic centimeter) and gives Sid a shot of a strong antibiotic. The bacteria will continue to grow for a period of time, reach a peak, and then decrease as the medication succeeds in overcoming the infection. After ten days, the infection has grown to 1600 bacteria per cc. After 15 days it has grown to 1875.

a.   Name three data points given in the problem statement.

b.   Make a rough sketch that will show the number of bacteria per cc over time.

c.   Find the equation of the parabola that contains the three data points.

d.   Based on the equation, how long will it take until the bacteria are eliminated?

e.   Based on the equation, how long had Sid been infected before he went to the doctor?

7-68.   THE COMMUTER

Sensible Sally has a job that is 35 miles from her home
and needs to be at work by 8:15 a.m. She wants to get
as much sleep as she can, leave as late as possible, and
still get to work on time. Sally discovered that if she
leaves at 7:10, it takes her 40 minutes to get to work.
If she leaves at 7:30, it takes her 60 minutes to get
work. If she leaves at 7:40, it takes her 50 minutes to
get to work. Since her commute time increases and
then decreases, Sally decided to use a parabola to model
her commute, assuming the time it takes her to get to
work varies quadratically with the number of minutes
after 7:00 that she leaves her house.

a.   If x = the number of minutes after 7:00 that Sally leaves, and y = the number of
      minutes it takes Sally to get to work, what three ordered pairs can you determine
      from the problem?

b.   Use the three points from part (a) to find the equation of a parabola in standard
      form that can be used to model Sally's commute.

c.   Will Sally make it to work on time if she leaves at 7:20?

7-69.   PAIRS PARABOLA CHALLENGE

Your challenge will be to work with a partner to create a parabola puzzle for another
pair of students to solve. Follow the directions below to create a puzzle that will make
them think and allow them to show off their algebra skills. When you are ready, you
will trade puzzles with another pair and attempt to solve theirs.

a.   With your partner, decide on an equation for a parabola and then identify three
      points that lie on its graph. Keep track of how you came up with your equation
      and how you chose your points. Be ready to share **strategies**.

b.   Write the coordinates of the three points on an index card or small slip of paper to
      give to another pair of students. Be sure you keep a copy of your equation so you
      can check their work later.

c.   Trade points with another pair and work with your partner to solve their puzzle.
      When you are confident of your equation, have the writers check your work.

7-70.   Make a conjecture about how you would find the equation $y = ax^3 + bx^2 + cx + d$ of a
         cubic function that passes through a given set of points when graphed. How many
         points do you think you would need to be given to be able to determine a unique
         equation? How could you extend the method you developed for solving a quadratic to
         solving a cubic?

7-71.   Solve the system of equations at right and then check your solution in each equation. Be sure to keep your work well organized.

$$x - 2y + 3z = 8$$
$$2x + y + z = 6$$
$$x + y + 2z = 12$$

7-72.   Find the equation in $y = ax^2 + bx + c$ form of the parabola that passes through the points $(1, 5)$, $(3, 19)$, and $(-2, 29)$.

7-73.   This problem is a checkpoint for graphing linear inequalities. It will be referred to as Checkpoint 12.

Complete parts (a) through (c) below for the system of inequalities at right.

$$y \leq -2x + 3$$
$$y \geq x$$
$$x \geq -1$$

a.   Draw the graph.

b.   Find the area of the shaded region.

c.   Check your graph by referring to the Checkpoint 12 materials located at the back of your book.

If you needed help graphing this system of inequalities correctly, then you need more practice graphing linear inequalities and systems of inequalities. Review the Checkpoint 12 materials and try the practice problems. Also, consider getting help outside of class time. From this point on, you will be expected to graph systems of inequalities such as this one easily and accurately.

7-74.   Simplify each expression in parts (a) through (c) below. Then complete part (d).

a. $xy(\frac{1}{x} + \frac{1}{2y})$ b. $ab(\frac{2}{a} + \frac{4a}{b})$ c. $2x(3 - \frac{1}{2x})$

d.   What expression would go in the box to make the equation $\Box(\frac{2}{x} + \frac{7}{y}) = 2y + 7x$ true?

7-75.   Change each of the following equations from logarithmic form to exponential form, or vice versa.

a. $y = \log_{12} x$ b. $x = \log_y 17$

c. $y = 1.75^{2x}$ d. $3y = x^7$

7-76.   Solve $\sqrt{3x-6}+6=12$ and check your solution.

7-77.   Find $m\angle C$ in each triangle below.

a.

b.

7-78.   Rewrite each expression below as an exponential expression with a base of 2.

a.   16   b. $\frac{1}{8}$ c. $\sqrt{2}$ d. $\sqrt[3]{4}$

7-79.   Solve the system of equations at right and then check your solution in each equation. Be sure to keep your work well organized.

$$x+2y-z=-1$$
$$2x-y+3z=13$$
$$x+y+2z=14$$

7-80.   Find an equation for the parabola that passes through the points $(-1,10)$, $(0,5)$, and $(2,7)$.

7-81.   Change each of the following equations from logarithmic form to exponential form, or vice versa.

a. $a=\log_b 24$ b. $3x=\log_{2y} 7$

c. $3y=2^{5x}$ d. $4p=(2q)^6$

7-82.   Consider the function defined as follows: The inputs are the numbers on a normal, fair die, and the outputs are the probability of that number coming up when the die is rolled. **Investigate** this function.

7-83. On their team test, Raymond, Sarah, Hannah, and Aidan were given $y = 4x^2 - 24x + 7$ to change into graphing form. Raymond noticed that the leading coefficient was a 4 and not a 1. His team agreed on a way to start rewriting, but then they worked in pairs and got two different solutions, shown below.

Raymond and Hannah

(1) $y = 4x^2 - 24x + 7$

(2) $y = 4(x^2 - 6x) + 7$

(3) $y = 4(x^2 - 6x + 3^2) + 7 - 36$

(4) $y = 4(x - 3)^2 - 29$

Aidan and Sarah

(1) $y = 4x^2 - 24x + 7$

(2) $y = 4(x^2 - 6x + 9) + 7 - 9$

(3) $y = 4(x - 3)^2 + 7 - 3^2$

(4) $y = 4(x - 3)^2 - 2$

Hannah says, *"Aidan and Sarah made a mistake in Step 3. Because of the factored 4 they really added 4(9) to complete the square, so they should subtract 36, not just 9."*

Is Hannah correct? **Justify** your answer by showing whether the results are equivalent to the original equation.

7-84. Use the correct method from problem 7-83 to change each of the following equations to graphing form. Then, without graphing, find the vertex and equation of the line of symmetry for each.

a. $y = 2x^2 - 8x + 7$

b. $y = 5x^2 - 10x - 7$

7-85. Given $f(x) = 2x^2 - 4$ and $g(x) = 5x + 3$, find the value of each expression below.

a. $f(a)$ b. $f(3a)$ c. $f(a + b)$

d. $f(x + 7)$ e. $f(5x + 3)$ f. $g(f(x))$

7-86. Complete the area model shown at right, then complete parts (a) through (c) below.

a. What is the sum of the areas of each of the rectangles that makes up the larger one?

b. What are the length and width of the large rectangle?

c. Write a statement of the form $l \cdot w = Area$ as a sum for this rectangle.

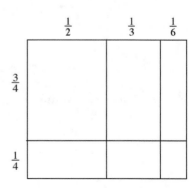

7.2.1 How can I solve exponential equations?

Using Logarithms to Solve Exponential Equations

In Chapter 6, you learned what a logarithm was, and you also learned several important facts about logs. In this lesson, you will learn about a property of logarithms that will prove very useful for solving problems that involve exponents.

7-87.   LOGARITHMS SO FAR

There are three important log facts you have worked with so far. Discuss these questions with your team to ensure everyone remembers these ideas. For each problem, make up an example to illustrate your ideas.

a.   What is a logarithm? How can log equations be converted into another form?

b.   What do you know about the logarithm key on your calculator?

c.   What does the graph of $y = \log(x)$ look like? Write a general equation for $y = \log(x)$.

7-88.   Marta was convinced that there had to be some way to graph $y = \log_2 x$ on her graphing calculator. She typed in $y = \log(2^x)$ and pressed $\boxed{\text{GRAPH}}$.

"It WORKED!" Marta yelled in triumph.

"Whaaaat?" said Celeste. *"I think $y = \log_2 x$ and $y = \log(2^x)$ are totally different, and I bet we can prove it by converting both of them to exponential form."*

"Yeah, I think you're wrong, Marta," said Sophia. *"I think we can prove $y = \log_2 x$ and $y = \log(2^x)$ are totally different by looking at the graphs."*

a.   Show that the two equations are different by using what you learned in previous lessons to sketch the graph of $y = \log_2 x$. Then sketch what your graphing calculator shows to be the graph of $y = \log(2^x)$.

b.   Now show that $y = \log_2 x$ and $y = \log(2^x)$ are different by converting both of them to exponential form.

7-89.   The work you did in problem 7-88 is a **counterexample**, which shows that in general, the statement $\log_b x = \log(b^x)$ is *false*. For each of the following log statements, use the **strategies** from problem 7-88 to determine whether they are true or false, and **justify** your answer. Be ready to present your conclusions and **justifications**.

   a. $\log_5(25) \overset{?}{=} \log_{25}(5)$ b. $\log(x^2) \overset{?}{=} (\log x)^2$

   c. $\log(7^x) \overset{?}{=} x \log(7)$ d. $\log(2x) \overset{?}{=} \log_2 x$

7-90.   In the previous problem only *one* of the statements was true.

   a. Use different numbers to make up four more statements that follow the same pattern as the one true statement, and test each one to see whether it appears to be true.

   b. Use your results to complete the following statement, which is known as the **Power Property of Logs**: $\log(b^x) =$ _____ .

7-91.   Do you remember solving problems like $1.04^x = 2$ in your homework? What method(s) did you and your teammates use to find x? In tonight's homework there are several more of these problems. (You probably wish there were a more efficient way!)

7-92.   THERE MUST BE AN EASIER WAY

   It would certainly be helpful to have an easier method than Guess and Check to solve equations like $1.04^x = 2$. Complete parts (a) through (c) below to discover an easier way.

   a. What makes the equation $1.04^x = 2$ so hard to solve?

   b. Surprise! In the first part of this lesson, you already found a method for getting rid of inconvenient exponents! Talk with your team about how your results from problems 7-89 and 7-90 can help you rewrite the equation $1.04^x = 2$. Be prepared to share your ideas with the class.

   c. Solve $1.04^x = 2$ using this new method. Be sure to check your answer.

7-93.   Solve the following equations. Be sure your answers are accurate to three decimal places, and also be sure to check your answers.

   a. $5 = 2.25^x$ b. $3.5^x = 10$

   c. $2(8^x) = 128$ d. $2x^8 = 128$

x	y
	1
	3
2	9
	27
4	
	243
6	
7	
8	

7-94.   Complete the table at right and find its equation.

7-95.   Margee thinks she can use logs to solve $56 = x^8$, since logs seem to make exponents disappear. Unfortunately, Margee is wrong. Explain the difference between equations like $2 = 1.04^x$, in which you can use logs, and $56 = x^8$, in which it does not make sense to use logs.

7-96.   What values must x have so that $\log(x)$ is greater than 2? **Justify** your answer.

7-97.   Simplify each expression below. If you are stuck, the ideas in problem 7-74 should be helpful.

a. $\dfrac{x}{1 - \frac{1}{x}}$

b. $\dfrac{\frac{1}{a} + \frac{1}{b}}{\frac{1}{b} - a}$

7-98.   Consider the questions below.

a.   What can you multiply 8 by to get 1?

b.   What can you multiply x by to get 1?

c.   Using the rules of exponents, find a way to solve $m^8 = 40$. Remember that logarithms will not be useful here, but the exponent key on your calculator *will* be. (Obtain the answer as a decimal approximation using your calculator. Check your result by raising it to the 8th power.)

d.   Now solve $n^6 = 300$.

e.   Describe a method for solving $x^a = b$ for x with a calculator.

7-99.   Adam keeps getting negative exponents and fractional exponents confused. Help him by explaining the difference between $2^{1/2}$ and 2^{-1}.

7-100.   Solve each inequality and graph its solution on a number line.

a. $|x| < 3$ b. $|2x + 1| < 3$ c. $|2x + 1| \geq 3$

7-101.   What is the equation of the line of symmetry for the graph of $y = (x-17)^2$?
Justify your answer.

7-102.   Solve each system of equations below.

a. $-4x = z - 2y + 12$
      $y + z = 12 - x$
      $8x - 3y + 4z = 1$

b. $3x + y - 2z = 6$
      $x + 2y + z = 7$
      $6x + 2y - 4z = 12$

c.   What does the solution in part (b) tell you about the graphs?

7.2.2 How can I rewrite it?

Investigating the Properties of Logs

You already know the basic rules for working with exponents. Since logs are the inverses of
exponential functions, they also have properties that are similar to the ones you already know.
In this lesson, you will explore these properties.

7-103.   Marta now knows that if she wants to find $\log_2(30)$, she cannot just type $\log(2^{30})$
into her calculator, since her calculator's log key cannot directly calculate logs with
base 2. But she still wants to be able to find what $\log_2(30)$ equals.

a.   First, use your knowledge of logs to estimate $\log_2(30)$.

b.   Now use what you learned in the previous lesson to get a better estimate.
Since you want to determine what $\log_2(30)$ equals, you can write $\log_2(30) = x$.
When working with a log equation, it is often easier to convert it to exponential
form. Rewrite this equation in exponential form.

c.   Use the methods you developed in class to solve this equation. Refer back to
your work on problem 7-92 if you need help.

d.   Congratulations! You are smarter than your calculator. You have just evaluated
a log with base 2, even though your calculator does not know how to do that.
Now you will have more practice. First estimate an answer, then apply the
method you have just developed to evaluate $\log_5(200)$.

e.   Apply the process you used in part (d) to evaluate the expression $\log_a b = x$.

7-104.   Since logs and exponentials are inverses, the properties of exponents (which you already know) translate to logs. The problems below will help you discover these new log properties.

  a.   Complete the two exponent rules below. In part (b), you will find the equivalent properties of logs.

$$x^a x^b = \text{_____} \quad \text{and} \quad \frac{x^b}{x^a} = \text{_____}$$

  b.   To help you find the equivalent log properties, use your calculator to solve for x in each problem below. Note that x is a whole number in parts (i) through (v). Look for patterns that would make your job easier and allow you to **generalize** in part (vi).

  $i.$ $\log(5) + \log(6) = \log(x)$ $ii.$ $\log(5) + \log(2) = \log(x)$

  $iii.$ $\log(5) + \log(5) = \log(x)$ $iv.$ $\log(10) + \log(100) = \log(x)$

  $v.$ $\log(9) + \log(11) = \log(x)$ $vi.$ $\log(a) + \log(b) = \log(\text{\_\_\_\_})$

  c.   What if the log expressions are being subtracted instead of added? Solve for x in each problem below. Note that x will not always be a whole number.

  $i.$ $\log(20) - \log(5) = \log(x)$ $ii.$ $\log(30) - \log(3) = \log(x)$

  $iii.$ $\log(5) - \log(2) = \log(x)$ $iv.$ $\log(17) - \log(9) = \log(x)$

  $v.$ $\log(375) - \log(17) = \log(x)$ $vi.$ $\log(b) - \log(a) = \log(\text{\_\_\_\_})$

7-105.   **LEARNING LOG**

The two properties you found in problem 7-104 work for logs in *any* base, not just base 10. (You will officially prove this later.) You now know three different log properties and you have developed a process for solving log problems that are not in base 10. Write and explain each of the log properties in your Learning Log. Be sure to include examples and add an example of a problem where you need to change to base 10. Title this entry "Log Properties" and label it with today's date.

7-106.   **LOG PROPERTY PUZZLES**

Obtain the Lesson 7.2.2 Resource Page from your teacher or copy the table below. Use the log properties to fill in the missing parts. Be sure to remember that in every row, each expression is equivalent to every other expression.

Product Property		Quotient Property	
$\log_3 60 =$ $\log_3 6 + $____ $=$	$\log_3 3 + $____ $=$	$\log_3 120 - $____	$= \log_3 240 - $____
$\log_7 36 =$	$=$	$=$	$=$
$= \log_6 9 + \log_6 2 =$		$=$	$=$
$=$	$=$	$= \log_{25} 75 - \log_{25} 1.5 =$	
$=$	$=$	$= \log 160 - \log 4$	$=$

7-107.   Use the properties of logs to write each of the following expressions as a single logarithm, if possible.

a. $\log_{1/2}(4) + \log_{1/2}(2) - \log_{1/2}(5)$ b. $\log_2(M) + \log_3(N)$

c. $\log(k) + x\log(m)$ d. $\frac{1}{2}\log_5 x + 2\log_5(x+1)$

e. $\log(4) - \log(3) + \log(\pi) + 3\log(r)$ f. $\log(6) + 23$

7-108.   What values must x have so that $\log(x)$ has a negative value? **Justify** your answer.

7-109.   The fact that for any base m (when $m > 0$), $\log_m a + \log_m b = \log_m ab$ is called the **Product Property of Logarithms**. To prove that this property is true, follow the directions below.

a.   Since logarithms are the inverses of exponential functions, each of their properties can be derived from a similar property of exponents. Here, you are trying to prove that "logs turn products into sums." First, recall similar properties of exponents. If $a = m^x$ and $b = m^y$, write $a \cdot b$ as a power of m.

b.   Rewrite $a = m^x$, $b = m^y$, and your answer to part (a) in logarithmic form.

c.   In the third equation you wrote for part (b), substitute for x and y to obtain a log equation of base m that involves only the variables a and b.

d.   The property $\log_m a - \log_m b = \log_m \frac{a}{b}$ is called the **Quotient Property of Logarithms**. Use $a = m^x$ and $b = m^y$ to express $\frac{a}{b}$ as a power of m. Then use a similar process to rewrite each into log form and prove the Quotient Property of Logs.

7-110.   The **Power Property of Logs** is a little trickier to prove. A proof is given below. As you copy each step onto your paper, work with your team to make sense of what was done. Give a reason for each step.

To prove that $\log_m a^n = n \log_m a$,

Let $\log_m a^n = p$ and $n \log_m a = q$

Convert to $m^p = a^n$

First rewrite to $\log_m a = \frac{q}{n}$ and then convert to $m^{q/n} = a$.

Using the two resulting equations, substitute for a and then simplify: $m^p = (m^{q/n})^n$

$$m^p = m^q$$

Therefore, $p = q$.

Remember that $p = \log_m a^n$ and $q = n \log_m a$, so $\log_m a^n = n \log_m a$, which was the goal of the proof.

ETHODS AND MEANINGS

MATH NOTES

Logarithm Properties

The following definitions and properties hold true for all positive $m \neq 1$.

Definition of logs: $\log_m(a) = n$ means $m^n = a$

Product Property: $\log_m(a \cdot b) = \log_m(a) + \log_m(b)$

Quotient Property: $\log_m(\frac{a}{b}) = \log_m(a) - \log_m(b)$

Power Property: $\log_m(a^n) = n \cdot \log_m(a)$

Inverse relationship: $\log_m(m)^n = n$ and $m^{\log_m(n)} = n$

7-111.   Solve each of the following equations to the nearest 0.001.

a. $(5.825)^{(x-3)} = 120$

b. $18(1.2)^{(2x-1)} = 900$

7-112. At right is a graph of $y = \log_b x$. Describe the possible values for b.

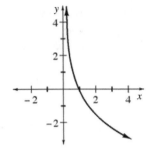

7-113. Use the definition of a logarithm to change $\log_2 7$ into a logarithmic expression of base 5.

7-114. Sketch the graph of $y = \log_3(x + 4)$ and describe the transformation from its parent graph.

7-115. The economy has worsened to the point that the merchants in downtown Hollywood cannot afford to replace their outdoor light bulbs when the bulbs burn out. On average, about thirteen percent of the light bulbs burn out every month. Assuming there are now about one million outside store lights in Hollywood, how long will it take until there are only 100,000 bulbs lit? Until there is only one bulb lit?

7-116. Raymond, Hannah, Aidan, and Sarah were working together to change $y = 3x^2 - 15x - 5$ into graphing form. They started by rewriting it as $y = 3(x^2 - 5x) - 5$, when Raymond said, "*Will this one work? Look, the perfect square would have to be $(x - 2.5)^2$.*"

After thinking about it for a while, Sarah said, "*That's OK. Negative 2.5 squared is 6.25, but because of the 3 we factored out, we are really adding $3(6.25)$.*"

"*Yes,*" Aidan added, "*So we have to subtract 18.75 to get an equivalent equation.*"

Hannah summarized with the work shown at right.

$$y = 3x^2 - 15x - 5$$
$$y = 3(x^2 - 5x) - 5$$
$$y = 3(x - 2.5)^2 - 5 - 18.75$$
$$y = 3(x - 2.5)^2 - 23.75$$

What do you think? Did they rewrite the equation correctly? If so, find the vertex and the line of symmetry of the parabola. If not, explain their mistakes and show them how to do it correctly.

7-117. Use the ideas developed in problem 7-116 to change each of the following quadratic equations into graphing form. Identify the vertex and the line of symmetry for each one.

a. $f(x) = 4x^2 - 12x + 6$

b. $g(x) = 2x^2 + 14x + 4$

7-118.   Consider the function $y = 3(x+2)^2 - 7$ as you complete parts (a) through (c) below.

a.   How could you restrict the domain to show "half" of the graph?

b.   Find the equation for the inverse function for your "half" graph.

c.   What are the domain and range for the inverse function?

7-119.   Eniki has a sequence of numbers given by the formula $t(n) = 4(5^n)$.

a.   What are the first three terms of Eniki's sequence?

b.   Chelita thinks the number 312,500 is a term in Eniki's sequence. Is she correct? **Justify** your answer by either giving the term number or explaining why it is not in the sequence.

c.   Elisa thinks the number 94,500 is a term in Eniki's sequence. Is she correct? Explain.

7-120.   Solve each of the following equations.

a. $\frac{x}{3} = x + 4$

b. $\frac{x+6}{3} = x$

c. $\frac{x+6}{x} = x$

d. $\frac{2x+3}{6} + \frac{1}{2} = \frac{x}{2}$

7-121.   Which of the following statements are true? If true, explain how you know, and if not, show why not.

a. $\frac{x+3}{5} = \frac{x}{5} + \frac{3}{5}$

b. $\frac{5}{x+3} = \frac{5}{x} + \frac{5}{3}$

7-122.   Two congruent overlapping squares are shown at right. If a point inside the figure is chosen at random, what is the probability that it will *not* be in the shaded region?

7.2.3 How can I find an exponential function?

Writing Equations of Exponential Functions

You have worked with exponential equations throughout this chapter. Today you will look at how you can find the equation for an exponential function using data.

7-123.   DUE DATE

Brad's mother has just learned that she is pregnant! Brad is very excited that he will soon become a big brother. However, he wants to know when his new sibling will arrive and decides to do some research. On the Internet, he finds the following article:

Hormone Levels for Pregnant Women

When a woman becomes pregnant, the hormone HCG (human chorionic gonadotropin) is produced to enable the baby to develop.

During the first few weeks of pregnancy, the level of HCG hormone grows exponentially, starting with the day the embryo is implanted in the womb. However, the rate of growth varies with each pregnancy. Therefore, doctors cannot use just a single test to determine how long a woman has been pregnant. They must test the levels over time. Commonly, the HCG levels are measured two days apart to look for this rate of growth.

Brad's mother says she was tested for HCG during her last two doctor visits. On March 21, her HCG level was 200 mIU/ml. Two days later, her HCG level was 392 mIU/ml.

a.   Assuming that the model for HCG levels is of the form $y = ab^x$, find an equation that models the growth of HCG for Brad's mother's pregnancy.

b.   Assuming that Brad's mother's level of HCG on the day of implantation was 5 mIU/ml, on what day did the baby most likely become implanted? How many days after implantation was his mother's first doctor visit?

c.   Brad learned that a baby is born approximately 37 weeks after implantation. When can Brad expect his new sibling to be born?

7-124.   SOLVING STRATEGIES

In problem 7-123, you and your team developed a **strategy** to find the equation of an exponential equation of the form $y = ab^x$ when given two points on the curve.

a.   What different **strategies** were generated by the other teams in your class? If no one shares your solving method with the class, be sure to share yours. Take notes on the different **strategies** that are presented.

b.   Did any team use a system of exponential equations to solve for a and b? If not, examine this **strategy** as you answer the questions below.

   i.   The doctor visits provide two data points that can help you find an exponential model: $(21, 200)$ and $(23, 392)$. Use each of these points to substitute for x and y into $y = ab^x$. You should end up with two equations in terms of a and b.

   ii.   Consider the **strategies** you already have for solving systems of equations. Are any of those **strategies** useful for this problem? Discuss a way to solve your system from part (i) for a and b with your team. Be ready to share your method with the class.

7-125.   The context in problem 7-123 required you to assume that the exponential model had an asymptote at $y = 0$ to find the equation of the model. But what if the asymptote is not at the x-axis? Consider this situation below.

a.   Assume the graph of an exponential function passes through the points $(3, 12.5)$ and $(4, 11.25)$. Is the exponential function increasing or decreasing? **Justify** your answer.

b.   If the horizontal asymptote for this function is the line $y = 10$, make a sketch of its graph showing the horizontal asymptote.

c.   If this function has the equation $y = ab^x + c$, what would be the value of c? Use what you know about this function to find its equation. Verify that as x increases, the values of y get closer to $y = 10$.

d.   Find the y-intercept of the function. What is the connection between the y-intercept and the asymptote?

7-126.   Janice would like to have $40,000 to help pay for college in 8 years. Currently, she has $1000. What interest rate, when compounded yearly, would help her reach her goal?

a.   What type of function would best model this situation? Explain how you know and write the general form of this function.

b.   If y represents the amount of money and x represents the number of years after today, find an equation that models Janice's financial situation. What interest rate does she need to earn?

c.   Janice's friend Sarah starts with $7800 and wants to have $18,400 twenty years from now. What interest rate does she need (compounded yearly)?

d.   Is Janice's goal or Sarah's goal more realistic? **Justify** your response.

7-127.   Ryan has the chickenpox! He was told that the number of pockmarks on his body would grow exponentially until his body overcomes the illness. He found that he had 60 pockmarks on November 1, and by November 3 the number had grown to 135. To find out when the first pockmark appeared, he will need to find the exponential function that will model the number of pockmarks based on the day.

a.   Ryan decides to find the exponential function that passes through the points $(3, 135)$ and $(1, 60)$. Use these points to write the equation of his function of the form $f(x) = ab^x$.

b.   According to your model, what day did Ryan get his first chickenpox pockmark?

7-128.   Give an example of an equation that requires the use of logarithms to solve it.

7-129.   Write three different, but equivalent, expressions for each of the following logs. For example: $\log(7^{3/2})$ can be written as $\frac{3}{2}\log(7)$, $\frac{1}{2}\log(7^3)$, $3\log(\sqrt{7})$, etc.

a. $\log(8^{2/3})$ b. $-2\log(5)$ c. $\log(na)^{bo}$

7-130.   Kendra just made a cup of hot chocolate that was too hot for her to drink. She set it aside so it could cool off. While she was waiting, her friend Lara called and Kendra forgot about her hot chocolate. Sketch a graph that shows the temperature of the hot chocolate since Kendra first set it aside. How cold will the hot chocolate get?

7-131. Simplify the following fractions.

a. $\dfrac{\frac{1}{a}-\frac{1}{b}}{\frac{1}{a}+\frac{1}{b}}$

b. $\dfrac{x+y}{\frac{1}{x}+\frac{1}{y}}$

7-132. Use $f(x)=3+\sqrt{2x-1}$ to complete parts (a) through (e) below.

a. What are the domain and range of $f(x)$?

b. What is the inverse of $f(x)$? Call it $g(x)$.

c. What are the domain and range of $g(x)$?

d. Find an expression for $f(g(x))$.

e. Find an expression for $g(f(x))$. What do you notice? Why does this happen?

7-133. Solve each of the following equations for x.

a. $x^3 = 243$

b. $3^x = 243$

7-134. Write the equation of each circle graphed below

a.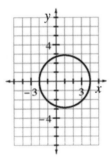

b.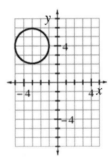

7-135. Add or subtract each expression below. Be sure to simplify.

a. $\dfrac{x^2}{x-5}-\dfrac{25}{x-5}$

b. $\dfrac{a^2}{a+5}+\dfrac{10a+25}{a+5}$

c. $\dfrac{x^2}{x-y}-\dfrac{2xy-y^2}{x-y}$

d. $\dfrac{x}{x+1}+\dfrac{1}{x-1}$

7-136. If $f(x)=x^4$ and $g(x)=3(x+2)$, find the value of each expression below.

a. $f(2)$ b. $g(2)$ c. $f(g(2))$ d. $g(f(2))$

e. Are $f(x)$ and $g(x)$ inverses of each other? **Justify** your answer.

7.2.4 Who killed Dr. Dedman?

An Application of Logarithms

7-137.   THE CASE OF THE COOLING CORPSE

The coroner's office is kept at a cool
17°C. Agent 008 kept pacing back and
forth trying to keep warm as he waited for
any new information about his latest case.
For more than three hours now,
Dr. Dedman had been performing an
autopsy on the Sideroad Slasher's latest
victim, and Agent 008 could see that the
temperature of the room and the deafening
silence were beginning to irritate even
Dr. Dedman. The Slasher had been
creating more work than Dr. Dedman
cared to investigate.

"Dr. Dedman, don't you need to take a break?" Agent 008 queried. *"You've been
examining this body for hours! Even if there were any clues, you probably wouldn't
see them at this point."*

"I don't know," Dr. Dedman replied, *"I just have this feeling something is not quite
right. Somehow the Slasher slipped up with this one and left a clue. We just have to
find it."*

"Well, I have to check in with headquarters," 008 stated. *"Do you mind if I step out
for a couple of hours?"*

"No, that's fine," Dr. Dedman responded. *"Maybe I'll have something by the time
you return."*

"Sure," 008 thought to himself. *"Someone always wants to be the hero and solve
everything himself. The doctor just does not realize how big this case really is. The
Slasher has left a trail of dead bodies through five states!"* Agent 008 left, closing the
door quietly. As he walked down the hall, he could hear the doctor's voice describing
the victim's gruesome appearance into the tape recorder fade away.

The hallway from the coroner's office to the elevator was long and dark. This was the
only way to Dr. Dedman's office. Didn't this frighten most people? Well, it didn't
seem to bother old Ajax Boraxo who was busy mopping the floor, thought 008.

He stopped briefly to use the restroom and bumped into one of the deputy coroners,
who asked, *"Dedman still at it?"*

Problem continues on next page. →

7-137. *Problem continued from previous page.*

"Sure is, Dr. Quincy. He's totally obsessed. He's certain there is a clue." As usual, when leaving the courthouse, 008 had to sign out.

"How's it going down there, Agent 008?" Sergeant Foust asked. Foust spent most of his shifts monitoring the front door, forcing all visitors to sign in, while he recorded the time next to the signature. Agent 008 wondered if Foust longed for a more exciting aspect of law enforcement. He thought if he were doing Foust's job he would get a little stir-crazy sitting behind a desk most of the day. Why would someone become a cop to do this?

"Dr. Dedman is convinced he will find something soon. We'll see!" Agent 008 responded. He noticed the time: ten minutes before 2:00. Would he make it to headquarters before the chief left?

"Well, good luck!" Foust shouted as 008 headed out the door.

Some time later, Agent 008 sighed deeply as he returned to the coroner's office. Foust gave his usual greeting: *"Would the secret guest please sign in?"* he would say, handing a pen to 008 as he walked through the door. *"Sign in again,"* he thought to himself. *"Annoying!"* 5:05 PM. Agent 008 had not planned to be gone so long, but he had been caught up in what the staff at headquarters had discovered about that calculator he had found. For a moment he saw a positive point to having anyone who came in or out of the courthouse sign in: He knew by quickly scanning the list that Dr. Dedman had not left. In fact, the old guy must still be working on the case.

As he approached the coroner's office, he had a strange feeling that something was wrong. He could not hear or see Dr. Dedman. When he opened the door, the sight inside stopped him in his tracks. Evidently, Dr. Dedman was now the *newest* victim of the Slasher. But wait! The other body, the one the doctor had been working on, was gone! Immediately, the security desk with its annoying sign-in sheet came to mind. Yes, there were lots of names on that list, but if he could determine the time of Dr. Dedman's death, he might be able to scan the roster to find the murderer! Quickly, he grabbed the thermometer to measure the Doctor's body temperature. He turned around and hit the security buzzer. The bells were deafening. He knew the building would be sealed off instantly and security would be there within seconds.

"Oh no!" Foust cried as he rushed in, *"How could this happen? I spoke to the Doctor less than an hour ago!"*

As the security officers crowded into the room, Agent 008 explained what he knew, which was almost nothing. He had stopped long enough to check the doctor's body temperature: 27°C. That was 10°C below normal. Then he remembered: the tape recorder! Dr. Dedman had been taping his observations; that was standard procedure. They began looking everywhere. The Slasher must have realized that the doctor had been taping and taken the tape recorder as well. Exactly an hour had passed during the search, and Agent 008 noticed that the thermometer still remained in Dr. Dedman's side. The thermometer clearly read 24°C. Agent 008 knew he could now determine the time of death.

Problem continues on next page. →

Coroner's Office – Please Sign In		
Name	**Time In**	**Time Out**
Lt. Borman	12:08	2:47
Alice Bingham	12:22	1:38
Chuck Miranda	12:30	2:45
Harold Ford	12:51	1:25
Ajax Boraxo	1:00	2:30
D. C. Quincy	1:10	2:45
Agent 008	1:30	1:50
Ronda Ripley	1:43	2:10
Jeff Dangerfield	2:08	2:48
Stacy Simmons	2:14	2:51
Brock Ortiz	2:20	2:43
Pierce Bronson	3:48	4:18
Max Sharp	3:52	5:00
Maren Ezaki	3:57	4:45
Caroline Cress	4:08	4:23
Milly Osborne	4:17	4:39
D.C. Quincy	4:26	4:50
Vinney Gumbatz	4:35	
Cory Delphene	4:48	4:57
Max Crutchfield	5:04	
Agent 008	5:05	
Security	5:12	

a. Make a sketch showing the relationship between body temperature and time. What type of function is it? **Justify** your answer.

b. Is there an asymptote for this relationship? If so, what does it represent? If not, explain why not.

c. Use your data and the general equation $y = km^x + b$ to find the equation that represents the temperature of the body at any certain time.

d. At approximately what time did Dr. Dedman die?

e. Who is the murderer?

7-138. A rule-of-thumb used by car dealers is that the trade-in value of a car decreases by 20% of its value each year.

a. Explain how the phrase "decreases by 20% of its value each year" tells you that the trade-in value varies exponentially with time (i.e., can be represented by an exponential function).

b. Suppose the initial value of your car is $23,500. Write an equation expressing the trade-in value of your car as a function of the number of years from now.

c. How much will your car be worth in four years?

d. In how many years will the trade-in value of your car be $6000?

e. If your car is really 2.7 years old now, what was its trade-in value when it was new?

7-139. Solve for x without using a calculator.

a. $x = \log_{25}(5)$

b. $\log_x(1) = 0$

c. $23 = \log_{10}(x)$

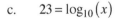

7-140. Using your calculator, solve the equations below. Round answers to the nearest 0.001.

a. $x^6 = 125$

b. $x^{3.8} = 240$

c. $x^{-4} = 100$

d. $(x+2)^3 = 65$

e. $4(x-2)^{12.5} = 2486$

7-141. Find the inverse of each of the functions below. Write your answers in function notation.

a. $p(x) = 3(x^3 + 6)$

b. $k(x) = 3x^3 + 6$

c. $h(x) = \frac{x+1}{x-1}$

d. $j(x) = \frac{2}{3-x}$

7-142. Kirsta was working with the function machine shown at right, but when she turned her back, her little brother Caleb dropped in a number. She didn't see what he dropped, but she did see what fell out: 9. What operations must she perform on 9 to undo what her machine did? Use this to find out what Caleb dropped in.

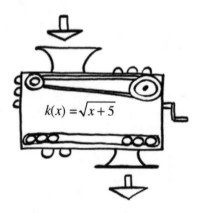

$k(x) = \sqrt{x} + 5$

7-143. Write a rule for a machine that will undo Kirsta's machine. Call it $c(x)$.

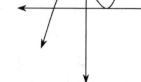

7-144. Consider the graph at right.

a. Is the graph a function? Explain.

b. Make a sketch of the inverse of this graph. Is the inverse a function? **Justify** your answer.

c. Must the inverse of a function be a function? Explain.

d. Describe what is characteristic about functions that do have inverse functions.

e. Could the inverse of a non-function be a function? Explain or give an example.

7-145.   This problem is a checkpoint for solving rational equations. It will be referred to as Checkpoint 13.

Solve each of the following rational equations.

a. $\frac{x}{3} = \frac{4}{x}$ b. $\frac{x}{x-1} = \frac{4}{x}$

c. $\frac{1}{x} + \frac{1}{3x} = 6$ d. $\frac{1}{x} + \frac{1}{x+1} = 3$

e.   Check your answers by referring to the Checkpoint 13 materials located at the back of your book.

If you needed help solving these equations correctly, then you need more practice solving rational equations. Review the Checkpoint 13 materials and try the practice problems. Also, consider getting help outside of class time. From this point on, you will be expected to solve equations such as these easily and accurately.

7-146.   The half-life of an isotope is 1000 years. A 50-gram sample of the isotope is sealed in a box.

a.   How much is left after 10,000 years?

b.   How long will it take to reduce to 1% of the original amount?

c.   How long will it take until all of the original sample of the isotope is gone? Support your answer.

7-147.   Suppose that a two-bedroom house in Nashville is worth $110,000 and appreciates at a rate of 2.5% each year.

a.   How much will it be worth in 10 years?

b.   When will it be worth $200,000?

c.   In Homewood, houses are depreciating at a rate of 5% each year. If a house is worth $182,500 now, how much will it be worth two years from now?

7.3.1 What is a matrix?

$$\begin{bmatrix} a & b & c \\ d & e & f \end{bmatrix}$$

Introduction to Matrices

A matrix is a type of table that is used to keep information organized in lists. With the rise of modern computing, matrices have become increasingly important for solving problems that involve many variables in science, economics, computer science, and mathematics. Matrices have their own notation and form, and their own unique arithmetic, which you will be learning in the next few lessons. Once you know how to represent problems using matrices and understand how they work, your calculator or computer can do the computations for you. At the end of this section, you will see how matrices can be used to solve complicated systems of equations.

7-148.   Otto Toyom's toy factory has become extremely successful. His cars and trucks are selling like crazy. He now has three major stores selling his toys: Bull's-Eye Discount Outlet, JC Nickles, and Marcey's Department Store. He needs an efficient way to

$$\text{vehicles} \begin{bmatrix} 4 & 2 & 1 \\ 6 & 1 & 3 \end{bmatrix}$$
(parts)

keep track of his profits, the number of cars ordered, and the number of parts needed to complete his orders. He begins by writing down a simple matrix (shown above) to represent the number of wheels, seats, and gas tanks needed to build his cars and trucks.

   a.   Otto has asked for your help. Copy the matrix and the labels "parts" and "vehicles" and title it the "Vehicle-by-Parts Matrix." Use the words *cars* and *trucks* to label the vehicle **rows** (rows run across), and use the words *wheels*, *seats*, and *gas tanks* to label the parts **columns** (columns run up and down).

   b.   This matrix is called a **2-by-3 matrix** (sometimes written "2 × 3") because it has 2 rows and 3 columns. If this matrix represents the special parts needed to build each car and truck, what do you think the matrix sum shown at right would represent, and what matrix would it equal?

$$\begin{bmatrix} 4 & 2 & 1 \\ 6 & 1 & 3 \end{bmatrix} + \begin{bmatrix} 4 & 2 & 1 \\ 6 & 1 & 3 \end{bmatrix}$$

   c.   Just as letters are used to represent numbers, letters are also used to represent matrices, only for matrices capital letters are always used. Use *A* to represent the original vehicles-by-parts matrix. How could you represent the matrix of parts needed to build 5 cars and 5 trucks?

   d.   Write a matrix that represents the numbers of parts needed for five cars and five trucks.

Algebra 2 Connections

7-149.   Otto has a question for you: *"Bull's-Eye just sent in their order for this week. They want 20 cars and 25 trucks. How many special parts will I need to complete that order?"*

   a.   Make a 1-by-2, store-by-vehicles matrix to represent the number of cars and trucks Otto wants to build. Label this matrix *B*. Make sure you label the row *BE* for Bull's-Eye and use cars and trucks to label the columns.

   b.   Write matrix *A* to the right of matrix *B* and find the total number of wheels Otto needs to build the cars and trucks requested by Bull's-Eye.

   c.   Now use the information in the two matrices to calculate the total number of seats and the total number of gas tanks Otto needs to complete the order.

   d.   Record the numbers of wheels, seats, and gas tanks Otto needs to complete the order in a 1-by-3 matrix (a store-by-parts matrix). Call this matrix *C* and label the row and columns appropriately.

7-150.   In the last problem, you performed a new operation called **matrix multiplication**. To find the total supplies needed, you multiplied matrices *B* and *A* together to get matrix *C*. Algebraically, this is written as $BA = C$.

   Write the problem again as an equation that shows the product of the store matrix times the parts matrix equal to the complete order matrix, and *carefully* describe each step of what you had to take to find each of the entries in matrix *C*. Pay close attention to the labels on the numbers you multiply, "Number of cars times number of wheels on a car," etc.

7-151.   Suppose a store requests *x* cars and *y* trucks. Show both the matrix multiplication representing the number of parts needed and the store-by-parts product matrix in terms of *x* and *y*.

$$\begin{bmatrix} x & y \end{bmatrix} \begin{bmatrix} 4 & 2 & 1 \\ 6 & 1 & 3 \end{bmatrix} = \begin{bmatrix} \_ & \_ & \_ \end{bmatrix}$$

   This process of multiplying-then-adding that you used to get each entry in the product matrix is the fundamental operation of matrix multiplication. It will be referred to as **multiplying a row into a column**.

7-152.   You have impressed Otto with your use of matrices, but he has more questions.
          JC Nickels Department store has called to place an order this week. They would like
          15 cars and 30 trucks by the end of the week. Otto would like you to show him how to
          represent this information with matrices.

          a.   Add a row to matrix B to include the quantities requested by JC Nickles. Be sure
                to label rows and columns appropriately.

          b.   Calculate the number of each special part (wheels, seats, gas tanks) that Otto
                needs to build the toys for JC Nickels and write a new well-labeled matrix C that
                shows the number of each special part (wheels, seats, gas tanks) for each store.
                Write the new C matrix with all appropriate labels.

          c.   With the expanded versions of B and C, it can still be said that $BA = C$. Rewrite
                this equation using the complete matrices. This example, in which each matrix
                has more than one row, shows a more general case of matrix multiplication.
                Describe or show how each entry in matrix C is calculated from B and A.

7-153.   Using your new matrix, C, what does the entry in the second row, third column mean?
          Note: A shorthand notation is $c_{2,3}$.

7-154.   With your team, determine which of the following are matrices and which are not. For
          each matrix that you find, specify the dimensions. For each that is not a matrix,
          explain why not.

$$A = \begin{bmatrix} -6 & 12 & 0.4 \\ 3.9 & 0 & -2x \end{bmatrix} \qquad B = \begin{bmatrix} 5 & 9 \\ 1 & \end{bmatrix} \qquad C = \begin{bmatrix} 8 & x & 3y \end{bmatrix}$$

$$D = \begin{bmatrix} Fred & Barney \\ Wilma & Betty \end{bmatrix} \qquad E = \begin{bmatrix} 5 & -9 \\ -\frac{3}{7} & 12 \end{bmatrix} \qquad F = \begin{bmatrix} 6 & 1 \\ & 3 & -2 \end{bmatrix}$$

$$G = \begin{bmatrix} 1 \\ 0 \end{bmatrix} \qquad H = \begin{bmatrix} 2 \end{bmatrix} \qquad I = \begin{matrix} 1 \\ 0 \end{matrix}$$

MⒺTHODS AND MEANINGS

Matrices

A **matrix** is a rectangular array of numbers or algebraic expressions enclosed in square brackets. (Some math texts use big parentheses instead.) Usually a matrix is represented by a capital letter. The plural of matrix is **matrices**. Each matrix has **rows** and **columns**. The rows are horizontal, and columns are vertical. If matrix M has 2 rows and 3 columns, it is said that the **dimensions** of M are 2 by 3, or M is a 2-by-3 matrix. $m_{2,1}$ is the **entry** in the second row and first column of matrix M; in general, $m_{r,c}$ is the entry in the rth row and c^{th} column. When you multiply a matrix by a number, as you did when you needed to find the numbers of special parts for 5 cars and 5 trucks, the number is called a **scalar**. In the expression $5A$, A represents a matrix, and 5 is a scalar.

In problem 7-149 you performed a new operation, **matrix multiplication**. To find the total supplies needed, you multiplied matrices B and A together to get matrix C. Algebraically, it is written $BA = C$.

To find the total number of wheels needed, you had to use the row of matrix B that contained the number of cars and trucks requested by Bull's-Eye and the column of matrix A that contained the number of wheels needed per car and per truck. For this to work, the row of matrix B had to match (i.e., have the same number of entries as) the columns of matrix A.

In this example, the product matrix gives you the number of wheels, seats, and gas tanks needed to complete the Bull's-Eye order. The store-by-vehicle matrix multiplied by the vehicle-by-parts matrix gives a store-by-parts matrix, as illustrated in the example below.

store-by-vehicle matrix $\qquad$ vehicle-by-parts matrix $\qquad$ store-by-parts matrix

$$BE \begin{array}{c} c \quad t \\ \left[20 \quad 25 \right] \end{array} \quad \cdot \quad \begin{array}{c} \quad w \quad s \quad g \\ c \\ t \end{array}\left[\begin{array}{ccc} 4 & - & - \\ 6 & - & - \end{array} \right] \quad = \quad BE \begin{array}{c} w \quad s \quad g \\ \left[230 \quad - \quad - \right] \end{array}$$

7-155.   Let G be the matrix shown at right.

$$G = \begin{bmatrix} 16 & 3 & -4 & 21 \\ 19 & 31 & 12 & 17 \\ 25 & -6 & 8 & 11 \end{bmatrix}$$

a.   What is $g_{1,3}$?

b.   Two matrices can be added only if they have the same dimensions. If matrix H can be added to matrix G, what must be the dimensions of H?

c.   All the entries of the zero matrix are 0. Write the zero matrix with the same dimensions as G.

d.   Create a matrix to add to matrix G to get the zero matrix. This is called the **additive inverse of a matrix**. What could you name your new matrix to show its relationship to G?

7-156.   Shola's Bakery uses sugar, eggs, and butter in all of its cakes, as well as in the frosting. Matrix C shows how many eggs, cups of sugar, and ounces of butter are used in each angel food cake and in each devil's food cake. Matrix F shows how many eggs, cups of sugar, and ounces of butter are used in the frosting for each cake.

$$C = \begin{matrix} & \begin{matrix} e & s & b \end{matrix} \\ \begin{matrix} af \\ df \end{matrix} & \begin{bmatrix} 6 & 1 & 5 \\ 3 & 1.5 & 4 \end{bmatrix} \end{matrix}$$

$$F = \begin{matrix} & \begin{matrix} e & s & b \end{matrix} \\ \begin{matrix} af \\ df \end{matrix} & \begin{bmatrix} 2 & 1 & 2 \\ 1 & 2 & 4 \end{bmatrix} \end{matrix}$$

a.   Write the matrix $C + F$, being sure to label the rows and columns, and explain what it represents.

b.   Write the matrix $3C$, with labels, and explain what it represents.

c.   Leora orders three angel food cakes and two devil's food cakes without frosting, as represented by the matrix L at right. Use matrix multiplication to write a matrix that shows how much sugar, eggs, and butter Shola will need to fill Leora's order.

$$L = \begin{matrix} \begin{matrix} af & df \end{matrix} \\ \begin{bmatrix} 3 & 2 \end{bmatrix} \end{matrix}$$

7-157.   Solve this system of equations:
$$5x - 4y - 6z = -19$$
$$-2x + 2y + z = 5$$
$$3x - 6y - 5z = -16$$

7-158.   Complete the square to change each equation below to graphing form. Find the domain and range of each relation and determine if it is a function.

a. $y = 2x^2 - 14x + 13$

b. $x = 2y^2 - 6y - 11$

7-159.   Graph each system below and shade the solution region.

a. $y \geq x^2 - 4$
      $y < -3x + 1$

b. $y < 2x + 5$
      $y \geq |x + 1|$

7-160.   Consider $\sqrt{5 - 2x} + 7 = 4$.

a.   Solve the equation and check your solution.

b.   Did you *really* check your solution? If not, do it now. What happened?

7-161.   Find $m\angle C$ in each triangle below.

a.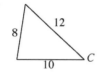

b.

7-162.   Solve $\sqrt{3x + 1} - x = -3$ and check your solution.

a.   You should have gotten two values for x when you solved. Did you? If not, rework the problem.

b.   Did you check *both* solutions? What happened?

7-163.   Consider the function $f(x) = \sqrt{x + 3}$.

a.   What are the domain and range of $f(x)$?

b.   If $g(x) = x - 10$, what is $f(g(x))$?

c.   What are the domain and range of $f(g(x))$?

d.   Is $f(g(x)) = g(f(x))$? **Justify** why or why not.

7-164.   Find the equation of the exponential function of the form $y = ab^x$ that passes through each of the following pairs of points.

a $(1, 18)$ and $(4, 3888)$

b. $(-2, -8)$ and $(3, -0.25)$

7.3.2 How can I multiply matrices?

Matrix Multiplication

In Lesson 7.3.1 you multiplied matrices together. In this lesson, you will continue to work with matrix multiplication as you learn which types of matrices can be multiplied together and which cannot.

7-165.   Congratulations! Otto has offered you a full-time position with his company. He would like you to expand the previous lesson's store-by-vehicle matrix (matrix B) to include his third retailer, Marcey's Department Store, which has requested 12 cars and 24 trucks.

a.   Show an expanded matrix B to include the information for Marcey's Department Store.

b.   Multiply the new matrix B with matrix A. What does the product matrix represent?

c.   In matrix B, the rows represent stores, and the columns represent vehicles. Therefore, matrix B is referred to as a stores-by-vehicles matrix. What would you call matrix A? What about matrix C? Describe the relationships of the labeling of the rows and columns in B and A to the labeling in the result C.

7-166.   Because each store sells its toys for a different amount, Otto has instructed you to keep all of the ordering information sorted by stores. He would like you to figure out his cost to fill each store's order. Each car costs Otto $2.75 to make, and each truck costs him $3.10. Make two new matrices to represent these costs, one a 1-by-2 matrix and the other a 2-by-1 matrix.

a.   Using the descriptive word labels for row-by-column, what does the 1-by-2 matrix represent?

b.   What does the 2-by-1 matrix represent?

c.   You need to multiply one of these matrices, call it matrix D, with the expanded matrix B from problem 7-165 to find Otto's cost to supply each store, but it is not always possible to multiply two matrices together. Which matrix would you use and in what order would you have to write the multiplication problem to make matrix multiplication possible? Discuss this with your team and be prepared to share your conclusions with the class.

d.   Find this product and label the matrix appropriately. Call this matrix E.

e.   What does the entry in the third row, first column of matrix E represent?

7-167.   Otto wants to figure out his profit on this week's order. Because he has expanded his
         business, he now charges an 86% markup beyond his costs on the vehicles he sells to
         Bull's-Eye, 74% on the vehicles he sells to JC Nickles, and a whopping 93% on the
         items he sells to Marcey's.

    a.   Make a matrix to represent Otto's profit percentages by store. Label it
          appropriately.

    b.   Multiply this profit-by-stores matrix with matrix E. What does this product
          matrix represent?

7-168.   Let $A = \begin{bmatrix} 1 & 2 \\ 3 & 4 \end{bmatrix}$ and $B = \begin{bmatrix} 5 & 6 \\ 7 & 8 \end{bmatrix}$.

    a.   Let C be the product of matrix A with matrix B (in symbols, $C = AB$). Find C.

    b.   Now find BA. Be careful. This time use the rows of B with the columns of A.

    c.   Since $ab = ba$ for any numbers a and b, it is said that multiplication of numbers
          is *commutative*. Is multiplication of matrices commutative? How do you know?

7-169.   LEARNING LOG

          Create a Learning Log entry that answers the following question:
          What has to be true about two matrices for it to be possible to
          multiply them? Be sure to use examples to illustrate your ideas.
          Title this entry "Conditions for Matrix Multiplication" and label it
          with today's date.

7-170.   With your team, make up a two matrices and find their product.

METHODS AND **M**EANINGS

More Matrix Multiplication

Matrices of any size can be multiplied as long as they fit correctly. That is, the number of columns in the first matrix must match the number of rows in the second. The entries of the product matrix can be obtained by finding sums of products of rows of the first matrix with columns of the second.

To get the $m_{r,\,c}$ entry of the product matrix, multiply the corresponding entries in the rth row of the first matrix and the cth column of the second matrix and add the products. Visually, it looks like this:

$$\begin{bmatrix} \boxed{r^{th}\ \text{row}} \\ \\ \end{bmatrix} \begin{bmatrix} \boxed{c^{th}\ \text{column}} \end{bmatrix} = \begin{bmatrix} \boxed{m_{r,c}} \\ \\ \end{bmatrix}$$

Review & Preview

7-171.   Abe, Barbara, and Cassie work at Budding Success Flower Shop. Each day, they plan to make bouquets in three styles in the quantities indicated by matrix E, an employees-by-bouquets matrix, shown at right.

Bouquet Styles

$$\text{Employees} \begin{array}{c} A \\ B \\ C \end{array} \begin{bmatrix} 6 & 4 & 7 \\ 4 & 8 & 5 \\ 5 & 6 & 6 \end{bmatrix}$$
$$\begin{array}{ccc} \#1 & \#2 & \#3 \end{array}$$

a.   How many #2 bouquets will Cassie make each day?

b.   Who makes the most bouquets?

c.   If all employees make their quota each day for a full workweek (Monday through Friday), write a matrix that shows how many bouquet styles each worker made.

d.   Represent your answer to part (c) in terms of E.

7-172.   Each #1 bouquet has 5 lilies, 4 roses, and 3 daisies. Each #2 bouquet has 4 lilies, 3 roses, and 3 daisies. Each #3 bouquet has 4 lilies, 6 roses, and 6 daisies.

    a.   Arrange this information in a new matrix with bouquet styles as rows. What will be the columns of this new matrix? Label the rows and columns of the matrix and call it matrix B.

    b.   Using the row-by-column labels, what will matrix B represent?

7-173.   Which matrix product makes sense: BE or EB? Show this matrix. What does it represent?

7-174.   Use your knowledge of shifting parent graphs to graph each equation below.

    a. $y = -2(x-3)^2 + 4$ b. $y = \frac{1}{2}(x+2)^3 - 3$

    c. $y = 2|x-5|$ d. $y = \sqrt{x-2} - 3$

7-175.   Change each equation to graphing form. Sketch the graph and label each vertex and axis of symmetry.

    a. $y = 2x^2 + 7x - 7$ b. $y = 3x^2 - x - 8$

7-176.   Solve each of the following equations. Be sure to check your solutions.

    a. $\frac{3}{x} + \frac{2}{x+1} = 5$ b. $x^2 + 6x + 9 = 2x^2 + 3x + 5$

    c. $8 - \sqrt{9 - 2x} = x + 3$.

7-177.   Solve each of the following equations.

    a. $(x+4)(2x-5) = 0$ b. $(x+4)(x^2 - 5x + 6) = 0$

    c. $3x(x+1)(2x-7)(3x+4)^2(x-13)(x+7) = 0$

    d.   Describe how to solve an equation made up of any number of factors all multiplied to equal zero.

7-178.   Find the equation of the parabola that passes through the points $(-2, 24)$, $(3, -1)$, and $(-1, 15)$.

7.3.3 How can I use a graphing calculator?

Matrix Multiplication with a Graphing Calculator

In today's lesson, you will learn how to use a graphing calculator to perform operations on matrices. Obtain a Lesson 7.3.3A or 7.3.3B resource page from your teacher, which contains instructions about using the calculator for matrix multiplication.

7-179. Look back to problems 7-171 and 7-172 for matrices B and E.

   a. Enter E and B into your graphing calculator.

   b. Use your calculator to find $E \cdot B$. Compare this to your answer for problem 7-173.

   c. Find $B \cdot E$. Write down the result and explain what it means to the problem.

7-180. Let matrix $A = \begin{bmatrix} 1 & 1 & 1 \end{bmatrix}$. Enter A into your graphing calculator.

   a. Find $A \cdot E$.   b. What does this product represent?

7-181. Suppose A is an m-by-n matrix and B is a p-by-q matrix.

   a. If AB is a valid matrix product, what do you know about m, n, p, and q?

   b. What will be the dimensions of AB?

7-182. Suppose you needed to multiply the matrices at right. Is it faster to multiply with or without a calculator? Have members of your team try it each way so that you can compare. What did you decide?
$\begin{bmatrix} 2 & 3 \\ 4 & 5 \end{bmatrix} \begin{bmatrix} 1 & 2 \\ 3 & 4 \end{bmatrix}$

7-183. At Budding Success Flower Shop, three different bouquet styles, each consisting of lilies, roses, and daisies, are assembled as shown in matrix B at right.

$\begin{array}{c} \text{Boquet Styles} \end{array} \begin{array}{c} \text{Flowers} \\ \begin{array}{ccc} l & r & d \end{array} \\ \begin{array}{c} \#1 \\ \#2 \\ \#3 \end{array} \begin{bmatrix} 5 & 4 & 3 \\ 4 & 3 & 3 \\ 4 & 6 & 6 \end{bmatrix} \end{array}$

   a. Suppose lilies cost $0.30 each, roses cost $0.45 and daisies cost $0.60. Write this information as a matrix in such a way that it makes sense to be multiplied by matrix B on the left. (That is, $B \cdot$ (your matrix) must make sense.) Title and label it as usual.

   b. Do the matrix multiplication $B \cdot$ (your matrix from part (a)) and explain the meaning of the resulting matrix.

7-184.   **LEARNING LOG**

In your Learning Log, write directions and clear examples for how to
multiply a matrix by a scalar, how to add two matrices, and how to
multiply two matrices. Title this entry "Matrix Operations" and label
it with today's date.

Review & Preview

7-185.   Perform the matrix multiplication at right without
using a calculator.

$$\begin{bmatrix} 2 & 3 & 7 \\ 5 & 1 & 0 \end{bmatrix} \begin{bmatrix} 4 \\ 6 \\ 1 \end{bmatrix}$$

7-186.   In the previous problem, the first matrix is a 2-by-3 matrix, and the second is a 3-by-1
matrix. What are the dimensions of the product matrix?

7-187.   Perform each of the following matrix operations without using a
calculator. If the operation is impossible, explain why.

a. $\begin{bmatrix} 4 & 9 & 2 \\ 6 & 0 & 5 \end{bmatrix} \begin{bmatrix} a \\ b \\ c \end{bmatrix}$

b. $2\begin{bmatrix} 4 & 9 & 2 \\ 6 & 0 & -5 \end{bmatrix} + \begin{bmatrix} 1 & 0 & -3 \\ 0 & 4 & 1 \end{bmatrix}$

c. $\begin{bmatrix} a & b \\ c & d \end{bmatrix} \begin{bmatrix} e & f \end{bmatrix}$

d. $\begin{bmatrix} a & b \\ c & d \end{bmatrix} + \begin{bmatrix} e & f \end{bmatrix}$

7-188.   Suppose you want to multiply a 5-by-11 matrix by a *c*-by-*d* matrix.

a.   For what value of *c* will the multiplication be defined?

b.   Given this value of *c*, what will be the dimensions of the product matrix?

7-189.　Given that $\log 2 \approx 0.3010$, $\log 3 \approx 0.4771$ and $\log 5 \approx 0.6990$, calculate each of the following logarithms without using a calculator.

a.　$\log 6$

b.　$\log 15$

c.　$\log 9$

d.　$\log 50$

7-190.　Several times throughout this course, you have solved equations involving radicals (square-root signs). You have found that it is important to check the solutions to these equations because sometimes solutions are **extraneous** (that is, they don't work when you substitute them back into the equation to check). Now you will see what else can happen with this type of equation. Solve $\sqrt{x} - \sqrt{5} = \sqrt{x-5}$.

a.　What happened when you squared both sides? Did you remember to use the distributive property correctly when you squared the left side? Did squaring both sides eliminate the radicals?

b.　After squaring both sides, the equation should look like previous equations involving radicals. Simplify, square again, and solve. Check your solution.

7-191.　Show how the Zero Product Property can be used to solve each of the following equations.

a.　$x(2x-1)(x-3) = 0$

b.　$2x^3 + x^2 - 3x = 0$

7-192.　Graph each equation below.

a.　$x^2 + (y-3)^2 = 9$

b.　$(x-5)^2 + (y-1)^2 = 4$

7-193.　Simplify each of the following expressions.

a.　$\dfrac{2x^3 + 5x^2 - 3x}{4x^3 - 4x^2 + x}$

b.　$\dfrac{3x^2 - 5x - 2}{2x^2 - 11x + 15} \cdot \dfrac{2x^2 - 5x}{3x^3 - 5x^2 - 2x}$

7.3.4 How can I use matrices?

$$\begin{bmatrix} a & b & c \\ d & e & f \end{bmatrix}$$

Writing Systems as Matrix Equations

In the past, you have solved systems of three equations with three variables. As you noticed, the algebraic manipulations can get complicated. Many applications in advanced mathematics and technology (such as computer drawing programs or switching and circuitry problems in telephone communications) can lead to the need to solve systems of one hundred equations with one hundred unknowns. That would take a lot of time and a lot of paper! In the next two lessons you will learn how matrices, along with calculators, can make solving these systems much simpler.

7-194.   Consider matrices A and X at right.

$$A = \begin{bmatrix} 9 & -3 & 1 \\ 1 & 1 & 1 \\ 16 & 4 & 1 \end{bmatrix} \quad X = \begin{bmatrix} x \\ y \\ z \end{bmatrix}$$

   a.   Find the product AX.

   b.   Explain how this product could be related to asystem of equations.

7-195.   Write the system at right as a matrix equation.

$$\begin{aligned} 2x + 7y + 5z &= -12 \\ 3x + y + 4z &= -22 \\ 6x + \quad\quad 9z &= -57 \end{aligned}$$

   This matrix equation can be abbreviated as $AX = B$, where A is the 3-by-3 matrix of coefficients, X is the single-column matrix of variables, and B is the single-column matrix of constants.

7-196.   Discuss with your team what you need to be able to do to solve the matrix equation $AX = B$ in problem 7-195.

7-197.   In the equation $AX = B$, AX represents a matrix multiplication problem. To solve this problem, you need to answer some questions. Is there a way to undo AX to find X? Is there an A^{-1}?

   Remember that when you first learned to solve an equation such as $\frac{2}{3}x = 14$, you used the reciprocal or multiplicative inverse of $\frac{2}{3}$ to write:

$$(\tfrac{3}{2})\tfrac{2}{3}x = 14(\tfrac{3}{2})$$

   Because $\frac{3}{2}(\frac{2}{3}) = 1$, which is the identity element for multiplication, the equation is solved and $x = 21$.

   To solve $AX = B$, there are two questions that have to be answered. First, what is the identity element? Second, what is the matrix multiplication inverse (A^{-1}) for matrix A? Parts (a) through (d) below address the first question.

Problem continues on next page. →

7-197.   *Problem continued from previous page.*

a.   Is the multiplicative identity for 2-by-2 matrices just a 2-by-2 matrix full of ones? That is, is the matrix product at right correct?
$$\begin{bmatrix} 1 & 1 \\ 1 & 1 \end{bmatrix} \begin{bmatrix} 3 & 5 \\ 1 & 2 \end{bmatrix} \overset{?}{=} \begin{bmatrix} 3 & 5 \\ 1 & 2 \end{bmatrix}$$

b.   Find a **multiplicative-identity** matrix for 2-by-2 matrices. Try out some possibilities, and work with your team to find a matrix that you can multiply by any 2-by-2 matrix (on the left or on the right) without changing its value. When you have found the identity matrix, name it I. Be prepared to **justify** your conclusions.

c.   Based on your previous results, guess the multiplicative identity for 3-by-3 matrices.

d.   In the matrix equations below, replace the blank matrix with your guess. Then check whether the matrix equations are true.

$$\begin{bmatrix} 2 & 7 & 5 \\ 3 & 1 & 4 \\ 6 & 0 & 9 \end{bmatrix} \begin{bmatrix} & & \\ & & \\ & & \end{bmatrix} = \begin{bmatrix} 2 & 7 & 5 \\ 3 & 1 & 4 \\ 6 & 0 & 9 \end{bmatrix} \qquad \begin{bmatrix} & & \\ & & \\ & & \end{bmatrix} \begin{bmatrix} 2 & 7 & 5 \\ 3 & 1 & 4 \\ 6 & 0 & 9 \end{bmatrix} = \begin{bmatrix} 2 & 7 & 5 \\ 3 & 1 & 4 \\ 6 & 0 & 9 \end{bmatrix}$$

7-198.   Rewrite the system of equations at right into a matrix equation of the form $AX = B$. With your team, discuss what you could do to solve this equation using matrices. In other words, how could you get X by itself?
$$9x - 3y + z = -7$$
$$x + y + z = -3$$
$$16x + 4y + z = 21$$

7-199.   What matrix could you multiply by $M = \begin{bmatrix} 2 & 1 \\ 4 & 0 \end{bmatrix}$ to get a result of $\begin{bmatrix} 1 & 0 \\ 0 & 1 \end{bmatrix}$?

Review & Preview

7-200.   Let A and B be the matrices defined at right. Complete each of the following matrix-multiplication problems.
$$A = \begin{bmatrix} 4 & -1 \\ 7 & 2 \end{bmatrix}$$
$$B = \begin{bmatrix} -5 & 0 \\ 3 & -8 \end{bmatrix}$$

a. $A - B$ b. $5A$

c. AB d. BA

7-201.   What matrix is the **additive identity** for 2-by-2 matrices?

7-202.   Represent each system of equations below with matrices. You do not have to solve the systems.

a. $p + 2q = 7$
      $3p + 4q = 11$

b. $4m - 5n = -2$
      $-3m + 4n = 9$

c. $4x - y + z = -5$
      $2x + 2y + 3z = 10$
      $5x - 2y + 6z = 1$

d. $7w - 3x + 2z = 41$
      $-2w + x - z = -13$
      $4w + y - 2z = 12$
      $2 - 3x = 1$

7-203.   Juan, Huang, and Danusha have pencils and pens in their backpacks. Juan has 3 pencils and 2 pens, Huang has 4 pencils and 5 pens, and Danusha has 6 pencils and 4 pens.

a.   Represent this information in a 3-by-2 matrix. Label rows and columns.

b.   Each pencil is worth 10 cents, and each pen is worth 25 cents. Represent this information in a matrix in such a way that you can multiply the first matrix by this one. Label rows and columns.

c.   Find the product matrix and interpret the 2, 1 entry.

7-204.   Suppose the entries in a 3-by-2 matrix are a, b, c, d, e, f (reading across the rows), and the entries in a second 2-by-1 matrix are g, h. Write the product matrix in terms of these letters.

7-205.   If x is a number, represent its reciprocal using exponents (not fractions).

7-206.   Add or subtract and simplify each of the following expressions. **Justify** that each step of your process makes sense.

a. $\frac{3}{(x-4)(x+1)} + \frac{6}{x+1}$

b. $\frac{x+2}{x^2-9} - \frac{1}{x+3}$

7-207.   Solve $\sqrt{2x+7} + \sqrt{x+48} = 10$ and check your solution. If your solution is incorrect, refer to parts (a) and (b) below.

a.   Did you remember you had to square twice?

b.   To solve this problem, you will have to square both sides twice, but you can make this problem a little easier first. Having one radical on each side of the equation simplifies the algebra slightly. If you did not rewrite the equation this way when you solved, try it now and solve the equation. Did you get the same solution? You should!

7-208.   Solve each of the following equations. Be sure to check your answers.

    a. $3|2x - 5| - 8 = -5$ b. $\sqrt{3x^2 + 11x} = 2$

7.3.5 How can I use matrices?

Using Matrices to Solve Systems of Equations

$$\begin{bmatrix} a & b & c \\ d & e & f \end{bmatrix}$$

In Lesson 7.3.4 you learned that a system of equations can be represented by a single *matrix equation* of the form $AX = B$. If you can find the numbers for the matrix X that make this equation true, you will have found the values of x, y, and z that solve the original system of equations. Solving matrix equations is very similar to solving other equations: a goal is to get X by itself. One complication is that there is no way to divide matrices, so you will need to learn how to use the **multiplicative inverse of a matrix**.

7-209.   Think about what you have learned about additive and multiplicative inverses of numbers.

    a.   What should you get when you multiply a number or a matrix by its multiplicative inverse?

    b.   Why would the multiplicative inverse of a matrix be useful in solving the matrix equation $AX = B$?

    c.   How can you determine whether two matrices are multiplicative inverses? Decided whether the matrices at right are multiplicative inverses and **justify** your decision.
$$\begin{bmatrix} 3 & 5 \\ 1 & 2 \end{bmatrix} \begin{bmatrix} 2 & -5 \\ -1 & 3 \end{bmatrix}$$

7-210.   The process of finding the inverse of a matrix A (denoted A^{-1}) is very complicated. Fortunately, your graphing calculator can do it with ease! If you are using a TI or Casio graphing calculator, the Lesson 7.3.3A or 7.3.3B Resource Page will show you how. Otherwise, ask your teacher for directions. Use the graphing calculator to find the inverse of matrix A from problem 7-195.

7-211.   To check the inverse, compute $[A]^{-1}[A]$. Do you see any strange entries? If so, talk with your team to figure out what they should be.

7-212.   Now you are ready to solve the system of equations in problem 7-195 by solving the equivalent matrix equation $AX = B$.

   a.   With your team, use what you know about inverses and your calculator to solve the system of equations.

   b.   In general, if $AX = B$ is a matrix equation, then what does X equal?

   c.   In general, would $X = BA^{-1}$ give the solution to the matrix equation $AX = B$? Explain why or why not.

7-213.   Write the linear system at right as a matrix equation of the form $AX = B$. Then enter matrices A and B in your graphing calculator and use the method of the previous problem to solve the system.

$$4x + 4y - 5z = -2$$
$$2x - 4y + 10z = 6$$
$$x + 2y + 5z = 0$$

7-214.   Professor Zipthrough wants to prove that the method of problem 7-212 always works to solve matrix equations of the form $AX = B$. He has written the steps on the board, but has not **justified** them. Help Professor Z **justify** each step below.

   Given: $AX = B$

   Step 1: $A^{-1}(AX) = A^{-1}B$ Step 2: $(A^{-1}A)X = A^{-1}B$

   Step 3: $IX = A^{-1}B$ Step 4: $X = A^{-1}B$

7-215.   Use the matrix method to solve the system of equations shown at right.

$$-4x + 7y - 12z = -3.8$$
$$5x - 8y = -14.8$$
$$x - 4y + 9z = 7.6$$

7-216.   The cubic function $g(x) = px^3 + qx^2 + rx + s$ passes through the points $(-2, -22)$, $(1, 2)$, $(2, -2)$, and $(5, 118)$.

   a.   Set up four equations using p, q, r, and s as variables.

   b.   Write these four equations as a single matrix equation.

   c.   Use your graphing calculator to solve this matrix equation and write the equation for $g(x)$.

7-217. How many points would you need to know to be able to set up a system of equations and the corresponding matrix equation to find the exact equation of a graph of the form $g(x) = a_7x^7 + a_6x^6 + a_5x^5 + a_4x^4 + a_3x^3 + a_2x^2 + a_1x + a_0$?

a. Describe the matrix equation you would need to set up.

b. How many points would you need to know to be able to set up a system of equations and the corresponding matrix equation to find $g(x) = a_nx^n + a_{n-1}x^{n-1} + a_{n-2}x^{n-2} + ... + a_1x + a_0$?

METHODS AND MEANINGS

MATH NOTES

Inverse of a Matrix

If A is a matrix, then its **multiplicative inverse** is denoted A^{-1}. Note that A^{-1} does *not* mean $\frac{1}{A}$. (A number cannot be divided by a matrix.) Instead, A^{-1} is the matrix with the property that $A^{-1}(A) = I$.

The identity matrix for 3-by-3 matrices is shown at right. Only square matrices can have inverses, and A^{-1} must have the same dimensions as A.

$$\begin{bmatrix} 1 & 0 & 0 \\ 0 & 1 & 0 \\ 0 & 0 & 1 \end{bmatrix}$$

In general, $AB \ne BA$ for matrices A and B. As a result, when referring to matrices, the word "multiply" alone is unclear; the terms **right-multiply** and **left-multiply** are used instead. To describe the product BA, one would say, "right-multiply B by A," or "left-multiply A by B."

Review & Preview

7-218. Show that each of the following pairs of matrices are inverses.

a. $\begin{bmatrix} 1 & 2 \\ 3 & 4 \end{bmatrix}$ and $\begin{bmatrix} -2 & 1 \\ 1.5 & -0.5 \end{bmatrix}$

b. $\begin{bmatrix} 4 & -5 \\ -3 & 4 \end{bmatrix}$ and $\begin{bmatrix} 4 & 5 \\ 3 & 4 \end{bmatrix}$

7-219. Use matrices to solve these systems. Check your answers by substituting them in the original equations. You will not need a calculator if you use the results of the previous problem.

a. $p + 2q = 7$
$3p + 4q = 11$

b. $4m - 5n = -2$
$-3m + 4n = 9$

Algebra 2 Connections

7-220. *P* is the product of two matrices, as shown at right. Show each result described below or explain why it cannot be shown.

$$P = \begin{bmatrix} 2 & -1 & 5 \\ -4 & 0 & 7 \end{bmatrix} \begin{bmatrix} -3 & 2 \\ 1 & -6 \\ 0 & 1 \end{bmatrix}$$

a.   *P*   b. $P_{1,2}$ c. $P_{2,3}$

7-221. If *M* is as shown below, find a matrix *I* such that $MI = IM = M$, or write "impossible" and explain why.

a. $M = \begin{bmatrix} 2 & -1 & 5 \\ -4 & 0 & 7 \end{bmatrix}$

b. $M = \begin{bmatrix} 2 & -1 \\ -4 & 0 \end{bmatrix}$

c. $M = \begin{bmatrix} 2 & -1 & 5 \\ -4 & 0 & 7 \\ 6 & -2 & 8 \end{bmatrix}$

7-222. Given that $\log_x 2 = a$, $\log_x 5 = b$, and $\log_x 7 = c$, write expressions using *a*, *b*, and/or *c* for each log expression below.

a. $\log_x 10$ b. $\log_x 49$ c. $\log_x 50$ d. $\log_x 56$

7-223. Solve each of the following equations.

a. $5^x = 72$ b. $2^{3x} = 7$ c. $3^{(2x+4)} = 17$

7-224. Solve $\sqrt{21x-3} - \sqrt{5x+1} = 6$ and check your solution. Remember: Square twice!

7-225. Add or subtract and simplify each of the following expressions. **Justify** that each step of your process makes sense.

a. $\dfrac{3x}{x^2+2x+1} + \dfrac{3}{x^2+2x+1}$

b. $\dfrac{3}{x-1} - \dfrac{2}{x-2}$

7-226. Graph each of the following systems of inequalities.

a. $y \geq 3(x-2)^2 - 4$
$y > -2|x-1| + 3$

b. $y > (x-1)^2 - 5$
$y > 3x - 5$
$y \leq \frac{1}{2}(x-1)^2 + 1$

Chapter 7 Closure What have I learned?

Reflection and Synthesis

The activities below offer you a chance to reflect on what you have learned in this chapter. As you work, look for concepts that you feel very comfortable with, ideas that you would like to learn more about, and topics with which you need more help. Look for connections between ideas as well as connections with material you have learned previously.

①   TEAM BRAINSTORM

With your team, brainstorm a list of topics. Be as detailed as you can. How long can you make your lists? Then brainstorm a list of all the connections among topics on your list and the mathematics you had already learned when you started this chapter. Challenge yourselves. Be prepared to share your team's ideas with the class.

Topics: What have you studied in this chapter? What ideas and words were important in what you learned? Remember to be as detailed as you can.

Connections: How are the topics, ideas, and words that you learned in previous courses connected to the new ideas in this chapter? Again, make your list as long as you can.

MAKING CONNECTIONS

Below is a list of the vocabulary used in this chapter. Make sure that you are familiar with all of these words and know what they mean. Refer to the glossary or index for any words that you do not yet understand.

3-D coordinate system	asymptote	isometric dot paper
line of symmetry	logarithm	ordered triple
plane	Power Property of Logs	Product Property of Logs
Quotient Property of Logs	solution	$y = x$

Make a concept map showing all of the connections you can find among the key words and ideas listed above. To show a connection between two words, draw a line between them and explain the connection, as shown in the example below. A word can be connected to any other word as long as you can **justify** the connection. For each key word or idea, sketch an example.

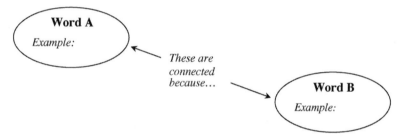

Your teacher may provide you with vocabulary cards to help you get started. If you use the cards to plan your concept map, be sure either to re-draw your concept map on your paper or to attach the vocabulary cards to a poster with all of the connections explained for others to see and understand.

While you are making your map, your team may think of related words or ideas that are not listed above. Be sure to include these ideas on your concept map.

③   GROWTH OVER TIME

This section gives you an opportunity to show growth in your understanding of key mathematical ideas over time as you complete this course.

Part 1: On a separate sheet of paper, explain everything that you know about $y = x^2 - 4$ and $y = \sqrt{x+4}$. Be sure to include everything you have learned since the last time you did this problem, and do not leave out anything you included in your earlier attempts.

Continues on next page. →

③   *Continued from previous page.*

Part 2: Compare your three responses to this "Growth Over Time" problem. Write an evaluation of your growth based on your responses. Consider each of the following questions as you write your answer.

- What new concepts did you include the second time you did the problem? In what ways was your response better than your first attempt?

- How was your final version different from the first two? What new ideas did you include?

- Did you omit anything in the final version that you used in one of the earlier versions? Why did you omit it?

- Rate your three attempts by making three bars like the ones below and shading each bar to represent how much you knew on each attempt.

First Attempt:
Second Attempt:
Final Attempt:

- Is there anything you want to add to your current version? If so, add it and keep this version for future reference.

④   SUMMARIZING MY UNDERSTANDING

This section gives you an opportunity to show what you know about certain math topics or ideas.

With your team, make a list of the *big ideas* of this chapter. Discuss the important ideas of the chapter and try to agree on a short list of no more than five big ideas. Be prepared to share your list in a whole-class discussion. When the class has reached agreement on a list, continue with parts (a) and (b) below.

a.   Write your own description of each big idea.

b.   For each big idea, provide one or more representative example problems. Solve each problem completely, using multiple representations, if applicable.

Your teacher may give you a "GO" page to work on (or you can download this from www.cpm.org). "GO" stands for "Graphic Organizer," a tool you can use to organize your thoughts and communicate your ideas clearly.

WHAT HAVE I LEARNED?

This section will help you recognize the types of problems you feel comfortable with and those with which you need more help. This section will appear at the end of every chapter to help you check your understanding. Even if your teacher does not assign this section, it is a good idea to try these problems and find out for yourself what you know and what you need to work on.

Solve each problem as completely as you can. The table at the end of this closure section has answers to these problems. It also tells you where you can find additional help and practice with similar problems.

CL 7-227. Graph in three dimensions.

    a.   (2, 3, 1)   b.   (–2, 3, 0)

    c. $2x + y - z = 6$

CL 7-228. Determine the point of intersection of the three planes.

    a. $x + y + z = 3$ b. $x + y + 4z = 5$

          $2x - y + 2z = 6$ $-2x \quad +2z = 3$

          $3x + 2y - z = 13$ $3x + y - 2z = 0$

CL 7-229. The parabola $y = ax^2 + bx + c$ passes through the points (2, 3), (–1, 6), and (0, 3). Determine:

    a.   The equation of the parabola.

    b.   The vertex of the parabola.

    c.   The x-intercepts of the parabola.

CL 7-230. Solve each equation to the nearest thousandth (0.001).

    a. $2^x = 17$ b. $5x^3 = 75$

    c. $5(3^{x+1}) = 85$ d. $\log_3(x + 1) = -2$

CL 7-231. Compute the value of each expression. No calculator is necessary.

    a. $\log(8) + \log(125)$ b. $\log_{25}(125)$

    c. $\frac{1}{2}\log(25) + \log(20)$ d. $7^{\log_7(12)}$

CL 7-232. An exponential function $y = km^x + b$ passes through (3, 7.5) and (4, 6.25). It also has an asymptote at $y = 5$.

    a.   Find the equation of the function.

    b.   If the equation also passes through (8, w), what is the value of w?

CL 7-233. A gallon of propane costs \$3.59. Inflation has steadily increased 4% per year.

    a.   What did a gallon of propane cost ten years ago?

    b.   If this trend continues, how much longer will it be until it costs \$10?

CL 7-234. Find the inverse of this equation: $y = 2 + \sqrt{2x - 4}$.

CL 7-235. Factor the following expressions completely.

    a. $y^2 + 2y - 35$ b. $2x^2 - x - 21$

    c. $m(3m + 2)(m - 1)$ d. $8ab^2 - 28ab + 12a$

CL 7-236. Given the matrices defined below, compute the following operations, if possible.

$$A = \begin{bmatrix} 3 & -1 & 6 \\ 8 & 9 & 0 \end{bmatrix} \quad B = \begin{bmatrix} 2 & 6 & -6 \\ 1 & 0 & 2 \end{bmatrix} \quad C = \begin{bmatrix} 2 & 1 & 3 \\ -1 & 2 & 0 \\ 3 & 2 & 1 \end{bmatrix}$$

    a. $A + B$ b. $B - A$

    c. BC d. CB

CL 7-237. Given the system of equations at right:

$$x + y + z = 3$$
$$2x - y + 2z = 6$$
$$3x + 2y - z = 13$$

    a.   Write the equivalent matrix equation.

    b.   Write the equivalent matrix solution. (Do not actually solve.)

CL 7-238. Check your answers using the table at the end of this section. Which problems do you feel confident about? Which problems were hard? Have you worked on problems like these in previous math classes? Sort the problems into three groups: the ones you are confident you can do, the ones you need more practice with, and the ones you need further help to understand.

⑥   HOW AM I THINKING?

This course focuses on five different **Ways of Thinking: investigating, reversing thinking, justifying, generalizing,** and **choosing a strategy**. These are some of the ways in which you think while trying to make sense of a concept or to solve a problem (even outside of math class). During this chapter, you have probably used each Way of Thinking multiple times without even realizing it!

With your team, review each of the five Ways of Thinking. Then choose three of these Ways of Thinking that you remember using while working on this chapter. Show and explain where and how you used each one. Describe why thinking in this way helped you solve a particular problem or understand something new. Be sure to include examples to demonstrate your thinking.

Answers and Support for Closure Activity #5
What Have I Learned?

Problem	Solutions		Need Help?	More Practice
CL 7-227.	a.		Lessons 7.1.1 and 7.1.2	Problems 7-6 and 7-19
			Math Notes boxes in Lessons 7.1.2 and 7.1.4	
	b.			
	c.			
CL 7-228.	a. $(4, 0, -1)$		Lesson 7.1.4	Problems 6-27, 7-47, 7-50, and 7-71, 7-79, 7-102, 7-157
	b. $(-1, 4, 0.5)$			
CL 7-229.	a. $y = x^2 - 2x + 3$		Lesson 7.1.5	Problems 7-64, 7-67, 7-68, 7-69, 7-72, 7-80, and 7-178
	b. $(1, 2)$		Learning Log entry from problem 7-63	
	c. No x-intercepts			
CL 7-230.	a. 4.087	b. 2.466	Lessons 6.2.2 and 7.2.1	Problems 6-28, 6-75, 6-86, 6-99, 7-11, 7-93, 7-111, 7-133, 7-140 and 7-223
	c. 1.579	d. −0.889		
CL 7-231.	a. 3	b. 1.5	Lessons 6.2.2 and 7.2.2	Problems 7-106, 7-107, 7-129, and 7-139, 7-189, and 7-222
	c. 2	d. 12	Math Notes box in Lesson 7.2.2	

Problem	Solutions	Need Help?	More Practice
CL 7-232.	a. $y = 20(\frac{1}{2})^x + 5$ b. $w = 5.078$	Lesson 7.2.3	Problems 7-125, 7-127, 7-137, and 7-138
CL 7-233.	a. $2.43 b. 26.1 years	Lessons 2.1.6 and 3.2.3	Problems 2-79, 2-87, 2-103, 2-154. 3-18, 3-40, CL 3-138, 4-33, 4-42, 4-73, 5-43, 5-65, 6-31, 5-93, 7-15, and 7-138, 7-147
CL 7-234.	a. $y = \frac{(x-2)^2}{2} + 2$	Lessons 6.1.1 and 6.1.3	Problems 6-4, 6-7, 6-39, 6-60, 7-118, 7-132, and 7-141
CL 7-235.	a. $(y+7)(y-5)$ b. $(x+3)(2x-7)$ c. $m(3m+2)(m-1)$ d. $4a(2b-1)(b-3)$	Lesson 2.2.2 Checkpoint 5	Problems 2-28, 2-90, 2-155, 3-29, 3-111, 3-124, 3-60, 4-82, and 7-41
CL-7-236.	a. $\begin{bmatrix} 5 & 5 & 0 \\ 9 & 9 & 2 \end{bmatrix}$ b. $\begin{bmatrix} -1 & 7 & -12 \\ -7 & -9 & 2 \end{bmatrix}$ c. $\begin{bmatrix} -20 & 2 & 0 \\ 8 & 5 & 5 \end{bmatrix}$ d. impossible	Lesson 7.3.2 Math Notes box in Lesson 7.3.2 Learning Log entries from problems 7-169 and 7-184	Problems 7-182, 7-185, 7-156, 7-168, 7-187, 7-200, 7-220
CL-7-237.	a. $\begin{bmatrix} 1 & 1 & 1 \\ 2 & -1 & 2 \\ 3 & 2 & -1 \end{bmatrix}\begin{bmatrix} x \\ y \\ z \end{bmatrix} = \begin{bmatrix} 3 \\ 6 \\ 13 \end{bmatrix}$ b. $\begin{bmatrix} 1 & 1 & 1 \\ 2 & -1 & 2 \\ 3 & 2 & -1 \end{bmatrix}^{-1}\begin{bmatrix} 3 \\ 6 \\ 13 \end{bmatrix} = \begin{bmatrix} x \\ y \\ z \end{bmatrix}$	Lessons 7.3.4 and 7.3.5	Problems 7-194, 7-195, 7-198, 7-202, 7-213, 7-212, and 7-219

CHAPTER 8 — Trigonometric Functions

This chapter begins with an experiment that will generate a new curve called a cyclic function. You will then explore the relationship between right-triangle trigonometry and this new curve. You will be introduced to a new representation that is useful for the study of cyclic functions: a unit circle. You will also learn how to use radians instead of degress to describe angles.

In the second section of this chapter, you will transform cyclic functions and find general equations for them. You will also learn about a new property that is charactaeristic of cyclic functions called a period. Then you will write equations for the curve that you generated in the experiment at the beginning of the chapter.

Guiding Questions

Think about these questions throughout this chapter:

What is the connection?

What does it mean?

How can I transform it?

What representations can I use?

In this chapter, you will learn:

➢ To recognize and create multiple representations of the functions $y = \sin\theta$ and $y = \cos\theta$.

➢ How to graph functions of the family whose parents are $y = \sin x$ and $y = \cos x$.

➢ The relationships between a unit circle and a graph of a cyclic function.

➢ How to use radians instead of degrees to measure lengths of arcs and angles.

Chapter Outline

Section 8.1 In this section, you will use your understanding of the trigonometric ratios in right triangles to build understanding of three new functions. You will also learn to use a new unit to measure angles.

Section 8.2 In this section, you will apply your expertise with transforming parent graphs to develop general equations for cyclic or trigonometric functions. You will also learn about a property particular to cyclic functions called a period.

8.1.1 What cyclic relationships can I model?

Introduction to Cyclic Models

In this chapter, you will learn about a new family of functions that are very useful for describing relationships that are **cyclic** (have repeating cycles), like the height of the ocean as the tides fluctuate between high and low or the distance of a swinging pendulum from its center point.

8-1.   EMERGENCY!

Nurse Nina rushes through the hospital with one hand on her clipboard and the other pulling a portable blood stand. The bags of blood swinging from the stand are needed in the emergency room (E.R.) *'stat'* for three patients in severe need. She is so intent on delivering the blood in time that she does not notice that one of the bags has a small hole in it and is dripping on the floor behind her. As she reaches the E.R., she is horrified to see a small pool of blood beginning to form on the floor. Looking down the corridor from where she came, she sees the trail of blood that dripped and notices that it forms a very interesting pattern.

What shape do you think the trail of blood created?

Your task: Use the materials and instructions provided by your teacher to re-create the pattern that the nurse saw on the hallway floor behind her. Make as many observations as you can about the shape you see and how that shape relates to what was happening to the bag of blood. Be sure to keep track of all the details. Be prepared to explain your observations to the class. (Note: Complete directions for conducting this experiment are on the next page.)

Directions for the Pendulum Experiment (Problem 8-1)

Find a space in the classroom where there is room to work. You may need to move your table or desks out of the way.

Set up your pendulum by attaching your bag of liquid to a meter stick using string, as shown at right.

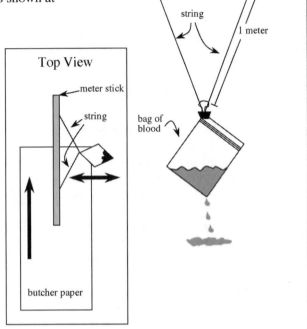

Assign the following tasks:

- One student holds the meter stick from which the pendulum swings.

- One student holds the bag, releases it when ready, and then stops it when it reaches the end of the paper.

- Two students hold the butcher paper, one at each end, and slide it *at a constant rate* underneath the swinging pendulum. Be sure to slide the paper parallel to the meter stick and perpendicular to the swing of the pendulum, as shown in the diagram at right.

Tips for a successful experiment:

- The student holding the meter stick should hold the places where the string attaches. Otherwise, the string has a tendency to slide toward the center of the meter stick.

- Use as much of the string as you can so that your pendulum is as long as possible.

- When you are ready, have your teacher cut a *very* small hole in the corner of the bag. The student holding the bag should pinch this hole closed until the pendulum begins swinging.

- Be sure to slide the butcher paper under the pendulum *at a constant rate*.

- As you pull the bag up to start the pendulum swinging, hold it taut from the bottom corner so that the bag remains in line with the string (see diagram at right).

- Have an extra bag ready to place the dripping bag into when the experiment is complete.

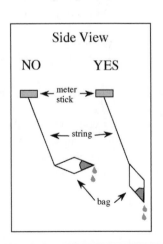

8-2.   Now you will make predictions about a new curve.

   a.   With your team, design your own curve similar to the one already created.
        Decide exactly how you want it to look. How long do you want each cycle?
        How tall do you want it to be? Where do you want it to be on your paper?
        Where do you want it to start? Once you have decided on your new curve, make
        a sketch of it on your paper.

   b.   Predict how you could conduct an experiment to get exactly the curve you have
        described. How fast should you move the paper? Where would you start it?
        How high would you start your pendulum? Be prepared to share your predictions
        and their **justifications** with the class.

8-3.   Draw a sketch of one of the shapes the class created with the drips from the swinging
         pendulum in Lesson 8.1.1.

   a.   Sketch what the shape would look like if the bag were pulled out farther before it
        was let go.

   b.   Sketch what the shape would look like if the paper underneath the pendulum
        traveled faster.

8-4.   Karin was working on graphing the function $f(x) = \frac{2}{x-3}$. She made a table (shown
         below), but she is not sure how to graph the values in the table. Show Karin how to
         make her graph and tell her everything you know about her function.

x	-3	-2	-1	0	1	2	3	4	5	6	7	8	9
$f(x)$	$-\frac{1}{3}$	$-\frac{2}{5}$	$-\frac{1}{2}$	$-\frac{2}{3}$	-1	-2	$*$	2	1	$\frac{2}{3}$	$\frac{1}{2}$	$\frac{2}{5}$	$\frac{1}{3}$

*undefined

8-5. In each of the following triangles, find the length of the side labeled x.

a.

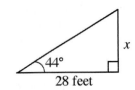

28 feet

b.

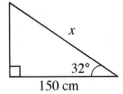

150 cm

c.

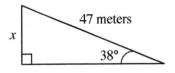

8-6. Copy the triangles at right and label the missing side lengths.

8-7. Find the equation of the parabola that passes through the points $(0, 0)$, $(3, 9)$, and $(6, 0)$.

8-8. Solve and check your solution: $2\sqrt{21 - x} - \sqrt{3x - 6} = 5$.

8-9. Find the inverse functions for the functions given below.

a. $f(x) = \sqrt[3]{4x - 1}$

b. $g(x) = \log_7 x$

8-10. Find the x- and y-intercepts of $y - 7 = 3^{(x+4)}$.

8-11. Change $x^2 - 2x + y^2 - 29 = 0$ to graphing form then sketch the graph and label the important points.

$8.1.2$ How can I graph it?

Graphing the Sine Function

Today you will use what you know about right-triangle relationships and about graphing functions to **investigate** a new function.

8-12.   *"HURRY!!! Let's get there before the line gets too long!"* shouts Antonio to his best friend René as they race to get on *The Screamer*, the newest attraction at the local amusement park.

"It's only been open for one day, and already everyone is saying it's the scariest ride at the park!" exclaims Antonio. *"I hear they really had to rush to get it done in time for summer."*

Antonio whistles as he screeches to a halt in front of the huge sign that says, *"Welcome to The Screamer, the Scariest Ride on Earth."* The picture below it shows an enormous wheel that represents *The Screamer*, with its radius of 100 feet. Half of the wheel is below ground level, in a very dark, murky pit with water at the bottom. As *The Screamer* rotates at dizzying speeds, riders fly up into the air before plunging downward through blasts of freezing air, hair-raising screams, and sticky spider webs into the pit where they splash through the dark, eerie water on their way back above ground.

René and Antonio wait impatiently to get on the ride, watching passengers load and unload. New passengers get on and strap themselves in as others emerge from the pit looking queasy. The ride rotates 15° to load and unload the next set of riders. As René straps himself in, he remembers Antonio's ominous words: *"I hear they really had to rush to get it done in time for summer."*

Sure enough, just as the ride plunges René and Antonio into the greasy water, they hear the piercing scream of metal twisting. Sparks fly and the pit fills with smoke as the ride grinds to a halt. To escape, all of the passengers must climb vertically to ground level from wherever they got stuck, either up from the pit or down from dizzying heights.

Problem continues on next page. →

8-12.   *Problem continued from previous page.*

Your task: Find a function that describes the
distance each passenger must climb in order to
escape from the broken ride, *The Screamer*.

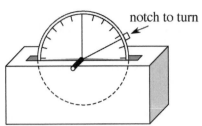
notch to turn

To help you gather data, your teacher will
provide you with the materials to build a
model of this situation. Layer your transparency circle on top of your cardboard
circle and insert a toothpick to act as an axle. Then slide the circles into the slit in
your cardboard box, as shown in the diagram at right.

a.   Use the transparent One Unit Ruler to measure the escape heights on the model
      for at least 16 different possible seat positions. The seat could be in the pit, high
      in the air, or right at ground level. Remember that this position depends on the
      angle of the ride's rotation when it broke down. The radius of the model wheel
      will be referred to as one unit. That is, a model height of one unit corresponds
      to an actual height of 100 feet on the ride, so an actual height of 80 feet on the
      ride will be represented by a measured height of 0.8 units on the model. Record
      your data in a table like the one shown below. Leave room for additional
      columns.

Degree of Rotation from $0°$ (Platform)	Measured Height $(0 \le y \le 1)$	Actual Height Above (or Below) Platform	

b.   Graph your data on a large graph.

c.   Suppose you were asked to add 20 more data points to your table. What
      shortcuts could you use to reduce the amount of work?

8-13.   What function can you use to model the situation in problem 8-12?
         To help you figure it out, sketch the right triangle shown in the
         diagram at right.

a.   With your team, write an equation and use it to calculate the
      height of the triangle. Does the escape height you calculated seem reasonable
      compared to the data you collected in problem 8-12?

b.   Write an equation representing the escape height $h(\theta)$ for *any* passenger, for
      any angle of rotation of *The Screamer*. (Note that the angle is represented by
      the Greek letter theta, which looks like this: θ.)

Problem continues on next page. →

Algebra 2 Connections

8-13.   *Problem continued from previous page.*

c.   Enter the data from the first two columns of your table into your grapher. Adjust the viewing window so you can see all of the data. Then graph $h(\theta)$ on top of the data. How well does $h(\theta)$ fit your data?

d.   Adjust the viewing window so that you can see more of the graph of $h(\theta)$. Describe the behavior of the graph as θ gets larger. Does this make sense? Why or why not?

e.   Use the 'table' function of your calculator to find its calculated values for $h(\theta)$. Add another column to your table from problem 8-12, label it with the equation you found for $h(\theta)$, and enter these values, rounding off to the nearest hundredth. How do the calculated values compare with your measured ones?

8-14.   René and Antonio finally make it home from the amusement park unhurt, but in need of a shower. As soon as they have cleaned up, they go over to a friend's house to share their scary experience on *The Screamer*. They draw a picture of the Ferris wheel and five of the seats, located at $15°$, $30°$, $45°$, $60°$, and $75°$ (shown at right and on the resource page provided by your teacher).

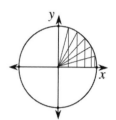

a.   Label each triangle with its *calculated* height. You can use your data from problem 8-12. If you do not have data for all of these angles, return to the 'table' function on your grapher. Plot these heights at their angle location on the coordinate system to the right of the circle. You will be plotting points in the form (x = angle in degrees, y = height).

b.   Draw five new triangles that are congruent to the first five, but that are located in the second quadrant. Label these with their angle measures (from 0°) and heights. Use the angle measures and heights to plot five new points on the graph that correspond to these five new points on the circle.

c.   Continue this process by drawing triangles in the third and fourth quadrants. You should have a total of twenty triangles drawn and twenty points plotted. Then label the points where the circle intersects the *x*- and *y*-axes with their angle measures and heights and then add points for them to the graph as well. Sketch a smooth curve through the points.

d.   Discuss with your team all of the relationships you can find among the points on the circle and between your unit circle and the graph. Be prepared to share your ideas with the class.

METHODS AND MEANINGS

Special Right-Triangle Relationships

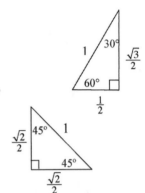

As you may recall from geometry, there are certain right triangles whose sides have special relationships that make certain calculations easier. One such triangle is half of an equilateral triangle and is known as a **30° – 60° – 90° triangle**, named after the degree measures of its angles.

The other special triangle is half of a square and is known as the **45° – 45° – 90° triangle**. Both triangles are shown at right.

Review & Preview

8-15.   Copy the triangles at right.

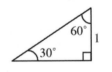

a.   Label the missing sides with their *exact* lengths. That is, leave your answers in radical form.

b.   The 30° – 60° – 90° triangle is sometimes called a half-equilateral. Draw a picture to illustrate this, and explain how that fact can be used to help label the missing sides in part (a).

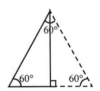

8-16.   Find the measure of angle *A* in the diagram at right.

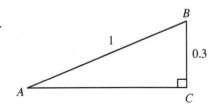

8-17. This is a Checkpoint problem for completing the square and finding the vertex of a parabola.

Complete the square to change the equation $y = 2x^2 - 4x + 5$ to graphing form, identify the vertex of the parabola, and sketch its graph.

If you needed help completing the square to change this equation to graphing form and identify the vertex, then you need more practice. Review the Checkpoint 14 materials and try the practice problems. Also, consider getting help outside of class time. From this point on, you will be expected to complete the square and identify the point (h, k) for equations such as these quickly and accurately.

8-18. Leadfoot Lilly was driving 80 miles per hour when she passed a parked highway patrol car. By the time she was half a mile past the spot where the patrol car was parked, the officer was driving after her at 100 miles per hour. If these rates remain constant, how long will it take the officer to catch up to Lilly? Write and solve an equation to represent this situation.

8-19. Evaluate each expression without using a calculator or changing the form of the expression.

    a. $\log(1)$

    b. $\log(10^3)$

    c. $10^{\log(4)}$

    d. $10^{3\log(4)}$

8-20. Complete the table of values for $f(x) = \frac{x^2 + 4x - 5}{x - 1}$.

x	-2	-1	0	1	2	3
y						

    a.   Graph the points in the table. What kind of function does it appear to be? Why is it not correct to connect all of the dots?

    b.   Look for a simple pattern for the values in the table. What appears to be the relationship between x and y? Calculate $f(0.9)$ and $f(1.1)$ and add the points to your graph. Is there an asymptote at $x = 1$? If you are unsure, calculate $f(0.99)$ and $f(1.01)$ as well.

    c.   Simplify the formula for $f(x)$. What do you think the complete graph looks like?

8-21.   In 1998, Terre Haute, Indiana had a population of 72,000 people. In 2000, the population had dropped to 70,379. City officials expect the population to level off eventually at 60,000.

   a.   What kind of function would best model the population over time?

   b.   Write an equation that would model the changing population over time.

8-22.   A semi-circular tunnel is 26 feet high at its highest point. A road 48 feet wide is centered under the tunnel. Bruce needs to move a house on a trailer through the tunnel. The load is 22 feet wide and 24 feet high. Will he make it? Use a diagram to help **justify** your reasoning completely.

8-23.   Find the value of x.

   a.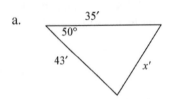

   b.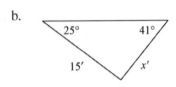

8-24.   Solve the system of equations shown at right.

$$x + y + z = 40$$
$$y = x - 5$$
$$x = 2z$$

8-25.   What is the domain of the entire graph of $h(\theta) = \sin\theta$? **Justify** your reasoning.

8-26.   Antonio's friend Jessica was also on *The Screamer* when it broke. Her seat was 65 feet above the ground. What was her seat's angle of rotation? Is there more than one possibility?

8-27.   Hilda was working on her homework. She completed the square to change $y = 3x^2 - 24x + 55$ to graphing form in order to identify the vertex of the parabola. She did the work at right and identified the vertex to be $(4, 39)$.

$$y = 3x^2 - 24x + 55$$
$$y = 3(x^2 - 8x) + 55$$
$$y = 3(x^2 - 8x + 16) + 55 - 16$$
$$y = 3(x - 4)^2 + 39$$

When she got back to class and checked her answers, she discovered that the vertex she found is incorrect, but she cannot find her mistake. Examine Hilda's work and explain to her what she did wrong. Then show her how to complete the square correctly and identify the vertex.

8-28. Consider the system of equations at right.

$$x^2 + y^2 = 25$$
$$y = x^2 + 3$$

    a. Solve the system graphically.

    b. Now solve the system algebraically. In this case, which variable is easier to solve for first? Do it. Now try to solve for the other variable first. What caused you to get stuck?

8-29. Mr. Keis wrote the following problem on the board and told his class, *"No calculators please. Simplify. You have sixty seconds!"*

$$\left(\tfrac{13^{12}}{14^{23}}\right)\left(\tfrac{27^3}{13^{11}}\right)\left(\tfrac{2^{10}}{27^4}\right)\left(\tfrac{14^{22}}{13}\right)\left(\tfrac{27}{2^9}\right)$$

Time yourself and simplify the expression. Did you meet the challenge?

8-30. Graph the system at right.

$$1 + x - y \geq 3x - 2y - 4$$
$$y < 2x^2 + 1$$

8-31. Solve each of the following equations and check your solutions.

    a. $\dfrac{1}{x} + \dfrac{5}{4x} = \dfrac{1}{x+1}$ Challenge: $\dfrac{1}{1-x} + \dfrac{1}{1+\sqrt{x}} = \dfrac{1}{1-\sqrt{x}}$

8-32. A function $W(x)$ is sketched at right.

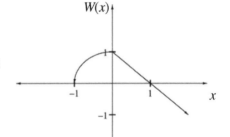

    a. Make your own copy of the graph, and then sketch the graph of the inverse of $W(x)$.

    b. Is the inverse a function? Explain.

8-33. Mary has an antique marble collection containing 40 marbles. She has five more red marbles than blue and twice as many red as green marbles. Write a system of equations and use matrices to find the number of each color of marble.

8.1.3 How are circles and sine graphs connected?

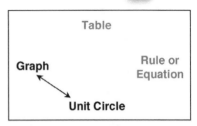

Unit Circle ↔ Graph

Throughout this course, you have used multiple representations (table, graph, equation, and situation) to solve problems, **investigate** functions, and **justify** conclusions. In Lesson 8.1.2 you found that a unit circle is one representation of a sine function. Today you will **investigate** the connections between the unit circle and the graph, as you build a deeper understanding of the sine function.

```
┌─────────────────────────────────┐
│              Table              │
│                                 │
│  Graph              Rule or     │
│     ↖               Equation    │
│        ↘                        │
│           Unit Circle           │
└─────────────────────────────────┘
```

8-34. Draw a circle on your paper. Draw a triangle that could represent René and Antonio's position on the wheel when *The Screamer* came to a sudden stop. Be sure to choose a different angle position from any of those you drew in problem 8-14.

   a. Label the triangle with its height and its angle measure (from 0°).

   b. Did any other riders have to climb the same distance to get to safety (up *or* down) as René and Antonio did? If so, draw the corresponding triangles and label them completely.

   c. What is the relationship between these triangles? Work with your team to **generalize** a method for finding all of the other corresponding angles when you are given just one angle.

8-35. In problem 8-34, you used a unit circle to find the height of a seat on *The Screamer*. Could you use your graph of $y = \sin\theta$ instead to find the height?

   a. Use the Lesson 8.1.3 Resource Page (a sine calculator) provided by your teacher to find the height of a seat that had rotated 130° from the starting platform.

   b. Are there any other seats at exactly the same height? If so, indicate them on your sine calculator.

   c. How can you use the symmetry of the graph to calculate which angles correspond to seats with the same height? Discuss this with your team and be prepared to share your **strategies** with the class.

   d. For each of the following angles, use the sine calculator from the resource page to find the height at that angle and to find another angle with the same height. Then sketch a small unit circle, draw in each pair of angles, and label the heights.

   i. 80°   *ii.* 200°   *iii.* 310°

8-36.   With your team, discuss the ways in which a unit circle and the graph of $s(\theta) = \sin\theta$ are connected. Be prepared to share your ideas with the class. Then record your ideas in a Learning Log. Use diagrams, arrows, and other math tools to help demonstrate your ideas. Label this entry "Unit Circle ↔ Graph for $s(\theta) = \sin\theta$" and label it with today's date.

8-37.   Sketch a graph of the first two cycles of $s(\theta) = \sin\theta$. Then label your graph to show the following positions of a passenger on *The Screamer*.

  a.   The passenger gets on initially.

  b.   The passenger reaches the bottom of the water pit.

  c.   The passenger is halfway between the highest point of *The Screamer* and the ground level.

8-38.   Each of the points on the graph at right represents the position of a rider on *The Screamer*. Draw a diagram of each rider's position on a unit circle and describe where the rider is.

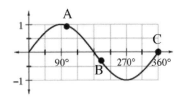

8-39.   While trying to measure the height of a tree, Julie noticed that a 3.5-foot post had a 4.25-foot shadow. If the tree's shadow is 100 feet long, how tall is the tree?

8-40.   Suppose you were to bend two whole sheets of $8\frac{1}{2}$-by-11 paper to form two cylinders (a tall, skinny one and a short, wide one). The volume of a cylinder can be calculated using the formula $V = (base\ area)(height)$ or $V = \pi r^2 h$.

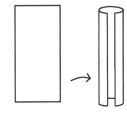

  a.   Do the two cylinders have the same volume? **Justify** your answer.

  b.   Is the result different if you start with $8\frac{1}{2}$-by-$8\frac{1}{2}$ paper?

8-41.   Find the x- and y-intercepts of the quadratic function $y = 3x^2 + 6x + 1$.

8-42.   Write the quadratic function in problem 8-41 in graphing form and sketch its graph.

8-43.   Solve $|x+5| = |x| - 5$ by graphing. Express your solution algebraically.

8-44.   Solve $\log_2 x = 2^x$ using any method.

8-45.   Maria Elena is collecting college pennants. She has five fewer pennants from Washington campuses than from California campuses and twice as many pennants from California campuses as from Pennsylvania campuses. She has 40 pennants in her collection. Write a system of equations to find the number of Pennants from each state.

8.1.4 How can I graph cosine?

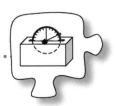

Graphing and Interpreting the Cosine Function

In this lesson, you will use your knowledge of right triangles again—this time to develop your understanding of another cyclic function.

8-46.   Work with your team to find the coordinates of point *P* on the unit circle shown at right. Is there more than one way to find point *P*? Be prepared to share your **strategies** with the class.

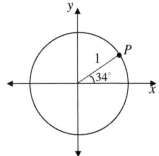

8-47.

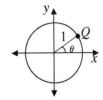

Now **generalize** what you found in problem 8-46 to write the coordinates of point *Q* on the unit circle shown at left.

8-48.   What can a sine value tell you about a point on a circle? What about a cosine value?

8-49.   If you know the sine of an angle in a unit circle, can you find its cosine? How? Work with your team to find a **strategy** and be prepared to share it with the class.

8-50.   Obtain a copy of the Lesson 8.1.4A Resource Page from your teacher. To graph the cosine function you will follow the same process as you did for the graph of the sine function in problem 8-14, but use the horizontal distance (or base of the triangle) instead of the height.

a.   Label the length of the base of each triangle in the unit circle. Plot these lengths at their angle location on the coordinate system to the right of the circle. You will be plotting points in the form (angle in degrees, base).

b.   Draw five new triangles that are congruent to the first five, but that are located in the second quadrant. Label the angle measure (from 0°) and the base for each triangle. Add five new corresponding points to the graph.

c.   Continue this process by drawing triangles in the third and fourth quadrants. You should have a total of twenty triangles drawn and twenty points plotted. Then find the four points where the circle crosses the axes and label them with both their angle measures and their horizontal distances from the origin. Add points for these to the graph on the right as well. Finally, sketch a smooth curve through the points.

d.   Compare this graph to the sine graph you got from graphing heights in problem 8-14. How are the two graphs similar? How are they different?

8-51.   Remember the scary Ferris wheel, *The Screamer*? LaRasha does! She was riding *The Screamer*, sitting 27 horizontal feet away from the central support pole, when the ride stopped. What was her seat's angle of rotation? Is there more than one possibility? **Justify** your answer using as many representations as you can.

8-52.   UNIT CIRCLE ↔ GRAPH

In problem 8-51, did you use a graph of $y = \cos\theta$ to find lengths of bases of triangles?

a.   Use the Lesson 8.1.4B Resource Page (a cosine-calculator graph) provided by your teacher to find the length of the base of a triangle formed by a seat on *The Screamer* that had rotated 130° from the starting platform.

b.   Are there any other triangles with the same base? If so, mark their corresponding points on your cosine calculator.

c.   How can you use the symmetry of the cosine-calculator graph to calculate the angle location of seats on *The Screamer* that have the same base? Is your method different than the one you used to find the heights?

8-53.   Find the coordinates of points *P* and *Q* on the unit circle at right.

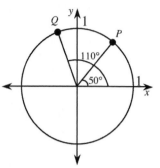

8-54.   The measure of ∠*ROS* in △*ROS* below is 60°.

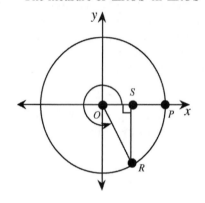

a.   The curved arrow represents the rotation of $\overline{OR}$, beginning from the positive *x*-axis. Through how many degrees has $\overline{OR}$ rotated?

b.   If $OR = 1$, what are the *exact* length of *OS* and *SR*?

c.   What are the *exact* coordinates of point *R*?

8-55.   What angle in the first quadrant could you reference to help you find the sine and cosine of each of the following angles?

a.   330°   b.   120°   c.   113°   d.   203°

8-56.   At right is a sequence of doodles and some numbers to go with them.

180	120	90	72

a.   Draw the next two doodles and state the numbers to go with them.

b.   What number would go with the 99th doodle? With the nth doodle?

8-57.   Solve $\frac{1}{1-\sqrt{x}} = 1 + \frac{\sqrt{x}}{1-\sqrt{x}}$.

8-58.   Solve $(\frac{1}{8})^{(2x-3)} = (\frac{1}{2})^{(x+2)}$.

8-59.   Sketch a graph of each equation below.

   a. $y = -2(x-2)^2 + 3$ b. $y = (x-1)^3 + 3$

8-60.   Solve $3^x + 5 = x^2 - 5$ using any method.

8-61.   Rip-Off Rentals charges $25 per day plus 50¢ per mile to rent a mid-sized car. Your teacher will rent you his or her family sedan and charge you only 3¢ if you drive one mile, 6¢ if you drive two miles, 12¢ if you drive three, 24¢ for four, and so on.

   a.   Write a rule that will give you the cost to rent each car.

   b.   If you plan to rent the car for a two-day road trip, which is the better deal if you drive 10 miles? 20 miles? 100 miles?

8-62.   Refer back to your solutions from problems 8-24, 8-33, and 8-45. Explain how these problems are related.

8-63.   Shinna was riding *The Screamer* when it broke down. Her seat was 53 horizontal feet from the central support pole. What was her seat's angle of rotation? How can you tell?

8-64.   Sketch a unit circle. In your circle, sketch in an angle that has:

   a.   A positive cosine and a negative sine.

   b.   A sine of −1.

   c.   A negative cosine and a negative sine.

   d.   A cosine of about −0.9 and a sine of about 0.4.

   e.   Could an angle have a sine equal to 0.9 and cosine equal to 0.8? Give an angle or explain why not.

8-65.   A 70° angle is drawn for you in the unit circle at right.

   a.   Approximate the coordinates of point *R*.

   b.   How could you represent the *exact* coordinates of point *R*?

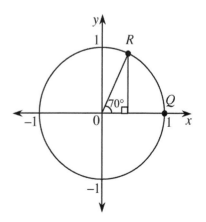

8-66. Daniel sketched the graphs at right for $y = \sin\theta$ and $y = \cos\theta$.

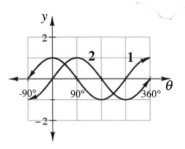

Unfortunately, he forgot to label the graphs, and now he cannot remember which graph goes with which equation. Explain to Daniel how he can tell (and remember!) which graph is $y = \sin\theta$ and which is $y = \cos\theta$.

8-67. Consider the system of equations $y = \cos x$ and $y = -1$.

    a.   Is it possible to solve this system by substitution? By the Elimination Method? By graphing?

    b.   List at least five possible solutions.

    c.   Consider the list of solutions you wrote in part (b) as a sequence and write a rule to represent *all* possible solutions.

8-68. This problem is a checkpoint for writing and solving exponential equations.

When rabbits were first brought to Australia, they had no natural enemies. There were about 80,000 rabbits in 1866. Two years later, in 1868, the population had grown to over 2,400,000!

    a.   Why would an exponential equation be a better model for this situation than a linear one? Would a sine function be better or worse? Why?

    b.   Write an exponential equation for the number of rabbits t years after 1866.

    c.   How many rabbits do you predict would have been present in 1871?

    d.   According to your model, in what year was the first pair of rabbits introduced into Australia? Is this reasonable?

    e.   Actually, 24 rabbits were introduced in 1859, so the model is not perfect, but is close. Is your exponential model useful for predicting how many rabbits there are now? Explain.

    f.   Check your answers to parts (a) through (e) by referring to the Checkpoint 15 materials at the back of your book.

If you needed help to complete any part of this problem, then you need more practice writing and solving exponential equations to solve problems. Review the Checkpoint 15 materials and try the practice problems. Also, consider getting help outside of class time. From this point on, you will be expected to write and solve exponential equations to solve problems quickly and accurately.

8-69.   Solve each equation.

   a. $\dfrac{3}{x+1} = \dfrac{4}{x}$

   b. $\dfrac{3}{x+1} + \dfrac{4}{x} = 2$

   c. $\dfrac{3}{x+2} + 5 = \dfrac{3}{x+2}$

   d.   Explain why part (c) has no solution.

8-70.   Write the equation of any line parallel to $3x - y = 2$. Then write the equation of a parabola that intersects your line but does *not* intersect the graph of $3x - y = 0$.

8-71.   A $5' \times 4' \times 3'$ box is made for the purpose of storage. What is the longest pole that can fit inside the box?

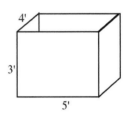

8-72.   While working on their homework on sequences, Davis was suddenly stumped!

   "This problem doesn't make sense!" he exclaimed. Tess was working on her homework as well.

   "What's the problem?" she asked.

   "This problem is about a SEQUENCE, $t(n) = 9n - 2$, but it is asking whether or not it is a function. How can a sequence be a function?"

   "Well of course a sequence is a function!" said Tess.

   Who is right? Should Davis be confused, or is Tess correct? Explain completely.

8.1.5 How else can I measure angles?

Defining a Radian

Whose idea was it to measure angles in degrees? And why are there 360° in a full turn? This decision actually dates back almost 4000 years! Degrees were created by the Babylonians, an ancient people who lived in the region that is now Iraq. The Babylonians also based their number system, called a sexigesimal system, on sixty.

Although you are familiar with measuring angles in degrees, this is not the only way to measure angles, nor is it necessarily the most useful. Today you will learn a different unit for measuring angles called a **radian**. Using radians instead of degrees is actually the standard across mathematics! When you take calculus, you will learn why radians are used in math more often than degrees.

8-73.   What word are you reminded of when you hear the word **radian**? Discuss this with your team and make a conjecture about how this might relate to a way to measure angles. Be prepared to share your ideas with the class.

8-74.   HOW TO MAKE A RADIAN

Imagine wrapping the radius of a circle around the circle. The angle formed at the center of the circle that corresponds to the arc that is one radius long has a measure of exactly one **radian**.

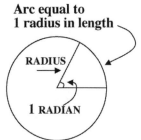

Arc equal to 1 radius in length

RADIUS

1 RADIAN

Your teacher will provide each member of your team with a differently sized circular object and some scissors.

a.   Trace your circular object onto a sheet of paper and carefully cut out the circle. Fold the paper circle in half and then in half again so that it is in the shape of a quarter circle, as in the diagram at right. How can you see the radius of your circular object in this new folded shape?

b.   Place your circular object onto another sheet of paper and trace it again, only this time leave the circular object in place. Roll (or wrap) a straight edge of your folded circle around your circular object and mark one radius length on the traced circle. Then mark another radius length that begins where the first one ended. Continue marking radius lengths until you have gone around the entire circle.

c.   Remove the circular object from your paper. On your traced circle, connect each radius mark to the center, creating central angles. Each angle you see, formed by an arc with a length of one radius, measures one **radian**. Label each of the radius lengths and each angle that measures one full **radian**. Write a short description of how you constructed an angle with measure one radian.

8-75.   Assume the radius of a circle is one unit.

    a.   What is the area of the circle? What is its circumference?

    b.   How many radii would it take to wrap completely around the circle? Express your answer as a decimal approximation *and* as an exact value.

    c.   Does the size of the circle matter? That is, does the number of radii it takes to wrap around the circle change as the radius of the circle gets larger or smaller? Why does this make sense?

    d.   Exactly how many radians are in 360°? In 90°?

    e.   How is a radian related to a radius? Explain your understanding of this relationship in your Learning Log. Use diagrams to support your explanation. Title this entry "Radians" and label it with today's date.

8-76.   Parts (a) through (g) below describe angles. Draw each angle on its own unit circle.

    a.   1 degree   b.   1 radian   c. π radians   d. $\frac{\pi}{2}$ radians

    e. $\frac{\pi}{4}$ radians   f. $\frac{\pi}{3}$ radians   g. $\frac{\pi}{6}$ radians

8-77.   Find your sine-calculator from Lesson 8.1.3. Use your new understanding of radians to convert the units on the θ axis from degrees to radians. Be prepared to share your conversion **strategies** with the class.

METHODS AND MEANINGS

Radians

A **radian** is defined as an angular measure such that an arc length of one radius on a circle of radius one produces an angle with measure one radian. It can also be thought of as the ratio of an arc length to the radius of the corresponding circle.

The circumference of a complete circle is $2\pi r$ units, so the corresponding radian measure is $\frac{2\pi r}{r} = 2\pi$. Thus, there are 2π radians in a complete circle.

Arc equal to
1 radius in length

RADIUS

1 RADIAN

8-78.   Your scientific or graphing calculator can function in both degrees and radians. See if you can figure out how to put your calculator in radian mode and then how to switch it back to degree mode. On most scientific calculators, a small "DEG" or "RAD" shows on the screen to let you know which mode you are in.

    a.   With your calculator in degree mode, find $\sin 60°$ and record your answer. Then switch to radian mode and find $\sin \frac{\pi}{3}$. Did you get the same answer? Explain why your answers should be the same or different.

    b.   Find $\sin \frac{\pi}{4}$. Which angles, measured in degrees, would have the same sine as $\sin \frac{\pi}{4}$?

8-79.   Calculate each of the following values. Express your answers exactly and as decimal approximations.

    a. $\sin(\frac{\pi}{4})$ b. $\sin(\frac{2\pi}{3})$

8-80.   Colleen and Jolleen both used their calculators to find $\sin 30°$. Colleen got $\sin 30° = -0.9880316241$, but Jolleen got $\sin 30° = 0.5$. Is one of their calculators broken, or is something else going on? Why did they get different answers?

8-81.   Recall the strategies developed in class for converting degrees to radians. How could you reverse that? Convert each of the following angle measures. Be sure to show all of your work.

    a. π radians to degrees   b. 3π radians to degrees

    c.   30 degrees to radians   d. $\frac{\pi}{4}$ radians to degrees

    e.   225 degrees to radians   f. $\frac{3\pi}{2}$ radians to degrees

8-82.   Greg was working on his homework. He completed the square to change $y = 2x^2 - 6x + 2$ to graphing form and identify the vertex of the parabola. He did the work at right and identified the vertex to be $(\frac{3}{2}, -\frac{1}{4})$. When he got back to class and checked his answers, he discovered that his vertex was wrong, but he cannot find his mistake. Examine Greg's work and explain to him where the mistake occured. Then show him how to correct the mistake and state the vertex.

$$y = 2x^2 - 6x + 2$$
$$y = 2(x^2 - 3x) + 2$$
$$y = 2(x^2 - 3x + \tfrac{9}{4}) + 2 - \tfrac{9}{4}$$
$$y = 2(x - \tfrac{3}{2})^2 - \tfrac{1}{4}$$

8-83.   Change each of the following equations to graphing form and then, without graphing, identify the vertex and axis of symmetry for each.

   a. $y = 3x^2 - 18x + 26$ b. $y = 3x^2 - 4x - 11$

8-84.   Solve each of the following equations for x.

   a. $171 = 3(5^x)$ b. $171y = 3(x^5)$

8-85.   Sketch a graph of $x^2 + y^2 = 100$.

   a.   Is it a function?

   b.   What are its domain and range?

   c.   Draw a central angle that measures $\frac{2\pi}{3}$ radians. If you remove this wedge of the circle, how much area remains?

8-86.   Find the equation for the inverse of the function $f(x) = 2\sqrt{\frac{(x-3)}{4}} + 1$. Sketch the graph of both the original and the inverse.

8.1.6 What do I know about a unit circle?

Building a Unit Circle

In this lesson, you will further develop your understanding of the unit circle and how useful it can be. By the end of the lesson, you should be able to answer the questions below.

> What can the unit circle help me understand about an angle?

> What does my information about angles in the first quadrant tell me about angles in other quadrants?

8-87.   There are some angles for which you know the *exact values* of sine and cosine. In other words, you can find the exact sine and cosine without using a calculator. Work with your team to find as many such angles (expressed in radians) as you can.

8-88.   Now you will build a unit circle. Obtain the Lesson 8.1.6 Resource Page from your teacher. There are points shown at $\frac{\pi}{12}, \frac{\pi}{6}, \frac{\pi}{4}, \frac{\pi}{3}, \frac{5\pi}{12}, \frac{7\pi}{12}, \frac{2\pi}{3}, \frac{3\pi}{4}, \frac{5\pi}{6}$, and $\frac{11\pi}{12}$ units along the circle, starting from the positive *x*-axis.

   a.   Find and label the exact coordinates, in (x, y) form, for three of the points shown in the *first quadrant*.

   b.   Mark *all* other points in the unit circle for which you can find *exact* coordinates. Not all of them are shown. Label each of these points with its angle of rotation (in radians) and its coordinates.

   c.   If you have not done so already, label each angle with its corresponding radian measure.

8-89.   Draw a new unit circle, label a point that corresponds to a rotation of $\frac{\pi}{12}$, and put your calculator in radian mode.

   a.   What are the coordinates of this point, correct to two decimal places?

   b.   Use the information you found in part (a) to determine each of the following values: (Hint: Drawing each angle on the unit circle will be very helpful.)

   i. $\sin(-\frac{\pi}{12})$ *ii.* $\cos\frac{13\pi}{12}$ *iii.*   Challenge: $\cos\frac{7\pi}{12}$

8-90.   For angle α in the first quadrant, $\cos\alpha = \frac{8}{17}$. Use that information to find each of the following values without using a calculator. Be prepared to share your **strategies** with the class.

   a. $\sin\alpha$

   b. $\sin(\pi + \alpha)$

   c. $\cos(2\pi - \alpha)$

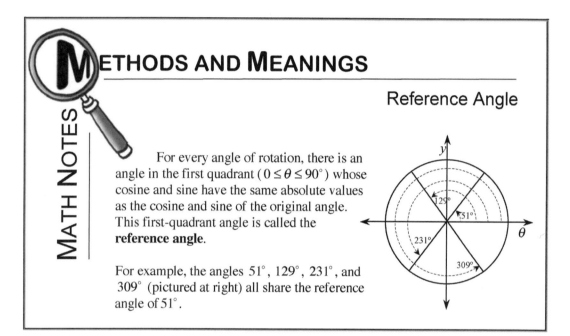

MᴇTHODS AND Mᴇᴀɴɪɴɢs

MATH NOTES

Reference Angle

For every angle of rotation, there is an angle in the first quadrant ($0 \le \theta \le 90°$) whose cosine and sine have the same absolute values as the cosine and sine of the original angle. This first-quadrant angle is called the **reference angle**.

For example, the angles $51°$, $129°$, $231°$, and $309°$ (pictured at right) all share the reference angle of $51°$.

8-91.   Calculate the value of each expression below. Each measure is given in radians.

   a. $\sin(4)$ b. $\sin(\frac{4\pi}{3})$

8-92.   Find the exact values of the angles that are solutions to the equation $\sin(\theta) = 0.5$. Express your solutions in radians.

8-93.   You have seen that you can calculate values of the sine function using right triangles formed by a radius of the unit circle. Values of θ that result in $30° - 60° - 90°$ or $45° - 45° - 90°$ triangles are used frequently on exercises and tests because their sines and cosines can be found exactly, without using a calculator. You should learn to recognize these values quickly and easily. The same is true for values of $\cos\theta$ and $\sin\theta$ that correspond to the x- and y-intercepts of the unit circle.

The central angles that correspond to these "special" values of x are $30°$, $45°$, $60°$, $90°$, $120°$, $135°$, $150°$, $180°$, $210°$, $225°$, $240°$, $270°$, $300°$, $315°$, and $330°$. What these angles have in common is that they are all multiples of $30°$ or $45°$, and some of them are also multiples of $60°$ or $90°$.

Copy and complete a table like the one below for all special angles between $0°$ and $360°$.

Degrees	0	30	45	60	90	120		
Radians	0	$\frac{\pi}{6}$						

8-94.   Draw a picture of an angle that measures 6 radians.

a.   Approximately how many degrees is this?

b.   Using only your picture, estimate the sine of 6 radians.

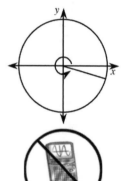

8-95.   Evaluate each expression without using a calculator or changing the form of the expression.

a. $\log(10)$

b. $\log(\sqrt{10})$

c. $\log(0)$

d. $10^{(2/3)\log(27)}$

8-96.   What interest rate (compounded annually) would you need to earn in order to double your investment in 15 years?

8-97.   Phana's garden is 2 meters wide and 5 meters long. She puts a walkway of uniform width around her garden. If the area of the walkway is 30 square meters, what are the outer dimensions of the walkway? Drawing a diagram will help you solve this problem.

8-98.   Solve each of the following equations.

a. $2(x-1)^2 = 18$

b. $2^x + 3 = 10$

8.1.7 What is tangent?

The Tangent Function

In the past several lessons, you have used your understanding of the sine and cosine ratios to develop and interpret the functions $s(\theta) = \sin\theta$ and $c(\theta) = \cos\theta$. In this lesson, you will expand your understanding by exploring the tangent ratio and graphing the function $t(\theta) = \tan\theta$.

8-99.   Jamal was working on his homework when he had a brilliant realization. He was drawing a triangle in a unit circle to estimate the sine of $\frac{\pi}{10}$, when he realized that this triangle is the same kind of triangle that he draws when he wants to find the slope of a line.

a.   How could you express the slope of the radius in terms of sine and cosine?

b.   Is there any other way you can use a trigonometric ratio to represent the slope? Discuss this with your team.

8-100.   THE TANGENT FUNCTION

Obtain the Lesson 8.1.7 Resource Page from your teacher. Use your knowledge of sine, cosine, and tangent to create a graph of the tangent function. Conduct a full **investigation** of the tangent function. Be prepared to share summary statements with the class.

Discussion Points

Does every angle have a tangent value?

How is the tangent graph similar to or different from the sine and cosine graphs?

Why does the tangent graph have asymptotes?

Further Guidance

8-101.   For each triangle in the first quadrant of the unit circle on your resource page, label the sine and cosine.

a.   Use your knowledge of tangent to complete a table like the one below. Start with the exact values for the sine and cosine.

θ	$\sin\theta$	$\cos\theta$	$\tan\theta$ (exact)	$\tan\theta$ (approximate to nearest 0.01)
$\frac{\pi}{6}$	$\frac{1}{2}$	$\frac{\sqrt{3}}{2}$	$\frac{1}{\sqrt{3}}$	
$\frac{\pi}{4}$	$\frac{\sqrt{2}}{2}$	$\frac{\sqrt{2}}{2}$		
$\frac{\pi}{3}$	$\frac{\sqrt{3}}{2}$	$\frac{1}{2}$		

b.   Plot the tangent values on the graph to the right of the unit circle.

c.   Draw five new triangles that are congruent to the first five, but that are located in the second quadrant. Add values for these new angles to your table and your graph.

d.   Continue this process by drawing triangles in the third and fourth quadrants. You should have a total of twenty triangles drawn and twenty angle values accounted for on your graph. If you have not done so already, add data to your table and points to your graph corresponding to the intercepts of the unit circle.

8-102.   **Investigate** the tangent graph by analyzing the following questions:

a.   Describe the domain and range of the tangent function.

b.   Describe any special points or asymptotes.

c.   Does it have symmetry? Describe any symmetry you see in the graph.

d.   How is the graph of $t(\theta) = \tan\theta$ different from the graphs of $s(\theta) = \sin\theta$ and $c(\theta) = \cos\theta$?

―――――   *Further Guidance*   ═══════
section ends here.

8-103.   Draw a new unit circle and label a point that corresponds to a rotation of $\frac{\pi}{6}$ radians.

a.   What are the coordinates of this point? Use exact values.

b.   Use this information to find each of the following values without a calculator. (Hint: Drawing each angle on the unit circle will be very helpful.)

   i: $\tan(\frac{7\pi}{6})$ *ii:* $\cos(\frac{13\pi}{6})$ *iii:* $\tan(\frac{2\pi}{3})$

METHODS AND MEANINGS

Sine, Cosine, and Tangent

MATH NOTES

For any real number θ, the **sine of θ**, denoted $\sin \theta$, is the y-coordinate of the point on the unit circle reached by a rotation of θ radians from **standard position** (counter-clockwise starting from the positive x-axis).

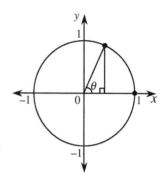

The **cosine of θ**, denoted $\cos \theta$, is the x-coordinate of the point on the unit circle reached by a rotation of θ radians from standard position.

The **tangent of θ**, denoted by $\tan \theta$, is the slope of the terminal ray of an angle (the radius) formed by a rotation of θ radians in standard position.

8-104. What central angle, measured in degrees, corresponds to a distance around the unit circle of $\frac{7\pi}{3}$?

    a. What other angles will take you to the same point on the circle?

    b. Make a sketch of the unit circle showing the resulting right triangle.

    c. Find $\sin(\frac{7\pi}{3})$, $\cos(\frac{7\pi}{3})$, and $\tan(\frac{7\pi}{3})$ exactly.

8-105. Evaluate each of the following trig expressions without using a calculator.

    a. $\sin(180°)$ b. $\sin(360°)$ c. $\sin(-90°)$

    d. $\sin(510°)$ e. $\cos(90°)$ f. $\tan(-90°)$

8-106. How do you convert from degrees to radians and from radians to degrees? Explain and **justify** your method completely.

Chapter 8: Trigonometric Functions

407

8-107.   Convert each of the following angle measures. Give exact answers

      a. $\frac{7\pi}{6}$ radians to degrees   b. $\frac{5\pi}{3}$ radians to degrees

      c.   45 degrees to radians   d. $100°$ to radians

      e. $810°$ to radians   f. $\frac{7\pi}{2}$ radians to degrees

8-108.   Simplify each of the following expressions, leaving only positive exponents in your answer.

      a. $(x^3 y^{-2})^{-4}$ b. $-3x^2(6xy - 2x^3 y^2 z)$

8-109.   Sketch a graph of $f(x) = \frac{1}{2}(x+1)^3$. Then sketch its inverse and write the equation of the inverse.

8-110.   Rewrite $f(x) = 2x^2 - 16x + 34$ in graphing form.

8-111.   The temperature of a pizza after it has been delivered depends on how long it has been sitting on the family-room table.

      a.   Sketch a reasonable graph of this situation. Be sure to label the axes.

      b.   Should your graph have an asymptote? Why or why not?

8-112.   Solve for x: $\frac{1}{ax} + \frac{1}{b} = \frac{1}{x}$

8.2.1 How can I transform a sine graph?

Transformations of $y = \sin x$

In Chapter 4, you developed expertise in **investigating** functions and transforming parent graphs. In this section, you will **investigate** families of cyclic functions and their transformations. By the end of this section, you will be able to graph any sine or cosine equation and write the equation of any sine or cosine graph.

8-113.   As you have seen with many functions in this and other courses, x is generally used to represent an input and y is used to represent the corresponding output. By this convention, sinusoidal functions should be written $y = \sin x$, $y = \cos x$, and $y = \tan x$. But beware! Something funny is happening.

With your team, examine the unit circle and the three graphs below. What do x and y represent in the unit circle? What do they represent in each of the graphs? Discuss this with your team and be prepared to share your ideas with the class.

a.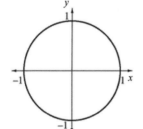

b.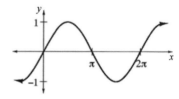

c.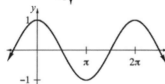

d.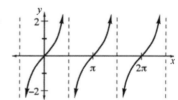

8-114.   With your team, you will apply your knowledge about transforming graphs of functions to transform the graphs of $y = \sin x$ and $y = \cos x$ and find their general equations.

Your task: As a team, **investigate** $y = \sin x$ and $y = \cos x$ completely. You should make graphs, find the domain and range, and label any important points or asymptotes. Then make a sketch and write an equation to demonstrate each transformation of the sine or cosine function you can find. Finally, find a general equation for a sine and a cosine function. Be prepared to share your summary statements with the class.

Discussion Points

What can we change in a cyclic graph?

Which points are important to label?

How can we apply the transformations we use with other functions?

Are there any new transformations that are special to the sine function?

Further Guidance

8-115.   Sketch a graph of at least one cycle of $y = \sin x$. Label the intercepts. Then work with your team to complete parts (a) through (c) below.

a.   Write an equation for each part below and sketch a graph of a function that has a parent graph of $y = \sin x$, but is:

   i. Shifted 3 units up.   *ii.* Reflected across the *x*-axis.

   iii. Shifted 2 units to the right.   *iv.* Vertically stretched.

i.
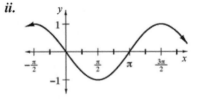

ii.

iii.
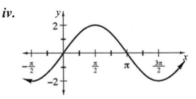

iv.

b.   Which points are most important to label in a periodic function? Why?

c.   Write a general equation for the family of functions with a parent graph of $y = \sin x$.

━━━━━━━━   *Further Guidance section ends here.*   ━━━━━━━━

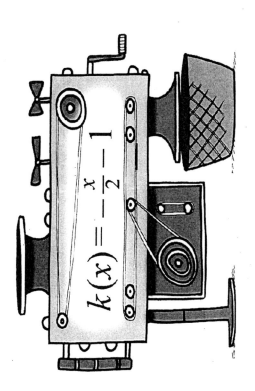

8-116.   Imagine the graph $y = \sin(x)$ shifted up one unit.

   a.   Sketch what it would look like.

   b.   What do you have to change in the equation $y = \sin x$ to move the graph *up* one unit? Write the new equation.

   c.   What are the intercepts of your new equation? Label them with their coordinates on the graph.

   d.   When you listed intercepts in part (c), did you list more than one *x*-intercept? Should you have?

8-117.   The graph at right was made by shifting the first cycle of $y = \sin x$ to the left.

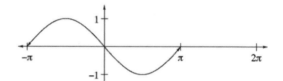

   a.   How many units to the left was it shifted?

   b.   Figure out how to change the equation of $y = \sin x$ so that the graph of the new equation will look like the one in part (a). If you do not have a graphing calculator at home, sketch the graph and check your answer when you get to class.

8-118.   Which of the situations below (if any) is best modeled by a cyclic function? Explain your reasoning.

   a.   The number of students in each year's graduating class.

   b.   Your hunger level throughout the day.

   c.   The high-tide level at a point along the coast.

8-119.   The CPM Amusement Park has decided to imitate *The Screamer* but wants to make it even better. Their ride will consist of a circular track with a radius of 100 feet, and the center of the circle will be 50 feet under ground. Passengers will board at the highest point, so they will begin with a blood-curdling drop. Write a function that relates the angle traveled *from the starting point* to the height of the rider above or below the ground.

8-120.   Should $y = \sin x$ and $y = \cos x$ both be parent graphs, or is one the parent of the other? Give reasons for your decision.

8-121.   Evaluate each of the following expressions exactly.

   a. $\tan\frac{2\pi}{3}$ b. $\tan\frac{7\pi}{6}$

8-122.   David Longshot is known for his long golf drives. Today he hit the ball 250 yards. He estimated that the ball reached a maximum height of 15 yards. Find a quadratic equation that would model the path of the golf ball.

8.2.2 What is missing?

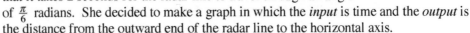

One More Parameter for a Cyclic Function

In this lesson, you will study one more transformation that is unique to cyclic functions. You will also extend your understanding of these functions to include those with input values that do not correspond to angles.

8-123.   Does the general equation $y = a\sin(x - h) + k$ allow for every possible transformation of the graph of $y = \sin x$? Are there any transformations possible *other than* the ones produced by varying values of *a*, *h*, and *k*? Look back at the graphs you made for the swinging bag of blood in the first lesson of this chapter. Discuss this with your team and be prepared to share your conjectures with the class.

8-124.   THE RADAR SCREEN

Brianna is an air traffic controller. Every day she watches the radar line (like a radius of a circle) go around her screen time after time. On one particularly slow travel day, Brianna noticed that it takes 2 seconds for the radar line to travel through an angle of $\frac{\pi}{6}$ radians. She decided to make a graph in which the *input* is time and the *output* is the distance from the outward end of the radar line to the horizontal axis.

Your task: Following the input and output specifications above, make a table and graph for Brianna's radar.

Discussion Points

How can we calculate the outputs?

How is this graph different from other similar graphs we have made?

How long does it take to complete one full cycle on the radar screen?
How can we see that on the graph?

8-125.   Now that you have seen that it is possible to have a sine graph with a cycle length that is not 2π, work with your team to make conjectures about how you could change your general equation to allow for this new transformation.

    a.   In the general equation $y = a\sin(x - h) + k$, the quantities a, h, and k are called **parameters**. Where could a new parameter fit into the equation?

    b.   Use your graphing calculator to test the result of putting this new parameter into your general equation. Once you have found the place for the new parameter, **investigate** how it works. What happens when it gets larger? What happens when it gets smaller?

    c.   Write a general equation for a sine function that includes the new parameter you discovered.

8-126.   Which of the following have a period of 2π? Which do not? How can you tell? If the period is not 2π, what is it?

    a.

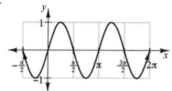

    b.   A pendulum takes 3 seconds to complete one cycle.

    c. $y = \sin\theta$

    d.   A radar line takes 1 second to travel through 1 radian.

8-127. Find an equation for each graph below.

a.

b.

c.

d.

8-128. Claudia graphed $y = \cos\theta$ and $y = \cos(\theta + 360°)$ on the same set of axes. She did not see any difference in their graphs at all. Why not?

8-129. This is a checkpoint for solving equations and inequalities involving absolute value.

Solve each absolute value equation or inequality below.

a. $2|2x+3|=10$

b. $|3x-5|>13$

c. $-|x+3|<10$

d.   Check your answers by referring to the Checkpoint 16 materials located at the back of your book.

If you needed help to solve these equations and inequalities correctly, then you need more practice solving equations and inequalities with absolute value. Review the Checkpoint 16 materials and try the practice problems. Also, consider getting help outside of class time. From this point on, you will be expected to solve equations and inequalities such as these quickly and accurately.

8-130. Find the x- and y-intercepts of the graphs of each of the following equations.

a. $y=2x^3-10x^2-x$

b. $y+2=\log_3(x-1)$

8-131. The average cost of movie tickets is \$9.50. If the cost is increasing 4% per year, in how many years will the cost double?

8-132. Change each equation to graphing form. For each equation, find the domain and range and determine if it is a function.

a. $y=-2x^2-x+13$

b. $y=-3x^2-6x+12$

8-133. Too Tall Thomas has put Rodney's book bag on the snack-shack roof. Rodney goes to borrow a ladder from the school custodian. The tallest ladder available is 10 feet long and the roof is 9 feet from the ground. Rodney places the ladder's tip at the edge of the roof. The ladder is unsafe if the angle it makes with the ground is more than 60°. Is this a safe situation? **Justify** your conclusion.

8-134. Deniz's computer is infected with a virus that will erase information from her hard drive. It will erase information slowly at first, but as time goes on, the rate at which information is erased will increase. In t minutes after the virus starts erasing information, $5,000,000(\frac{1}{2})^t$ bytes of information remain on the hard drive.

a.   Before the virus starts erasing, how many bytes of information are on Deniz's hard drive?

b.   After how many minutes will there be 1000 bytes of information left on the drive?

c.   When will the hard drive be completely erased?

8-135.   Graph $f(x) = |x - 6| - 4$.

    a.   Explain how you can graph this without making an $x \rightarrow y$ table, but using parent graphs.

    b.   Graph $g(x) = \|x - 6| - 4\|$. Explain how you can graph $g(x)$ without making an $x \rightarrow y$ table by using your earlier graph.

8-136.   Find the value of x in each triangle.

    a.
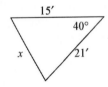

    b.

8.2.3 What is the period of a function?

Period of a Cyclic Function

In Lesson 8.2.2, you found a place for a new parameter in the general form of a trigonometric equation and discovered that it must have something to do with the period. By the end of this lesson, you will have the tools you need to find the equation for any sine or cosine graph and will be able to graph any sine or cosine equation. In other words, you will learn the equation $\leftrightarrow$ graph connection. The following questions can help your team stay focused on the purpose of this lesson.

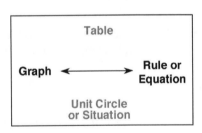

How can we write the equation for any sine or cosine graph?

How can we graph any sine or cosine function?

8-137.   Find the period for each of the following situations:

    a.   The input is the angle θ in the unit circle, and the output is the cosine of θ.

    b.   The input is time, and the output is the average daily temperature in New York.

    c.   The input is the distance Nurse Nina has traveled along the hallway, and the output is the distance of bloody drips from the center-line of the hallway.

8-138. Put your graphing calculator in radian mode. Set the domain and range of the viewing window so that you would see just one complete cycle of $y = \sin x$. What is the domain for one cycle? Range?

a. Graph $y = \sin x$, $y = \sin(0.5x)$, $y = \sin(2x)$, $y = \sin(3x)$, and $y = \sin(5x)$. Make a sketch and answer the following questions for each equation.

    i. How many cycles of each graph appear on the screen?

    ii. What is the amplitude (height) of each graph?

    iii. What is the period of each graph?

    iv. Is each equation a function?

b. Make a conjecture about the graph of $y = \sin(bx)$ with respect to each of the questions (*i*), (*ii*), (*iii*), and (*iv*) above. If you cannot make a conjecture yet, try more examples.

c. Create at least three of your own examples to check your conjectures. Be sure to include sketches of your graphs.

d. What is the relationship between the period of a sine graph and the value of b in its equation?

8-139. Take the graph you made by swinging a pendulum in Lesson 8.1.1. Decide where to draw x- and y-axes and find the equation of your graph. Is there more than one possible equation? Be prepared to share your **strategies** with the class.

8-140. *Without* using a graphing calculator, describe each of the following functions by stating the amplitude, period, and vertical and horizontal shifts. Then sketch the graph of each function. *After* you have completed each graph, check your sketch with the graphing calculator and correct and explain any errors.

a. $y = \sin 2(x - \frac{\pi}{6})$ b. $y = 3 + \sin(\frac{1}{3}x)$

c. $y = 3\sin(4x)$ d. $y = \sin\frac{1}{2}(x + 1)$

e. $y = -\sin 3(x - \frac{\pi}{3})$ f. $y = -1 + \sin(2x - \frac{\pi}{2})$

8-141.   Farah and Thu were working on writing the
          equation of a sine function for the graph at right.
          They figured out that the amplitude is 3, the
          horizontal shift is $\frac{\pi}{4}$ and the vertical shift is –2.
          They can see that the period is π, but they disagree
          on the equation. Farah has written
          $f(x) = 3\sin 2(x - \frac{\pi}{4}) - 2$ and Thu has written
          $f(x) = 3\sin(2x - \frac{\pi}{4}) - 2$.

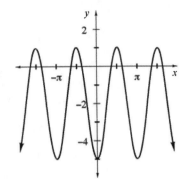

          a.   Whose equation is correct? How can you be
                sure?

          b.   Graph the incorrect equation and explain how it is different from the original
                graph.

8-142.   Look back at the general equation you wrote for the family of sine functions in
          problem 8-114. Now that you have figured out how period affects the equation, work
          with your team to add a new parameter (call it b) that allows your general equation to
          account for any transformation of the sine function, including changes in the length of
          each cycle. Be prepared to share your general equation with the class.

8-143.   Based on your explorations in class, complete parts (a) through (c) below.

          a.   Describe what the graph of $y = 3\sin(\frac{1}{2}x)$ will look like compared to the graph
                of $y = \sin x$.

          b.   Sketch both graphs on the same set of axes.

          c.   Explain the similarities and differences between the two graphs.

8-144.   What is the period of $y = \sin(2\pi x)$? How do you know?

8-145.   Sketch the graph of each equation below.

a. $y = \sin(2\pi x)$

b. $y = 3\sin(\pi x)$

c. $y = 2\sin(2\pi x) + 1$

8-146.   Match each equation with the appropriate graph. Do this without using a graphing calculator.

a. $y = \sin(x + \frac{\pi}{2})$

b. $y = \sin(2x)$

c. $y = 2\sin(\frac{x}{2})$

d. $y = \sin(x) - 3$

e. $y = -\sin[2(x - \frac{\pi}{8})]$

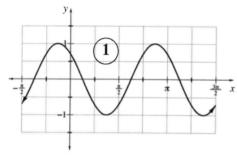
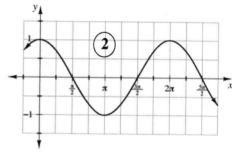
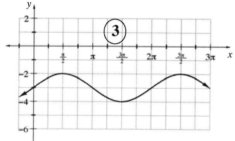
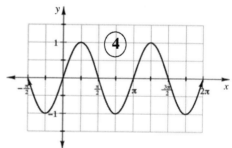
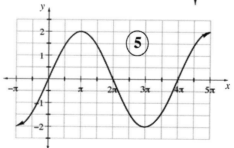

8-147.   Ceirin's teacher promised a quiz for the next day, so Ceirin called
          Adel to review what they had done in class. *"Suppose I have
          $y = \sin 2x$,"* said Ceirin, *"what will its graph look like?"*

          "It will be horizontally compressed by a factor of 2," replied Adel,
          "so the period must be π."

          *"Okay, now let's say I want to shift it one unit to the right. Do I just subtract 1 from x,
          like always?"*

          "I think so," said Adel, *"but let's check on the graphing calculator."* They proceeded
          to check on their calculators. After a few moments they both spoke at the same time.

          "Rats," said Ceirin, *"it isn't right."*

          "Cool," said Adel, *"it works."*

          When they arrived at school the next morning, they compared the equations they had
          put in their graphing calculators while they talked on the phone. One had
          $y = \sin 2x - 1$, while the other had $y = \sin 2(x - 1)$.

          Which equation was correct? Did they both subtract 1 from x? Explain. Describe the
          rule for shifting a graph one unit to the right in a way that avoids this confusion.

8-148.   George was solving the equation $(2x - 1)(x + 3) = 4$ and he got the
          solutions $x = \frac{1}{2}$ and $x = -3$. Jeffrey came along and said, *"You made
          a big mistake! You set each factor equal to zero, but it's not equal to
          zero, it's equal to 4. So you have to set each factor equal to 4 and then
          solve."* Who is correct? Show George and Jeffrey how to solve this
          equation. To be sure that you are correct, check your solutions.

8-149.   Complete the square to change $3x^2 + 6x + 3y^2 - 18y + 5 < 0$ to graphing form.
          Identify key points. Find the domain and range. Sketch the graph.

8-150.   Simplify each expression without using a calculator.

          a. $25^{-1/2}$ b. $(\frac{1}{27})^{-1/3}$

          ]c. $9^{3/2}$ d. $16^{-3/4}$

8-151.   Consider the equation $f(x) = 3(x + 4)^2 - 8$.

          a.   Find an equation of a function $g(x)$ such that $f(x)$ and $g(x)$ intersect in only
                one point.

          b.   Find an equation of a function $h(x)$ such that $f(x)$ and $h(x)$ intersect in no
                points.

8.2.4 What are the connections?

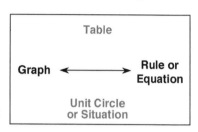

Graph ↔ Equation

In the past few lessons, you have been developing the understanding necessary to graph a cyclic equation without making a table and to write an equation from a cyclic graph. In today's lesson, you will strengthen your understanding of the connections between a cyclic equation and its graph. By the end of this lesson, you will be able to answer the following questions:

Table
Graph ⟷ Rule or Equation
Unit Circle or Situation

Does it matter if we use sine or cosine?

What do we need to know to make a complete graph or write an equation?

8-152.   What do you need to know about the sine or cosine functions to be able to graph them or write their equations? Talk with your team and write a list of all of the attributes of a sine or cosine function that you need to know in order to write an equation and graph it.

8-153.   CREATE-A-CURVE

Split your team into partners. With your partner, you will create your own sine or cosine function, write its equation, and draw its graph. Be sure to keep your equation and graph a secret! Start by choosing whether you will work with a sine or a cosine function.

a.   Half the distance from the highest point to the lowest point is called the **amplitude**. You can also think of amplitude as the vertical stretch. What is the amplitude of your function?

b.   How far to the left or right of the y-axis will your graph begin? In other words, what will be the **horizontal shift** of your function?

c.   How much above or below the x-axis will the center of your graph be? In other words, what will be the **vertical shift** of your function?

d.   What will the **period** of your function be?

e.   What will the **orientation** of your graph in relation to $y = \sin x$ or $y = \cos x$ be? Is it the same or is it flipped?

f.   Now that you have decided on all of the attributes for your function, write its equation.

8-154.   Copy the equation for your curve from problem 8-153 on a clean sheet of paper. Trade papers with another pair of students.

a.   Sketch a graph of the equation you received from the other pair of students.

b.   When you are finished with your graph, give it back to the other pair so that they can check the accuracy of your graph.

8-155.   When you look at a graph and prepare to write an equation for it, does it matter if you choose sine or cosine? Which will work best?

With your team, find *at least four* different equations for the graph at right. Be prepared to share your equations with the class.

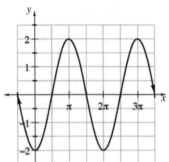

a.   Does it matter if you choose sine or cosine?

b.   Which of your equations do you prefer? Why?

8-156.   Sarita was watching her little sister bounce on a trampoline and she decided to take some data, so she started her stopwatch. Half a second later, her sister reached the highest point, 15 feet above the ground! When the stopwatch read 1.4 seconds, Sarita's sister was at the lowest point, stretching the trampoline down to just one foot above the ground. Find a cyclic equation that models the height of Sarita's sister over time if she continues to bounce in the same way.

8-157.   LEARNING LOG

In your Learning Log, write your ideas about the target questions for this lesson: *Does it matter if I use sine or cosine? What do I need to know to make a complete graph or write an equation?* Title this entry "Cyclic Equations and Graphs" and label it with today's date.

METHODS AND **M**EANINGS

MATH NOTES

General Equation for Sine Functions

The **general equation** for the **sine function** is $y = a\sin[b(x - h)] + k$.

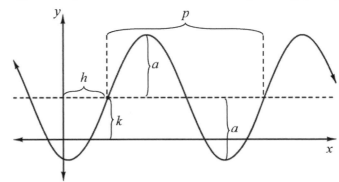

The **amplitude** (half of the distance between the highest and the lowest points) is **a**.

The **period** is the length of one cycle. It is labeled **p** on the graph.

The number of cycles in 2π is **b**.

The **horizontal shift** is **h**.

The **vertical shift** is **k**.

8-158.   Susan knew how to shift $y = \sin x$ to get the graph at right, but she wondered if it would be possible to get the same graph by shifting $y = \cos x$.

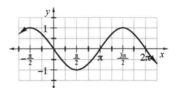

   a.   Is it possible to write a cosine function for this graph?

   b.   If you think it is possible, find an equation that does it. If you think it is impossible, explain why.

   c.   Adlai said, *"I can get that graph without shifting to the right or left."* What equation did he write?

8-159.   In the function $y = 4\sin(6x)$, how many cycles of sine are there from 0 to 2π? How long is each cycle (i.e., what is the period)?

8-160.   Write the equation of a cyclic function that has an amplitude of 7 and a period of 8π. Sketch its graph.

8-161.   Sketch a graph of each of the following trigonometric functions.

   a. $y = \sin(0.5(x - \pi))$ b. $y = 10\sin(3x) - 2$

   c. $y = 5\cos(x + \frac{\pi}{4})$ d. $y = \cos(2(x - \frac{\pi}{4}))$

8-162.   Find the exact value for each of the following trig expressions. For parts (g) and (h), assume that $0 \le \theta \le 2\pi$.

   a. $\cos(\frac{3\pi}{4}) =$ b. $\tan(\frac{4\pi}{3}) =$ c. $\sin(\frac{11\pi}{6}) =$ d. $\sin(\frac{3\pi}{4}) =$

   e. $\tan(\frac{5\pi}{4}) =$ f. $\tan(\frac{17\pi}{6}) =$ g. $\tan(\theta) = 1$ h. $\tan(\theta) = -1$

8-163.   Use the Zero Product Property to solve each equation in parts (a) and (b) below.

   a. $x(2x + 1)(3x - 5) = 0$ b. $(x - 3)(x - 2) = 12$

   c.   Write an equation and show how you can use the Zero Product Property to solve it.

8-164.   Find a quadratic equation whose graph has each of the following characteristics:

   a.   No x-intercepts and a negative y-intercept.

   b.   One x-intercept and a positive y-intercept.

   c.   Two x-intercepts and a negative y-intercept.

8-165.   A two-bedroom house in Seattle was worth $400,000 in 2005. If it appreciates at a rate of 3.5% each year:

   a.   How much will it be worth in 2015?

   b.   When will it be worth $800,000?

   c.   In Jacksonville, houses are depreciating at 2% per year. If a house is worth $200,000 now, how much value will it have lost in 10 years?

Chapter 8 Closure   What have I learned?

Reflection and Synthesis

The activities below offer you a chance to reflect on what you have learned in this chapter. As you work, look for concepts that you feel very comfortable with, ideas that you would like to learn more about, and topics you need more help with. Look for connections between ideas as well as connections with material you learned previously.

①   TEAM BRAINSTORM

With your team, brainstorm a list for each of the following three categories. Be as detailed as you can. How long can you make your list? Challenge yourselves. Be prepared to share your team's ideas with the class.

Topics: What have you studied in this chapter? What ideas and words were important in what you learned? Remember to be as detailed as you can.

The Web: Which connections on the multiple-representations web have you learned about for cyclic functions? Which are strongest and most useful? Which are less useful for you?

Connections: How are the topics, ideas, and words that you learned in previous courses connected to the new ideas in this chapter? Again, make your list as long as you can.

② MAKING CONNECTIONS

Below is a list of the vocabulary used in this chapter. Make sure that you are familiar with all of these words and know what they mean. Refer to the glossary or index for any words that you do not yet understand.

amplitude	angle	asymptotes
cosine	cyclic function	parameter
pendulum	period	radian
reference angle	sine	tangent
trigonometric functions	unit circle	

Make a concept map showing all of the connections you can find among the key words and ideas listed above. To show a connection between two words, draw a line between them and explain the connection, as shown in the example below. A word can be connected to any other word as long as you can **justify** the connection. For each key word or idea, provide a sketch of an example.

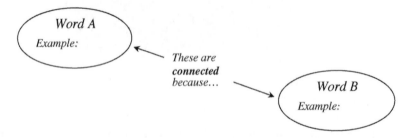

Your teacher may provide you with vocabulary cards to help you get started. If you use the cards to plan your concept map, be sure either to re-draw your concept map on your paper or to glue the vocabulary cards to a poster with all of the connections explained for others to see and understand.

While you are making your map, your team may think of related words or ideas that are not listed above. Be sure to include these ideas on your concept map.

③ GROWTH OVER TIME

This section gives you an opportunity to show growth in understanding of key mathematical ideas over time as you complete this course.

Part 1: On a separate sheet of paper, explain everything that you know about $f(x) = 2^x - 3$. Be sure to include everything you have learned since the last time you did this problem, and do not leave out anything you included in your earlier attempts.

Part 2: Compare your three responses to this "Growth Over Time" problem. Write an evaluation of your growth based on your responses. Consider each of the following questions as you write your answer.

- What new concepts did you include the second time you did the problem? In what ways was your response better than your first attempt?

- How was your final version different from the first two? What new ideas did you include?

- Did you omit anything in the final version that you used in one of the earlier versions? Why did you omit it?

- Rate your three attempts by making three bars like the ones below and shading each bar to represent how much you knew on each attempt.

  First Attempt:
  Second Attempt:
  Final Attempt:

- Is there anything you want to add to your current version? If so, add it and keep this version for future reference.

④ SUMMARIZING MY UNDERSTANDING

This section gives you an opportunity to show what you know about certain math topics or ideas.

With your team, make a list of the **big ideas** of this chapter. Discuss the important ideas of the chapter and try to agree on a short list of no more than five big ideas. Be prepared to share your list in a whole class discussion. When the class has reached agreement on a list, continue with parts (a) and (b) below.

a. Write your own description of each big idea.

b. For each big idea, provide one or two representative example problems. Solve each problem completely, using multiple representations, if applicable.

Your teacher may give you a "GO" page to work on (or you can download this from www.cpm.org). "GO" stands for "Graphic Organizer," a tool you can use to organize your thoughts and communicate your ideas clearly.

WHAT HAVE I LEARNED?

This section will help you evaluate which types of problems you feel comfortable with and which you need more help with. This section will appear at the end of every chapter to help you check your understanding. Even if your teacher does not assign this section, it is a good idea to try these problems and find out for yourself what you know and what you need to work on.

Solve each problem as completely as you can. The table at the end of this closure section has answers to these problems. It also tells you where you can find additional help and practice on similar problems.

CL 8-166. Describe how you can tell the difference between the graphs of $y = \sin x$ and $y = \cos x$. Be sure to **justify** your ideas.

CL 8-167. Convert the following angles to radians.

    a. $225°$ b. $75°$ c. $-15°$ d. $330°$

CL 8-168. Sketch each of the following angles in its own unit circle.

    a.   An angle that has a positive cosine and a negative sine.

    b.   All angles that have a sine of 0.5.

    c.   An angle that measures $\frac{4\pi}{3}$ radians. Find its exact sine.

    d.   An angle with a negative cosine and a positive tangent.

CL 8-169. Without using a calculator, give the exact value of each expression.

    a. $\sin 60°$ b. $\cos 180°$ c. $\tan 225°$

    d. $\sin \frac{\pi}{4}$ e. $\cos \frac{2\pi}{3}$ f. $\tan \frac{3\pi}{2}$

CL 8-170. If an angle between 0 and 2π radians has a sine of -0.5, what is its cosine? How do you know?

                                                                Algebra 2 Connections

CL 8-171. Find the exact values of x and y in the drawings below.

a.

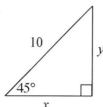

b.

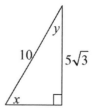

CL 8-172. For each equation determine the amplitude, period, locator point and sketch part of the graph.

a. $y = 3\cos(2x)$

b. $y = \tan(x - \frac{\pi}{2})$

CL 8-173. Write an equation for each of the following graphs. If you have a graphing calculator, use it to check your equation (be sure to set your window to match the picture).

a.

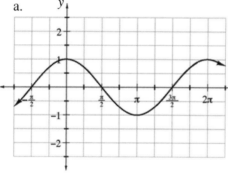

b.

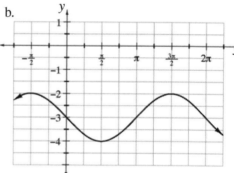

c.

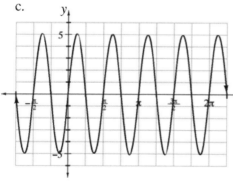

d.

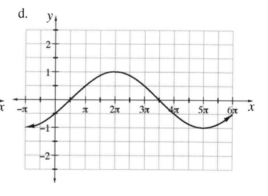

CL 8-174. Rewrite each equation below in graphing form and sketch its graph. Then state the domain and range and whether or not it is a function.

a. $y = 3x^2 + 30x - 2$

b. $x^2 + y^2 - 6x + 4y + 4 = 0$

CL 8-175. Solve each equation to the nearest thousandth.

a. $2 \cdot 3^x = 40.8$

b. $3x^4 = 27$

c. $\log_5(2x + 1) = 3$

d. $\log(x) + \log(2x) = 5$

CL 8-176. Find an equation for an exponential function that passes through the points $(1, 22)$ and $(3, 20.125)$ and has a horizontal asymptote at $y = 20$.

CL 8-177. Check your answers using the table at the end of this section. Which problems do you feel confident about? Which problems were hard? Have you worked on problems like these in previous chapters math classes? Sort the problems into three groups: the ones you are confident you can do, the ones you need more practice with, and the ones you need further help to understand.

⑥   HOW AM I THINKING?

This course focuses on five different **Ways of Thinking**: **justifying, generalizing, choosing a strategy, investigating**, and **reversing thinking**. These are some of the ways in which you think while trying to make sense of a concept or attempting to solve a problem (even outside of math class). During this chapter, you have probably used each Way of Thinking multiple times without even realizing it!

Review each of the five Ways of Thinking described in the closure sections of Chapters 1 through 5. Then choose three of these Ways of Thinking that you remember using while working on this chapter. Show and explain where and how you used each one. Describe why thinking in this way helped you solve a particular problem or understand something new. Be sure to include examples to demonstrate your thinking.

Answers and Support for Closure Activity #5
What Have I Learned?

Problem	Solutions	Need Help?	More Practice
CL 8-166.	The graph of $y = \cos x$ has a y-intercept of 1 because $\cos 0 = 1$ and the base of the triangle at 0 degrees in the unit circle is 1 unit long. The graph of $y = \sin x$ has a y-intercept of 0 because $\sin 0 = 0$ and the height of the triangle at 0 degrees in the unit circle is 0 units.	Lessons 8.1.2, 8.1.3, and 8.1.4 Math Notes box in Lesson 8.1.7 Learning Log entry from problem 8-157	Problems 8-14, 8-37, 8-48, 8-49, 8-50, 8-51, 8-53, 8-63, 8-64, 8-66, and 8-114
CL 8-167.	a. $\frac{5\pi}{4}$ b. $\frac{5\pi}{12}$ c. $-\frac{\pi}{12}$ d. $\frac{11\pi}{6}$	Lesson 8.1.5	Problems 8-78, 8-81, 8-93, 8-106, 8-107
CL 8-168.	a. b. c. $\sin\frac{4\pi}{3} = -\frac{\sqrt{3}}{2}$ d.	Lessons 8.1.3 and 8.1.6 Math Notes box in Lesson 8.1.5	Problems 8-64, 8-76, 8-104
CL 8-169.	a. $\frac{\sqrt{3}}{2}$ b. -1 c. 1 d. $\frac{\sqrt{2}}{2}$ e. $-\frac{1}{2}$ f. undefined	Lessons 8.1.5 and 8.1.6	Problems 8-79, 8-91, 8-104, 8-105, 8-121, and 8-162
CL 8-170.	$\frac{\sqrt{3}}{2}$ or $-\frac{\sqrt{3}}{2}$; If the sine is negative, the angle must lie in the 3rd or 4th quadrant and 0.5 is one leg of a 30°-60°-90° triangle.	Lessons 8.1.3, 8.1.4, and 8.1.6 Math Notes box in Lesson 8.1.7	Problem 8-35, 8-52, 8-64, 8-78, 8-104

Problem	Solutions	Need Help?	More Practice
CL 8-171.	a. $x = 5\sqrt{2}$, $y = 5\sqrt{2}$ b. $x = 60°$, $y = 30°$	Math Notes box in Lesson 8.1.2	Problems 8-6, 8-15
CL 8-172.	a. Locator: $(0, 3)$, Amplitude: 3, Period: π 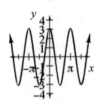 b. Locator: $(\frac{\pi}{2}, 0)$, Period: π, There is no amplitude 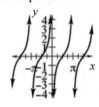	Lessons 8.1.2, 8.1.7, 8.2.1, 8.2.3, and 8.2.4	Problems 8-115, 8-127, 8-140, 8-143, 8-145, 8-146 8-153, 8-159, and 8-161
CL 8-173.	a. $y = \sin x$, $y = \sin(x + \frac{\pi}{2})$ or $y = -\sin(x - \frac{\pi}{2})$ b. $y = -3 - \sin x$, c. $y = 5\sin 4x$, d. $y = \sin\frac{1}{3}(x - \frac{\pi}{2})$	Lessons 8.2.1, 8.2.2, 8.2.3, and 8.2.4 Math Notes box in Lesson 8.2.4, Learning Log entry from problem 8-157	Problems 8-127, 8-141, 8-146, 8-155, 8-161
CL 8-174.	a. $y = 3(x - 5)^2 - 2$, $-\infty < x < \infty, y \geq -2$; it is a function. b. $(x - 3)^2 + (y + 2)^2 = 9$, $0 \leq x \leq 6$, $-5 \leq y \leq 1$; it is not a function. 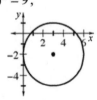	Lessons 4.1.3, 4.3.1, and 4.3.2 Math Notes box in Lesson 4.2.2 Checkpoint 14	Problems 4-38, 4-71, 4-108, 4-121, 4-132, 4-135, 4-137, 4-146, 4-149, 5-66, 5-72, 6-52, 7-84, 7-158, 7-175, 8-17, 8-42, 8-110, 8-132, 8-149

Problem	Solutions				Need Help?	More Practice
CL 8-175.	a. 2.745		b. ≈ 1.732		Lessons 7.2.1 and 7.2.2	Problems 7-111, 7-133, 7-139, 7-140, 7-223, CL 7-230,8-19 and 8-84
	c. 62		d. 223.607			
CL 8-176.	$y = 8(\frac{1}{4})^x + 20$				Lesson 7.2.3 Checkpoint 15	Problems 7-125, 7-127, 7-164, CL 7-232, 8-21, 8-68, and 8-134

POLYNOMIALS
9
RIDE the world's FIRST UNDERGROUND ROLLERCOASTER!

CHAPTER 9

Polynomials

In this chapter you expand your knowledge of families of functions to include polynomial functions. As you **investigate** the equation $\leftrightarrow$ graph connection for polynomials, you will learn how to search for factors (which can help you find x-intercepts) and how to use division to find additional factors.

When you **investigate** the graphs of polynomials and systems involving polynomials, you will see many that appear not to intersect. As you **investigate** these systems further, you will learn about imaginary and complex numbers.

In the last section of the chapter, you will apply your knowledge of polynomials to model some of the attractions at a county fair.

Guiding Questions

Think about these questions throughout this chapter:

How can I model this situation?

How can I find the other solutions?

How can I graph it?

What is an imaginary number?

In this chapter you will learn:

➤ How to sketch complete graphs of polynomial functions.

➤ How to divide one polynomial expression by another.

➤ How to solve some equations you could not solve earlier by expanding the set of numbers you use.

➤ What imaginary and complex numbers are, their properties, and how they are related to graphs that do not have real intersections.

➤ How to find solutions for factorable polynomial equations of one variable.

➤ How to write polynomial equations given their graphs and how to use polynomial functions to represent some situations.

Chapter Outline

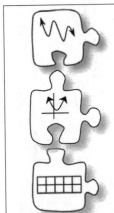

Section 9.1 You will **investigate** polynomial functions and learn how to sketch them without using a graphing calculator. You will also learn how to find polynomial equations from their graphs.

Section 9.2 Here you will be introduced to a number system called *complex numbers*. You will see how these numbers relate to quadratic equations that have no real solutions and to the roots of other polynomial equations.

Section 9.3 In this section, you will learn how to divide polynomials by applying your knowledge of generic rectangles and factoring. You will solve equations using polynomial division to factor polynomials.

9.1.1 How can I predict the graph?

Sketching Graphs of Polynomial Functions

In previous courses and chapters, you learned how to graph many types of functions, including lines and parabolas. Today you will work with your team to apply what you know to more complicated **polynomial** equations. Just as quadratic polynomial equations can be written in standard or factored form, other polynomial equations can be written in standard or factored form. For example, $y = x^4 - 4x^3 - 3x^2 + 10x + 8$ is in standard form, and it can be written in factored form as $y = (x+1)^2(x-2)(x-4)$.

During this lesson, you will develop techniques for sketching the graph of a polynomial function from its equation, and you will **justify** why those techniques work.

9-1.   The Mathamericaland Carnival Company has decided to build a new roller coaster to use at this year's county fair. The new coaster will have a very special feature: part of the ride will be underground. The designers will use polynomial functions to describe different pieces of the track. Part of the design is shown at right. Your task is to guess a possible equation to represent the track and test it on your graphing calculator. To help get an idea of what to try, start by checking the graphs of the equations given below. Think about how the graphs are the same and how they are different.

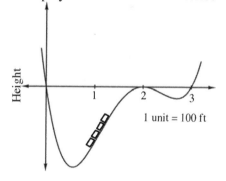

1 unit = 100 ft

$y = x(x-2)$

$y = (x-2)^2$

$y = x(x-2)(x-3)$

Your task: Use the information you found by graphing the above equations to help you make guesses about the equation that would produce the graph of the roller coaster. Once you have found a graph that has a shape close to this one, try zooming in or changing the viewing window on your graphing calculator to see the details better. Keep track of what you tried and the equations you find that fit most accurately.

9-2.   POLYNOMIAL FUNCTION INVESTIGATION

In this **investigation**, you will determine which information in a
polynomial equation can help you sketch its graph.

Your task: With your team, create summary statements explaining the
relationship between a polynomial equation and its graph. To accomplish this task,
first divide up the equations listed below so each team member is responsible for two
or three of them. Make a complete graph of each of your functions. Whenever
possible, start by making a sketch of your graph without using a graphing calculator.
Then, as a team, share your observations including your responses to the "Discussion
Points." Choose two or three equations that can be used to represent all of your
findings. You can choose them from the list below, or you can create new ones as a
team.

The form of your presentation to the class can be on a poster, transparencies or as a
PowerPoint^{TM} presentation. Whichever format your teacher decides, make sure you
include complete graphs and summary statements that are well **justified**.

$$P_1(x) = (x-2)(x+5)^2$$ $$P_2(x) = 2(x-2)(x+2)(x-3)$$

$$P_3(x) = x^4 - 21x^2 + 20x$$ $$P_4(x) = (x+3)^2(x+1)(x-1)(x-5)$$

$$P_5(x) = -0.1x(x+4)^3$$ $$P_6(x) = x^4 - 9x^2$$

$$P_7(x) = 0.2x(x+1)(x-3)(x+4)$$ $$P_8(x) = x^4 - 4x^3 - 3x^2 + 10x + 8$$

Discussion Points

What can we predict from looking at the equation of a polynomial?
Why does this make sense?

Which form of a polynomial equation is most useful for making a graph?
What information does it give?

How can we use the equation to help predict what a useful window might be?

Which examples are most helpful in finding the connections between
the equation and the graph?

How does changing the exponent on one of the factors change the graph?

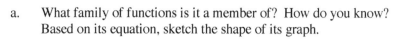

9-3.   As a team, examine the first polynomial $P_1(x) = (x-2)(x+5)^2$.

   a.   What family of functions is it a member of? How do you know?
         Based on its equation, sketch the shape of its graph.

   b.   Now use your graphing calculator to graph $P_1(x)$. Label the
         x-intercepts. How are the x-intercepts related to the equation?
         "Reading" from left to right along the x-axis, describe the graph before the first
         x-intercept, between x-intercepts, and after the last x-intercept.

9-4.   Continuing as a team, examine the equation $P_2(x) = 2(x-2)(x+2)(x-3)$.

   a.   How many distinct (different) factors are there? How many x-intercepts would
         you predict for its graph? Draw the graph and label the x-intercepts. How is this
         graph similar to or different from the graph of $P_1(x)$?

   b.   Does the factor 2 have any effect on the x-intercepts? On the shape of the graph?
         On the y-intercepts? How would the graph change if the factor 2 were changed to
         be a factor -2?

9-5   What is different about $P_3(x) = x^4 - 21x^2 + 20x$? What x-intercept(s) can you
       determine from the equation, before graphing with the calculator? Explain how you
       know. Use the graph to figure out exactly what the other intercepts are. Explain how
       you can prove that your answers are exact.

9-6.   With your team, divide up the work to **investigate** $P_4(x)$ through $P_8(x)$ and continue
        your **investigation**, referring back to the "your task" statement and the discussion
        points in problem 9-2.

───────────   *Further Guidance*   ───────────
                section ends here.

9-7.   Based on what your team learned and on the class discussion, record
        your own list of useful **strategies** for graphing polynomial functions.
        Use as many of the new vocabulary words as you can and write down
        the ones you are not sure of yet. You will add to and refine this list
        over the next several lessons.

METHODS AND MEANINGS

Polynomials, Degree, Coefficients

A **polynomial** in one variable is an expression that can be written as the sum or difference of terms of the form:

$$\left(\text{any number}\right) \cdot x^{\left(\text{whole number}\right)}$$

Polynomials with one variable (often x) are usually arranged with powers of x in order, starting with the highest, left to right. Polynomials can include only the operations of addition, subtraction, or multiplication.

The highest power of the variable in a polynomial of one variable is called the **degree** of the polynomial. The numbers that multiply each term are called **coefficients**. See the examples below.

Example 1: $f(x) = 7x^5 + 2.5x^3 - \frac{1}{2}x + 7$ is a polynomial function of degree 5 with coefficients 7, 0, 2.5, 0, $-\frac{1}{2}$, and 7. Note that the last term, 7, is called the **constant** term but represents the variable expression $7x^0$, since $x^0 = 1$.

Example 2: $y = 2(x+2)(x+5)$ is a polynomial in factored form with degree 2 because it can be written in standard form as $y = 2x^2 + 14x + 20$. It has coefficients 2, 14, and 20.

The following are not polynomial functions: $y = 2^x - 3$, $f(x) = \frac{1}{x^2 - 2x} + x$, and $y = \sqrt{x-2}$.

9-8.   For each equation below, make tables that include x-values from -2 to 2 and draw each graph.

    a. $y = (x-1)^2(x+1)$

    b. $y = (x-1)^2(x+1)^2$

    c. $y = x^3 - 4x$

    d.   What are the parent functions for these equations?

9-9.   **Polynomials** are expressions that can be written as a sum of terms of the form:

$$(\text{any number}) \cdot x^{(\text{whole number})}$$

Which of the following equations are polynomial equations? For those that are not polynomials, explain why not. Check the lesson 9.1.1 Math Notes box for further details about polynomials.

a. $f(x) = 8x^5 + x^2 + 6.5x^4 + 6$ b. $y = \frac{3}{5}x^6 + 19x^2$

c. $y = 2^x + 8$ d. $f(x) = 9 + \sqrt{x} - 3$

e. $P(x) = 7(x-3)(x+5)^2$ f. $y = x^2 + \frac{1}{x^2+5}$

g.   Write an equation for a new polynomial function and then write an equation for a new function that is not a polynomial.

9-10.   Describe the possible numbers of intersections for each of the following pairs of graphs. Sketch a graph for each possibility. For example, a circle could intersect a line twice, once, or not at all. Your solution to each part should include all of the possibilities and a sketched example of each one.

a.   Two different lines.   b.   A line and a parabola.

c.   Two different parabolas.   d.   A parabola and a circle.

9-11.   Solve the following system: $y = x^2 - 5$
$y = x + 1$

9-12.   A table can be used as a useful tool for finding some inverse functions. When the function has only one x in it, the function can be described with a sequence of operations, each applied to the previous result. Consider the following table for $f(x) = 2\sqrt{x-1} + 3$.

	1st	2nd	3rd	4th
What f does to x:	subtracts 1	$\sqrt{}$	multiplies by 2	adds 3

Since the inverse must undo these operations, in the opposite order, the table for $f^{-1}(x)$ would look like the one below.

	1st	2nd	3rd	4th
What does f^{-1} to x:	subtracts 3	divides by 2	$(\ )^2$	adds 1

a.   Copy and complete the following table for $g^{-1}(x)$ if $g(x) = \frac{1}{3}(x+1)^2 - 2$

	1st	2nd	3rd	4th
What g does to x:	adds 1	$(\ )^2$	divides by 3	subtracts 2
What g^{-1} does to x:				

b.   Write the equations for $f^{-1}(x)$ and $g^{-1}(x)$.

9-13.   Describe the difference between the graphs of $y = x^3 - x$ and $y = x^3 - x + 5$.

9-14.   Solve the equations below.

a. $\frac{3x}{x+2} + \frac{7}{x-2} = 3$

b. $\frac{x-7}{x-5} = \frac{6}{x}$

9-15.   An arithmetic sequence starts out $-23, -19, -15 \ldots$

a.   What is the rule?

b.   How many times must the generator be applied so that the result is greater than 10,000?

9-16.   Artemis was putting up the sign at the County Fair Theater for the movie "ELVIS RETURNS FROM MARS." He got all of the letters he would need and put them in a box. He reached into the box and pulled out a letter at random.

a.   What is the probability that he got the first letter he needed when he reached into the box?

b.   Once he put the first letter up, what is the probability that he got the second letter he needed when he reached into the box?

9-17.   Without a calculator, find two solutions $0° \le \theta < 360°$ that make each of the following equations true.

a. $\cos \theta = \frac{1}{2}$ b. $\tan \theta = -1$ c. $\sin \theta = \frac{\sqrt{3}}{2}$ d. $\cos \theta = -\frac{\sqrt{3}}{2}$

9-18.   Which of the following equations are polynomial functions? For each one that is not, **justify** why not.

a. $y = 3x^2 + 2x^2 + x$

b. $y = (x-1)^2(x-2)^2$

c. $y = x^2 + 2^x$

d. $y = 3x - 1$

e. $y = (x-2)^2 - 1$

f. $y^2 = (x-2)^2 - 1$

g. $y = \frac{1}{x^2} + \frac{1}{x} + \frac{1}{2}$

h. $y = \frac{1}{2}x + \frac{1}{3}$

i. $y = x$

j. $y = -7$

9-19. Samantha thinks that the equation $(x-4)^2+(y-3)^2=25$ is equivalent to the equation $(x-4)+(y-3)=5$. Is she correct? Are the two equations equivalent? Explain how you know. If they are not equivalent, explain Samantha's mistake.

9-20. Find the **roots** (the solutions when $y=0$) of each of the following polynomial functions.

    a. $y=x^2-6x+8$

    b. $f(x)=x^2-6x+9$

    c. $y=x^3-4x$

9-21. Sketch a graph of $y=x^2-7$.

    a.   How many roots does this graph have?

    b.   What are the roots of the function?

9-22. Solve $x^2+2x-5=0$.

    a.   How many x-intercepts does $y=x^2+2x-5$ have?

    b.   Approximately where does the graph of $y=x^2+2x-5$ cross the x-axis?

9-23. This is a checkpoint for finding the equation for the inverse of a function.

Consider the function $f(x)=2\sqrt{3(x-1)}+5$.

    a.   Find the equation for the inverse of $f(x)$.

    b.   Sketch the graph of both the original and the inverse.

    c.   Check your results by referring to the Checkpoint 17 materials located at the back of your book.

If you needed help to write the equation of the inverse of this function, then you need more practice with inverses. Review the Checkpoint 17 materials and try the practice problems. Also, consider getting help outside of class time. From this point on, you will be expected to write equations for inverses of functions such as this one quickly and easily.

9-24. Graph the inequality $x^2 + y^2 \leq 25$, and then describe its graph in words.

9-25. Find x if $2^{p(x)} = 4$ and $p(x) = x^2 - 4x - 3$.

9-26. Start with the graph of $y = 3^x$, then write new equations that will shift the graph as described below.

   a. Down 4 units.   b. Right 7 units.

9-27. THE COUNTY FAIR FERRIS WHEEL

Consider this picture of a Ferris wheel. The wheel has a 60-foot diameter and is drawn on a set of axes with the Ferris wheel's hub (center) at the origin. Use a table like the one below and draw a graph that relates the angle (in standard position) of the spoke leading to your seat to the approximate height of the top of your seat above or below the height of the central hub. The table below starts at –90°, your starting position before you ride around the wheel.

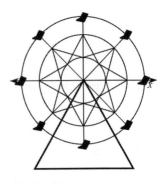

x (angle)	–90°	–45°	0°	45°	90°	135°	180°	....	270°
y (height)	–30'								

   a. The wheel goes around (counter-clockwise) several times during a ride. How could you reflect this fact in your graph? Update your graph.

   b. What is the maximum distance above or below the center that the top of your seat attains during the ride?

   c. Find an equation to fit the County Fair Ferris wheel ride.

9.1.2 How can I predict the graph?

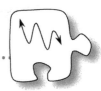

・・・

More Graphs of Polynomials

Today you will use what you learned in the "Polynomial Function Investigation" to respond to some questions. Thinking about how to answer these questions should help you clarify and expand on some of your ideas as well as help you learn how to use the vocabulary involved with polynomials.

9-28.   Use your finger to trace an approximate graph of polynomial functions in the air, as directed by your teacher. Or you may sketch each of the polynomial functions below quickly on paper. Just sketch the graph without the x- and y- axes.

a. $P(x) = (x+10)(x+7)(x-12)$ b. $Q(x) = (x+6)(x+3)(x-5)(x-8)$

c. $R(x) = -(x+4)(x+2)(x-6)(x-10)$ d. $W(x) = (x+7)^2(x-7)^2$

e. $S(x) = (x+6)(x+3)(x-5)(x-8)(x-12)$

9-29.   Look back at the work you did in Lesson 9.1.1 (problem 9-2, "Polynomial Function Investigation"). Then answer the following questions.

a.   What is the maximum number of roots a polynomial of degree 3 can have? Sketch an example.

b.   What do you think is the maximum number of roots a polynomial of degree n can have?

c.   Can a polynomial of degree n have fewer than n roots? Under what conditions?

9-30.   For each polynomial function shown below, state the minimum degree its equation could have.

i.   *ii.*    *iii.*   *iv.*

a.   Which of the graphs above show that as the x-values get very large the y-values continue to get larger and larger?

b.   How would you describe the other graphs for very large x-values?

c.   When the y-values of a graph get very large as the x-values get large, the graph has **positive orientation**. When the y-values of a graph get very small as the x-values get large, the graph has **negative orientation**. How is each of the above graphs oriented?

9-31.   For each graph in problem 9-30, you decided what the minimum degree of its equation
          could be. Under what circumstances could graphs that look the same as these have
          polynomial equations of a *higher* degree?

          Consider the graphs of $y = (x-1)^2$ and $y = (x-1)^4$.

          a.   How are these graphs similar? How are they different?

          b.   Could the equation for graph (*ii*) from the previous problem have degree 4?

          c.   Could it have degree 5? Explain.

          d.   How is the graph of $y = x^3$ similar to or different from the graph of $y = x^5$?

          e.   How do the shapes of graphs of $y = (x-2)^3$ and $y = (x+1)^5$ differ from the
               shapes of graphs of equations that have three or five factors that are all different?

9-32.   In $P_1(x) = (x-2)(x+5)^2$ (the first example from the "Polynomial Function
          Investigation"), $(x+5)^2$ is a factor. This produces what is called a **double root** of the
          function.

          a.   What effect does this have on the graph?

          b.   Check your equations for a **triple root**. What effect does a triple root have on the
               graph?

9-33.   We can use a number line to represent the *x*-values for which a polynomial graph is
          above or below the *x*-axis. The bold parts of each number line below show where the
          output values of a polynomial function are positive (that is, where the graph is above
          the *x*-axis). The open circles show locations of the *x*-intercepts or roots of the
          function. Where there is no shading, the value of the function is negative. Sketch a
          possible graph to fit each number line, and then write a possible equation. (Each
          number line represents the *x*-axis for a different polynomial.)

          a.      b.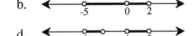

          c.      d.

9-34.   What can you say about the graphs of polynomial functions with an even degree
          compared to the graphs of polynomial functions with an odd degree? Use graphs from
          the "Polynomial Functions Investigation" (and maybe some others), to **justify** your
          response.

9-35. Choose three of the polynomials you graphed in the "Polynomial Functions Investigation" (problem 9-2) and create number lines for their graphs similar to the ones in problem 9-33.

9-36. Create a new number-line description (like the ones in problem 9-33) and then trade with a partner. (Each team member should create a different number line.) After you have traded, find a possible graph and equation for a polynomial function to fit the description you have received. Then **justify** your results to your team and check your team members' results.

9-37. Without using a calculator, sketch rough graphs of the following functions.

a. $P(x) = -x(x+1)(x-3)$

b. $P(x) = (x-1)^2(x+2)(x-4)$

c. $P(x) = (x+2)^3(x-4)$

ⓜETHODS AND MEANINGS

Roots and Zeros

The **roots** of a polynomial function, $p(x)$, are the **solutions** of the equation $p(x) = 0$. Another name for the roots of a function is **zeros of the function** because at each root, the value of the function is zero. The real roots (or zeros) of a function have the same value as the x-values of the x-intercepts of its graph because the x-intercepts are the points where the y-value of the function is zero.

Sometimes roots can be found by factoring. In the "Parabola Lab" (problems 4-13 and 4-14), you discovered how to make a parabola "sit" on the x-axis (the polynomial has one root), and you looked at ways of making parabolas intersect the x-axis in two specific places (two roots).

9-38. Where does the graph $y = (x+3)^2 - 5$ cross the x-axis?

9-39. If you were to graph the function $f(x) = (x-74)^2(x+29)$, where would the graph intersect the x-axis?

9-40.   For each pair of intercepts given below, write an equation for a quadratic function in standard form.

a. $(-3, 0)$ and $(2, 0)$

b. $(-3, 0)$ and $(\frac{1}{2}, 0)$

9-41.   What is the degree of each polynomial function below?

a. $P(x) = 0.08x^2 + 28x$

b. $y = 8x^2 - \frac{1}{7}x^5 + 9$

c. $f(x) = 5(x+3)(x-2)(x+7)$

d. $y = (x-3)^2(x+1)(x^3+1)$

9-42.   Are parabolas polynomial functions? Are lines polynomial functions? Are cubics? Exponentials? Circles? In all cases, explain why or why not.

9-43.   A sequence of pentagonal numbers is started at right.

a.   Find the next three pentagonal numbers.

b.   What kind of sequence do the pentagonal numbers form?

c.   What is the equation for the nth pentagonal number?

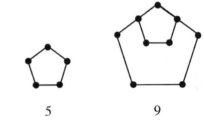

1   5   9

9-44.   A circle with its center on the line $y = 3x$ in the 1st quadrant is tangent to the y-axis.

a.   If the radius is 2, what is the equation of the circle?

b.   If the radius is 3, what is the equation of the circle?

9-45.   Sketch the graph of each function below on the same set of axes.

a. $y = 2^x$

b. $y = 2^x + 5$

c. $y = 2^x - 5$

9-46.   For each equation, find two solutions $0° \le \theta < 360°$, which make the equation true. You should not need a calculator.

a. $\sin\theta = \frac{1}{2}$

b. $\tan\theta = \sqrt{3}$

c. $\cos\theta = \frac{\sqrt{3}}{2}$

d. $\sin\theta = -\frac{\sqrt{2}}{2}$

9.1.3 How can I find the equation?

Stretch Coefficients for Polynomial Functions

In Lesson 9.1.2 you found possible equations for the graphs of polynomial functions based on their x-intercepts. Many of the sketches you used did not even include the scale on the y-axis. In this lesson, you will focus on figuring out equations that represent *all* of the points on the graphs.

9-47.   Find reasonable equations for each of the following polynomial functions. Without using a graphing calculator, how can you check the accuracy of your equations? How can you check to see whether the y-values (or stretch factor) are accurate? Show how you checked the accuracy in each case. Were your equations accurate?

a.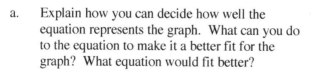

b.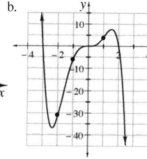

c.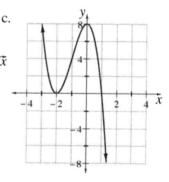

9-48.   What is the difference between the graphs of the functions $y = x^2(x - 3)(x + 1)$ and $y = 3x^2(x - 3)(x + 1)$?

9-49.   ARE THE INTERCEPTS ENOUGH?

Melvin wrote the equation $y = (x + 3)(x + 1)(x - 2)^2$ to represent the graph at right. How well does this equation represent the graph?

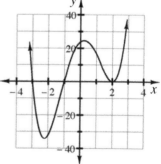

a.   Explain how you can decide how well the equation represents the graph. What can you do to the equation to make it a better fit for the graph? What equation would fit better?

b.   Before you figured it out, you could have written the polynomial for this graph as $P(x) = a(x + 3)(x + 1)(x - 2)^2$. What if you did not have a graphing calculator, but you were told that the graph goes through the point (1, 16)? How could you use that information to determine the exact equation? Once you have decided on a method with your team, try it. How can you test the accuracy of your equation?

9-50.   THE COUNTY FAIR COASTER RIDE

Now that you have more expertise with
polynomial equations and their graphs, the
Mathamericaland Carnival Company has
hired your team to find the *exact* equation
to represent its roller-coaster track.

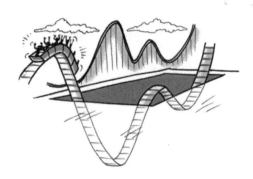

The numbers along the x-axis are in
hundreds of feet. At 250 feet, the track
will be 20 feet below the surface. This
gives the point $(2.5, -0.2)$.

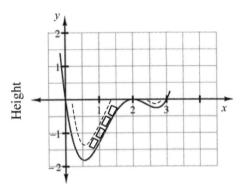

a.   What degree polynomial represents
the portion of the roller coaster
represented by the graph at right?

b.   What are the roots?

c.   Find an exact equation for the
polynomial that will generate the
curve of the track.

d.   What is the deepest point of the roller
coaster's tunnel?

9-51.   Write an exact equation for each graph below.

a.

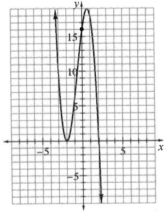

b.

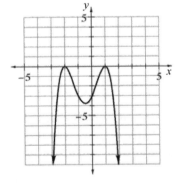

9-52.   Write a polynomial equation for a function with a graph that bounces off the x-axis at
$(-1, 0)$, crosses it at $(4, 0)$, and goes through the point $(-2, -18)$.

9-53.   Armando came up with the equation $y = 3(x+1)^4(x-4)$ for problem 9-52. Does his
equation fit all of the given criteria? Why or why not? Is it the same as the equation
you came up with?

9-54. What if problem 9-52 also had said that the graph went through the point $(1, -36)$? Is there still more than one possible equation? Explain.

9-55. What information about the graph of a polynomial function is necessary to determine exactly one correct equation? Discuss this with your team.

MATH NOTES

LOOKING DEEPER

Notation for Polynomials

A general equation to represent all polynomials: The general equation of a second-degree (quadratic) polynomial is often written in the form $f(x) = ax^2 + bx + c$, and the general equation of a third-degree (cubic) polynomial is often written in the form $f(x) = ax^3 + bx^2 + cx + d$.

For a polynomial with an undetermined degree n, it is unknown how many letters will be needed for the coefficients, so instead of using a, b, c, d, e, etc., mathematicians use only the letter a, and they put on subscripts, as shown below.

$$f(x) = (a_n)x^n + (a_{n-1})x^{(n-1)} + \ldots + (a_1)x^1 + a_0$$

This general polynomial has degree n and coefficients a_n, a_{n-1}, ..., a_1, a_0.

For example, for $7x^4 - 5x^3 + 3x^2 + 7x + 8$, the degree is 4. In this specific case, a_n is a_4 and $a_4 = 7$, a_{n-1} is $a_3 = -5$, a_{n-2} is $a_2 = 3$, $a_1 = 7$, and $a_0 = 8$.

Review & Preview

9-56. What is the stretch factor (the value of a) for the equation of the graph in part (c) of problem 9-47? Write the exact equation of the function.

9-57. For each of the following polynomial expressions, find the degree, list the coefficients, and then label them a_0 through a_n. Refer to the example in the Lesson 9.1.3 Math Notes box above about polynomial notation.

a. $6x^4 - 3x^3 + 5x^2 + x + 8$

b. $-5x^3 + 10x^2 + 8$

c. $-x^2 + x$

d. $x(x - 3)(x - 5)$

e. x

f. 10

9-58. Write a polynomial equation for a graph that has three x-intercepts: $(-4, 0)$, $(1, 0)$, and $(3, 0)$, and passes through the point $(-1, 60)$.

9-59. The x-intercepts of a quadratic polynomial are given below. Find a possible quadratic equation in standard form.

    a. $x = \frac{3}{4}, x = -2$ b. $x = -\sqrt{5}, x = \sqrt{5}$

9-60. Consider the functions $y = \frac{1}{2}$ and $y = \frac{16}{x^2 - 4}$. Find the coordinates where the graphs of the functions intersect.

9-61. Find the center and radius of each circle below.

    a. $(y - 7)^2 = 25 - (x - 3)^2$ b. $x^2 + y^2 + 10y = -9$

    c. $x^2 + y^2 + 18x - 8y + 47 = 0$ d. $y^2 + (x - 3)^2 = 1$

9-62. Without using a calculator, write the solution to each equation.

    a. $2^x = 17$ b. $\log_3(x + 1) = 5$

    c. $\log_3(3^x) = 4$ d. $4^{\log_4(x)} = 7$

9-63. Consider the function $y = x^2 + 5x + 7$.

    a.   Complete the square to find the vertex.

    b.   Find the y-intercept.

    c.   Use the vertex, the y-intercept, and the symmetry of parabolas to find a third point and sketch the graph.

9-64. Write a possible equation for the graph at right.

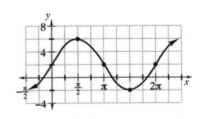

$9.2.1$ What are imaginary numbers?

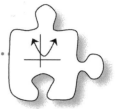

Introducing Imaginary Numbers

In the past, you have not been able to solve some quadratic equations like $x^2 + 4 = 0$ and $x^2 + 1 = 0$, because there are no real numbers you can square to get a negative answer. To solve this issue, mathematicians created a new, expanded number system based on one new number. But this was not the first time mathematicians had invented new numbers! To read about other such inventions, refer to the Math Notes box that follows problem 9-65.

In this lesson, you will learn about imaginary numbers and how you can use them to solve equations you were previously unable to solve.

9-65. Consider the equation $x^2 = 2$.

    a. How do you "undo" squaring a number?

    b. When you solve $x^2 = 2$, how many solutions should you get?

    c. How many x-intercepts does the graph of $y = x^2 - 2$ have?

    d. Solve the equation $x^2 = 2$. Write your solutions both as radicals and as decimal approximations.

OOKING DEEPER

Historical Note: Irrational Numbers

MATH NOTES

In Ancient Greece, people believed that all numbers could be written as fractions of whole numbers (what are now called **rational numbers**). Many individuals realized later that some numbers could not be written as fractions (such as $\sqrt{2}$), and these individuals challenged the accepted beliefs. Some of the people who challenged the beliefs were exiled or outright killed over these challenges.

The Greeks knew that for a one-unit square, the length of the diagonal, squared, yielded 2. When it was shown that no rational number could do that, the existence of what are called *irrational numbers* was accepted and symbols like $\sqrt{2}$ were invented to represent them.

The problem $x^2 = 3$ also has no rational solutions; fractions can never work exactly. The rational (i.e., decimal) solutions that calculators and computers provide are only approximations; the exact answer can only be represented in radical form, namely, $\pm\sqrt{3}$.

9-66.   Mathematicians throughout history have resisted the idea that some equations may not
         be solvable. Still, it makes sense that $x^2 + 1 = 0$ cannot be solved because the graph
         of $y = x^2 + 1$ has no x-intercepts. What happens when you try to solve $x^2 + 1 = 0$?

(L)OOKING DEEPER

Historical Note: Imaginary Numbers

MATH NOTES

In some ways, each person's math education parallels the history of
mathematical discovery. When you were much younger, if you were
asked, *"How many times does 3 go into 8?"* or *"What is 8 divided by 3?"* you
might have said, *"3 doesn't go into 8."* Then you learned about numbers other
than whole numbers, and the question had an answer. Of course, in some
situations you are only interested in whole numbers, and then the first answer is
still the right one. Later, if you were asked, *"What number squared makes 5?"*
you might have said, *"No number squared makes 5."* Then you learned about
numbers other than rational numbers, and you could answer that question.

Similarly, until about 500 years ago, the answer to the question, *"What number
squared makes –1?"* was, *"No number squared makes –1."* Then something
remarkable happened. An Italian mathematician named Bombelli used a
formula for finding the roots of third-degree polynomials. Within the formula
was a square root, and when he applied the formula to a particular equation, the
number under the square root came out negative. Instead of giving up, he had a
brilliant idea. He had already figured out that the equation had a solution, so he
decided to see what would happen if he pretended that there *was* a number he
could square to make a negative. Remarkably, he was able to continue the
calculation, and eventually the "imaginary" number disappeared from the
solution. More importantly, the resulting answer worked; it solved his original
equation. This led to the acceptance of these so-called **imaginary numbers**.
The name stuck, and mathematicians became convinced that all quadratic
equations do have solutions. Of course, in some situations you will only be
interested in real numbers (that is, numbers not having an imaginary part), and
then the original answer, that there is no solution, is still the correct one.

9-67.   In the 1500s, an Italian mathematician named Rafael Bombelli invented the imaginary
         number $\sqrt{-1}$, which is now called i. $\sqrt{-1} = i$ implies that $i^2 = -1$. After this
         invention, it became possible to find solutions for $x^2 + 1 = 0$; they are i and $-i$.
         What would be the value of $\sqrt{-16} = \sqrt{16(-1)} = \sqrt{16i^2} = ?$ Use the definition of i to
         rewrite each of the following expressions.

         a. $\sqrt{-4}$ b. $(2i)(3i)$ c. $(2i)^2(-5i)$ d. $\sqrt{-25}$

9-68.   Graph the function $y = x^2 - 4x + 5$.

   a.   Does the graph cross the x-axis? Should the equation $x^2 - 4x + 5 = 0$ have real solutions?

   b.   Use the Quadratic Formula to solve $x^2 - 4x + 5 = 0$. Use your new understanding of imaginary numbers to simplify your results as much as possible.

   c.   A real number plus (or minus) a multiple of i (like each of the solutions to $x^2 - 4x + 5 = 0$) is called a **complex number**. Check one of your solutions from part (b) by substituting it into the equation for x and simplifying the result.

9-69.   When a graph crosses the x-axis, the x-intercepts are often referred to as the **real roots** of the equation that results when $y = 0$. You have seen that solutions to equations can be real or complex, so it follows that roots can also be real or complex. Compare and contrast what happens with the graphs and equations for the three cases in parts (a) through (c) below.

   a.   Sketch the graph of $y = (x + 3)^2 - 4$. What are the roots?

   b.   Sketch the graph of $y = (x + 3)^2$. What are the roots?

   c.   Sketch the graph of $y = (x + 3)^2 + 4$. Can you find the roots by looking at the graph? Why or why not? Find the roots by solving $(x + 3)^2 + 4 = 0$.

   d.   Make **general** statements about the relationship between graphs of parabolas and the kinds of roots their equations have.

9-70.   Consider the equations $y = x^2$ and $y = 2x - 5$.

   a.   On one set of axes, sketch the graphs and label the intersection.

   b.   Use algebra to solve the system of equations.

   c.   Discuss your results with your team. What could these solutions mean?

9-71.   Do the graphs of $y = \frac{1}{x}$ and $y = -x + 1$ intersect? What kind of algebraic solutions will this system have? Verify your answer by solving the system.

METHODS AND MEANINGS

Imaginary and Complex Numbers

MATH NOTES

The **imaginary number** that solves the equation $x^2 = -1$ is i, so $i^2 = -1$, and the two solutions of the equation are i and $-i$.

In general, i follows the rules of real number arithmetic. The sum of two imaginary numbers is imaginary (unless it is 0). Multiplying the imaginary number i by every possible real number would yield the set of all the imaginary numbers.

The set of numbers that solve equations of the form $x^2 =$ (a negative real number) is called the set of **imaginary numbers**. Imaginary numbers are not positive, negative, or zero. The collection (set) of positive and negative numbers (integers, rational numbers (fractions), and irrational numbers), are referred to as the **real numbers**.

The sum of a real number (other than zero) and an imaginary number, such as $2 + i$, is generally neither real nor imaginary. Numbers such as these, which can be written in the form $a + bi$, where a and b are real numbers, are called **complex numbers**. Each complex number has a real component, a, and an imaginary component, bi. The real numbers are considered to be complex numbers with $b = 0$, and the imaginary numbers are complex numbers with $a = 0$.

9-72.   Write each of the following expressions in the form $a + bi$.

   a. $-18 - \sqrt{-25}$ b. $\frac{2 \pm \sqrt{-16}}{2}$

   c. $5 + \sqrt{-6}$

9-73.   Explain why $i^3 = -i$. What does i^4 equal?

9-74.   If $f(x) = x^2 + 7x - 9$, calculate the values in parts (a) through (c) below.

   a. $f(-3)$ b. $f(i)$ c. $f(-3 + i)$

9-75.   Is $5 + 2i$ a solution to $x^2 - 10x = -29$? How can you be sure?

9-76.   Solve $16^{(x+2)} = 8^x$.

9-77.   Is $(x - 5)^2$ equivalent to $(5 - x)^2$? Explain why or why not.

9-78.   Calculate the value of each expression below.

   a. $\sqrt{-49}$ b. $\sqrt{-2}$ c. $(4i)^2$ d. $(3i)^3$

9-79.   Find the inverse functions below.

   a.   If $f(x) = 2x - 3$, then what does $f^{-1}(x)$ equal?

   b.   If $h(x) = (x - 3)^2 + 2$, then what does $h^{-1}(x)$ equal?

9-80.   Solve each equation.

   a. $5.2(3.75)^x = 100$ b. $4 + 3x^4 = 81$

9.2.2 What are complex roots?

Complex Roots

In this lesson, you will solve equations as well as **reverse your thinking** to **investigate** the relationship between the complex solutions to a quadratic equation and the equation they came from.

9-81.   Find the roots of each of the following quadratic functions by solving for x when $y = 0$. Does the graph of either of these functions intersect the x-axis?

   a. $y = (x+5)^2 + 9$ b. $y = x^2 - 4x + 9$

9-82.   What do you notice about the complex solutions in problem 9-81? Describe any patterns you see. Discuss these with your team and write down everything you can think of.

9-83.   In parts (a) through (d) below, look for patterns as you calculate the sum and the product for each pair of complex numbers. Use what you find to answer parts (e) through (g).

   a. $2+i,\ 2-i$ b. $3-5i,\ 3+5i$

   c. $-4+i,\ -4-i$ d. $1+i\sqrt{3}, 1-i\sqrt{3}$

   e.   What complex number can you multiply $3+2i$ by to get a real number?

   f.   What happens when you multiply $(-4+5i)(-4+3i)$?

   g.   What complex number can you multiply $a+bi$ by to get a real number?

9-84.   WHAT EQUATION HAS THESE SOLUTIONS?

Each of the four pairs of complex numbers in problem 9-83 could be the roots of a quadratic function.

Your task: With your team, create a quadratic equation for each pair of complex numbers in parts (a) through (d) of problem 9-83 such that those numbers are the roots. Discuss the methods you use for writing the equations and write summary statements describing your methods.

Discussion Points

How can we **reverse** the process of solving and work backwards?

How can we use what we know about factors and zeros?

How are the solutions related to the standard form of the equation?

Further Guidance

9-85.   Problem 9-83 made Mariposa curious about sums and products. She decided to solve the equation $x^2 - 6x + 25 = 0$ and look at the sums and products of its solutions. What patterns can you help her find that might give her ideas about the equation once she knows the solutions?

9-86.   Austin had another idea. He knew that if 3 and –5 were solutions of a quadratic equation then $(x - 3)$ and $(x + 5)$ would be factors that could be multiplied to get a quadratic polynomial. How could his idea be used with the pairs of complex solutions in problem 9-83? Choose one pair and show how to use your idea.

9-87.   Melvin had still another idea. *"Why not just let $x = -4 \pm i$ and work backwards?"* He asked. Would his idea work?

══════════   *Further Guidance*   ══════════
section ends here.

9-88.   For each pair of numbers below, find a quadratic equation that has these numbers as solutions.

a. $\frac{3}{4}$ and –5   b. $3i$ and $-3i$

c. $5 + 2i$ and $5 - 2i$ d. $-3 + \sqrt{2}$ and $-3 - \sqrt{2}$

METHODS AND MEANINGS

The Discriminant and Complex Conjugates

For any quadratic equation $ax^2 + bx + c = 0$, you can determine whether the roots are real or complex by examining the part of the quadratic formula that is under the square-root sign. The value of $b^2 - 4ac$ is known as the **discriminant**. The roots are real when $b^2 - 4ac \geq 0$ and complex when $b^2 - 4ac < 0$.

For example, in the equation $2x^2 - 3x + 5 = 0$, $b^2 - 4ac = (-3)^2 - 4(2)(5) = -31 < 0$, so the equation has two complex roots and the parabola $y = 2x^2 - 3x + 5$ does not intersect the x-axis.

Complex roots of quadratic equations with real coefficients will have the form $a - bi$ and $a + bi$, which are called **complex conjugates**. The sum and product of two complex conjugates are always real numbers.

For example, the conjugate for the complex number $-5 + 3i$, is $-5 - 3i$. $(-5 + 3i) + (-5 - 3i) = -10$ and $(-5 + 3i)(-5 - 3i) = 25 - 9i^2 = 34$.

Note: With the introduction of complex numbers, the use of the terms *roots* and *zeros* of polynomials expands to include complex numbers that are solutions of the equations when $p(x) = 0$.

Review & Preview

9-89. For each of the following sets of numbers, find the equation of a function that has these numbers as roots.

a. $-3 + i$ and $-3 - i$

b. $5 + \sqrt{3}$ and $5 - \sqrt{3}$

c. -2, $\sqrt{7}$, and $-\sqrt{7}$

d. 4, $-3 + i$, and $-3 - i$

9-90. Raul claims that he has a shortcut for deciding what kind of roots a function has. Jolene thinks that a shortcut is not possible. She says you just have to solve the quadratic equation to find out. They are working on $y = x^2 - 5x - 14$.

Jolene says, "*See, I just start out by trying to factor. This one can be factored $(x - 7)(x + 2) = 0$, so the equation will have two real solutions and the function will have two real roots.*"

"*But what if it can't be factored?*" Raul asked. "*What about $x^2 + 2x + 2 = 0$?*"

"*That's easy! I just use the Quadratic Formula,*" says Jolene. "*And I get... let's see... negative two plus or minus the square root of... two squared... that's 4... minus... eight...*"

"*Wait!*" Raul interrupted. "*Right there, see, you don't have to finish. 2^2 minus $4 \cdot 2$, that gives you −4. That's all you need to know. You'll be taking the square root of a negative number so you will get a complex result.*"

"*Oh, I see,*" said Jolene. "*I only have to do part of the solution, the part you have to take the square root of.*"

Use Raul's method to tell whether each of the following functions has real or complex roots without completely solving the equation. Note: Raul's method is summarized in the Math Notes box for this lesson.

a. $y = 2x^2 + 5x + 4$

b. $y = 2x^2 + 5x - 3$

9-91. Decide which of the following equations have real roots, and which have complex roots without completely solving them.

a. $y = x^2 - 6$

b. $y = x^2 + 6$

c. $y = x^2 - 2x + 10$

d. $y = x^2 - 2x - 10$

e. $y = (x - 3)^2 - 4$

f. $y = (x - 3)^2 + 4$

9-92. Consider this geometric sequence: $i^0, i^1, i^2, i^3, i^4, i^5, ..., i^{15}$.

a. You know that $i^0 = 1$, $i^1 = i$, and $i^2 = -1$. Calculate the result for each term up to i^{15}, and describe the pattern.

b. Use the pattern you found in part (a) to calculate i^{16}, i^{25}, i^{39}, and i^{100}.

c. What is i^{4n}, where n is a positive whole number?

d. Based on your answer to part (c), simplify i^{4n+1}, i^{4n+2}, and i^{4n+3}.

e. Calculate i^{396}, i^{397}, i^{398}, and i^{399}.

9-93.   Use the pattern from the previous problem to help you to evaluate the following expressions.

   a. i^{592} b. i^{797} c. $i^{10,648,202}$

9-94.   Describe how you would evaluate i^n where n could be any integer.

9-95.   Consider the graph below.

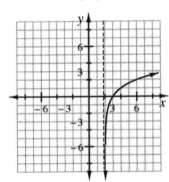

   a.   What is the parent for this function?

   b.   What is the equation of the vertical asymptote?

   c.   Write a possible equation for this graph.

9-96.   In one of the games at the county fair, people pay to shoot a paint pistol at the target shown at right. The center has a radius of one inch. Each concentric circle has a radius one inch larger than the preceding circle. Assuming the paint pellet hits the target randomly, what is the probability that it hits:

   a.   The 50-point ring?

   b.   The 20-point ring?

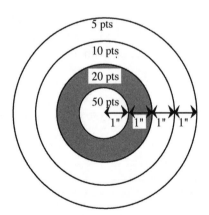

9-97.   Given $C = \begin{bmatrix} 3 & -2 \\ -5 & 1 \end{bmatrix}$, $D = \begin{bmatrix} 0 & 3 \\ 4 & -3 \end{bmatrix}$ find:

   a. CD b. $C + D$

   c. C^2 d. X if $2X + C = D$

9.2.3 Where are the complex numbers?

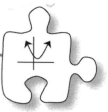

More Complex Numbers and Equations

If the number line is filled with real numbers, how can imaginary and complex numbers be represented geometrically? In this lesson, you will learn a way to graph complex numbers and interpret the graphical meaning of complex solutions.

9-98.   Avi and Tran were trying to figure out how they could represent complex numbers geometrically. Avi decided to make a number line horizontal like the *x*-axis to represent the real part as well as a vertical line like the *y*-axis to represent the imaginary part.

   a.   Draw a set of axes and label them as Avi described.

   b.   How could Avi and Tran graph a point to represent the complex number $3 + 4i$? Be prepared to share your **strategies** with the class.

   c.   Use the method you developed in part (b) to plot points to represent the six numbers below.

   i. $2 + 5i$ *ii.* $6 - i$ *iii.* $-5 - 3i$

   iv. 4 *v.* $7i$ *vi.* $-4 + 2i$

9-99.   On a new set of **complex axes** (like those drawn by Avi and Tran in problem 9-98), locate points representing all of the following complex numbers

   a. $3 + 4i$, $3 - 4i$, $-3 + 4i$, and $-3 - 4i$.

   b.   The four complex numbers represented by $\pm 4 \pm 3i$.

   c. 5, -5, $5i$, and $-5i$.

   d.   What do you notice about your graph? How far from $(0, 0)$ is each point?

9-100.   On the real number line, the distance from 0 to a point on the line is defined as the absolute value of the number. Similarly, in the **complex plane** (the plane defined by a set of complex axes), the **absolute value** of a complex number is its distance from zero or the origin (0, 0). In the previous problem, the absolute value of all of those complex numbers was 5. For each of the following questions, a sketch in the complex plane will help in visualizing the result.

   a.   What is the absolute value of $-8 + 6i$?

   b.   What is the absolute value of $7 - 2i$?

   c.   What is $|4 + i|$?

   d.   What is the absolute value of $a + bi$?

9-101.   Based on the following graphs, how many *real* roots does each polynomial function have?

   a. 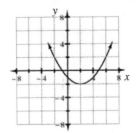   b.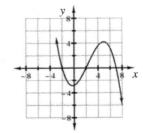

   Graphs (a) and (b) above have been vertically shifted to create graphs (c) and (d) shown below. How many *real* roots does each of these new polynomial functions have?

   c. 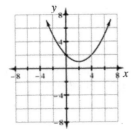   d.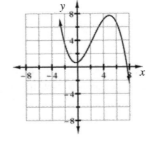

   The polynomials in parts (c) and (d) do not have fewer roots. Polynomial (c) still has *two* roots, but now the roots are complex. Polynomial (d) has *three* roots: two are complex, and only one is real.

9-102.   Recall that a polynomial function with degree n crosses the x-axis at most n times. For instance, $y = (x+1)^2$ intersects the x-axis once, while $y = x^2 + 1$ does not intersect it at all. The function $y = x^2 - 1$ intersects it twice. These graphs are shown below.

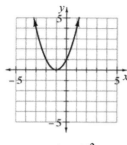 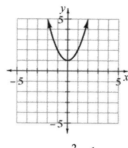 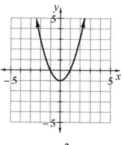

$$y = (x+1)^2 \qquad\qquad y = x^2 + 1 \qquad\qquad y = x^2 - 1$$

a.   A third-degree equation might intersect the x-axis one, two, or three times. Make sketches of all these possibilities.

b.   Can a third-degree equation have zero real roots? Explain why or why not.

9-103.   Now consider the graph of $y = x^3 - 3x^2 + 3x - 2$.

a.   How many real solutions could $x^3 - 3x^2 + 3x - 2 = 0$ have?

b.   Check to verify that $x^3 - 3x^2 + 3x - 2 = (x-2)(x^2 - x + 1)$.

c.   Find all of the solutions of $x^3 - 3x^2 + 3x - 2 = 0$.

d.   How many x-intercepts does $y = x^3 - 3x^2 + 3x - 2$ have? How many real roots and how many non-real roots (complex)?

9-104.   Sketch the graph of $f(x) = x^2 + 4$ and solve the equation $x^2 + 4 = 0$ to find its roots.

a.   Describe the parabola. Be sure to include the vertex and the equation of its axis of symmetry.

b.   With a partner, obtain a copy of the Lesson 9.2.3 Resource Page from your teacher, and follow the directions below to make a 3-D model that will show the location of the complex roots in a complex plane that is perpendicular to the real plane in which you drew the graph of the parabola.

    i.   Fold the paper on the line marked bi and $-bi$. This is a "mountain" fold, so the printing is on the outside.

Problem continues on next page. →

9-104.   *Problem continues from previous page.*

    ii. Cut the paper exactly along the dotted line. Do not cut beyond the dotted portion.

    iii. Now make "valley" folds on the two lines parallel to the first fold.

    iv. Hold the two ends of the paper and push them toward the center so the center pops up, and then fold the top and bottom of the paper back on the line marked "center."

You should have a three-dimensional coordinate system with the *xy*-plane facing you and the *i*-axis coming out toward you. The equation $f(x) = x^2 + 4$ should be in the lower right corner. Now locate the roots of the function on your 3-D model.

METHODS AND MEANINGS

MATH NOTES

Graphing Complex Numbers

To represent imaginary numbers, an imaginary axis and a plane are needed. Real numbers are on the horizontal axis and imaginary numbers are on the vertical axis, as shown in the examples below. Complex numbers are graphed using the same method that coordinate points are: the number $2 + 3i$ is located at $(2, 3)$, and the number i or $0 + 1i$ is located at $(0, 1)$. The number -2 or $-2 + 0i$ is located at $(-2, 0)$. This representation is called the **complex plane**.

In the complex plane, $a + bi$ is located at the point (a, b). Its distance from the origin is its **absolute value.** To find the absolute value, calculate the distance from $(0, 0)$ to (a, b):

$$|a + bi| = \sqrt{a^2 + b^2}$$

Examples:

$$|-2 + 3i| = \sqrt{(-2)^2 + 3^2} = \sqrt{13}$$

$$|-1 - i| = \sqrt{(-1)^2 + (-1)^2} = \sqrt{2}$$

$$|5i| = 5$$

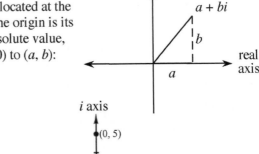

9-105. In parts (a) through (d) below, for each polynomial function $f(x)$, the graph of $f(x)$ is shown. Based on this information, tell how many linear and quadratic factors the factored form of its equation should have and how many real and complex (non-real) solutions $f(x) = 0$ might have. (Assume a polynomial function of the lowest possible degree for each one.)

Example: $f(x)$ at right will have three linear factors, therefore three real roots and no complex roots.

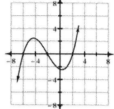

a.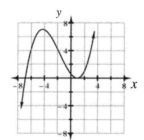

b.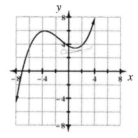

c.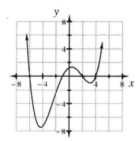

d.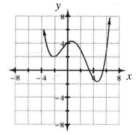

9-106. Make a sketch of a graph $p(x)$ so that $p(x) = 0$ would have the indicated number and type of solutions.

    a.   5 real solutions

    b.   3 real and 2 complex

    c.   4 complex

    d.   4 complex and 2 real

    e.   For parts (a) through (d), what is the lowest degree each function could have?

9-107.   Consider the function $y = x^3 - 9x$.

   a.   What are the roots of the function? (Factoring will help!)

   b.   Sketch a graph of the function.

9-108.   Make rough sketches of the graphs of each of the following polynomial functions. Be sure to label the x- and y- intercepts.

   a. $y = x(2x + 5)(2x - 7)$ b. $y = (15 - 2x)^2(x + 3)$

9-109.   The management of the Carnival Cinema was worried about breaking even on their movie "Elvis Returns from Mars." To break even, they had to take in $5000 on the matinee. They were selling adult tickets for $8.50 and children's tickets for $5.00. They knew they had sold a total of 685 tickets. How many of those tickets would have to have been adult tickets for them to meet their goal?

9-110.   You are given the equation $5x^2 + bx + 20 = 0$. For what values of b does this equation have real solutions?

9-111.   Show that each of the following equations is true.

   a. $(i - 3)^2 = 8 - 6i$ b. $(2i - 1)(3i + 1) = -7 - i$

   c. $(3 - 2i)(2i + 3) = 13$

9-112.   Kahlid is going to make a table to graph $y = \sqrt{x^2}$, but Aaron says that it would be a waste of time to make a table because the graph is the same as $y = x$.

   a.   Use Kahlid's equation to make the table and draw the graph.

   b.   As you can see, Aaron was wrong, but you did get a graph that you have seen before. What other equation has the same graph? Explain why this is reasonable.

9-113.   Multiply each of the following expressions.

   a. $(x - 3)^2$ b. $2(x + 3)^2$ c. $(a - b)(a^2 + ab + b^2)$

9.3.1 How can I divide polynomials?

Polynomial Division

When you graphed polynomial functions in the first section of this chapter, you learned that the factored form of a polynomial is very useful for finding the roots of the function or the x-intercepts of the graph. But what happens when you do not have the factored form and you need to find all of the roots?

9-114. Andre needs to find the exact roots of the function $f(x) = x^3 + 2x^2 - 7x - 2$. When he uses his graphing calculator, he can see that one of the x-intercepts is 2, but there are two other intercepts that he cannot see exactly. What does he need to be able to do to find the other roots?

Andre remembers that he learned how to multiply binomials and other polynomials using generic rectangles. He figures that since division is the inverse (or undo) operation for multiplication, he should be able to **reverse** the multiplication process to divide. As he thinks about that idea, he comes across the following news article.

Polydoku Craze Sweeping Nation!

(CPM) – Math enthusiasts around the nation have entered a new puzzle craze involving the multiplication of polynomials. The goal of the game, which enthusiasts have named Polydoku, is to fill in squares so that the multiplication of two polynomials will be completed.

	1	2	3	4	5
A	$\times$	$2x^3$	$-x^2$	$+3x$	-1
B	$3x$	$6x^4$	$-3x^3$	$9x^2$	$-3x$
C	-2	$-4x^3$	$2x^2$	$-6x$	2

$$6x^4 \quad -7x^3 \quad +11x^2 \quad -9x \quad +2$$

The game shown at right, for example, represents the multiplication of $(3x - 2)(2x^3 - x^2 + 3x - 1) = 6x^4 - 7x^3 + 11x^2 - 9x + 2$.

Most of the squares are blank at the start of the game. While the beginner level provides the factors (in the gray squares), some of the factors are missing in the more advanced levels.

9-115.   Andre decided to join the craze and try some Polydoku puzzles, but he is not sure how to fill in some of the squares. Help him by answering parts (a) and (b) below about the Polydoku puzzle in the news article he read (found in problem 9-114), then complete part (c).

a.   Explain how the term $2x^2$ in cell C3 of the news article was generated.

b.   What values were combined to get $-7x^3$ in the news article answer?

c.   Copy and complete the Polydoku puzzle at right.

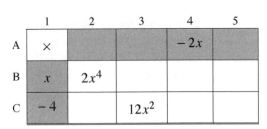

	1	2	3	4	5
A	×	$4x^3$	$+6x^2$	$-2x$	-5
B	$2x$				
C	-3				

9-116.   POLYDOKU TEAM CHALLENGE

Work with your team to complete the puzzle at right. Find the factors and the product for the puzzle. If you get stuck, you can consult parts (a) through (c) below for ideas.

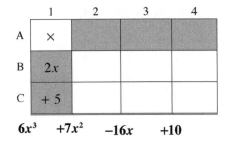

	1	2	3	4	5
A	×			$-2x$	
B	x	$2x^4$			
C	-4		$12x^2$		

$12x$

a.   How is cell B2 related to the answer?

b.   How did you find the third term in the answer?

c.   What cells did you use to get the value in cell B5?

9-117.   Jessica is about to start the intermediate-level Polydoku puzzle shown at right. Show Jessica how to complete the puzzle. Make sure you can **justify** your solution.

Use your results to complete the statements below.

	1	2	3	4
A	×			
B	$2x$			
C	$+5$			

$6x^3$ $+7x^2$ $-16x$ $+10$

$$\frac{6x^3 + 7x^2 - 16x + 10}{2x + 5} = \underline{\hspace{2cm}} \text{ and } (2x+5) \cdot \underline{\hspace{2cm}} = \underline{\hspace{2cm}}$$

9-118.   Unfortunately, Jessica made a mistake when she copied the problem. The constant term of the original polynomial was supposed to have the value + 18 (not + 10). She does not want to start all over again to solve the puzzle.

   a.   Jessica realizes that she now has 8 remaining from the original expression. What is the significance of this 8?

   b.   Jessica writes her work as shown below:

   $$\frac{6x^3 + 7x^2 - 16x + 18}{2x + 5} = \frac{(6x^3 + 7x^2 - 16x + 10) + 8}{2x + 5} = 3x^2 - 4x + 2, \text{ remainder 8.}$$

   Gina thinks that there is a way to write the answer without using the word "remainder." Discuss this with your team and find another way to write the result. Be prepared to share your results and your reasoning with the class.

   c.   Use Jessica and Gina's method to divide $(6x^3 + 11x^2 - 12x - 1) \div (3x + 1)$.

9-119.   Create your own Polydoku puzzles that can be used to solve each of the polynomial-division problems below. Express any remainders as fractions and use your results to write a multiplication and a division statement such as those in problem 9-117.

   a. $\dfrac{6x^4 - 5x^3 + 10x^2 - 18x + 5}{3x - 1}$ b. $(x^4 - 6x^3 + 18x - 4) \div (x - 2)$

   c. $x - 3 \overline{)x^3 + x^2 - 14x + 3}$ d. $\dfrac{x^5 - 1}{x - 1}$

9-120.   Now work with your team to help Andre solve his original problem (problem 9-114). Find all of the roots (exact zeros) of the polynomial.

METHODS AND MEANINGS

MATH NOTES

Polynomial Division

The examples below show two methods for dividing $x^4 - 6x^3 + 18x - 1$ by $x - 2$. In both cases, the remainder is written as a fraction.

Using long division:

$$
\begin{array}{r}
x^3 - 4x^2 - 8x + 2 \\
x - 2 \overline{)\,x^4 - 6x^3 + 0x^2 + 18x - 1} \\
\underline{x^4 - 2x^3} \\
-4x^3 + 0x^2 \\
\underline{-4x^3 + 8x^2} \\
-8x^2 + 18x \\
\underline{-8x^2 + 16x} \\
2x - 1 \\
\underline{2x - 4} \\
3
\end{array}
$$

Answer: $x^3 - 4x^2 - 8x + 2 + \frac{3}{x-2}$

Using generic rectangles:

	x^3	$-4x^2$	$-8x$	$+2$	Remainder
x	x^4	$-4x^3$	$-8x^2$	$+2x$	3
-2	$-2x^3$	$+8x^2$	$+16x$	-4	

$$x^4 - 6x^3 \quad + 0x^2 \quad + 18x \quad - 1$$

Answer: $x^3 - 4x^2 - 8x + 2 + \frac{3}{x-2}$

Therefore, $(x^4 - 6x^3 + 18x - 1) \div (x - 2) = x^3 - 4x^2 - 8x + 2 + \frac{3}{x-2}$ and

$(x - 2)(x^3 - 4x^2 - 8x + 2 + \frac{3}{x+2}) = x^4 - 6x^3 + 18x - 1$

9-121.   Carlos is always playing games with his graphing
          calculator, but now his calculator has contracted a
          virus. The $\boxed{\text{TRACE}}$, $\boxed{\text{ZOOM}}$, and $\boxed{\text{WINDOW}}$ functions on
          his calculator are not working. He needs to solve
          $x^3 + 5x^2 - 16x - 14 = 0$, so he graphs
          $y = x^3 + 5x^2 - 16x - 14$ and sees the graph at right in
          the standard window.

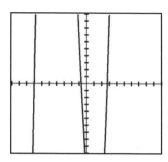

   a.   From the graph, what appears to be an integer
         solution to the equation?

   b.   Check your answer from part (a) in the equation.

   c.   Since $x = -7$ is a solution to the equation, what is the factor associated with this
         solution?

   d.   Use polynomial division to find the other factor.

   e.   Use your new factor to complete this equation:

$$x^3 + 5x^2 - 16x - 14 = (x + 7)(other\ factor) = 0$$

   f.   The "other factor" leads to two other solutions to the equation. Find these two
         new solutions and give all three solutions to the original equation.

9-122.   Now Carlos needs to solve $2x^3 + 3x^2 - 8x + 3 = 0$, but his calculator will still only
          create a standard graph. He sees that the graph of $y = 2x^3 + 3x^2 - 8x + 3$ crosses the
          x-axis at $x = 1$. Find all three solutions to the equation.

9-123.   Without actually multiplying, decide which of the following polynomials could be the
          product of $(x - 2)(x + 3)(x - 5)$. **Justify** your choice.

   a. $x^3 - 4x^2 - 11x - 5$ b. $2x^3 - 4x^2 - 11x + 30$

   c. $x^3 - 4x^2 - 11x + 30$ d. $2x^3 - 4x^2 - 11x - 5$

9-124.   Which of the following binomials could be a factor of $x^3 - 9x^2 + 19x + 5$? Explain your reasoning.

a. $x - 2$ b. $x - 5$ c. $x + 3$ d. $x + 2$

9-125.   Now divide $x^3 - 9x^2 + 19x + 5$ by the factor that you chose in the preceding problem. If it is a factor, use it and the resulting factor to find all the zeros of the polynomial. If it is not a factor, reconsider your answer to the preceding problem and try a different factor.

9-126.   Consider the equation $5x^2 - 7x - 6 = 0$ as you answer the questions in parts (a) through (d) below.

a.   What are the factors of $5x^2 - 7x - 6$?

b.   What are the solutions to the equation?

c.   Explain the relationship between the factors of the polynomial expression and the solutions to the equation.

d.   How are the solutions to the equation related to the lead coefficient and constant term in the original polynomial?

9-127.   This is a checkpoint for solving systems of three equations and three unknowns.

Use elimination or matrix multiplication to solve the system of equations at right.

$$x + y - z = 12$$
$$3x + 2y + z = 6$$
$$2x + 5y - z = 10$$

Check your solution by referring to the Checkpoint 18 materials located at the back of your book.

If you needed help to solve this system correctly, then you need more practice solving 3×3 systems. Review the Checkpoint 18 materials and try the practice problems. Also, consider getting help outside of class time. From this point on, you will be expected to solve systems such as these accurately.

9-128.   Given the equation: $3x + y - z = 6$.

a.   Draw a graph.

b.   Is $(1, 2, -1)$ on the graph? **Justify** your answer.

9-129. Frank says that $\frac{a}{x+b} = \frac{a}{x} + \frac{a}{b}$, while Fred does not think that the two expressions are equivalent. Who is correct? **Justify** your answer.

9-130. The area of $\triangle ABC$ is 24 square inches. If $\overline{AB} \perp \overline{BC}$ and $BC = 8$ inches, find AC.

9.3.2 How can I solve it?

Factors and Integral Roots

You already know several methods for solving quadratic equations, such as factoring, completing the square, and using the Quadratic Formula. Mathematicians have developed formulas for solving third- and fourth-degree polynomial equations, but these formulas are far more complicated and messy than the Quadratic Formula is, and they are rarely used. Furthermore, for polynomials of degree greater than four, there is no single formula to use. For many polynomials, you can develop more useful methods than a formula based on what you already know.

9-131. SEARCHING FOR ROOTS OF POLYNOMIALS

By combining what you know about graphing, factoring, and polynomial division, and then applying what you know about solving quadratic equations, you will be able to find the roots of the higher-degree polynomial functions in this lesson.

Your task: Find all of the zeros of the polynomial below and then write the polynomial in factored form with factors of degree 2 or 1.

$$P(x) = x^4 - x^3 - 5x^2 + 3x + 6$$

Discussion Points

What are some possible linear factors?

How can the graph help us decide which factors to try?

How can we use the known factors to figure out other factors?

What do we need to do to write the polynomial in factored form and find the zeros?

9-132.   Using only integers for a, and just by looking at the polynomial expression, list all of the possible linear factors $(x \pm a)$ for the polynomial $P(x) = x^4 - x^3 - 5x^2 + 3x + 6$.

   a.   Could $x - 5$ be included on your list of possible linear factors? Explain.

   b.   Not all of the *possibilities* will actually be factors. Use your graphing calculator to decide which members of your list are the best possibilities.

   c.   Now that you have shortened the list of possibilities, which factors on the shortened list really are factors of $P(x)$? **Justify** your answer.

   d.   If you haven't already divided, divide the polynomial by one of the factors from part (c) and write the polynomial as a product of a linear and a cubic factor.

   e.   Now divide the cubic factor from part (d) by the other linear factor that worked, and write the original polynomial as a product of two linear factors and one quadratic factor.

   f.   From the factored form, you can find all of the solutions to $x^4 - x^3 - 5x^2 + 3x + 6 = 0$ and the exact x-intercepts for the graph of $P(x)$. What are they?

───────────   *Further Guidance*   ───────────
                section ends here.

9-133.   **LEARNING LOG**

   As a team, look back over the work you did to find the linear factors of $P(x)$ and make a list of steps you can use to find all of the zeros of a given polynomial. Then record your ideas in your Learning Log. Use diagrams, arrows, and other math tools to help demonstrate your ideas. Label the list "Factors and Roots of Polynomial Functions."

9-134.   Your teacher will assign your team one of the following polynomial functions. Use the list of steps your team developed to factor the polynomial and find all of its roots. Then prepare a poster in which you illustrate and **justify** each of your steps. Be sure to include the graph on your poster and clearly explain the relationship between the solutions of the equation and the x-intercepts.

   a. $Q_1(x) = x^3 + 3x^2 + 1x - 5$ b. $Q_2(x) = 6x^4 + 7x^3 - 36x^2 - 7x + 6$

   c. $Q_3(x) = x^4 + 2x^3 + 10x^2 + 18x + 9$ d. $Q_4(x) = x^4 - 8x^3 + 18x^2 - 16x + 5$

   e. $Q_5(x) = x^5 - 4x^3 - x^2 + 4$ f. $Q_6(x) = x^3 + x^2 - 7x - 7$

9-135.   LEARNING LOG

Make additions and adjustments to your Learning Log entry from
problem 9-133 to reflect what you leaned from the posters.

9-136.   Use the procedures you developed to factor each of the following polynomial
expressions. Each final answer should be a linear factor times a quadratic factor. Look
for patterns in the factors.

a. $x^3 - 1$ b. $x^3 + 8$ c. $x^3 - 27$ d. $x^3 + 125$

9-137.   If you **generalize** the patterns for the factors in problem 9-136, you will discover a
shortcut for factoring cubic polynomials that are described as the sum or difference of
two cubes. Write the factors for each polynomial expression below.

a. $x^3 + a^3$ b. $x^3 - b^3$

c.   Write a description of how to get the factors without having to divide.

9-138.   Are there similar patterns for $x^4 + a^4$ and $x^4 - b^4$? Explain.

9-139.   BUILDING POLYNOMIALS

For each of the following descriptions of polynomial functions with integral
coefficients, answer each question below.

  i.   What are the possible numbers of real zeros?

  ii.   How many complex zeros are possible?

  iii. For each number of possible real zeros, give an example of a polynomial in
        factored form.

a.   A third-degree polynomial function.

b.   A fourth-degree polynomial function.

c.   A fifth-degree polynomial function.

METHODS AND MEANINGS

The Factor and Integral Zero Theorems

Factor Theorem: If a is a zero of a polynomial function, then $(x - a)$ is a factor of the polynomial, and if $(x - a)$ is a factor of the polynomial, then a is a zero.

Example: We know that -3, $\frac{1}{2}$, and $1 \pm i\sqrt{7}$ are zeros of the polynomial $p(x) = 2x^4 + x^3 + 22x^2 + 80x - 24$. (You can test each value by substituting it into the equation to verify that the resulting value of the function is 0.) According to the Factor Theorem, $(x + 3)$, $(x - \frac{1}{2})$, $(x - (1 + i\sqrt{7}))$, and $(x - (1 - i\sqrt{7}))$ are factors of the polynomial. Notice that the theorem does not state that they are the *only* factors of the polynomial. In order to show that these are factors, we must show that they can each be part of a product that results in $p(x)$. We start by multiplying the factors together. To make the operations simpler, we multiply the complex factors first, as shown below.

$$(x + 3)(x - \tfrac{1}{2})(x - (1 + i\sqrt{7}))(x - (1 - i\sqrt{7}))$$
$$= (x + 3)(x - \tfrac{1}{2})(x^2 - 2x + 8)$$

We then notice that if we multiply this expression by 2, we can eliminate the fraction in $(x - \frac{1}{2})$ without changing the roots. For convenience, we multiply $2(x - \frac{1}{2})$ first and then multiply the rest of the factors together.

$$2(x + 3)(x - \tfrac{1}{2})(x^2 - 2x + 8)$$
$$= (x + 3)(2x - 1)(x^2 - 2x + 8)$$
$$= 2x^4 + x^3 + 22x^2 + 80x - 24 = p(x)$$

Integral Zero Theorem: For any polynomial with integral coefficients, if an integer is a zero of the polynomial, it must be a factor of the constant term.

Example: Suppose the integers a, b, c, and d are zeros of a polynomial. Then, according to the Factor Theorem, $(x - a)(x - b)(x - c)(x - d)$ are factors of the polynomial.

When you multiply these factors together, the constant term will be $abcd$, so a, b, c, and d are factors of the constant term.

9-140.   Carlo was trying to factor the polynomial
$p(x) = x^4 - 4x^3 - 4x^2 + 24x - 9$ and find all of its
roots. He had already found one factor by making a
guess and trying it, so he had
$p(x) = (x - 3)(x^3 - x^2 - 7x + 3)$. He was trying to
factor $x^3 - x^2 - 7x + 3$, and he had tried $(x + 3)$,
$(x + 1)$, and $(x - 1)$, but none worked. Then Teo came
by and said, *"You should look at the graph."*

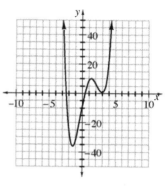

a.   How does the graph help?

b.   Complete the problem.

9-141.   Spud has a problem. He knows that the solutions for a quadratic equation are
$x = 3 + 4i$ and $x = 3 - 4i$, but in order to get credit for the problem he was supposed to
have written down the equation. Unfortunately, he lost the paper with the original
equation on it. His friends are full of advice.

a.   Alexia says, *"Look, just remember when we made polynomials. If you wanted
7 and 4 to be the answers, you just used $(x - 7)(x - 4)$. So you just do x minus
the first one times x minus the other."* Use $(x - (3 + 4i))(x - (3 - 4i))$ to find the
quadratic expression.

b.   Hugo says, *"No, no, no. You can do it that way, but that's too complicated.
I think you just start with $x = 3 + 4i$ and work backward. So $x - 3 = 4i$, then,
hmmm. Yeah, that'll work."* Try Hugo's method.

c.   Which way do you think Spud should use? Explain your choice.

9-142.   So far you have been able to extend the rules for real numbers to add, subtract, and
multiply complex numbers, but what about dividing? Can you use what you know
about real numbers to divide one complex number by another? In other words, if a
problem looks like this:

$$\frac{3 + 2i}{-4 + 7i}$$

What needs to be done to get an answer in the form of a single complex number,
$a + bi$?

Natalio had an idea. He said, *"I'll bet we can use the conjugate!"*

"How?" asked Ricki.

Problem continues on next page. →

9-142.   *Problem continued from previous page.*

"Well, it's a fraction. Can't we multiply the numerator and denominator by the same number?" Natalio replied.

a.   Natalio was not very clear in his explanation. Show Ricki what he meant they should do.

b.   Using Natalio's ideas you probably still came up with a fraction in part (a), but the denominator should be a whole number. To write a complex number such as $\frac{c+di}{m}$ in the form $a+bi$, just use the distributive property to rewrite the result as $\frac{c}{m}+\frac{d}{m}i$. Rewrite your result for part (a) in this form.

9-143.   Use the method developed in problem 9-142 to do the following division problems.

a. $\frac{2-5i}{1-2i}$

b. $(-3+i) \div (2+3i)$

9-144.   Find the inverse of $g(x) = (x+1)^2 - 3$ with the domain $x \geq -1$. Sketch both graphs and tell the domain and range of the inverse function.

9-145.   Sketch the graph of each polynomial function below and find all of the zeros.

a. $y = x^3 + 1$

b. $y = x^3 - 8$

9-146.   Solve the system of equations at right for (x, y, z).

$$x = y + z$$
$$2x + 3y + z = 17$$
$$z + 2y = 7$$

9-147.   Sketch the graph of each equation below.

a. $y = 3 \sin (x + \frac{\pi}{2})$

b. $y = -2 \sin (4x)$

9-148.   Spud has done it again. He's lost another polynomial function. This one was a cubic, written in standard form. He knows that there were two complex zeros, $-2 \pm 5i$ and one real zero, -1. What could his original function have been?

480

9-149.   Given the equation $x^3 - 6x^2 + 7x + 2 = 0$.

      a.   Verify that $x = 2$ is a solution.

      b.   What is one factor of $x^3 - 6x^2 + 7x + 2$?

      c.   Use (b) to find another factor.

      d.   What are all the solutions of $x^3 - 6x^2 + 7x + 2 = 0$?

9-150.   Rewrite each of the following division problems as a single complex number.

      a. $\frac{5+3i}{5-3i}$ b. $\frac{7+3i}{1-i}$

9-151.   Where do the graphs below intersect? You should be able to do these without a graphing calculator.

      a. $2x + y = 10$ b. $2x + y = 10$

            $x + y = 25$ $x^2 + y^2 = 25$

9-152.   Sketch both the circle $x^2 + y^2 = 25$ and the parabola $y = x^2 - 13$.

      a.   How many points of intersection are there?

      b.   Find the coordinates of these points algebraically.

9-153.   Solve each equation. Be sure to check your answers.

      a. $\sqrt{x} + 2 = x$ b. $\sqrt{x} + 2 = \sqrt{x+6}$

9-154.   Find the distance between each pair of points.

      a.   (2, 3) and (4, 7)   b.   (2, 3) and (x, y)

9-155.   For each equation, find two solutions $0 \le x < 2\pi$, which make the equation true. No calculator necessary.

      a. $\cos x = -\frac{1}{2}$ b. $\tan x = \frac{\sqrt{3}}{3}$ c. $\sin x = 0$ d. $\cos x = \frac{\sqrt{2}}{2}$

9-156.   Rewrite each of the following division problems as a single complex number in simplest form.

a. $\frac{2-6i}{4+2i}$

b. $\frac{5}{1+2i}$

9-157.   A long lost relative died and left you $15,000! Your parents say that you need to save the money for college, so you put it an account that pays 8% interest compounded annually. How many years will it take until your account is worth $25,000?

9-158.   Solve each equation.

a. $\log_3(2x-1) = -2$

b. $5^{\log_5(x)} = 3$

c. $\log_2(x) - \log_2(3) = 4$

d. $\log_3(5) = x$

9-159.   Verify that the graphs of the equations $x^2 + y^3 = 17$ and $x^4 - 4y^2 - 8xy = 17$ intersect at $(3, 2)$.

9-160.   The graphs of $y = \log_2(x-1)$ and $y = x^3 - 4x$ intersect at two points: $(2, 0)$ and approximately $(1.1187, -3.075)$. Use that information to solve $\log_2(x-1) = x^3 - 4x$.

9-161.   Each dartboard below is a target at the county fair dart-throwing game. What is the probability of hitting the darkened region of each target? Assume you always hit the board but the location on the board is random.

a.    b. 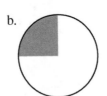   c.   d.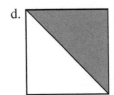

60°

e. 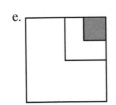   f.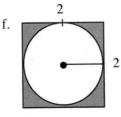

2

2

9-162.   Use your knowledge of the unit circle to explain why the graphs of $y = \sin\theta$ and $y = \cos(\theta - \frac{\pi}{2})$ are the same.

9-163.   For homework, Londa was asked to simplify the expression $\sqrt{-7} \cdot \sqrt{-7} =$. She got the answer 7, but when she checked, she learned that the correct answer was -7.

a.   Show Londa the steps she could take to get -7.

b.   What steps do you think Londa took to get 7 as a result?

c.   What does she need to consider in order to avoid making this mistake in the future?

d.   Londa's example means that it is not always true that $\sqrt{a} \cdot \sqrt{b} = \sqrt{ab}$ for real numbers a and b. What restriction needs to be placed on the numbers a and b?

9-164.   Change each angle from degrees to radians.

a. $60°$ b. $75°$ c. $210°$ d. $225°$

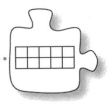

An Application of Polynomials

In this lesson, you will have the opportunity to use the equation and graph of a polynomial function to solve a problem involving a game at the county fair.

9-165.   COUNTY FAIR GAME TANK

The Mathamericaland Carnival Company wants to create a new game. It will consist of a tank filled with ping-pong balls of different colors. People will pay for the opportunity to crawl around in the tank blindfolded for 60 seconds, while they collect ping-pong balls. Most of the ping-pong balls will be white, but there will be a few of different colors. The players will win $100 for each red, $200 for each blue, and $500 for each green ping-pong ball they carry out of the tank.

The tank will be rectangular, open at the top, and will be made by cutting squares out of each corner of an 8.5-meter by 11-meter sheet of translucent miracle material that can be bent into shape. The owner of the company thinks that she will make the greatest profit if the tank has maximum volume. She has hired your team to figure out the exact dimensions of the tank that creates the maximum value.

Your task: Your team will write a report of your findings to the Carnival Company that includes each of the following elements.

- Any data or conjectures your team made based on experimental paper tanks.

- A diagram of the tank with the dimensions clearly labeled with appropriate variables.

- A graph of the volume function that you found with notes on a reasonable domain and range.

- An equation that matches your graph.

- Your conclusions and observations.

Further Guidance

9-166.   Use a full sheet of 8.5" x 11" paper, which is the same shape as the material for the tank. Each member of your team should choose a different sized square to cut out of the corners. Measure the side of the square you cut out and write along the edge of the large piece of paper. Use either inches or centimeters. Your paper should look like the figure at right.

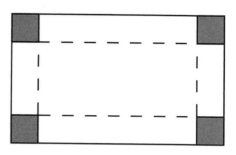

Fold the paper up into an open box (fold on the dotted lines). Then tape the cut parts together so that the box holds its shape. Measure the dimensions of the tank. Record the dimensions directly on the model tank.

9-167.   Make a table like the one below for your team's results. Consider "extreme" tanks, the ones with the largest possible cutout and the smallest possible cutout. For example, imagine cutting a square out of each corner zero inches on a side.

Height of Tank	Width of Tank	Length of Tank	Volume of Tank

a.   Examine the data in the table with your team and make some conjectures about how to find the maximum volume.

b.   Label the height as x. Using x for the height, find expressions for the length and width.

c.   Write an equation to represent the volume of the tank.

d.   Sketch the graph of your function by using the roots and determining the orientation.

e.   What domain and range make sense for your function?

f.   Approximate the maximum volume of the tank and the dimensions of the tank that will generate this volume.

9-168.   Use your graph and your tank model to write your report. Include your answers to the following questions.

   a.   Which points on the graph represent tanks that can actually be made? Explain.

   b.   How are the dimensions of the tank related? In other words, what happens to the length and width as the height increases?

   c.   Make a drawing of your tank. (You may want to use isometric dot paper.) Label your drawing with its dimensions and its volume.

─────────   *Further Guidance*   ─────────
             section ends here.

MⒺTHODS AND MEANINGS

Factoring Sums and Differences

The difference of two squares can be factored: $a^2 - b^2 = (a+b)(a-b)$

The sum of two cubes can be factored: $a^3 + b^3 = (a+b)(a^2 - ab + b^2)$

The difference of two cubes can be factored: $a^3 - b^3 = (a-b)(a^2 + ab + b^2)$

─────────   **Review & Preview**   ─────────

9-169.   A polynomial function has the equation $P(x) = x(x-3)^2(2x+1)$. What are the x-intercepts?

9-170.   Sketch a graph of a fourth-degree polynomial that has no real roots.

9-171.   Generally, when you are asked to factor, it is understood that you are only to use integers in your factors. If you are allowed to use irrational or complex number, *any* quadratic can be factored.

By setting the polynomial equal to zero and solving the quadratic equation, you can work backwards to "force factor" any quadratic. Use the solutions of the corresponding quadratic equation to write each of the following expressions as a product of two linear factors.

   a. $x^2 - 10$ b. $x^2 - 3x - 7$ c. $x^2 + 4$ d. $x^2 - 2x + 2$

9-172.   Sketch the graphs and find the area of the intersection of the inequalities below.

$$y > |x + 3|$$
$$y \leq 5$$

9-173.   Determine whether $x = -2$ is a solution to the equation $x^4 - 4x = 8x^2 - 40$. Show why or why not.

9-174.   Use your solving skills to complete parts (a) and (b) below.

   a.   Solve $\frac{x+3}{x-1} - \frac{x}{x+1} = \frac{8}{x^2-1}$ for x.

   b.   In part (a), the result of solving the equation is $x = 1$, but what happens when you substitute 1 for x? What does this mean in relation to the solutions for this equation?

9-175.   The roots of two quadratic polynomials are given below. Write possible quadratic functions in standard form.

   a. $x = -i$, $x = i$ b. $x = 1 + \sqrt{2}$, $x = 1 - \sqrt{2}$

9-176.   Graph two cycles of each function.

   a. $y = -2\cos(x + \frac{\pi}{2})$ b. $y = \sin(x - \frac{\pi}{2})$

Chapter 9 Closure What have I learned?

Reflection and Synthesis

The activities below offer you a chance to reflect on what you have learned in this chapter. As you work, look for concepts that you feel very comfortable with, ideas that you would like to learn more about, and topics you need more help with. Look for connections between ideas as well as connections with material you learned previously.

①   TEAM BRAINSTORM

With your team, brainstorm a list for each of the following categories. Be as detailed as you can. How long can you make your list? Challenge yourselves. Be prepared to share your team's ideas with the class.

Topics: What have you studied in this chapter? What ideas and words were important in what you learned? Remember to be as detailed as you can.

Connections: How are the topics, ideas, and words that you learned in previous courses connected to the new ideas in this chapter? Again, make your list as long as you can.

②   MAKING CONNECTIONS

Below is a list of the vocabulary used in this chapter. Make sure that you are familiar with all of these words and know what they mean. Refer to the glossary or index for any words that you do not yet understand.

coefficient	complex	conjugate
degree	discriminant	factor
imaginary	integral roots	polynomial
quotient	real	remainder
root	solution	x-intercept
zero		

Make a concept map showing all of the connections you can find among the key words and ideas listed above. To show a connection between two words, draw a line between them and explain the connection, as shown in the example below. A word can be connected to any other word as long as you can **justify** the connection. For each key word or idea, provide a sketch of an example.

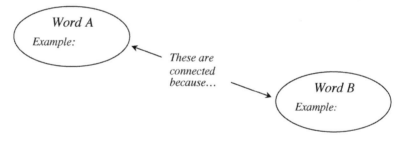

Your teacher may provide you with vocabulary cards to help you get started. If you use the cards to plan your concept map, be sure either to re-draw your concept map on your paper or to glue the vocabulary cards to a poster with all of the connections explained for others to see and understand.

While you are making your map, your team may think of related words or ideas that are not listed above. Be sure to include these ideas on your concept map.

③ GROWTH OVER TIME

This section gives you an opportunity to show growth in your understanding of key mathematical ideas over time as you complete this course.

Part 1: Answer the following question on a separate sheet of paper. Be sure to include everything you have learned since the last time you did this problem, and do not leave out anything you included in your earlier attempts.
How many different kinds of graphs can you create that have

i.   No x-intercepts?   ii.   One x-intercept?

iii. Two x-intercepts?   iv.   Three or more x-intercepts?

For each type of graph, show a sketch, label the key points, and give its equation. Make sure that each graph you give as an example represents a different family and describe the family in words or with a general equation. Show how to calculate the x-intercepts of each of your sample graphs.

Part 2: Compare your three responses to this "Growth Over Time" problem. Write an evaluation of your growth based on your responses. Consider each of the following questions as you write your answer.

- What new concepts did you include the second time you did the problem? In what ways was your response better than your first attempt?

- How was your final version different from the first two? What new ideas did you include?

- Did you omit anything in the final version that you used in one of the earlier versions? Why did you omit it?

- Rate your three attempts by making three bars like the ones below and shading each bar to represent how much you knew on each attempt.

First Attempt:	
Second Attempt:	
Final Attempt:	

- Is there anything you want to add to your current version? If so, add it and keep this version for future reference.

④ SUMMARIZING MY UNDERSTANDING

This section gives you an opportunity to show what you know about certain math topics or ideas.

With your team, make a list of the **big ideas** of this chapter. Discuss the important ideas of the chapter and try to agree on a short list of no more than five big ideas. Be prepared to share your list in a whole class discussion. When the class has reached agreement on a list, continue with parts (a) and (b) below.

a.   Write your own description of each big idea.

b.   For each big idea, provide one or two representative example problems. Solve each problem completely, using multiple representations, if applicable.

WHAT HAVE I LEARNED?

This section will help you evaluate which types of problems you feel comfortable with and which you need more help with. This section will appear at the end of every chapter to help you check your understanding. Even if your teacher does not assign this section, it is a good idea to try these problems and find out for yourself what you know and what you need to work on.

Solve each problem as completely as you can. The table at the end of this closure section has answers to these problems. It also tells you where you can find additional help and practice on similar problems.

CL 9-177. Decide if each of the following equations is a polynomial. If it is, state the degree. If it is not, explain how you know.

a. $f(x) = 3x^3 - 2x + 5$

b. $y = 0.25x^7 - 5x$

c. $y = 3^x - x^2$

d. $f(x) = x^2 - \sqrt{x} + 2$

e. $Q(x) = 3(x - 4)^2(x + 2)$

f. $y = x^2 - 3x + 5 - \frac{2}{x-2}$

CL 9-178. Where do the graphs of each of the following functions cross the x-axis?

a. $f(x) = (x - 2)^2 - 3$

b. $f(x) = (x - 19)^2(x + 14)$

CL 9-179. Write a polynomial equation for a graph that has three x-intercepts at $(-3, 0)$, $(2, 0)$, and $(5, 0)$, and passes through the point $(1, 56)$.

CL 9-180. Decide if each of the following functions has real or complex roots.

a. $y = 3x^2 + 5x + 4$

b. $y = 3x^2 + 5x - 4$

CL 9-181. Make a sketch of a graph $q(x)$ such that $q(x) = 0$ would have the number and type of solutions indicated below.

a.   7 real solutions

b.   5 real and 2 complex solutions

c.   4 complex solutions

d.   2 complex and 4 real solutions

CL 9-182. Sketch graphs of each of the following polynomial functions. Be sure to label the x- and the y-intercepts of each graph.

    a. $y = x(2x+3)(2x-5)$
    b. $y = (11-2x)^2(x-2)$

CL 9-183. Simplify each expression

    a. $(3+4i)+(7-2i)$
    b. $(3+5i)^2$

    c. $(7+i)(7-i)$
    d. $(3i)(2i)^2$

    e. i^3
    f. i^{32}

CL 9-184. Divide: $(2x^3 + x^2 - 19x + 36) \div (x+4)$

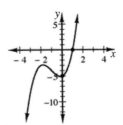

CL 9-185. The graph of $f(x) = x^3 + 3x^2 + x - 5$ is shown at right. Use it to determine all real and complex roots.

CL 9-186. The roots of a quadratic polynomial are given below. Find a possible quadratic equation in standard form.

    a. $x = 2i, \ x = -2i$
    b. $x = 2+\sqrt{3}, \ x = 2-\sqrt{3}$

CL 9-187. Use the system at right to answer each of the following questions.

$$y = 2x$$
$$y = x^2 + 5$$

    a.   Without graphing, what is the solution to the system?

    b.   What does the solution to the system tell you about the graphs?

CL 9-188. Check your answers using the table at the end of this section. Which problems do you feel confident about? Which problems were hard? Have you worked on problems like these in math classes you have taken before? Use the table to make a list of topics you need help on and a list of topics you need to practice more.

⑥ HOW AM I THINKING?

This course focuses on five different **Ways of Thinking**: **justifying, generalizing, choosing a strategy, investigating,** and **reversing thinking**. These are some of the ways in which you think while trying to make sense of a concept or attempting to solve a problem (even outside of math class). During this chapter, you have probably used each Way of Thinking multiple times without even realizing it!

Review each of the five Ways of Thinking described in the closure sections of Chapters 1 through 5. Then choose three of these Ways of Thinking that you remember using while working on this chapter. Show and explain where and how you used each one. Describe why thinking in this way helped you solve a particular problem or understand something new. Be sure to include examples to demonstrate your thinking.

Answers and Support for Closure Activity #5
What Have I Learned?

Problem	Solutions	Need Help?	More Practice
CL 9-177.	a. yes; degree 3 b. yes; degree 7 c. no; it contains a power of x d. no; it contains a power of $\frac{1}{2}$ e. yes; degree 3 f. no; it contains a negative power of x	Math Notes boxes in Lessons 9.1.1 and 9.1.3	Problems 9-9, 9-18, 9-30, 9-41, and 9-57
CL 9-178.	a. $x = \pm\sqrt{3} + 2$ b. $x = 19$ and $x = -14$	Math Notes box in Lesson 9.1.2	Problems 9-20, 9-21, 9-22, 9-38, 9-39, 9-107, 9-126, 9-134, and 9-169
CL 9-179.	$y = 3.5(x + 3)(x - 2)(x - 5)$	Lesson 9.1.3	Problems 9-40, 9-47, 9-49, 9-50, 9-51, 9-52, 9-58, and 9-59
CL 9-180.	a. complex roots b. real roots	Lessons 9.2.1 and 9.2.2 Math Notes boxes in Lessons 9.2.2 and 9.3.2	Problems 9-68, 9-69, 9-81, 9-91, 9-103, and 9-139

Problem	Solutions		Need Help?	More Practice
CL 9-181.	a. b. c. d.		Math Notes box in Lesson 9.2.3	Problems 9-69, 9-101, 9-102, 9-103, 9-104, 9-105, 9-106, and 9-170
CL 9-182.	a. b. 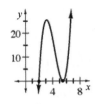		Lessons 9.1.1 and 9.1.2	Problems 9-3, 9-4, 9-8, 9-37, and 9-108
CL 9-183.	a. $10 + 2i$ b. $-16 + 30i$ c. 50 d. $-12i$ e. $-i$ f. 1		Lesson 9.2.1 Math Notes box in Lesson 9.2.1	Problems 9-67, 9-72, 9-73, 9-78, 9-83, and 9-111
CL 9-184.	$2x^2 - 7x + 9$		Math Notes box in Lesson 9.3.1	Problems 9-117, 9-118, 9-119, and 9-125
CL 9-185.	$x = 1, -2 \pm i$		Lesson 9.3.2	Problems 9-120, 9-121, 9-122, 9-125, 9-134, and 9-145
CL 9-186.	a. $y = x^2 + 4$ b. $y = x^2 - 4x + 1$		Lessons 9.1.2 and 9.1.3 Math Notes boxes in Lessons 9.1.2 and 9.3.2	Problems 9-40, 9-47, 9-51, 9-52, 9-58, 9-59, 9-88, 9-89, and 9-175
CL 9-187.	a. $(1 \pm 2i, 2 \pm 4i)$ b. graphs do not intersect		Lesson 9.2.1	Problems 9-11, 9-60, 9-70, 9-71, and 9-151

CHAPTER 10   Probability and Counting

In this chapter, you will develop your understanding of probability, which is often important when making decisions in business or politics. Your knowledge of probability will most likely impact future decisions you will make.

As you work through this chapter, you will learn **strategies** for counting the number of possible outcomes of a situation. You will also discover that the order of events and whether they can occur repeatedly makes a difference in the total possibilities.

Knowing how to calculate the number of **permutations** or **combinations** in a given situation can make some problems much easier. In this chapter, you will work on a wide range of problems, from carnival games and games of chance, to making decisions on social issues.

In this chapter, you will learn:

> The fundamental principle for counting the number of outcomes by multiplying.

> How to count possibilities in situations that require a particular order and in situations where order is not important.

> How to use counting principles to calculate probabilities.

> New connections between algebra, geometry, and probability.

Guiding Questions

Think about these questions throughout this chapter:

How many outcomes are there?

Are they equally likely?

Does order matter?

What tools can I use?

What are the connections?

Chapter Outline

Section 10.1   In the first section, you will use tree and area diagrams, probability, independent events, and expected value to solve problems and resolve questions of fairness.

Section 10.2   Here, you will use the Fundamental Principle of Counting, permutations, and combinations, both to count outcomes for complex situations and to compute probabilities.

10.1.1 Is this game fair?

Probability and Expected Value

In this lesson you will review ideas of probability as you use strategic lists, tree diagrams, and area models. You will find that certain tools may work better for particular problems. In one problem a tree diagram or list might be most efficient, while in another problem an area model may be the best choice.

You will also be asked to decide whether a game is **fair** and to think about **expected values**. A game is **fair** if over many plays, a person would expect to neither win nor lose points or money by playing the game. **Expected value** is what you expect to win per play, on average, based on playing the game many times. Discuss the following focus questions as you work:

> What are the possible outcomes?
>
> Are the outcomes equally likely?
>
> Will a tree diagram, list, or area model help?

10-1.   ROCK, PAPER, SCISSORS

Your team will play a variation of "Rock, Paper, Scissors" (sometimes called "Rochambeau") and record points. You will need to work in a team of four. Have one person act as recorder while the other three play the game.

a.   List the names of the people in your team alphabetically. The first person on the list is Player A, the next is Player B, the third is Player C, and the fourth is the recorder. Write down who has each role.

b.   Your team will play "Rock, Paper, Scissors." The recorder should record the winner for each round. Assign points as follows:

  • Player A gets a point each time all three players match.

  • Player B gets a point each time two of the three players match.

  • Player C gets a point each time none of the players match.

First, discuss with your team which player you think will receive the most points by the end of the game. Now, play "Rock, Paper, Scissors" at least 20 times.

c.   Does this game seem fair? How could you calculate the theoretical probabilities of each outcome (Player A, Player B, or Player C winning)? Discuss this with your team and be prepared to share your ideas with the class.

Problem continues on next page.→

10-1. *Problem continued from previous page.*

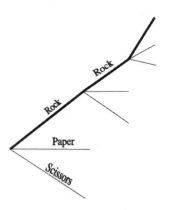

d. Jenna is Player A in her team and she has decided to make a tree diagram to help her calculate the probability that she will win. The diagram she started is shown at right. Work with your team to complete this diagram. How many of the branches represent Jenna winning? Which ones? Calculate the probability that Jenna will win.

e. Calculate the probabilities that Player B will win and that Player C will win. Is this a fair game?

10-2.

BASKETBALL: Shooting One-and-One Free Throws

Rimshot McGee has a 70% free throw average. The opposing team is ahead by one point. Rimshot is at the foul line in a one-and-one situation with just seconds left in the game. (A one-and-one situation means that the player shoots a free throw. If he makes the shot, he is allowed to shoot another. If he misses the shot, he gets no second shot. Each shot made is worth one point.)

a. First, take a guess. What do you think is the most likely outcome for Rimshot: zero points, one point, or two points?

b. Draw a tree diagram to represent this situation.

c. Jeremy is working on the problem with Jenna and he remembers that area models are sometimes useful for solving problems related to probability. They set up the area model at right. Discuss this model with your team. Which part of the model represents Rimshot getting one point? How can you use the model to help calculate the probability that Rimshot will get exactly one point?

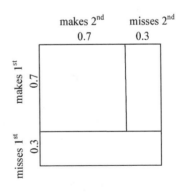

Problem continues on next page. →

Algebra 2 Connections

10-2.   *Problem continued from previous page.*

d.   Use either your tree diagram or the area model to help you calculate the probabilities that Rimshot will get either 0 or 2 points. What is the most likely of the three outcomes?

e.   Many people, when faced with this same problem, guess that one point is the most likely outcome. Their confusion comes from their intuitive understanding of **expected value**, which is the average number of points you would expect over many repetitions of the situation. In this case, if Rimshot McGee were in 100 one-and-one free throw situations, what would we expect to be his average number of points? Discuss this with your team and be ready to share your ideas with the class.

10-3.   With your team, take a minute to examine the area model for problem 10-2.

a.   What are the dimensions of the rectangle? Explain why these dimensions make sense.

b.   What is the total area of the model? Express the area as a product of the dimensions and as a sum of the parts.

c.   What probability is represented by the entire area of the model?

10-4.   DOUBLE SPIN

"Double Spin" is a new game at the fair. The player gets to spin a spinner twice, but wins only if the same amount comes up both times. The $100 sector is $\frac{1}{8}$ of the circle. Make an area model or tree diagram to show the probabilities of every outcome of two spins and then answer the following questions.

a.   What is the probability of winning $100 ?

b.   What is the probability of winning anything at all?

c.   How did your team choose whether to use an area model or a tree diagram? Now that you have calculated the probabilities, do you think you made the right choice? Why or why not?

d.   What is the **expected value** for a winner of this game? That is, what is the average amount of money the carnival should expect to pay to players each turn over a long period of time?

e.   If it costs $3.00 for you to play this game, should you expect to break even in the long run?

10-5.   Marty and Gerri had just lost playing "Double Spin" when they ran into another game
         they had never heard of called "Pick a Tile," in which the player has to reach into a bag
         and choose one square tile and one circular tile. The bag contains three yellow,
         one blue and two red squares as well as one yellow and two red circles. In order to win
         the game (and a large stuffed animal), a player must choose one blue square and
         one red circle.

         Since it costs $2 to play the game, Marty and Gerri decided to calculate the probability
         of winning before deciding whether to play.

         Gerri suggested making a list of all the possible color combinations,
         squares first then circles: *RY*   *BY*   *YY*
                                              RR   *BR*   *YR*

         "So," says Gerri, "the answer is $\frac{1}{6}$."

         *"That doesn't seem quite right," says Marty. "There are more yellow squares in there
         than blue ones. I don't think the chance of getting a yellow square and a red circle
         should be the same as getting a blue square and a red circle. Maybe we need to
         account for all three yellow squares with Y_1, Y_2, Y_3."*

         a.   Make a tree diagram or a systematic list of all the possibilities, using subscripts to
               account for the colors for which there is more than one square or circle.

         b.   Find the probability of a player choosing the blue-red combination.

         c.   Should Gerri and Marty play this game? Would you? Why or why not?

10-6.   How could the area model at right help Marty and Gerri calculate all of the
         probabilities?

         a.   Complete the area model and use it to calculate
               the probability of each possible color
               combination of a square and a circular tile.

         b.   Talk with your team about how this model is
               related to the systematic list or tree diagram
               that you made in problem 10-5. Find as many
               connections as you can and be prepared to
               share your ideas with the class.

$P(R) =$ $P(Y) =$

$P(Y) =$

$P(R) =$

$P(B) =$

10-7.   BASKETBALL: Shooting One-and-One Free Throws Revisited

Dunkin' Delilah Jones has a 60% free throw average.

a.   What would be the most likely result when she shoots a one-and-one?

b.   Is it more likely that Delilah would make no points or that she would score some points? Explain.

c.   On average, how many points would you expect Dunkin' Delilah to make in a one and one free throw situation? That is, what is the expected value?

d.   Try at least three other possible free throw percentages and make a note of the most likely outcome.

e.   Is there some free-throw percentage that would make two points and zero points equally likely outcomes? If so, find this percentage.

f.   If you did not already do so, draw an area model or tree diagram for part (e) using x as the percentage and write an equation to represent the problem. Write the solution to the equation in simplest radical form.

10-8.   Suppose that you were going to flip three coins: a penny, a nickel, and a dime.

a.   Make a systematic list that shows all the possible outcomes. This list of all the possible outcomes is known as the **sample space** for this experiment. Does it matter which coin is flipped first?

b.   How many outcomes are there?

c.   Find the probability of flipping each of the following. Be sure to show your thinking clearly:

i.	Three heads	*ii.*	At least two heads
iii.	One head and two tails	*iv.*	At least one tail
v.	Exactly two tails	*vi.*	At least one head and one tail

d.   Which is more likely, flipping at least 2 heads or at least 2 tails? Explain.

e.   If you have not done so already, represent this sample space with an area model or a tree diagram. Is there one model that makes more sense than the other in this situation? Explain.

10-9.   For what kinds of probability problems might area models be most useful? What about tree diagrams? Are there any types of problems in which either model would be impossible to use? Explain.

ETHODS AND MEANINGS

Probability Models

When all the possible outcomes of an event are **equally likely** (in other words have the same probability), the probability of a sequence of such events can be found by making a simple **systematic list**. However, when some outcomes are more likely than others, a more sophisticated model is required.

Spinner #1

$P(I) = \frac{1}{2}$
$P(U) = \frac{1}{6}$
$P(A) = \frac{1}{3}$

Spinner #2

$P(T) = \frac{1}{4}$
$P(F) = \frac{3}{4}$

One such model is an **area model**. In this type of model, the situation is represented by a square with dimensions 1X1 so that the areas of the parts are the probabilities of the different events that can occur. For example, suppose you spin the two spinners shown above. The probabilities of the outcomes are represented as the lengths along the sides of the area model at right. Notice that the "U" column takes up $\frac{1}{6}$ of the width of the table since $P(U) = \frac{1}{6}$. Similarly, the "T" row takes up $\frac{1}{4}$ of the height of the table, since $P(T) = \frac{1}{4}$. Then the probability that the spinners come out "U" and "T" is equal to the area of the $P(U) \times P(T)$ rectangle in the table: $\frac{1}{6} \cdot \frac{1}{4} = \frac{1}{24}$.

Spinner #1

	$I(\frac{1}{2})$	$A(\frac{1}{3})$	$U(\frac{1}{6})$
$T(\frac{1}{4})$	IT	AT	UT
$F(\frac{3}{4})$	IF	AF	UF

(Spinner #2 labels the rows)

The situation can also be represented with a **tree diagram**. In this model, the branching points indicate the events, and the branches stemming from each event indicate the possible outcomes for the event. For example, in the tree diagram at right the first branching point represents spinning the first spinner.

The first spinner can come out "I" "A" or "U", so each of those options has a branch. The number next to each letter is the probability that the letter occurs.

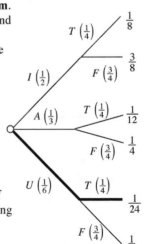

The numbers at the far right of the table represent the probabilities for each sequence of events. For example, $P(U \text{ and } T)$ can be found at the end of the bold branch of the tree. This probability, $\frac{1}{24}$, can be found by multiplying the fractions that appear on the bold branches.

10-10.   Eddie told Alfred, *"I'll bet if I flip three coins I can get exactly two heads."* Alfred replied, *"I'll bet I can get exactly two heads if I flip four coins!"* Eddie scoffed, *"Well, so what? That's easier."* Alfred argued, *"No, it's not. It's harder."* Who is correct? Show all of your work and be prepared to defend your conclusion.

10-11.   Use an area model or a tree diagram to represent the sample space for rolling two standard six-sided dice.

   a.   In the standard casino dice game the roller wins on the first roll if he rolls a sum of 7 or 11. What is the probability of winning on the first roll?

   b.   The player loses on the first roll if he rolls a sum of 2, 3, or 12. What is the probability of losing on the first roll?

   c.   If the player rolls any other sum, he continues to roll the dice until that sum comes up again or until he rolls a 7, whatever happens sooner. What is the probability that the game continues after the first roll?

10-12.   What is the probability that $x^2 + 7x + k$ is factorable if $0 \le k \le 20$ and k is an integer?

10-13.   Rondal High School had a student enrollment of 1245 in 2005, 1328 in 2006, and 1413 in 2007. School officials predicted that the 2008 enrollment would be 1505. The capacity of the school is 1800 students.

   a.   Graph this data. Determine the line of best fit and write a possible equation for that line.

   b.   What do the slope and y-intercept of the line represent?

   c.   Based on this information, when do you predict that the school will reach its capacity?

   d.   According to your graph and data, estimate the enrollment of Rondal High in the year 2000.

   e.   When do you think that Rondal High was built? Explain your thinking.

10-14.   Find all values of a for which the equation $ax^2 + 5x + 6 = 0$ has a solution that is a real number. Express a in terms of one or more inequalities.

10-15.   Solve each equation for $0 \le \theta \le 360$. You may need your calculator, but remember that your calculator only gives *one* answer. Most of these problems have more than one answer. Think about all four quadrants.

   a. $\sin \theta = 0.5$ b. $\cos \theta = -0.5$ c. $4 \tan \theta - 4 = 0$ d. $3 \sin^2 \theta = 1$

10-16.   Verify algebraically that $g(x) = \frac{5x-2}{3}$ is the inverse function of $f(x) = \frac{3x+2}{5}$.

10-17.   As you may remember, earthquake magnitudes are measured by the amount of energy
          that is released. Since the amount of energy released from a large earthquake can be
          millions of times greater than the energy released by a small quake, a scale was created
          (the **Richter scale**) to give magnitudes in numbers that are easy to use. An earthquake
          measuring 3.4 on the Richter scale, for example, releases $10^{3.4}$ kilojoules of energy.

          a.   How many times more energy is released by an earthquake that measures 6.5 on
                the Richter scale than an earthquake that measures 5.5?

          b.   How many times more energy is released by an earthquake that measures 5.1
                than an earthquake that measures 4.3? Give your answer both as a power of 10
                and as a decimal.

          c.   What would the magnitude be of an earthquake that released half as much energy
                as an earthquake measuring 6.2 on the Richter scale?

10-18.   A Nevada roulette wheel has 38 slots numbered
          00, 0, 1, 2, 3, ... , 36. Eighteen of the numbers
          1, 2, ..., 36 are red and 18 are black; 0 and
          00 are green.

          a.   What is the probability of landing on red?

          b.   What is the probability of not landing on
                red?

          c.   The bettor put his money on red twice in a
                row. Use an area or a tree diagram to
                show how to find the probability that he won
                both bets.

10-19.   One way to win in a game with two dice is to roll a sum of six before getting a sum of
          seven. (Anything else that happens – sums of 2, 3, 4, 5, 8, 9, 10, 11, or 12 – are
          ignored.)

          a.   How many ways are there to get a sum of six?

          b.   How many ways are there to get seven?

          c.   How many possible outcomes are important in this problem?

          d.   What is the probability of getting a six before a seven?

10-20.   Harold sorted his jellybeans into two jars. He likes purple ones best and the black ones next best, so these are both in one jar. His next favorites are yellow, orange, and white, and these are in another jar. He threw all the rest in the garbage. Harold allows himself to eat only one jellybean from each jar per day. He wears a blindfold when he selects his jellybeans so he cannot choose his favorites first. What is the probability that Harold gets one black jellybean and one orange jellybean, if the first jar has 60% black and 40% purple jellybeans and the second jar has 30% yellow, 50% orange, and 20% white jellybeans?

10-21.   Solve this system for y and z: $\frac{z+y}{2} + \frac{z-y}{4} = 3$

$\frac{4z-y}{2} + \frac{5z+2y}{11} = 3$

10-22.   Solve each equation.

   a. $\log_2(x) + \log_2(x-2) = 3$ b. $\log(2x) - \log(x^2) = -2$

10-23.   Convert the following angle measurements from degrees to radians.

   a. $30°$ b. $15°$ c. $-75°$ d. $630°$

10-24.   Find the exact equation of this graph.

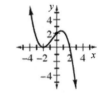

10-25.   Find the value of x.

   a. 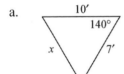   b.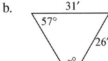

10-26.   A conveyor belt carries grain to the top of a barn, where it drops the grain so that it forms a pile on the ground. The pile is in the shape of a cone. Recall that $V = \frac{1}{3}\pi r^2 h$ is the formula for the volume of a cone.

   a.   Find the volume of the grain when the height of the pile is ten feet and the radius of the base is four feet.

   b.   The cone-shaped piles during each stage of grain dropping are all similar. If the radius of the base is four feet when the height is ten feet, what is the radius of the base when the height is 15 feet?

   c.   Consider the angle the side of the cone-shaped pile makes with the ground. Is this angle changing? **Justify** your answer. If not, what is the measure of the angle?

10.1.2 What are the chances if...?

Conditional Probabilities

In some problems (such as problems 10-2 and 10-7 involving basketball), you need to find the probability of an event when you know that some other event that could affect it has already happened. In other words, you need to find the **conditional probability**. In cases where the other event does not affect the one you are interested in, the two events are called **independent events**. Discuss the following questions as you work with your team:

How can we represent the different probabilities with a tree diagram?
Or with an area model?

What representation is most helpful for understanding the problem?

Which representation is most useful for solving the problem?

10-27.   On the midway at the county fair, there are many popular games to play. One of them is "Flip to Spin or Roll." You start by flipping a coin. If heads comes up, you get to spin the big wheel, which has ten equal sectors: three red, three blue, and four yellow. If the coin shows tails, you get to roll a cube with three red sides, two yellow sides, and one blue side. If your spin lands on blue, or if the blue side of the cube comes up, you win a stuffed animal.

   a.   Draw *both* an area diagram and a tree diagram to represent the sample space for this game.

   b.   Which diagram was easier to make? From which diagram is most useful for showing what result is most likely?

   c.   What is the probability of winning a stuffed animal, P(blue)?

   d.   About how many times would you expect to have to play this game in order to win a stuffed animal?

   e.   If it cost a dollar to play the game and the stuffed animal could have been purchased at the Bob's Bargain Basement for $3.50, was it worth the money? Explain.

   f.   Suppose that you know that Tyler won a stuffed animal. Talk with your team and use your area model to help you figure out what the probability that he started off with heads is? Be prepared to share your ideas with the class.

   g.   In part (f), you calculated the conditional probability of having started with heads given that you knew you rolled or spun blue. Which diagram shows this relationship most clearly? Explain.

10-28.   Imagine rolling two standard six-sided dice. Use an area model to represent all possible combinations of numbers.

a.   What is the probability of rolling a sum of eight?

b.   Maribelle has a sum of eight. What is the probability that she rolled a three and a five?

10-29.   BUILD-A-FARM

In the children's game, "Build-a-Farm," each player first spins a spinner. Half of the time the spinner comes up red. Half of the time the spinner comes up blue. If the spinner is red, you reach into the red box. If the spinner is blue, you reach into the blue box. The red box has 10 chicken counters, 10 pig counters, and 10 cow counters, while the blue box has 5 chicken counters, 4 pig counters, and 1 cow counter.

a.   Sketch an area diagram for the situation where a child spins and then draws. Note that the parts corresponding to the two boxes of animal markers will be quite different.

b.   Shade the parts of the diagram corresponding to getting a pig counter. What is $P(\text{pig})$?

c.   Find P(cow counter), the probability of getting a cow counter.

d.   Now, supposing you got a cow counter, what is the probability that your spin was red?

e.   Find the conditional probability that if you got a cow counter, your spin was blue.

10-30.   If Letitia studies for her math test tonight, she has an 80% chance of getting an A. If she does not study, she only has a 10% chance. Whether she can study or not depends on whether she has to work at her parents' store. Earlier in the day, her father said he was feeling sick and there is a 50% chance he will not be able to work tonight.

a.   Draw a diagram for the situation.

b.   Find the probability that Letitia gets an A.

c.   What are the chances that Letitia studied, given that she got an A?

10-31.   La Troy has been studying very hard for his English test. He thinks that given any
          question, he has a 99% chance of getting it right.

          a.   What is the probability that he gets the first three questions right?

          b.   If the test has fifty questions, what is the probability that he gets them all correct?

          c.   Suppose La Troy wanted a 90% chance he would get every question on the test
                correct. What would his chances of getting each question correct have to be?

          d.   If you did not do so already, write an equation to represent part (c) and solve it.

10-32.   When he was in first grade, Harvey played games with
          spinners. One game he especially liked had two spinners
          and several markers that you moved around a board.
          You were only allowed to move if your color came up on
          both spinners. Harvey always chose purple because that
          was his favorite color.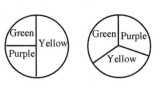

          a.   What was the probability that Harvey could move his marker?

          b.   What was the probability for the better choice of color?

          c.   How often did no one get to move?

          d.   There are at least two ways to figure out part (c). Discuss your solution method
                with your team and show a second way to solve part (c).

10-33.   Sometimes it is easier to figure out the probability that something will *not* happen than
          the probability that it *will*. Show two ways to solve the problem below and decide
          which way you prefer and explain why.

          Crystal is spinning the spinner at right and claims she has a good
          chance of having the spinner land on red at least once in three tries.
          What is the probability that the spinner will land on red at least once in
          three tries?

Algebra 2 Connections

10-34.   Eddie is arguing with Tana about the probability
of flipping three coins. They decided to flip a
penny, nickel, and a dime. If they flipped three
coins, would a tree diagram or an area model be
better for determining the sample space? **Justify**
your answer.

a.   How many outcomes are in the sample
space?

b.   What is the probability of getting each of the
following outcomes? Show all of your reasoning.

i.   Three tails?   *ii.*   At least two tails?

iii.   Exactly two tails?   *iv.*   At least one head?

c.   How would the probabilities change if Tana found out that Eddie was using
weighted coins, coins that were not fair, so that the probability of getting heads
for each coin was $\frac{4}{5}$ instead of $\frac{1}{2}$? Would this change the size of the sample
space? Recalculate the probabilities in part (b) based on the new information.

10-35.   A spinner has just two colors, red and blue. The probability the spinner will land on
blue is x.

a.   What is the probability it will land on red?

b.   Sketch an area diagram for spinning twice.

c.   When it is spun twice, what is the probability it will land on the same color
both times?

d.   Given that it lands on the same color twice, what is the probability that it landed
on blue both times?

10-36.   On another spinner, blue occurs a fraction x of the time, while the red and green
portions have equal area. There are no other colors.

a.   Represent the probability that the spinner will land on green.

b.   Sketch an area diagram for spinning twice.

c.   Shade the region on your area diagram corresponding to getting the same color
twice.

d.   What is the probability that both spins give the same color?

e.   If you know that you got the same color twice, what is the conditional probability
that the color was blue?

10-37.   LEARNING LOG

Looking back at the problems in the last two lessons, examine the use of systematic lists, tree diagrams, and area models. For what types of problems or subproblems is a systematic list most helpful? Tree diagrams? Area models? Reflect on these strategies. Explain how they can be used to represent the sample space in a problem and how they can help find probabilities. Title this entry "Representing Sample Spaces using Systematic Lists, Tree Diagrams, and Area Models" and label it with today's date.

METHODS AND **M**EANINGS

MATH NOTES

Sample Spaces, Events, Probability, Expected Values, Fair Games

A **sample space** is the set of all possible outcomes of an experiment, and an **event** is a group of outcomes within the sample space.

If an experiment has n equally likely outcomes, the **probability** of an event, E, with $m \le n$ equally likely outcomes is:

$$P(E) = \tfrac{m}{n} \text{ and } 0 \le P(E) \le 1$$

To calculate the **expected value** of a set of mutually exclusive events (events that cannot happen at the same time), multiply the probability of each event by the value (or pay-off) for that event, and add the results together. For example, suppose a game-show contestant rolls one die to determine her grand prize. If she rolls a 6, she wins $10,000, but if she rolls anything else she wins $1000. The expected value for her prize is:

$$\tfrac{1}{6}(\$10,000) + \tfrac{5}{6}(\$1000) = \$2500$$

In a **fair game**, the cost to play equals the expected value. If you play a game against several people, then the game is fair if the individual expected values are equal.

Review & Preview

10-38.   Guess what? Another spinner. This time the spinner lands on red half of the time and on green one third of the time. The rest of the time it lands on blue.

a.   Draw an area diagram for spinning twice and shade the region that corresponds to getting the same color on both spins, for each of the three colors.

b.   Suppose you know that the spinner landed on the same color twice. What is the probability that that color was green?

10-39.   What is the probability that $x^2 + kx + 12$ will factor if $0 \le k \le 8$ and k is an integer? Make an organized list (sample space) to help you determine the probability.

10-40.   You decide to park your car in a parking garage that charges $3.00 for the first hour and $1.00 for each hour (or any part of an hour) after that.

    a.   How much will it cost to park your car for 90 minutes?

    b.   How much will it cost to park your car for 118 minutes? 119 minutes?

    c.   How much will it cost to park your car for 120 minutes? 121 minutes?

    d.   Graph the cost in relation to the length of time your car is parked.

    e.   Is this function continuous?

10-41.   Victoria is playing with her balance scale and balances 3 blue blocks and 2 red blocks on one side with 5 blue blocks and a red block on the other. Later, her brother balances 2 red blocks and a blue block with a 40-gram weight. How much does each block weigh?

10-42.   Factor and reduce to simplify: $\dfrac{3x+6}{x^2+7x+10}$. **Justify** each step.

10-43.   Simplify and add $\dfrac{x-4}{x+2} + \dfrac{4x+12}{x^2+5x+6}$. **Justify** each step.

10-44.   After paying $20,000 for a car you read that this model has decreased in value 15% per year over the last several years. If this trend continues, in how many years will your car be worth only half of what you paid for it?

10-45.   Change the angle measurements below from radians to degrees or from degrees to radians.

    a. $144°$ b. $300°$ c. $\dfrac{5\pi}{9}$

    d. $\dfrac{17\pi}{12}$ e. $\dfrac{19\pi}{2}$ f. $220°$

10-46. Antonio and Giancarlo are playing a board game that uses three spinners, which are shown in the diagrams at right. The first is two-thirds red and one-third green. The second is all red and split into four equal parts with the numbers 0, 2, 4, and 6 in each quarter. The third is all green and split into three unequal sections, marked with a 6, a 4, and a 2. On each turn the player has to spin two of the spinners to determine how far he gets to move his marker. The color that comes up on the first spinner determines which of the other two spinners the player has to spin to get the number of spaces to move.

Spinner #1

Spinner #2
Red

a. Make an area model or tree diagram to represent the possible outcomes.

b. What is the probability that Giancarlo will get to move his marker 4 or 6 spaces?

Spinner #3
Green

c. What is the probability he will have to stay put?

d. What is the probability that he will get to move?

e. Antonio was moving his marker 2 spaces. What is the probability that he had spun green on the first spinner?

10-47. Rearrange each equation into a more useful form for graphing. State the locator point and draw the graph.

a. $y = 2x^2 + 8x + 5$

b. $x^2 + y^2 - 2x - 6y = 0$

10-48. Solve the system of equations at right.

$$8x - 3y - 2z = -8$$
$$-2x + 8y + 7z = 26$$
$$4x + y - 5z = 23$$

10-49. Divide: $(x^3 - 2x^2 + 25x - 50) \div (x - 2)$.

10-50. Use your answer from the previous problem to solve $x^3 - 2x^2 + 25x - 50 = 0$.

10-51. Write the reciprocal of each of the following in simplest form.

a. $\sqrt{2} + \sqrt{2}i$

b. $1 - \sqrt{3}$

10-52. If $\cos\theta = \frac{8}{17}$, find $\sin\theta$.

10-53.   Simplify each expression.

a. $\dfrac{1}{x+2}+\dfrac{3}{x^2-4}$

b. $\dfrac{3}{2x+4}-\dfrac{x}{x^2+4x+4}$

c. $\dfrac{x^2+5x+6}{x^2-9}\cdot\dfrac{x-3}{x^2+2x}$

d. $\dfrac{4}{x-2}\div\dfrac{8}{2-x}$

10-54.   Solve each equation.

a. $\dfrac{15}{x-2}=\dfrac{16}{x}$

b. $\dfrac{1}{x}+\dfrac{1}{2x}=9$

10-55.   Graph $y\geq|x+2|-3$ and $y\leq2$ on the same set of axes.

10.2.1 What if the sample space is very large?

The Fundamental Principle of Counting

Phone numbers in the U.S. are composed of a three-digit area code followed by seven digits. License plates in some states are made up of three letters followed by a three-digit number. Postal ZIP codes are made up of five digits, and another four digits are often added. To win the lottery in one state you need to select the right five numbers from all the possible choices of five numbers out of 56. Consider these questions:

- How likely is it that you could win the lottery?
- Are there enough phone numbers for the exploding increase in cell phones?
- Jay wants to know the probability of randomly getting JAY on his license plates so he can avoid paying the extra amount for a special plate.

The sample spaces for these questions are huge. Imagine trying to draw a tree diagram! Tree diagrams with three or four branches, branching two or three times, are messy enough. You need a way to count possibilities without having to draw a complete diagram. In this and the next two lessons, you and your team will develop some strategies that will allow you to account for all possibilities without having to make a complete list or draw a complete tree diagram. As you work on the problems in this lesson, discuss the following questions with your team:

What decisions are we making when we make a systematic list?

How many decisions do we need to make?

How many ways are there to make each decision?

How can we use the patterns in a tree diagram to find the total number of branches?

10-56.   Nick came across the following problem: If a 4-digit number is randomly selected from all of the 4-digit numbers that use the digits 1, 2, 3, 4, 5, 6, and 7, with repeated digits allowed, what is the probability that the selected number is 2763? Nick knew that he had to figure out how many such numbers were possible, in order to know the size of his sample space.

   a.   Nick started to make a systematic list of the possibilities, but after the first few he gave up. What is the difficulty here in trying to create a list?

   b.   Next he started a tree diagram. What problem did he encounter with the tree?

   c.   He decided he needed a shortcut strategy for organizing this problem; otherwise he was going to be up all night. He started by asking himself, *"How many decisions (about the digits) do I need to make?"* With your team discuss his first question and then consider his next, *"How many choices do I have for each decision (each digit)?"*

   d.   Audrey was working alone at home on the same problem at the same time. She was thinking of a tree diagram, when she asked herself, *"How many branch-points will this tree have?"* and *"How many branches at each point?"* Were these the same questions Nick was pondering?

   e.   At the same moment they text messaged each other that they were stuck. When they talked, they realized they were on the same track. The problem asks for *four-digit numbers*, so there are *four* decisions. Simultaneously they said, "We need a **decision chart**."

   $$\underline{\hspace{3cm}} \quad \underline{\hspace{3cm}} \quad \underline{\hspace{3cm}} \quad \underline{\hspace{3cm}}$$
   1st digit   2nd digit   3rd digit   4th digit

   How many choices are there for each decision? How many four digit numbers are there?

   f.   What is the probability that the randomly selected number will be 2763?

10-57.   How many four-digit numbers could you make with the digits 1, 2, 3, 4, 5, 6, and 7 if you could not use any digit more than once in the four-digit number? Show a decision chart. Explain the similarities and differences between this situation and the one described in problem 10-56.

10-58.   Use a decision chart to answer each question below.

   a.   A game contains nine discs, each with one of the numbers 1, 2, 3, 4, 5, 6, 7, 8, or 9 on it. How many different three-digit numbers can be formed by choosing any three discs, without replacing the discs?

Problem continues on next page. →

10-58.   *Problem continued from previous page.*

   b.   A new lotto game called "Quick Spin" has three wheels, each with the numbers 1, 2, 3, 4, 5, 6, 7, 8, and 9 equally spaced around the rim. Each wheel is spun once, and the number the arrow points to is recorded. How many three-digit numbers are possible?

   c.   Explain the similarities and differences between part (a) and part (b).

10-59.   Marcos is selecting classes for next year. He plans to take English, physics, government, pre-calculus, Spanish, and journalism. His school has a six-period day, so he will have one of these classes each period. How many different schedules are possible?

   a.   What is the probability that Marcos will get first-period pre-calculus?

   b.   What is the probability that Marcos will get both first-period pre-calculus *and* second-period physics?

10-60.   On your calculator, find a button labeled $n!$ or $!$. On many graphing calculators, it is a function in the math menu and probability submenu. This is the **factorial** function button.

   a.   Find the value of 8 factorial (written 8!), then 7!, then 6!, 5!, ... , 1!

   b.   Which result is the same as the number of Marcos's possible schedules?

   c.   What do you think 6! means? Why does it give the correct solution to the possible number of ways to arrange Marcos's schedule?

   d.   Explain why 4! gives the correct solution to the possible number of ways to arrange the letters **M   A   T   H**.

10-61.   Remembering what $n!$ means can help you do some messy calculations quickly, as well as help you do problems that might be too large for your calculator's memory.

   For instance, if you wanted to calculate $\frac{9!}{6!}$, you could use the $n!$ button on your calculator and find that $9! = 362{,}880$ and $6! = 720$, so $\frac{9!}{6!} = \frac{362880}{720} = 504$.

   You could also use a simplification technique. Since $9! = 9 \cdot 8 \cdot 7 \cdot 6 \cdot 5 \cdot 4 \cdot 3 \cdot 2 \cdot 1!$ and $6! = 6 \cdot 5 \cdot 4 \cdot 3 \cdot 2 \cdot 1$, you can rewrite $\frac{9!}{6!} = \frac{9 \cdot 8 \cdot 7 \cdot 6 \cdot 5 \cdot 4 \cdot 3 \cdot 2 \cdot 1}{6 \cdot 5 \cdot 4 \cdot 3 \cdot 2 \cdot 1} = 9 \cdot 8 \cdot 7 = 504$.

   Use this simplification technique to simplify each of the following problems before computing the result.

   a. $\frac{10!}{8!}$ b. $\frac{20!}{18!2!}$ c. $\frac{7!}{4!3!}$ d. $\frac{75!}{72!}$

Review & Preview

10-62. A Scrabble® player has four tiles with the letters A, N, P, and S.

    a. How many arrangements of these letters are possible?

    b. Draw a tree diagram that shows how to get the arrangements and explain how a decision chart represents the tree.

    c. What is the probability of a two-year-old randomly making a word using the four letters?

10-63. How many different batting orders can be made from the nine starting players on a baseball team? Write the answer using factorials and as a number.

10-64.   How many distinct rearrangements of the letters in the word FRACTIONS are there?

10-65.   Five students are running for Junior class president. They must give speeches before the election committee. They draw straws to see who will go first, second, etc. In how many different orders could they give their speeches?

10-66.   If $f(n) = n!$, evaluate each of the following ratios.

a. $\dfrac{f(5)}{f(3)}$ b. $\dfrac{f(6)}{f(4)}$ c. $\dfrac{f(9)}{f(7)f(2)}$

10-67.   Eight friends go to the movies. They want to sit together in a row with a student on each aisle. (Assume the row is 8 seats wide including 2 aisle seats.)

a.   How many ways can they sit in the row?

b.   If Kristen wants to sit in an aisle seat, how many ways can they all sit in the row?

c.   If Annabeth wants to sit on an aisle seat with Ian next to her, how many ways can the eight students sit?

10-68.   In the casino game of Roulette, some players think that when the ball lands on red several times in a row that it will be more likely to land on black on the next spin. You can calculate to the conditional probability to demonstrate that this is not the case. In other words, the outcome of one spin of an honest roulette wheel does not have any effect on the outcome of the next one.

a.   Make an area diagram for two spins of the wheel. Remember that there are 18 red numbers, 18 black numbers, and two greens.

b.   What is the probability that the ball will land on red twice in a row?

c.   Based on your diagram what is the total probability that the ball will land on red on the second spin? (P(RR, BR, GR))

d.   Calculate the conditional probability that the first spin was red given that the second spin is red.

e.   How do your answers to parts (d) compare to the simple probability of the ball landing on red for any single spin? The fact that they are all the same means you have demonstrated that the probability of the ball landing on red is independent of where it landed before.

10-69.   How many solutions are there to the system of equations at right? $y = x^2 - 2x + 2$
          Justify your response. $y = 2x - 2$

10-70.   Graph $y = \sqrt{(4 - x^2)}$. Imagine revolving this graph around the *x*-axis, faster and faster,
          so that it appears to form a sphere. Sketch the sphere and then find its volume. Note:
          The volume of a sphere is given by $V = \frac{4}{3}\pi r^3$.

10.2.2 How can I count arrangements?

Permutations

There are many kinds of counting problems. In this chapter you will learn to recognize problems
that involve arrangements and others that do not. In some cases outcomes will be repeated, but in
others they will not. A list of **permutations** includes different arrangements of distinct objects
chosen from a set of objects. In other words, permutations are arrangements of elements without
using any element more than once, or without repetition. As you work on the problems in this
lesson discuss the following questions with your team:

> When we make a decision chart, how many choices do we have after we make the
> first choice? The second? The third? ...
>
> Can we use the same choice we already made again?
>
> Can this situation be represented as a list of permutations?
>
> What patterns can we find in these problems?

10-71.   Jasper finally managed to hold on to some money long enough to open a savings
          account at the credit union. When he went in to open the account, the accounts
          manager told him that he needed to select a four-digit pin (personal identification
          number). She also said that he could not repeat a digit, but that he could use any of the
          digits 0, 1, 2, ..., 9 for any place in his four-digit pin.

          a.   How many pins are possible?

          b.   Notice that the decision chart for this problem looks like the beginning of 10!, but
                it does not go all the way down to 1. Factorials can be used to represent this
                problem, but you must compensate for the factors that you do not use, so you can
                write $\frac{10!}{6!}$. Discuss with your team how this method gives the same result as your
                decision chart.

10-72.   Twenty-five art students submitted sculptures to be judged at the county fair. Awards will be given for the six best sculptures. You have been asked to be the judge. You must choose and arrange in order the best six sculptures.

   a.   If you did this randomly, in how many ways could you choose the six best?

   b.   Show how to simplify the expression: $\frac{25!}{19!}$.

   c.   Where did the 19 come from in the original expression? How could you know the 19 from the numbers in the original problem? Why did 19! in the denominator become an important step in coming up with an answer to the problem? Discuss this with your team.

10-73.   With your team, discuss how you could use factorials to represent each of the following situations. Then find the solutions. Four of the five problems involve permutations, and one does not. As you work, discuss with your team which problems fit the definition for permutations and why or why not.

   a.   Fifty-two contestants are vying for the Miss Teen pageant crown. In how many different ways can the judges pick the next Miss Teen and the runners-up one, two, and three?

   b.   The volleyball team is sponsoring a mixed-doubles sand court volleyball tournament and sixteen pairs have signed up for the chance to win one of the seven trophies and cash prizes. In how many different ways can the teams be chosen and arranged for the top seven slots?

   c.   Carmen is getting a new locker at school, and the first thing she must do is decide on a new locker combination. The three-number locker combination can be picked from the numbers 0 through 35. How many different locker combinations could she make up if none of the numbers can be repeated?

   d.   How many three-digit locker combinations could Carmen make up if zero could only be the second or third number and none of the numbers can be repeated?

   e.   How many locker combinations can Carmen have if she can use any of the numbers 0 through 35 and she can repeat numbers? Is this still a list of permutations?

10-74. Problems about batting orders and questions about how many numbers you could make without repeating any digits are called **permutations**. The following lists give some more examples for determining what is or is not a permutation.

Permutations:

i. All the arrangements a child can make on a line on the refrigerator door with three magnetic letters A, B, and C.

ii. All the 4-digit numbers you could make using seven square tiles numbered 2, 3, 4, 5, 6, 7, and 8.

iii. From a group of 8 candidates, one will become president, one vice-president, and one secretary of the school senate.

Not-permutations:

iv. All of the possible three letter license plates using A, B, and C.

v. The possible 4-digit numbers you could write if you could choose any digit from the numbers 2, 3, 4, 5, 6, 7, 8.

vi. From a group of 8 candidates, three will be selected to be on the spirit committee.

a. Below is a list of all of the license plate letter triples that can be made with the letters A, B, and C.

AAA	BBB	CCC	AAB	ABA
BAA	AAC	ACA	CAA	ABB
BAB	BBA	ACC	CAC	CCA
ABC	ACB	CAB	BAC	CBA
BCA	BCC	CBC	CCB	CBB
BCB	BBC			

How is this list different from the list of arrangements of three cards with the letters A, B, and C printed on them? Explain and make the list of cards to demonstrate your ideas.

b. Imagine two lists of three selected from 8 candidates (for descriptions *iii* and *vi* above). How do they differ? Which list would be longer?

c. What are the important characteristics that a counting problem has to have in order to classify it as a permutations problem?

d. Discuss with your team a *general* method for solving the examples above in the "Permutation" column and write a description for your general method that would work for any problem that could be identified as a permutations problem.

10-75. For the homecoming football game the cheerleaders printed each letter of the name of your school's mascot on a large card. Each card has one letter on it, and each cheerleader is supposed to hold up one card. At the end of the first quarter, they realize that someone has mixed up the cards.

a. How many ways are there to arrange the cards?

b. If they had not noticed the mix up, what would be the probability that the cards would have correctly spelled out the mascot?

ETHODS AND MEANINGS

Fundamental Principle of Counting and *n*!

The **fundamental principle of counting** provides a shortcut for counting the branches of a symmetric tree diagram (finding the size the sample space) by multiplying.

For independent events, if an event A can occur in *m* different ways and an event B can occur in *n* different ways, then event A followed by event B can happen in $m \cdot n$ different ways. For a sequence of independent events, a **decision chart** is a useful tool.

For example: Ivan always has a sandwich for lunch. He may choose from three kinds of bread (white, wheat, or rye), four lunch meats (salami, ham, bologna, or pastrami), and two greens (lettuce or sprouts). Thus, he has three decisions to make: which bread, which lunchmeat, and which green. The decision chart for this situation is shown below.

$$\underbrace{\quad 3 \quad}_{1st\ decision} \cdot \underbrace{\quad 4 \quad}_{2nd\ decision} \cdot \underbrace{\quad 2 \quad}_{3rd\ decision} = 24\ choices$$

Factorial is shorthand for the product of a list of consecutive, descending whole numbers from the largest down to 1:
$$n! = n(n-1)(n-2)...(3)(2)(1)$$

For example, 4 factorial or $4! = 4 \cdot 3 \cdot 2 \cdot 1 = 24$ and $6! = 6 \cdot 5 \cdot 4 \cdot 3 \cdot 2 \cdot 1 = 720$.

Review & Preview

10-76.   Mr. Dobson is planning to give a quiz to his class tomorrow. Unfortunately for his students, Mr. Dobson is notorious for writing quizzes that seem to have no relevance to the subject. With this in mind, his students know that their efforts will be purely guesswork. If the quiz contains ten questions that the students will have to match with ten given answers, what is the probability that Rodney Random will get all ten questions matched correctly?

10-77.   Which is bigger: $(5-2)!$ or $(5-3)!$? Justify your answer.

10-78.   Write an equivalent expression for each of the following situations that does not include the factorial (!) symbol.

    a.   The first five factors of $(n-3)!$

    b.   The first five factors of $(n+2)!$

    c. $\frac{n!}{(n-3)!}$

    d. $\frac{(n+2)!}{(n-2)!}$

10-79.   What do you think 0! is equal to?

    a.   Try it on your calculator to see what you get.

    b.   What does $_8P_8$ mean? What *should* $_8P_8$ be equal to? Write $_8P_8$ using the factorial formula. Why is it necessary for 0! to equal 1?

    c.   Do you remember how to show that $2^0 = 1$? You can use a sequence of powers of 2 ($\frac{2^4}{2} = 2^3$, $\frac{2^3}{2} = 2^2$, $\frac{2^2}{2} = 2^1$, so $\frac{2^1}{2} = 2^0$), but we also know that $\frac{2^1}{2} = 1$. Therefore $2^0 = 1$.

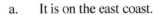

        You can construct a similar pattern for 0!, starting with $\frac{5!}{5} = 4!$ and then $\frac{4!}{4} = 3!$. Continue the pattern and make an argument to justify that 0! = 1.

10-80.   A state is chosen at random from the 50 states. Find the probability that the state meets each of the following criteria:

    a.   It is on the east coast.

    b.   It has at least one representative in the House of Representatives.

    c.   It has three U.S. senators.

    d.   It does not border an ocean or the Gulf of Mexico.

10-81.   Compute the quotient $\frac{(4-7i)}{(8-9i)}$.

10-82.   In the year 2006, the Postal Service required 39 cents postage on a first-class letter weighing less than, but not equal to 1 ounce. An additional 23 cents was added for each ounce, or part of an ounce above that. Graph the relationship between price and weight for first-class mail in 2006.

10-83.   Graph at least two cycles of the following functions.

    a. $f(x) = 3\sin 2(x - \frac{\pi}{4}) + 1$ b. $g(x) = \frac{1}{2}\cos\frac{1}{4}(x + \pi)$

10.2.3 How many groups are possible?

Combinations

In the previous lesson you learned a method for counting arrangements, or permutations. In this lesson you will consider questions such as how many five-card poker hands are possible, how many spirit committees can be selected from the Junior class, or your chances of winning the lottery.

In a five-card poker hand, the **arrangement** of the cards does *not* matter. Since all the spirit committee members have equal status, the **order** in which they are selected does *not* matter. If you have a winning lottery ticket, you will not care about the order in which the numbers are drawn. In these situations, you need to count the **combinations**. As you work with your team on the problems in this lesson, use the following questions to help focus your discussion:

Does the particular arrangement matter?

What are the relationships among these situations?

10-84.   Five members of the Spirit Club have volunteered for the club governing board. These members are Al, Barbara, Carl, Dale, and Ernie. The club members will select three of the five as board members for the next year. One way to do this would be to elect a governing committee of three in which all members would have the same title. A second way would be to select a president, vice-president, and secretary.

a.   How many different lineups of officers are possible? This means a president, vice-president, and a secretary are chosen. Al as president, Barbara as vice-president, and Carl as secretary is considered a different possibility from Al as president, Barbara as secretary, and Carl as vice-president.

b.   How many different governing committees are possible? In this case, it is a good idea to make a list of all the possibilities, which are called **combinations**.

c.   Felicia decides that she wants to volunteer as well.

i.   How many different possibilities for officers are possible now?

ii.   How many different governing committees are possible now? Again, make the list of all of the possibilities, or combinations.

Problem continues on next page. →

10-84.   *Problem continues from previous page.*

    d.   Since there are more volunteers, the spirit club has decided to appoint another committee member.

        i.   If they add a treasurer to the list of officers, how many different ways are there to select the four officers are possible?

        ii.   If they choose a governing committee of four, how many possibilities are there?

10-85.   Compare the results you got for each set of numbers in problem 10-84 when the roles were determined (permutations) and when there were no specific roles (combinations).

    a.   Work with your team to develop a conjecture about the mathematical relationship between permutations and combinations chosen from the same sized groups. Be prepared to share your thinking with the class.

    b.   Test your conjecture by calculating the number of permutations and combinations of 2 items chosen from 6. Does it work?

    c.   How can you generalize your conjecture so that it can be applied to permutations and combinations of r items chosen from n? Write a formula relating permutations (written $_nP_r$) and combinations (written $_nC_r$).

10-86.   Now you will use your graphing calculator to test the formula you wrote in problem 10-85. Try 4 items chosen from 20. Does your formula work?

    a.   How many possibilities would you have to test to be sure that your formula is correct?

    b.   With your team, find a way to justify the logic of your formula. How can you convince someone that it has to be correct for all numbers?

10-87.   In one state lottery there are 56 numbers to choose from. How many ways are there to choose 6 of the 56 numbers? How many combinations of 6 numbers can be chosen from the list of 56? Does the order in which the numbers are chosen matter?

    a.   Find the number of possible combinations for the lottery.

    b.   What is the probability of selecting the six winning numbers?

10-88.   In the game of poker called "Five-Card Draw," each player is dealt five cards from a standard deck of 52 cards. While players tend to arrange the cards in their hands, the order in which they get them does not matter. How many five-card poker hands are possible? Use the methods you developed in today's investigation.

METHODS AND MEANINGS

Permutations

MATH NOTES

Eight people are running a race. In how many different ways can they come in first, second, and third?

This is a problem of counting **permutations,** or arrangements, and the result can be represented $_8P_3$, which means the number of ways to **choose and arrange** three different (not repeated) things from a set of eight. There are several ways to write $_8P_3$:

$$_8P_3 = 8 \cdot 7 \cdot 6 = \frac{8 \cdot 7 \cdot 6 \cdot 5 \cdot 4 \cdot 3 \cdot 2 \cdot 1}{5 \cdot 4 \cdot 3 \cdot 2 \cdot 1} = \frac{8!}{5!} = \frac{8!}{(8-3)!} = 336$$

In general, $_nP_r = \frac{n!}{(n-r)!} = n(n-1)(n-2)...(n-r+1)$ for n items chosen r at a time.

10-89.   There are twelve people signed up to play darts during lunch. How many ways can a three-person dart team be chosen?

10-90.   Find the value of each permutation below.

   a. $_5P_3 = ?$ b. $_7P_4 = ?$ c. $_8P_2 = ?$ d. $_{10}P_3 = ?$

10-91.   The first four factors of 7! are 7, 6, 5, and 4 or 7, $(7-1)$, $(7-2)$, and $(7-3)$.

   a.   Show the first four factors of 12! in the same way the factors of 7! are shown above.

   b.   What are the first six factors of $n!$?

   c.   What is $_nP_6$?

Chapter 10: Probability and Counting   525

10-92.   On a six-person bowling team, only
          four players bowl in any game. How
          many different four-person teams can
          be made if the order in which they
          bowl does not matter?

10-93.   How many different bowling lineups of
          four players can be made in the
          previous problem if order does matter?

10-94.   Here is another way to think about the question: *"What is 0! ?"*

    a.   How many ways are there to choose all five items from a group of five items?
          What happens when you substitute into the factorial formula to compute $_5C_5$?
          Since you know (logically) what the result has to be, use this to explain what 0!
          must be equal to.

    b.   On the other hand, how many ways are there to choose *nothing* from a group of
          five items? And what happens when you try to use the factorial formula to
          compute $_5C_0$?

10-95.   In the card game called "Twenty-One," two cards
          are dealt from a randomly shuffled deck (a regular
          deck of 52 cards). The player's goal is to get the
          sum of his or her cards to be as close to 21 as
          possible, without going over 21. To establish the
          sample space for this problem, you need to think of
          choosing two from a set of 52.

    a.   How many ways are there to do this?

    b.   The tens, jacks, queens, and kings all have a
          value of 10 points. There are four of each in a
          standard deck. How many ways are there to choose two cards with a value of
          10 out of the 16 that are in the deck? What is the probability of being dealt two
          ten-valued cards?

    c.   If you did not already do so, write your solution to part (b) in the form $\frac{_aC_b}{_dC_e}$.

    d.   What is the probability of being dealt two face cards? (Face cards are Kings,
          Queens and Jacks, the cards that have faces.)

    e.   If you did not already do so, write your solution to part (d) in the form $\frac{_aC_b}{_dC_e}$.

10-96.　Given seven points in a plane, no three of which are collinear:

　　a.　How many different lines are determined by these points?

　　b.　How many distinct triangles can be formed?

　　c.　How many distinct quadrilaterals can be formed?

　　d.　Explain why the answers to parts (b) and (c) are the same.

10-97.　If $n > 3$, write a shorter equivalent expression for $n \cdot (n-1) \cdot (n-2) \cdot (n-3)$.

10-98.　Find the value of each of the following combinations.

　　a.　$_{10}C_8$　　　　b.　$_{12}C_7$　　　　c.　$_7C_1$

10-99.　Simplify each expression below. Think about how you could use rules of exponents, the Distributive Property, and the multiplicative property of one to find shortcuts.

　　a.　$3^{-2} \cdot 3^4$　　　　　　　　　　b.　$3^{-4} \cdot 3^4$

　　c.　$(3^{-1} + 3^{-3}) \cdot 3^4$　　　　　d.　$\frac{3^{-2} - 3^{-1}}{3^{-3} + 3^{-4}}$

10.2.4 What kind of counting problem is this?

Categorizing Counting Problems

One of the biggest challenges in solving problems that involve counting techniques is deciding which method of counting to use. Selecting a counting method depends on whether different arrangements of elements will be considered to be different outcomes and on whether elements can be repeated or not in an outcome. As you work with your team on the Ice Cream Shop problem, starting a list of possibilities will be a useful strategy. The list may be too long to complete, but starting it should help.

10-100. **THE ICE-CREAM SHOP**

Friday was the seventh day of the heat wave with temperatures over 95°, and DJ's Gourmet Ice-Cream Shop had only five flavors left: chocolate fudge, French vanilla, maple nut, lemon custard, and blueberry delight. Some customers ordered their ice cream in cones and some in a dish, but everyone ordered three scoops, the maximum DJ was allowing to ensure that the inventory would last.

On Saturday the temperature hit 100°. DJ still had five flavors, but he decided to allow no more than one scoop of a particular flavor per customer in order to keep a balanced variety on hand. On Friday, the customers had more choices because they could order a cone (which most people eat from the top down) or a dish (where scoops can be eaten in any order) and they could have different flavors or more than one scoop of their favorite.

DJ's advertises ***Over 100 Choices!*** When his customers complained that he did not have 100 flavors, he responded, "But I still offer over 100 *choices*!" Was that true on both days?

Your task: There are four counting problems here, two for Friday and two for Saturday. Describe each situation and show how to calculate the number of choices customers have once they decide on a cone or a dish.

Discussion Points

What are some possible outcomes for this situation? Can we start a list?

Does the arrangement or order of the scoops matter?

Can the choices be repeated?

Does our description of the outcomes for this situation fit any of the
counting formulas we know?

Further Guidance

10-101.   It is useful to organize the information in a large 2×2 chart with columns for Friday and Saturday and rows for dishes and cones. With your team set up a 2×2 chart or obtain the Lesson 10.2.4 Resource Page from your teacher and use it to organize the different possibilities. Describe each problem in relation to whether it involves arrangements or repeats elements, and make a prediction about which situation has the greatest number of choices and which has the least.

10-102.   Use what you have learned about the Fundamental Principal of Counting, permutations, and combinations to solve three of the four problems.

10-103.   The fourth problem is more cumbersome because the order of the scoops does not matter and all of the scoops could be different, two could be the same and one different, or all could be the same. This problem has a number of subproblems, and for at least one of them you may need to make a list. Work with your team to identify and solve each subproblem.

_____   *Further Guidance*   _____
                  section ends here.

10-104.   Charlie and his nephew Jake, who is a bottomless hunger pit, went to the state fair. Charlie had promised he would buy Jake three snacks, one when they arrived, one mid-afternoon, and one when they were about to leave. As they were arriving, Jake was trying to negotiate to get them all at once. At the food stand the menu included seven items:

Corn Dogs	Popcorn
Root Beer	Orange Soda
Sno Cones	Cotton Candy
Candied Apples	

Jake has a dilemma. He likes everything on the menu so much that he would not mind having any three items or even any two or three of the same thing. Uncle Charlie thinks variety is good so he wants Jake to choose three different things.

Your task: With your team, categorize the alternatives for Jake and Charlie in terms of arrangements and repetition. Then describe and justify the solution method you would use to count the number of possibilities for each situation. Finally, figure out how many possible ways there are for Jake to choose his snacks for each situation.

10-105. When Jake and Charlie disagree, Jake has a two-thirds chance of getting his way. Draw an area model or tree diagram and calculate the probability that Charlie prevails and Jake has to order three different items and have his snacks spread out.

10-106. LEARNING LOG

Explain the difference between combinations, permutations, and other counting problems that involve the Fundamental Principle of Counting. Make your explanation so clear and thorough that a student who is just transferring into your class can understand counting techniques. Include information about whether arrangements are important and whether elements can be repeated and give examples that illustrate the different possibilities. Title this entry, "Counting Problems and Strategies" and label it with today's date.

Ⓜ ETHODS AND MEANINGS

Combinations

In selecting committees, it matters who is selected but not the **order** of selection or any **arrangement** of the groups. Selections of committees, or of lists of groups without regard to the order within the group, are called **combinations**. Note that **combinations** do not include repeated elements.

For example: Eight people are eligible to receive $500 scholarships, but only three will be selected. How many different ways are there to select a group of three?

This is a problem of counting **combinations**. $_8C_3$ represents the number of ways to choose three from a set of eight. This is sometimes read as "eight **choose** three."

To compute the number of combinations, first calculate the number of permutations and then divide by the number of ways to arrange each permutation.

$$_8C_3 = \frac{_8P_3}{3!} = \frac{8!}{5!3!} = 56$$

In general:

$$\text{Number of ways to choose} = \frac{\text{\# of ways to choose and arrange}}{\text{\# of ways to arrange}}$$

$$_nC_r = \frac{_nP_r}{r!} = \frac{n!}{(n-r)!r!}$$

10-107. On Friday, Randy Random went to DJ's to get a cone.

a. If he made a random selection, what is the probability that he got *all* three scoops the same?

b. What is the probability that he got all three different?

10-108. Connie and Nora went into Ready Scoop to get ice cream cones, but Nora can't make up her mind. The have 23 flavors and she wants 3 scoops.

a. If Nora is very particular about the order of the scoops, how many choices does she have if all of the scoops are different?

b. Nora changes her mind. She wants a dish, not a cone, but she still wants three different flavors, how many ways can she order?

c. Connie says, *"I still want a cone with dark chocolate on the bottom and then any other two scoops."* How many cones are possible with dark chocolate on the bottom?

d. Vlad came in as they were leaving and saw Connie's cone. He said, *"Oh, that's what I want, a cone with chocolate on the bottom and then two other flavors."* The clerk, said, *"Okay, but we have four kinds of chocolate."* Vlad replied, *"Any kind of chocolate will do."* How many different cones could fill Vlad's order?

10-109. John has to graph a set of parabolas of the form $y = x^2 - 4x + 2^n$ where n is an integer and $0 \le n \le 6$. What is the probability that one of these parabolas, chosen at random, will have:

a. One x-intercept?

b. Two x-intercepts?

c. No x-intercepts?

10-110. If $\tan\theta = \frac{1}{2}$ and $\pi \le \theta \le \frac{3\pi}{2}$, what is the value of $\sin\theta$?

10-111.   Jenny and Gina were trying to solve $\sqrt{x+5}+\sqrt{x}=5$. They knew they would have to square the equation to get rid of the radicals, but when they tried it, they got $x+5+2\sqrt{x(x+5)}+x=25$, which did not look much easier to deal with. Gina had an idea.

"*Let's start by putting the radicals on opposite sides of the equation and then squaring.*" she said. Her work is shown at right.

$$\sqrt{x+5}+\sqrt{x}=5$$
$$\sqrt{x+5}=5-\sqrt{x}$$
$$x+5=25-10\sqrt{x}+x$$

"*But there's still a radical!*" she exclaimed, disappointed.

"*That's okay,*" said Jenny, "*there's only one now, so we can get the term with the radical by itself and then square everything again.*"

a.   Follow Jenny's advice and solve this equation.

b.   Use Jenny and Gina's method to solve $\sqrt{2x-2}-\sqrt{x}=1$.

10-112.   If you deposit $1000 into an account that pays 6% interest compounded monthly, how long do you have to wait until the account is worth $4000?

10-113.   Graph each of the following trig functions:

a. $y=2\sin(x)$ and $y=\cos(x)$ on the same set of axes.

b.   Use your answer to part (a) to graph $y=2\sin(x)+\cos(x)$.

10-114.   You are given a bag that you are told contains eight marbles. You draw out a marble, record its color, and put it back.

a.   If you repeat this eight times and you do not record any red marbles, can you conclude that there are not any red marbles in the bag? Explain.

b.   If you repeat this 100 times and you do not record any red marbles, can you conclude that there are not any red marbles in the bag? Explain.

c.   How many times do you have to draw marbles (putting them back each time) to be absolutely certain that there are no red marbles in the bag?

10-115.   Divide (x^3+8) by $(x+2)$. Then use your answer to factor x^3+8.

10-116.   If $a = 2 + 3i$ and $b = 1 - i$, compute each of the following operations:

a. $a + b$ b. $a - b$ c. ab d. $\frac{a}{b}$

10.2.5 What kind of problem is this?

Choosing Counting Methods

The problems in this lesson will require you to use of a variety of counting strategies. You will need to work with your team to interpret each problem in relation to whether arrangements matter and repetition is allowable and whether the situation can be seen as one set of outcomes or must be treated as several alternative sets of outcomes. Discuss these issues as you encounter each problem. The following questions can help focus your discussions.

What does an outcome look like? What are its elements?

Will a different arrangement of the same elements count as a different outcome?

Is it okay to repeat elements within one outcome?

Are there several alternative types of outcomes here?

10-117.   Joaquin is getting a new locker at school and the first thing he must do is decide on a new combination. The three number locker combination can be selected from the numbers 0 through 21.

a.   How many different locker combinations can Joaquin choose if none of the numbers can be repeated?

b.   With your understanding of permutations, combinations, and factorials, discuss with your team whether the name "combination lock" is appropriate.

c.   How many mathematical combinations are possible?

d.   How many choices would there be if you could repeat a number, but not use the same number twice in a row?

10-118. The new worker at Pauli's Pizza Parlor made up a
whole rack of three topping individual pizzas but forgot
to label the boxes. He made one pizza for each possible
choice of three different toppings of the ten that were
available.

a. How many pizzas are on the rack?

b. How many have Canadian bacon, pineapple, and
one other topping?

c. What is the probability of getting a pizza that has mushrooms on it?

10-119. For each of the following problems you may need to consider several subproblems.

a. How many numbers less than 500 can you make using the digits 0, 2, 4, 6, 8?

b. How many numbers less than 500 are there if the digits 0, 2, 4, 6, 8 cannot be
repeated?

10-120. ANAGRAMS

a. How many distinct ways can the letters in the word MASH be arranged?

b. How many distinct ways can the letters in the word SASH be arranged?

c. How many distinct ways can the letters in the word SASS be arranged?

d. What makes each of the problems above different? How are they related?

10-121. If a coin is flipped 10 times, in how many different sequences can heads or tails
come up?

a. How many ways can 10 heads come up?

b. In how many ways can 5 of the 10 coins show heads?

c. In how many ways can 0, 1, 2 or 3 heads show, with the rest tails?

d. Calculate the probability that each of the events in parts (a), (b), and (c) occurs.

e. What is the probability that at least 4 heads come up?

10-122.   Four brown dogs and two white dogs are in a large dog house. Someone tells you that exactly two dogs are asleep.

    a.   What is the probability that the two dogs are brown?

    b.   What is the probability that the two dogs are both white?

    c.   What is the probability that one dog is white and the other is brown?

    d.   If someone also told you the two sleeping dogs were the same color, what is the probability they are brown?

10-123.   LEARNING LOG

Reread your Learning Log entry from Lesson 10.2.4, which contains an explanation of the difference between combinations, permutations, and other counting problems that involve the Fundamental Principle of Counting. Revise your explanation to include any new information you learned from this lesson and add any examples that could remind you of what to look for in a new problem. Add today's date to this entry.

Review & Preview

10-124.   A pizza parlor has 12 toppings other than cheese. How many different pizzas can they create with five *or fewer* toppings? List all subproblems and calculate the solution.

10-125.   Andrea has just purchased a five-digit combination lock. It allows her to set up her own combination. She can use the numbers 0 through 9 for her combination, and she must use five digits.

    a.   How many five-digit combinations can she make so that no digit is repeated?

    b.   How many five-digit combinations are possible if she *can* repeat the digits, but cannot use the same digit twice in a row?

10-126.   Beethoven wrote nine symphonies and Mozart wrote 27 piano concertos.

     a.   If the local radio station KALG wants to play two pieces, a Beethoven symphony and then a Mozart concerto, in how many ways can this be done?

     b.   The station manager has decided that on each successive night (seven days a week), a Beethoven symphony will be played, followed by a Mozart concerto, followed by a Schubert string quartet (there are 15 of those). How long could this policy be continued before exactly the same program would have to be repeated?

10-127.   Solve each absolute value inequality.

     a. $|2x+1| < 5$ b. $2|3x-2| \geq 10$

10-128.   The roots of a polynomial are given below. Find two linear factors and the corresponding quadratic factor.

     a. $x = -2 + \sqrt{3},\ x = -2 - \sqrt{3}$ b. $x = -2 + i,\ x = -2 - i$

10-129.   Graph the inequalities $y \geq |x-2|$ and $y \leq 4 - |x|$ then find the area of the enclosed region.

10-130.   Joanne was making repairs to her deck and needed to buy some supplies. She purchased two posts, three boards, and four piers for $52. Needing more materials, she went back to the lumberyard and bought one post and five boards for $13. Realizing she did not need the piers she made a third trip where she bought three more boards, returned the four piers and ended up with a refund of $34. What was the cost of each item?

10-131.   Use the equation $f(x) = (x+3)^3 - 1$ to complete each of the following tasks.

     a.   Find the inverse equation.

     b.   Graph the inverse equation.

     c.   Is the inverse a function? Explain.

10.2.6 What are my chances of winning?

Some Challenging Probability Problems

In this lesson, you will have the opportunity to apply what you have learned about probability and counting principles to solve some interesting (and very challenging) problems. As you work with your team on one of the following problems, you will probably get stuck at some point along the way. Below are discussion questions that can help to get started again.

What subproblems do we need to solve?

What simpler problem would help us to understand this problem?

How would we start a tree or a list?

Does order matter? Are the outcomes combinations, permutations, or something else?

Are these separate groups of outcomes? Are the probabilities independent?
Should we add or do we need to multiply?

Would it be easier to consider what is *not* an outcome?

10-132.   THE CANDY DISH

A bowl contains three candies: two red and one green. Work with a partner and decide who is player A and who is player B. Then take turns choosing a candy from the bowl without looking. Player A takes one and keeps it, then player B takes one. If the colors match, player A gets a point; if they differ, player B gets a point. Is this a fair game? First try the game experimentally. Then show your analysis of the probabilities.

Now put four candies in the bowl, three of one color and one of another. Will this game be fair? Again, check experimentally then give your analysis using probabilities.

Are there other ways to put different numbers of two colors of candy in the bowl that would lead to a fair game while keeping the rest of the rules the same as in the previous two problems? Try a number of different possibilities (up to at least a total of 20 candies). Analyze each one using probability, make some hypotheses, and report any patterns you see in the results, conclusions, or generalizations that you can **justify** mathematically.

Your task: Prepare a report or poster to be evaluated based on:
*   The number and variety of cases you investigate and analyze.
*   Your organization of the data, your analyses, and your general conclusions.
*   The extent to which you can mathematically generalize your observations and justify your generalizations.

10-133.   CASINO DICE GAME

To play this game, you roll two
dice. If your total on the first
roll is 7 or 11 points, you win.
If your total is 2, 3, or 12 points,
you lose. If you get any other
number (4, 5, 6, 8, 9, or 10), that
number becomes your point.
You then continue to roll until
your point comes up again or
until a 7 comes up. If your point
comes up first, you win. If
7 comes up first, you lose. You
ignore any outcomes that are not
your point or 7.

In pairs, play the game ten times.
Record how many wins and
losses your team has. Combine
your information with other
teams working on the problem.
Are the results fairly even or were there many more wins or losses?

The game you have been playing is the basic dice game played in casinos worldwide.
What is the probability of winning?

Your task: To calculate the probability of winning, you will need to identify and solve
several subproblems. Prepare a report that shows each of the subproblems clearly, as
well as how you solved each one. Your report should also show the exact probability
of winning as a fraction as well as a decimal approximation.

10-134.   **An extra challenge:** Most casinos allow bettors to bet against the dice roller. In this
case, the bettor wins whenever the roller would lose *except when the roller gets a 12 on
the first roll*. When 12 comes up, the bettor does not win or lose and he or she just
waits for the next roll. What is the probability of winning a bet against the roller?
Which is the better bet, for or against? By how much?

10-135. Start with a list of the ways to get each sum 2, 3, ..., 12. For the remaining parts of the dice game, it will help to keep answers in fraction form.

    a. Find the probability of winning on the first roll.

    b. Find the probability of losing on the first roll.

    c. Find the probability of the game ending on the first roll.

10-136. Now consider the other ways to win by rolling the point before rolling a 7.

    a. Find the probability of rolling a 4.

    b. Find the probability of rolling a 4 before a 7. (Note that you are only interested in 4's and 7's for this problem.)

    c. Find the probability of rolling a 4 and then rolling another 4 before a 7. In other words, what is the probability of getting the outcome in parts (a) and then the outcome in part (b)?

    d. Find the probability of rolling a 5.

    e. Find the probability of rolling a 5 before a 7. (You only care about 5's and 7's here.)

    f. Find the probability of rolling a 5 and another 5 before a 7.

    g. Find the probabilities for winning when your first roll is 6, 8, 9, or 10. Look for symmetry as you do this.

10-137. Make a list of the all the ways to win.

    a. What is the probability of winning?

    b. If you won the game, what is the probability that you won by throwing 7 or 11 on the first throw?

    c. What is the probability of losing this game?

    d. Is it a fair game? Is it close to fair? Explain why casinos can allow betting on this game without expecting to lose money.

*Further Guidance
section ends here.*

10-138.   TRIANGLES BY CHANCE

Obtain three dice from your teacher. You may also want some string, linguini, a compass, or some other building material. Roll the three dice and use the numbers on the dice to represent the lengths of sides of a triangle. Build (or draw) the triangle. Record the three numbers in a table according to the type of triangle formed (scalene, isosceles, equilateral, or no triangle). For example, if 3, 3, and 5 came up on the dice, you would record 3,3, 5 under the heading **isosceles** since a triangle with sides of length 3, 3, and 5 is isosceles. Repeat this ten times, and then combine your information with the other teams working on this problem. Examine the data and discuss the results. Based on your discussion, make an estimate for the probability of each outcome. Then calculate the theoretical probabilities.

Your task: Complete a team report or poster that includes:

- Initial estimates of probabilities with your team **justification** for each one.

- The subproblems you solved, including how you counted the possible outcomes.

- The theoretical probability for each case.

Further Guidance

10-139.   First you will need to calculate the size of the sample space for rolling three dice.

a.   How many ways come up so that the result is an equilateral triangle?

b.   How many ways can the dice come up so that the result is an isosceles triangle?

c.   How many ways can the dice come up so that the result is a scalene triangle?

d.   How many outcomes lead to no triangle?

e.   Use your results from parts (a) through (d) to compute the probabilities for each outcome.

=========   *Further Guidance*   =========
          section ends here.

10-140.   POKER

In the basic game of five-card-draw poker, five
cards are dealt to each player from a standard
deck of 52 cards. Players place bets based on
their estimate of their chances of winning.
They then draw any number of cards (up to
five) to see if they can improve their hands,
and they make another round of placing bets.

The winning poker hands (assuming no wild
cards) are described below, in order from best
to worst. Poker is a game that has been played
for many centuries. Players had established
the order of winning hands centuries before mathematicians developed the counting
techniques, which verified that the order was actually mostly correct.

(Note: In the list below, J stands for Jack, Q stands for Queen, K stands for King,
A stands for Ace, and X stands for any card.)

   1.   Royal flush: 10-J-Q-K-A, all the same suit.

   2.   Straight flush: 7-8-9-10-J, any five in a row, all the same suit (A can be
        used before 2 or after K).

   3.   Four of a kind: 2-2-2-2-X, four of a number or face card, and any other
        card.

   4.   Full house: 7-7-7-A-A-, three of one kind and two of another.

   5.   Flush: any five cards of the same suit, not all consecutive.

   6.   Straight: 3-4-5-6-7, any five in a row, a mixture of 2 or more suits.

   7.   Three of a kind: 8-8-8-J-A, three of a number or face card, the other two
        different.

   8.   Two pair: 9-9-5-5-2, pairs of two different numbers or face cards, with one
        other number or face card.

   9.   Two of a kind: A-A-7-8-J, any pair with three random others that do not
        match.

  10.   Bust: no matches, no runs of five in a row, different suits.

Your task: Calculate the number of five-card hands that can be selected from a deck of
52 cards, and then, for the first six of the above hands, calculate the number of ways
the hand can be dealt, and the probability that a player will be dealt that hand. Prepare
a team report or poster that describes your work on both the counting problems and the
probabilities.

10-141.   The most difficult Poker hand to get is a royal flush. To calculate the probability of getting a royal flush, you first need to determine the size of the sample space. How many five-card hands are possible if there are 52 cards to choose from? Then decide how many ways there are to make a royal flush.

   a.   What is the probability of getting a royal flush?

   b.   How many straight flushes are there that are all spades? Making a list will help you decide. Then how many straight flushes are there altogether?

   c.   What is the probability of getting a straight flush that is not a royal flush?

10-142.   Flushes are five cards of one suit.

   a.   How many flushes are possible?

   b.   What is the probability of getting a flush?

10-143.   Straights are five cards in a row, such as 4-5-6-7-8 of any suit.

   a.   How many straights are possible that include 2 or more suits? In other words, how many straights are possible that are not also straight flushes or royal flushes?

   b.   What is the probability of getting a straight?

10-144.   How many ways are there to draw four cards that are the same number? Making a list will help. And how many ways are there to get the fifth card? What do you need to do to get the total number of five-card hands that contain four of a kind?

   a.   What is the probability of getting four of a kind?

   b.   Now consider a full house. First, think of listing the number of ways to get exactly three cards that are the same number. Once you know the three cards, how many ways are there to get the other two cards in your hand the same? What should you do with these two results to get the number of full houses possible?

   c.   What is the probability of getting a full house?

   d.   Recall your result for the number of ways to get three of a kind and figure out how many ways there are to get two cards that are different from the rest of the deck. Use this information to calculate the number of five-card hands with three matching numbers.

Problem continues on next page.→

10-144.   *Problem continued from previous page.*

   e.   What is the probability of getting three of a kind?

   f.   Use a similar method for calculating the number of ways to get one pair and the probability of getting another pair.

   g.   Think about how you calculated the number of full houses and about how you calculated the number of hands with four of a kind. Then calculate the number of hands with two pairs.

   h.   What is the probability of drawing a hand that is a "bust?" How can you use the probabilities you have already calculated?

<hr> *Further Guidance*
section ends here. <hr>

MATH NOTES

(M)ETHODS AND MEANINGS

Definition of 0!

The use of the combinations formula when $r = n$ (when the number to be chosen is the same as the total number in the group) leads to a dilemma, as illustrated in the following example.

Suppose the Spirit Club has a total of three faithful members. Only one three-member governance committee is possible. If we apply the formula for combinations, we get $_3C_3 = \frac{_3P_3}{3!} = \frac{3!}{(3-3)!3!} = \frac{3!}{0!3!} = 1$. Does this make sense?

To resolve this question and make the formulas useful for all cases, mathematicians decided on this definition: $0! = 1$.

Review & Preview

10-145.   Jean Luc's favorite Asian restaurant has six dishes on its lunch menu. He wants to get their three-item combo for lunch and is reminded by the counter-person that he can order two or three servings of the same selection. How many different ways could he order lunch?

10-146.   Make a sketch of the graph of each of the following functions. Describe the graphs.

   a. $y = (x+1)^2(x-2)^2(x-5)^2$ b. $y = -(x+1)^2(x-2)^2(x-5)^2$

10-147.   You roll three different-colored dice and use the numbers on the dice to determine the lengths of the sides of a triangle. For example, 3-3-5 would be an isosceles triangle with base 5. What is the probability of building a right triangle?

10-148.   Given the function $h(x) = -2(x+3)^2 + 2$:

   a.   What are the intercepts?   b.   What are the domain and range?

10-149.   Rewrite each equation in graphing form and identify the key points.

   a. $y = \frac{1}{4}x^2 + \frac{1}{2}x + \frac{5}{8}$ b. $y = \frac{1}{4}x^2 + 5x + 41$

10-150.   Rewrite each of the following in simplest complex or radical form.

   a. $\frac{\sqrt{2}+\sqrt{2}i}{\sqrt{2}-\sqrt{2}i}$ b.   The reciprocal of $\frac{1}{2} + \frac{\sqrt{5}}{2}$

10-151.   Find the distance between the two points.

   a. (x, y) and $(-3, y)$ b. (x, y) and $(-3, 2)$

10-152.   Imagine a circle with a radius of 4 units and a center at $(5, 6)$. This circle is rotated around the x-axis, always staying the same distance from the axis. It sweeps out a three-dimensional figure. What shape is formed? Make a sketch.

10-153.   Your teacher has decided that one person in your class will get an extra 50 points of credit. The lucky person has been narrowed down, so now it is between you and Newton. The teacher says, *"I'm thinking of a number between 0 and 10. Whoever can choose the number closest to it gets the 50 points."* Quickly, Newton yells out, *"Three!"* What number would you choose? **Justify** and explain your answer.

10-154.   Another pizza parlor is having a super special. They have a rack of small pizzas, each with three or four different toppings. The price is really low because they forgot to indicate on the boxes what toppings were on each pizza. They had eight toppings available, and they made one pizza for each of the possible combinations of three or four toppings.

   a.   How many pizzas are on the rack?

   b.   What is the probability of getting a pizza that has mushrooms on it?

10-155. Use the properties of logarithms to rewrite each expression as an equivalent one using only one logarithm.

    a. $\log_3(5) + \log_3(m)$ b. $\log_6(p) - \log_6(m)$

    c. $\log_2(r) + 3\log_6(z)$ d. $\log(90) + \log(4) - \log(36)$

10-156. Simplify each expression.

    a. $\dfrac{x+2}{x^2-2x-3} + \dfrac{x}{x^2-2x}$ b. $\dfrac{2}{x} - \dfrac{x}{x-2}$

    c. $\dfrac{x^2-x-6}{x^2-x-20} \cdot \dfrac{x^2+6x+8}{x^2-x-6}$ d. $\dfrac{x^3+8}{x} \div \dfrac{x+2}{x^2}$

10-157. Solve each equation.

    a. $\dfrac{x+1}{5} = \dfrac{5}{x-1}$ b. $\dfrac{1}{x} + \dfrac{1}{x+2} = 3$

10-158. Graph in three dimensions.

    a. $(2, -1, -3)$ b. $6x - 3y + 9z = 18$

10-159. Find the distance between each pair of points.

    a. $(17, 29)$ and $(-1, -1)$ b. (x, y) and $(-1, -1)$

10-160. In the diagram at right, the point (x, y) is the same distance from $(-3, 4)$ as it is from $(2, -1)$. There are many possibilities for (x, y). Algebraically, what do they have in common?

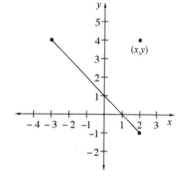

    a.   What is the distance from (x, y) to $(-3, 4)$?

    b.   What is the distance from (x, y) to $(2, -1)$?

    c.   Write the equation that states that the two expressions in (a) and (b) are equal and simplify.

    d.   What is the specific name of the geometric object represented by your equation from part (c)?

Chapter 10 Closure What have I learned?

Reflection and Synthesis

The activities below offer you a chance to reflect on what you have learned in this chapter. As you work, look for concepts that you feel very comfortable with, ideas that you would like to learn more about, and topics you need more help with. Look for connections between ideas as well as connections with material you learned previously.

①   TEAM BRAINSTORM

With your team, brainstorm a list for each of the following categories. Be as detailed as you can. How long can you make your list? Challenge yourselves. Be prepared to share your team's ideas with the class.

Topics: What have you studied in this chapter? What ideas and words were important in what you learned? Remember to be as detailed as you can.

Connections: How are the topics, ideas, and words that you learned in previous courses connected to the new ideas in this chapter? Again, make your list as long as you can.

②   MAKING CONNECTIONS

Below is a list of the vocabulary used in this chapter. Make sure that you are familiar with all of these words and know what they mean. Refer to the glossary or index for any words that you do not yet understand.

arrangement	choose	combination
conditional probability	decision chart	equally likely
event	expected value	experimental
factorial	fair game	independent
order	outcome	permutation
probability	repetition	subproblems
sample space	theoretical	

Make a concept map showing all of the connections you can find among the key words and ideas listed above. To show a connection between two words, draw a line between them and explain the connection, as shown in the example below. A word can be connected to any other word as long as there is a **justified** connection. For each key word or idea, provide a sketch of an example.

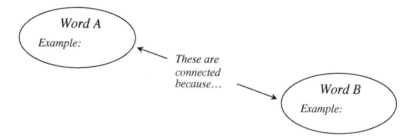

Your teacher may provide you with vocabulary cards to help you get started. If you use the cards to plan your concept map, be sure either to re-draw your concept map on your paper, or to glue the vocabulary cards to a poster with all of the connections explained for others to see and understand.

While you are making your map, your team may think of related words or ideas that are not listed above. Be sure to include these ideas on your concept map.

③ SUMMARIZING MY UNDERSTANDING

This section gives you an opportunity to show what you know about certain math topics or ideas.

With your team, make a list of the **big ideas** of this chapter. Discuss the important ideas of the chapter and try to agree on a short list of no more than five big ideas. Be prepared to share your list in a whole class discussion. When the class has reached agreement on a list, continue with parts (a) and (b) below.

a.   Write your own description of each big idea.

b.   For each big idea, provide one or two representative example problems. Solve each problem completely, using multiple representations, if applicable.

Your teacher may give you a "GO" page to work on (or you can download this from www.cpm.org). "GO" stands for "Graphic Organizer," a tool you can use to organize your thoughts and communicate your ideas clearly.

④ WHAT HAVE I LEARNED?

This section will help you evaluate which types of problems you feel comfortable with and which you need more help with. This section appears at the end of every chapter to help you check your understanding. Even if your teacher does not assign this section, it is a good idea to try these problems and find out for yourself what you know and what you need to work on.

Solve each problem as completely as you can. The table at the end of this closure section has answers to these problems. It also tells you where you can find additional help and practice on similar problems.

CL 10-161. Next June, Joanna is taking a vacation. She will make four stops while she is gone. They will be Pittsburgh, Washington D.C., Philadelphia, and New York City. Joanna is not sure in what order to visit these places. In how many ways can she organize her vacation?

CL 10-162. Four fair coins are flipped. What is the probability of getting three or more heads?

CL 10-163. Part one of the final exam for Algebra 2 contains 10 questions and you get to choose any eight to answer.

    a.   How many different ways could you choose the eight problems?

    b.   If everyone must answer the first two questions, how many ways could you choose the remaining problems?

CL 10-164. How many permutations of all the letters in the word PYRAMID do not end with the letter D?

CL 10-165. A game at the County Fair has two spinners as shown at right. Each spinner is spun once.

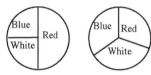

    a.   What is the probability of both spinners landing on red?

    b.   What is the probability of both spinners landing on the same color?

    c.   What is the probability of both spinners landing on different colors?

    d.   If both spinners landed on the same color, what is the probability that is was blue?

CL 10-166. If you pay $2 to spin the spinners in the previous problem, you have a chance to win more money! The County Fair will pay you $7 if both spinners land on red, $5 if both spinners land on white, and $3 if both spinners land on blue. Is this game fair? What is the expected value?

CL 10-167. A bag contains eight blue marbles and four gold marbles. You choose three without replacement.

    a.   What is the probability of getting (in this order) blue, gold, and blue?

    b.   What is the probability of getting (in any order) two blues and a gold?

CL 10-168. Simplify each of the following expressions.

    a. $\frac{(n-1)!}{(n-3)!}$ b. $\frac{n!}{(n-2)!}$

CL 10-169. If five cards are dealt from a shuffled deck of playing cards:

     a.   What is the probability of getting a five-card hand that is all red?

     b.   Express your solution to part (a) in the form $\frac{_aC_b}{_dC_e}$.

     c.   What is the probability of getting a five-card hand that is all clubs?

     d.   Express your solution to part (c) in the form $\frac{_aC_b}{_dC_e}$.

     e.   What is the probability of getting 5 cards from any one suit?

CL 10-170. Consider the following anagrams.

     a.   How many distinct ways can the letters in the word SAKE be arranged?

     b.   How many distinct ways can the letters in the word SEEK be arranged? Be careful!

     c.   How many distinct ways can the letters in the word SEES be arranged?

     d.   What makes these counts different?

CL 10-171. Check your answers using the table at the end of this section. Which problems do you feel confident about? Which problems were hard? Have you worked on problems like these in math classes you have taken before? Use the table to make a list of topics you need help with and a list of topics you need to practice more.

⑤   HOW AM I THINKING?

This course focuses on five different **Ways of Thinking**: justifying, generalizing, choosing a strategy, investigating, and reversing thinking. These are some of the ways in which you think while trying to make sense of a concept or attempting to solve a problem (even outside of math class). During this chapter, you have probably used each Way of Thinking multiple times without even realizing it!

Review each of the five Ways of Thinking described in the closure sections of Chapters 1 through 5. Then choose three of these Ways of Thinking that you remember using while working on this chapter. Show and explain where and how you used each one. Describe why thinking in this way helped you solve a particular problem or understand something new. Be sure to include examples to demonstrate your thinking.

Answers and Support for Closure Activity #4
What Have I Learned?

Problem	Solutions	Need Help?	More Practice
CL 10-161.	$_4P_4 = 4 \cdot 3 \cdot 2 \cdot 1 = 24$	Lesson 10.2.1 Math Notes boxes in Lessons 10.2.2 and 10.2.3	Problems 10-56, 10-57, 10-58, 10-59, 10-60, 10-62, 10-63, 10-64, 10-65, and 10-75
CL 10-162.	$\frac{5}{16}$	Lessons 10.1.1 and 10.1.2 Math Notes box in Lesson 10.1.1	Problems 10-1, 10-5, 10-8, 10-34, and 10-100, and 10-121
CL 10-163.	a. $_{10}C_8 = 45$ b. $_8C_6 = 28$	Lesson 10.2.3	Problems 10-87, 10-88, 10-89, 10-92, and 10-96
CL 10-164.	$7! - 6! = 4320$	Lessons 10.2.1 and 10.2.4	Problems 10-60, 10-119, 10-120, and 10-125
CL 10-165.	a. $\frac{1}{6}$ b. $\frac{1}{6} + \frac{1}{12} + \frac{1}{12} = \frac{1}{3}$ c. $1 - \frac{1}{3} = \frac{2}{3}$ d. $\frac{1}{12} \div \frac{1}{3} = \frac{1}{4}$	Lessons 10.1.1 and 10.1.2 Math Notes box in Lesson 10.2.1	Problems 10-2, 10-4, 10-27, 10-29, 10-30, 10-32, 10-33, 10-38, and 10-122
CL 10-166.	$7(\frac{1}{6}) + 5(\frac{1}{12}) + 3(\frac{1}{12}) \approx \$1.83 < \$2$ so no, but it is close.	Lesson 10.1.1	Problems 10-2, 10-4, and 10-5
CL 10-167.	a. $\frac{8}{12} \cdot \frac{4}{11} \cdot \frac{7}{10} = \frac{28}{165} \approx 0.17$ b. $\frac{_8C_2 \cdot _4C_1}{_{12}C_3} = \frac{28}{55} \approx 0.51$	Lessons 10.2.1 and 10.2.3 Math Notes box in Lesson 10.2.4	Problems 10-29, 10-59, 10-95, 10-118, and 10-122
CL 10-168.	a. $(n-1)(n-2) = n^2 - 3n + 2$ b. $n(n-1) = n^2 - n$	Lesson 10.2.2	Problems 10-78 and 10-91
CL 10-169.	a. 0.0253 b. $\frac{_{26}C_5}{_{52}C_5}$ c. 0.000495 d. $\frac{_{13}C_5}{_{52}C_5}$ e. 0.0019808	Lessons 10.2.3 and 10.2.6 Math Notes box in Lesson 10.2.4	Problems 10-95, 10-118, 10-142, 10-143, and 10-144

Problem	Solutions	Need Help?	More Practice
CL 10-170.	a. 24 b. 12 c. 6 d. When the letters are repeated, we cannot distinguish between them.	Lessons 10.2.1 10.2.2, 10.2.4, and 10.2.5	Problems 10-62, 10-75, 10-120, and 10-125

CHAPTER 11   Conic Sections

To begin this chapter, you will revisit the parabola by **investigating** the principle that makes a satellite dish work. You will discover a new way to define a parabola and will use that new definition to redevelop its equation.

Then you will analyze the shapes that result from slicing a cone with a plane. These shapes are called **conic sections**. Some of them will already be familiar! You will use your algebraic skills to derive new equations and learn how to sketch graphs of these shapes quickly. Finally, you will see how equations of all conic sections are related to one general equation.

In this chapter, you will:

➢ Learn about the special property of parabolas that makes satellite dishes work.

➢ Name and analyze the shapes that result from slicing a cone with a plane.

➢ Learn new definitions of familiar shapes such as parabolas, hyperbolas, and circles.

➢ Complete the square to change equations of conic sections into graphing form.

Guiding Questions

Think about these questions throughout this chapter:

What is the connection?

What do they all have in common?

How can I transform it?

How can I describe it algebraically?

Chapter Outline

Section 11.1 In this section, you will discover a very useful property of parabolas. You will also learn a new way to create a parabola and derive its equation.

Section 11.2 Here, you will identify and analyze the shapes that result from slicing a cone with a plane. You will use your algebraic skills to derive equations and will develop techniques for graphing them efficiently.

Section 11.3 You will further develop techniques for graphing conic sections and will identify what they all have in common. In this section, you will also create your own conic section and analyze it completely.

11.1.1 What is special about a parabola?

A Special Property of Parabolas

In this chapter, you will study new ideas about a group of shapes, some of which you have seen before. In this lesson, you will take a closer look at a parabola and discover a property of parabolas that makes them extremely useful in devices such as high-powered telescopes and satellite dishes.

11-1. What makes a parabola so special? Discuss this with your team. Have you ever heard of parabolas being useful outside of your math class? If so, what have you heard? If not, think of some parabolas you can see in the physical world.

11-2. Have you ever wondered how a satellite dish works? If you slice a satellite dish in half, you will find that the cross section of the dish is parabolic. In this activity, you will learn about a special property of parabolas that make a satellite dish work.

Your teacher will provide you and your partner with the Lesson 11.1.1A Resource Page, a viewfinder, a ruler, a set of colored pens or pencils, a flat mirror, a round-topped pin, and possibly a piece of dry spaghetti.

a. Choose a color and mark a point at the intersection of one of the dotted lines with the **bold** line at the bottom of the resource page. Fold the page so that the colored dot lands on the point shown in the center of the page (called the center point). Make a firm crease, unfold the paper, and use a ruler and the same color to draw a line along the crease.

b. Use another color to mark another point along the **bold** line where it intersects a dotted line, and make another fold so that the new point lands on the center point. Again, make a firm crease, unfold the paper, and use a ruler and the same color to draw a line along the crease.

c. Repeat part (b) until you have at least nine lines drawn in as many different colors as possible.

d. Tape the piece of spaghetti along the line at the top of the page to serve as a guide for the viewfinder, and tape the pin so its head is on the center point. Have one partner place the edge of a flat mirror along one of the colored lines, as shown in the diagram at right. Place the viewfinder behind the piece of spaghetti. The other 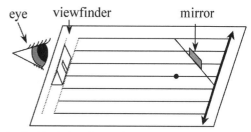 partner will look through the viewfinder along the dotted line that intersects the point that is the same color as the line the mirror is on. Adjust the viewfinder and mirror until you can see a clear image of the pinhead in the mirror. When you see it, mark the spot on the dotted line in front of the mirror.

Problem continues on next page.→

11-2.   *Problem continued from previous page.*

   e.   Repeat part (d) for each of the fold lines drawn in pencil. When you are finished, you should have at least nine marks.

   f.   Draw a smooth curve through all of the points you sighted. What shape is formed?

11-3.   Now that you have seen that focusing reflections to one point can form a parabola and you know that the cross section of a satellite dish is a parabola, how are these ideas connected? How does a satellite dish work? What happens to signals that hit the dish on a path parallel to its axis of symmetry? Discuss this with your team.

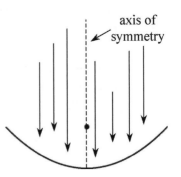

   a.   Draw a diagram like the one at right and complete it to show what happens to the signals that hit the dish.

   b.   If you were building a satellite dish, where would you put the receptor that can read the signals coming in from the satellite? Explain.

   c.   Describe in as much detail as you can why a satellite dish is parabolic. What does the parabolic shape allow it to do?

11-4.   **Investigate** the distance of each point on your parabola from the bold line (called the **directrix**) and compare it to the distance to the marked point on the axis of symmetry (called the **focus**). What do you notice? Create a summary statement about this relationship and be prepared to share it with the class.

11-5.   What is special about a parabola? How can it be used in a telescope or satellite dish? What do all of the points of a parabola have in common? Answer these questions in your Learning Log. Title this entry "Parabolas" and label it with today's date.

11-6.   Graph each of the following functions and label the *x*- and *y*-intercepts.

   a. $f(x) = 3(x-4)^2 - 5$ b. $g(x) = 2x^2 - 3x - 5$

11-7.   For the function $f(x) = 5x^2 + 4x + 20$, find the roots and the vertex of the graph. Then rewrite the equation in graphing form.

11-8.   Solve $\sqrt{x^2 + 6} = x + 2$.

11-9.   Find the distance between each of the following pairs of points.

   a. $(-6, 9)$ and $(2, -4)$ b. (x, y) and $(5, 2)$

11-10.   If Emily bought three pounds of oranges and four pounds of bananas for $8.53 and Beth bought four pounds of oranges and two pounds of bananas for $7.74, how much should Jenel expect to pay for nine pounds of oranges and seven pounds of bananas?

11-11.   For what values of *n* does the equation $2x^2 + nx + 9 = 0$ have exactly one root?

11-12.   Consider the graph of $f(x) = \sin(x)$.

   a.   Describe the graph.

   b.   Could this graph be an example of any other function? Explain why $f(x) = \sin(x)$ cannot be a polynomial function.

11-13.   State the degree of $f(x) = (x+4)(x+1)^2(x-2)$ and sketch its graph.

11-14.   Find the equation of a third degree polynomial that has the roots 3, 2, and −1 and passes through the point (1, 1).

11.1.2 How can I describe it algebraically?

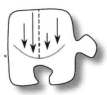

Constructing and Analyzing Parabolas

In Lesson 11.1.1 you learned that one way to define a parabola is the set of all points that are an equal distance from a line and a point that is not on the line. In this lesson, you will use that understanding to construct a parabola with your team and analyze it algebraically.

11-15. Obtain the Lesson 11.1.2A Resource Page and a compass from your teacher. Each team member should choose two different distances to work with. For example, if one team member chooses 4 and 8 units, the other three members of your team could choose 6 and 10, 5 and 12, and 3 and 7 units.

a. Adjust your compass so its radius measures the first number of units you have chosen, using the grid on the resource page to measure units. Using the focus as the center, sketch an arc with your compass that is the correct number of units from the focus point.

b. Now locate the two points on the circle that are exactly one radius length from the directrix. Make sure that the distance you measure from the circle to the directrix is the shortest possible (the perpendicular distance) and is the same as the distance from the circle back to its center. Find these points and darken them on your circle. Then repeat the process for the second length you have chosen. Check to be sure that all of your teammates have done the same on their own papers.

c. Obtain a Lesson 11.1.2A Resource Page transparency and an overhead pen from your teacher. Line up the focus and directrix from the transparency with your own focus and directrix and trace your four points onto the transparency. In the same way, collect points from all team members. Use your overhead pen to sketch the curve that passes through all of your team's points.

d. There is one length where there is only one point equidistant from the center of the circle and the line. What length is this and what point does it give?

e. What should be true of all of the points on your parabola? In other words, what do they all have in common?

Algebra 2 Connections

11-16.   Now you will use your understanding of the points on the parabola to find its equation. Obtain a Lesson 11.1.2B Resource Page from your teacher.

   a.   With your team, place your transparency parabola on the axes on your resource page such that the vertex of the parabola lies on the origin, it is oriented upward, and it is symmetrical about the *y*-axis.

   b.   Mark a point on your parabola *P* (it can be any point on the curve) and label its coordinates (x, y). Draw a line from the point you marked to the focus and another line from your point perpendicular to the directrix. Write an expression that represents the distance from your point *P* to the focus of your parabola. (Note that you are intentionally using the variables *x* and *y* here and not number coordinates. This allows you to **generalize** for any point.)

   c.   Write an expression for the distance between the point (x, y) and the directrix of your parabola.

   d.   What is the relationship between these two distances for a parabola? Use this relationship to write an equation for your parabola. Simplify your equation and solve it for *y*.

   e.   Does your equation make sense? Use your previous knowledge of parabolas to **justify** your decision.

11-17.   How many equations can you find? Choose at least three different ways to place your parabola over the axes provided. You can even rotate it 90°. Use the equal distances (as you did in problem 11-16) to find a new equation for each placement. Be prepared to share your **strategies** and your equations with the class.

11-18.   On graph paper, sketch the parabola that is the set of all points equidistant from the focus (0, 7) and the directrix $y = -3$.

   a.   Find and simplify the equation of the parabola.

   b.   Change the equation of this parabola to shift the graph five units to the right. What would the vertex of your new parabola be?

Review & Preview

11-19.   On graph paper, sketch the parabola that is the set of all points equidistant from the focus (3, 0) and the directrix $x = -5$.

   a.   Find and simplify the equation of the parabola.

   b.   Change the equation of the parabola to shift the graph up 3 units. What would the vertex of the new parabola be?

11-20. Complete the square to convert each of the following quadratic functions to graphing form. State the vertex and sketch the graph.

a. $f(x) = x^2 + 6x + 7$

b. $f(x) = x^2 - 10x$

11-21. Solve each system of equations below.

a. $x - 2y = 7$
$2x + y = 3$

b. $\frac{x+4y}{3} - \frac{6y-x}{4} = -3$
$\frac{x}{10} + 5y = 2$

11-22. Convert the following degree measures to radians.

a. $45°$
b. $75°$
c. $-15°$
d. $450°$

11-23. Verify that $3 + i\sqrt{2}$ is a solution of $x^2 - 6x + 11 = 0$.

11-24. Show and explain why the equation $2^x = 5 - x$ has only one real solution.

11-25. Compute each complex product.

a. $(1+i)^2$

b. $(1+i)^3$

11-26. Sketch a graph of $y = -x^2(x-2)^2(x+2)^2$.

11-27. The mascot for Sacramento High School is the DRAGONS.

a. How many ways can the cheerleaders rearrange the letters in the school mascot?

b. How many ways can the letters be rearranged if the first and last letters are correctly placed?

11-28. A bag contains eight blue marbles and four gold marbles. If you choose three marbles without looking, what is the probability of getting:

a. All blue marbles?

b. Two blue and one gold?

c. All gold marbles?

d. One blue and two gold marbles?

e. Show two different ways to calculate the answer to part (d).

$11.2.1$ What happens when I slice a cone?

· ·

Sections of a Cone

In this lesson, you will **investigate** the shapes that result from slicing a three-dimensional cone with a plane. You will look at these shapes both geometrically, as the intersection of a cone and a plane, and algebraically, as solutions to three-dimensional systems of equations.

11-29.   What will the graph of $z^2 = x^2 + y^2$ look like? Discuss this with your team and make a prediction. Then check your prediction on the class grapher. What shape do you see?

11-30.   What will the graph of $z = 2 - x$ look like? What will happen when the graph of $z = 2 - x$ is graphed on the same set of axes as the graph of $z^2 = x^2 + y^2$?

       a.   Consider the graph of this system on the class grapher. Sketch the graph on your paper.

       b.   What shape do the solutions form?

       c.   Solve the system algebraically. Does your algebraic result make sense when you look at the graph? Explain.

11-31.   Is it possible to get an intersection of a cone and a plane that form a different shape? Discuss this with your team. On your paper, sketch any shapes you think are possible.

11-32.   Now your teacher will change the equation of the plane to $z = 2$, so that it is parallel to the xy-plane.

       a.   What will the intersection look like? Make a prediction with your team.

       b.   Your teacher will graph the system at right on the class grapher. What shape do the solutions form? Was your prediction correct?

$$z^2 = x^2 + y^2$$
$$z = 2$$

       c.   Solve your system algebraically and explain the result.

11-33.   How else could you orient a plane to create a different kind of cross section? Be prepared to share your ideas with the class.

11-34.   Now the plane will change again. Consider the graphs of the cone and the plane represented by the system below on the class grapher.

a.   What shape do the solutions form?

b.   Solve the system algebraically.

$$z^2 = x^2 + y^2$$
$$z = 2 - 0.5x$$

11-35.   Now your teacher will change the equation of the plane that slices the cone to $z = 2 - 3x$, so it makes a steeper angle than the side of the cone.

a.   What will the intersection look like now? Sketch your prediction.

b.   Consider the graph of the system at right. Does the shape of the solutions look familiar? What is it? Is it similar to your prediction?

$$z^2 = x^2 + y^2$$
$$z = 2 - 3x$$

c.   Solve the system algebraically.

11-36.   Are there any other shapes you could generate by making a cone and a plane intersect? As your teacher graphs each of the following systems, sketch the system and describe the intersection.

a. $z^2 = x^2 + y^2$
      $z = 0$

b. $z^2 = x^2 + y^2$
      $x = 0$

c. $z^2 = x^2 + y^2$
      $z = x$

11-37.   Your teacher will assign your team one of the conic sections. Create a poster that shows your conic section as a graphical *and* algebraic solution to a system of three-dimensional equations. Use $z^2 = x^2 + y^2$ as the equation of your cone. You can use the planes given in the preceding problems, or you can choose from the planes given below.

Planes parallel to the *xy*-plane: $z = 4$, $z = 3$, $z = -5$

Planes less steep than the side of the cone: $z = 3 - 0.5x$, $z = 0.25x + 2$

Planes parallel to the side of the cone: $z = 3 - x$, $z = 1 - y$, $z = x + 4$

Planes steeper than the side of the cone: $z = 3 - 3x$, $z = 2x + 3$, $z = 2 - 1.5y$

11-38.   Solve the following systems of equations and describe the shapes of the intersections.

   a. $z^2 = x^2 + y^2$
          $z = x + 2$

   b. $z^2 = x^2 + y^2$
          $z = 7$

11-39.   Find the vertex of the parabola given by each quadratic equation below.

   a. $f(x) = x^2 + 8x + 12$

   b. $g(x) = x^2 - 2x + 3$

11-40.   Where do the graphs of $x^2 - y = 4$ and $y = 2x - 1$ intersect?

11-41.   Solve each equation below for x. Show all of your work. (Your answers will contain the variables a, b, and/or c.)

   a. $cx - a = b$

   b. $\frac{x}{a} - b = c$

   c. $(x - a)(x - b) = 0$

   d. $ax^2 - acx = 0$

   e. $\frac{x}{a+b} = \frac{1}{c}$

   f. $\frac{1}{x} + a = b$

11-42.   Your midterm exam contains 12 questions and you must answer any 10.

   a.   How many different combinations of questions are possible?

   b.   If everyone must answer questions one, two and three, how many different combinations are possible?

11-43.   The big math test is tomorrow! You know that if you have time to study there is a 90% chance of getting a good grade, but if you cannot study there is only a 40% chance of earning a good grade. Your family uses a spinner to see who will have to work at the family business tonight. The spinner has five evenly divided sections and your name is on one section. If you have to work tonight there will be no time to study. What is the probability of getting a good grade? An area model or a tree diagram may be helpful in solving this problem.

11-44.   Graph each plane in three dimensions.

    a. $2x - 3y + 4z = 12$ b. $2x - 3y = 12$

11-45.   Use reference angles, the symmetry of a circle, and the knowledge that $\cos(\frac{\pi}{3}) = \frac{1}{2}$ to write three other true statements using cosine and angles that are multiples of $\frac{\pi}{3}$.

11-46.   The Flat Building's roof is 32 feet wide and 60 feet long. An antenna rises 25 feet above the center of the roof, and wires connect from the top of the antenna to each corner of the roof and to the midpoint of each edge, as shown in the picture at right.

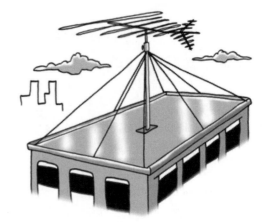

    a.   What is the total length of wire needed (without counting any extra needed for attaching it)?

    b.   The wires that attach to the corners of the building form an angle with the roof. Find the measure of that angle.

    c.   Suppose the height of the antenna is x feet (instead of 25 feet). Represent the total length of the wires in terms of x.

11.2.2 How else can I see it?

Multiple Perspectives on Parabolas and Circles

In Lesson 11.2.1, you learned that a parabola is one of the shapes that can result from slicing a cone with a plane. You have many other ideas about parabolas also. In this lesson, you will focus on parabolas and bring together all of the ways you have of looking at this interesting shape. You will then extend one of your newest ideas about a parabola to help you define a circle in a new way.

11-47.   Polly Parabola, CEO of Professional Parabola Productions, is very confused! She has sent your team the following memo.

> *Dear Study Team,*
>
> *My parabola laboratory has been making parabolas for a very long time now, and we thought we were experts! – until recently. I have heard two rumors that suggest that there may be more to a parabola than we had thought: something about making a parabola from a point and a line and something else about a cone and a plane.*
>
> *Please investigate these new rumors for me. If they turn out to be true, they may help us to design more efficient ways to make parabolas and streamline our ordering process, allowing us to offer an even wider variety of parabolas to our customers.*
>
> *Please have a report on my desk by the end of the day with your findings.*
>
> *Thank you,*
> *Ms. Polly Parabola*

Your task: With your team, demonstrate *all* of the mathematical ways you can describe a parabola. Be sure to use complete summary statements to explain your findings clearly, so that Polly Parabola can understand you.

Discussion Points

How can we create the equation of a parabola algebraically?

How can we make a parabola on a two-dimensional graph without using an equation?

How can we make a parabola on a three-dimensional graph?

Are all parabolas functions?

11-48.   In Chapter 4, you used the equation $y = x^2$ as a parent equation for the family of quadratic functions.

    a.   What was the general equation that you found for the family of quadratic functions?

    b.   You also looked briefly at the family of sleeping parabolas. What was their general equation?

11-49.   In Section 11.1, you learned about a special property of parabolas and a new way to define a parabola.

    a.   Write this new definition of a parabola in your own words.

    b.   Show how you can use this definition to draw a parabola.

11-50.   In Lesson 11.2.1, you learned that the equation of a parabola can be the solution to a three-dimensional system of equations.

    a.   What are the three-dimensional shapes that can form a parabola when they intersect?

    b.   Use algebra to show that a three-dimensional system representing the shapes in part (a) can have a quadratic solution.

Further Guidance
section ends here.

11-51.   The set of all points with a given set of characteristics is called a **locus** of points. A line through the origin is a locus of points where the ratio of the y-coordinate to the x-coordinate is constant. A parabola is a locus of points, and one of the ways to describe a parabola is by using its **locus definition**.

    a.   What is the locus definition of a parabola? In other words, what is true about each and every point of a parabola?

    b.   What do all of the points in a circle have in common? Work with your team to write a locus definition of a circle based on what all points of a circle have in common. Be prepared to share your ideas with the class.

11-52.   Draw a circle with its center at the origin and a radius of 5. Mark a point P on the circle and label it with the coordinates (x, y).

    a.   Write an expression for the distance between point P and the center of the circle.

    b.   Since you know the radius of the circle, you can turn your distance expression into an equation that describes all of the points in the circle. Write and simplify the equation of this circle.

11-53.   Now draw a circle with center $(3, 5)$ and radius 4 units. Again, label a point P with the coordinates (x, y).

    a.   Write an expression for the distance between point P and the center of the circle.

    b.   What is the exact distance between any point on your circle and the center of the circle? Use this distance with your expression from part (a) to write an equation and then simplify the result.

11-54.   Work with your team to **generalize** this process to find the equation of a circle with any radius r and center (h, k). How does your result compare to your previous understanding of the equation of a circle?

11-55.   LEARNING LOG

In your Learning Log, write the locus definitions for a circle and a parabola and show how these definitions can help you find equations. Title this entry "Locus Definitions for a Circle and Parabola" and label it with today's date.

LOOKING DEEPER

Focus and Directrix of a Parabola

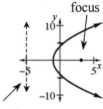

focus

A parabola can be defined in relationship to a line (called its **directrix**) and a point (called its **focus**). All of the points that make up the parabola are equidistant from the focus and the directrix. For the parabola shown at right, the directrix is the line $x = -5$ and the focus is the point $(3, 0)$.

directrix

The focus is also the point at which the reflections of parallel rays (perpendicular to the directrix) from a parabolic mirror will intersect. The distance p from the vertex to the focus is called the **focal length** of the parabola, and it is related to the stretch factor. In the parabola shown above, $p = 4$. Below are some equations of parabolas along with their **foci** (plural of focus).

- The parabola described by $y = x^2$ has its focus at $(0, \frac{1}{4})$.

- The parabola described by $y = 3x^2$ has its focus at $(0, \frac{1}{12})$.

- The parabola described by $y = \frac{1}{8}x^2$ has its focus at $(0, 2)$.

- In general, the parabola described by $y = ax^2$ has focal length $p = \frac{1}{4a}$. Its focus is located at the point $(0, \frac{1}{4a})$, and the directrix is $y = -\frac{1}{4a}$.

Review & Preview

11-56.   On graph paper, sketch the parabola that is the set of all points equidistant from the focus $(0, -5)$ and the directrix $y = 7$.

a.   Find and simplify the equation of the parabola.

b.   Change the equation of the parabola to shift the graph up 3 units. What would the vertex of the new parabola be?

c.   What would the new focus point be, and what line would be the new directrix?

11-57.   Find the equation of a circle with center $(-2, 7)$ that passes through the point $(3, 11)$.

11-58.   Draw a circle and a line tangent to it at any point P on the circle. Now draw a line from the center of the circle through point P.

   a.   What do you know about these two lines?

   b.   What do you know about the slopes of the lines?

11-59.   Using a graph of $y = \sin x$ as a reference, graph $y = |\sin x|$.

11-60.   Solve each equation below for x.

   a. $1234x + 23456 = 987654$ b. $\frac{10}{x} + \frac{20}{x} = 5$

   c. $5x^2 - 6x + 1 = 0$ d. $x^3 - 3x^2 + 2x = 0$

11-61.   Factor and simplify each expression below.

   a. $\frac{x^2-4}{x^2+4x+4}$ b. $\frac{2x^2-5x-3}{4x^2+4x+1}$

   c.   **Justify** each step in simplifying the expression in part (a).

11-62.   For each equation below, state the amplitude, period, and locator point, and then sketch two cycles of the graph.

   a. $y = \tan(x)$ b. $y = \tan(x - \pi)$

11-63.   Solve each equation.

   a. $\log_5(2x) = 3$ b. $\log_5(x+1) = -1$

   c. $\log(4) - \log(x) = 2$ d. $2\log_3(6) + \log_3(y) = 4$

11-64.   Calculate $(2+i)(3-5i) - (1-4i)^2$.

11.2.3 How can I find the equation?

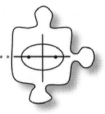

Equations of Ellipses

In Lesson 11.2.2, you wrote locus definitions for a circle and a parabola. An ellipse has a locus definition as well. In this lesson, you will construct your own ellipse and use a locus definition to find its equation.

11-65.   An **ellipse** can be defined as the locus of points for which the sum of their distances from two fixed points remains constant. In this activity, you will use this definition to make your own ellipse.

Directions for constructing an ellipse:

- Obtain a piece of cardboard, tape, two pins, a string, and the Lesson 11.2.3 Resource Page from your teacher.

- Tape the Lesson 11.2.3 Resource Page on top of the cardboard and place your pins on the points $(5, 0)$ and $(-5, 0)$.

- Make two loops on your string 20 units apart, as shown at right. (Measure this on your resource-page grid.) Put a loop over each pin.

- Use your pencil to stretch the string as far as it will go in any direction.

- Move your pencil as far as you can around the pins, *keeping the string taut.*

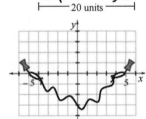

The length of the string is the sum of the distances from your pencil to each of the two pins (or **foci**). As long as you do not add or remove any string and the string remains taut, this sum remains constant and the shape you see on your paper is an ellipse.

11-66.   Choose at least five points on the ellipse you have constructed. For each point, measure the distances to each of the foci and calculate the sum. Does the sum truly remain constant?

11-67.   Mark a point P on your ellipse and label it with the coordinates (x, y).

   a.   Write an expression for the sum of the distances from your point P to each of the pins. (These points are called **foci**, which is plural for **focus**.)

   b.   The length of your string is the sum of the distances from any point on the ellipse to the foci. Use this distance with your expression from part (a) to create an equation.

   c.   Work with your team to simplify the equation you wrote in part (b). Be prepared to share your simplification **strategies** with the class.

11-68.   With your team, compare the ellipse you constructed with its equation. How do the numbers in the equation relate to the graph? Be prepared to share all of your ideas about the possible connections between the equation and the graph with the class.

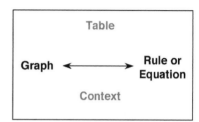

OOKING DEEPER

Foci of an Ellipse

MATH NOTES

Suppose an ellipse has its center at the origin, with x-intercepts at $(\pm a, 0)$ and y-intercepts at $(0, \pm b)$, where $a > b$. Then there are two points on the x-axis at $(\pm c, 0)$, with $c^2 = a^2 - b^2$, which are called the **foci** of the ellipse.

Ellipses also have unique geometric properties; not every oval is an ellipse. To understand the geometric properties of the ellipse, imagine a pool table in the shape of an ellipse, with only one pocket, located at one focus. If you place a ball on the other focus and hit it *in any direction*, it will bank off the rail and go into the pocket. Also, no matter where the ball hits the rail, it will always travel the same distance before reaching the pocket.

11-69. Find the equation of the ellipse you would form using the same process as in problem 11-65 but with a string 15 units long.

Extra challenge: See how far you can get rewriting it to fit the form of your result from problem 11-65.

11-70. Find the distance between each of the following pairs of points.

a. $(8, 4)$ and $(12, 20)$

b. (x, y) and $(-3, -5)$

11-71. Solve each of the following equations.

a. $\frac{x}{x+1} = \frac{5}{7}$

b. $\frac{2}{y} = \frac{3}{y+5}$

c. $\frac{x}{x+1} + \frac{2}{x-1} = \frac{8}{x^2-1}$

d. $\frac{2}{y+5} - \frac{3}{y} = \frac{3}{y+5}$

11-72. Solve for x and y in each system below.

a. $2x + y = 12$
   $xy = 16$

b. $2x + y = 12$
   $xy = 20$

c. Explain how the graphs of (a) and (b) relate to the solutions to each system of equations.

11-73. Sketch the graph of $y = (x + 2)^3 + 4$.

a. Rewrite the equation $y = (x + 2)^3 + 4$ without parentheses. Remember the order of operations.

b. How would the graph in part (a) differ from the graph of the original equation?

c. What is the parent equation of $y = (x + 2)^3 + 4$? Of $y = x^3 + 6x^2 + 12x + 12$?

11-74.   A sequence starts 24, 12, ... Use that information to complete parts (a) and (b) below.

    a.   If the sequence is arithmetic:

         i.   Find $t(3)$.

         ii.   Find $t(n)$.

         iii.   What is the shape of its graph?

         iv.   Which term is –624?

    b.   If the sequence is geometric:

         i.   Find $t(3)$.

         ii.   Find $t(n)$.

         iii.   What is the shape of its graph?

         iv.   Which term is $\frac{3}{128}$?

11-75.   Before radios and satellite communication systems, ships would communicate with each other by using a string of colored flags. With four blue flags and two red flags, how many six flag signals are possible?

11-76.   Use reference angles, the symmetry of a circle, and the knowledge that $\tan(20°) \approx 0.3640$ to write three other true statements using tangent.

11-77.   Use the properties of logarithms to rewrite each equation and then solve. Check for extraneous roots.

    a. $\log(x) + \log(x + 21) = 2$ b. $2\log_4(x) - \log_4(3) = 2$

    c. $\log_2(9x + 5) - \log_2(x^2 - 1) = 2$ d. $\log_7(x + 1) + \log_7(x - 5) = 1$

11.2.4 How can I graph it quickly?

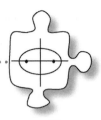

Equation ↔ Graph for Ellipses

In Lesson 11.2.3, you constructed an ellipse and found its equation. In this lesson, you will **investigate** the connections between the equation and the graph of an ellipse and will develop methods that enable you to sketch a graph quickly from an equation.

11-78. EQUATION ↔ GRAPH

With your team, find as many connections as you can between the graph of the ellipse you constructed in Lesson 11.2.3 and its equation. How could you use the equation to make the graph? Be prepared to share your ideas with the class.

11-79. Consider the equation $\frac{x^2}{16} + \frac{y^2}{9} = 1$.

a. Use your ideas from problem 11-78 to help you make a graph.

b. Work with your team to write a general equation for an ellipse centered at the origin with x-intercepts $(a, 0)$ and $(-a, 0)$, and y-intercepts $(0, b)$ and $(0, -b)$.

c. For this equation, the length of the **major axis** of this ellipse is the distance between the two x-intercepts. What is the length of the **major axis** for this graph? What is it in general?

d. For this equation, the length of the **minor axis** of this ellipse is the distance between the two y-intercepts. What is the length of the **minor axis** for this graph? What is it in general?

11-80. How could you change the equation $\frac{x^2}{16} + \frac{y^2}{9} = 1$ to make each of the following transformations? Be prepared to share your equations with the class.

a. The graph moves 3 units to the right.

b. The graph moves 2 units down.

c. The center of the ellipse is $(5, 1)$.

d. What information can you get from looking at an equation of *any* ellipse that can help you sketch a graph?

11-81.   The 16 and the 9 in the equation $\frac{x^2}{16} + \frac{y^2}{9} = 1$ give useful information about the graph of the ellipse.

   a.   What information do the 16 and the 9 give?

   b.   If the ellipse is shifted so that its center is not on the origin (like $\frac{(x-5)^2}{16} + \frac{(y-1)^2}{9} = 1$), what information do the 16 and the 9 give now?

   c.   The four points on an ellipse, the one farthest to the right, one farthest to the left, one highest, and one lowest are called the **vertices** of the ellipse. Find the coordinates of the vertices of $\frac{(x-5)^2}{16} + \frac{(y-1)^2}{9} = 1$ and sketch the graph. Be prepared to share your strategies with the class.

11-82.   Find the equation of the ellipse at right. When you have decided on an equation, test it on the class grapher.

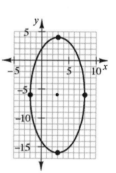

11-83.   Use the information from each equation below to make graphs of the ellipses. Label the center and the vertices of each graph.

   a. $\frac{x^2}{9} + \frac{y^2}{64} = 1$

   b. $\frac{(x-3)^2}{16} + \frac{(y+2)^2}{9} = 1$

   c. $\frac{(x-2)^2}{25} + (y+1)^2 = 1$

   d. $x^2 + \frac{(y-4)^2}{9} = 1$

11-84.   Write the general equation for an ellipse centered at (h, k) with a horizontal major axis of length $2a$ and a vertical minor axis of length $2b$.

11-85.   LEARNING LOG

   In your Learning Log, explain everything you know about the connections between the graph of an ellipse and its equation. Title this entry "Equation $\leftrightarrow$ Graph for Ellipses" and label it with today's date.

METHODS AND MEANINGS

Ellipses and Eccentricity

The line segment that connects the two farthest extremes of the ellipse in the long direction is called the **major axis** of the ellipse, and the distance from the center of the ellipse to one end of the major axis is called the **semi-major axis**. The line segment that connects the two closer extremes is called the **minor axis** of the ellipse, and the distance from the center of the ellipse to one end of the minor axis is called the **semi-minor axis**. If a is the length of the semi-major axis, b is the length of the semi-minor axis, and (h, k) is the center, the equation of the ellipse can be written:

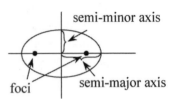

semi-minor axis

foci   semi-major axis

$$\frac{(x-h)^2}{a^2} + \frac{(y-k)^2}{b^2} = 1 \text{, if the major axis is horizontal, or}$$

$$\frac{(x-h)^2}{b^2} + \frac{(y-k)^2}{a^2} = 1 \text{, if the major axis is vertical.}$$

Eccentricity is a term that refers to a measure of the shape of the ellipse. Eccentricity can be calculated with the formula $e = \frac{c}{a}$, where c is the distance from the center to the focus, and $c^2 = a^2 - b^2$. Since $c < a$, the eccentricity of an ellipse is always between 0 and 1. The larger the eccentricity of an ellipse, the more elongated the ellipse appears. The smaller the eccentricity, the more the shape of an ellipse resembles a circle.

Review & Preview

11-86.   Graph each of the following ellipses.

a. $\frac{x^2}{25} + \frac{y^2}{100} = 1$

b. $\frac{(x-4)^2}{64} + \frac{(y+3)^2}{9} = 1$

11-87.   Find the distance from the point $(4, 10)$ to each line or point described below.

a.   The line $x = -4$.

b.   The line $y = 7$.

c.   The point $(3, 7)$.

d.   The point $(5, -4)$.

11-88.   Solve the following equations.

a. $\frac{3}{x} + \frac{5}{x-7} = -2$

b. $\frac{2x+3}{4} - \frac{x-7}{6} = \frac{2x-3}{12}$

11-89.   Betty's Quick Stop makes a 15% profit on its lunches and a 22% profit on its dinners. If Betty took in $2700 on Tuesday and made $513.01 profit, how much did Betty take in on lunch? Write one or two equations, then solve.

11-90.   Show how to solve the equations below *without* using your calculator. You will have radicals or logarithms in your answers.

a. $3^x = 17$

b. $x^3 = 17$

11-91.   Write the equation of the line tangent to the graph of $(x-7)^2 + (y-2)^2 = 169$ at the point $(12, 14)$. (Hint: Drawing a diagram will help.)

11-92.   For the polynomial function $f(x) = x^3 - 5x^2 + 11x - 15$, which of the following are possible factors?

a. $(x+1)$ b. $(x-2)$ c. $(x+4)$ d. $(x-3)$

11-93   Using your answers to the previous problem:

a.   Factor $f(x) = x^3 - 5x^2 + 11x - 15$.

b.   Solve $f(x) = 0$.

11-94.   For an object shot into the air, its height h in feet above the ground after t seconds is given by the equation $h = 80t - 16t^2$. Use this equation to answer the following questions.

a.   For what times is the object on the ground?

b.   For what domain is this function reasonable?

c.   How long did it take the object to hit the ground?

d.   For what times is the height greater than 64 feet?

11.2.5 What if I use a constant difference?

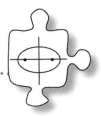

A New Conic Section

Imagine mathematicians studying the conic sections before their equations were known. They had just finished studying the ellipse, which has to do with a *sum* of distances. Now they are curious about what would happen, if instead of considering a *sum* of distances, they considered a *difference* of distances. They wondered what shape would result from the set of points where the *difference* of distances from two fixed points to any point on the curve remained constant. In other words, what is the curve that is the locus of points where the *difference* in the distances to two given points is always the same?

11-95.   How would the algebraic
analysis of a conic section
change if you were considering
a difference instead of a sum?

a.   Draw a set of axes on
graph paper and draw two
focus points at $(5, 0)$ and
$(-5, 0)$. Then mark a
point P somewhere else
and label it (x, y). You
will assume that this point
is on your new curve.

b.   With your team, write an expression for the difference of distances from any
point P to each of the foci. You can look back at your work with the ellipse in
problem 11-67 to help you.

c.   Any real number will work for the constant distance, but some numbers are more
convenient than others. A constant difference of 6 units works well. To find out
what will happen, set the expression you got for the difference in part (b) equal to
6 to write an equation.

d.   Work with your team to simplify the equation you got in part (c). Again, you can
look at the work you did with the equation of the ellipse to help you, but be
careful with the negative signs. Be prepared to share your **strategies** and results
with the class.

11-96.   Now that you have the equation, it is time to figure out what the graph looks like. What information can you get from the equation that can help you draw a graph?

   a.   Can you find the x- and y-intercepts from the equation? Explain. Do you have enough information to figure out the shape of the graph?

   b.   Make an $x \rightarrow y$ table with enough entries to make a complete and accurate graph. What happens when you try 0, ±1, or ±2 for x? Describe the shape of the graph. Does it look like anything you have seen before? What is the domain for this relation?

11-97.   The curve that you have just graphed is a hyperbola, and, as you may recall, it is one of the shapes resulting from slicing a cone with a plane. You may remember from graphing hyperbolas in the past that hyperbolas have asymptotes.

   a.   Sketch a graph of the hyperbola described by $y = \frac{5}{x}$. What are the equations of its asymptotes?

   b.   The hyperbola that you graphed in problem 11-96 is shown at right, along with its asymptotes. How are its asymptotes different from the ones that you have seen before?

   c.   Work with your team to estimate the equations of the asymptotes of the hyperbola described by $\frac{x^2}{9} - \frac{y^2}{16} = 1$. Be prepared to share your **strategies** and results with the class.

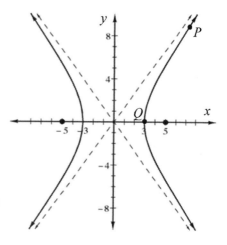

11-98.   With your team, compare your hyperbola with its equation. How do the numbers in the equation relate to the graph? Be prepared to share your ideas about the possible connections between the equation and the graph of a hyperbola.

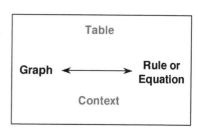

![L](magnifying glass) OOKING DEEPER

MATH NOTES

Orientation of Conic Sections

Why was the directrix for the parabola always either horizontal or vertical? In other words, why are the parabolas you analyzed oriented either directly up, down, left, or right? What if the directrix were some other line and the parabola was oriented in a different direction?

At right is a parabola with directrix $y = -x$ and focus $(3, 3)$. Notice the point P on the parabola labeled with the coordinates (x, y). The expression for the distance between point P and the focus of the parabola is simple to write; it is $\sqrt{(x-3)^2 + (y-3)^2}$.

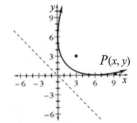

The expression for the shortest distance between point P and the directrix, on the other hand, is very challenging to write, because the directrix is neither horizontal nor vertical. Similarly, when analyzing a hyperbola from its locus definition, it is much simpler to orient it directly left-right or up-down.

At right is a sketch of the function $f(x) = \frac{5}{x}$. Notice that its lines of symmetry are $y = x$ and $y = -x$. If the hyperbola were rotated $45°$ clockwise, the new lines of symmetry would be $x = 0$ and $y = 0$.

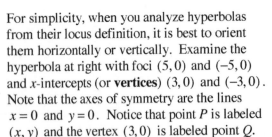

For simplicity, when you analyze hyperbolas from their locus definition, it is best to orient them horizontally or vertically. Examine the hyperbola at right with foci $(5, 0)$ and $(-5, 0)$ and x-intercepts (or **vertices**) $(3, 0)$ and $(-3, 0)$. Note that the axes of symmetry are the lines $x = 0$ and $y = 0$. Notice that point P is labeled (x, y) and the vertex $(3, 0)$ is labeled point Q.

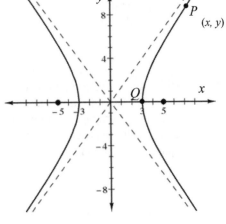

The difference of the distances from point P to each of the focus points is given by $\left| \sqrt{(x+5)^2 + y^2} - \sqrt{(x-5)^2 + y^2} \right|$. The difference of distances from the vertex Q to each of the focus points is 6 units. When you set these differences equal to each other, you get the equation of the hyperbola $\left| \sqrt{(x+5)^2 + y^2} - \sqrt{(x-5)^2 + y^2} \right| = 6$, which simplifies to $\frac{x^2}{9} - \frac{y^2}{16} = 1$.

11-99.   Graph each of the following ellipses.

a. $\dfrac{x^2}{4} + \dfrac{y^2}{9} = 1$

b. $\dfrac{(x+2)^2}{25} + \dfrac{(y-1)^2}{16} = 1$

11-100.   Find the equation of the line tangent to the circle $x^2 + y^2 = 25$ at each of the following points.

a. $(5, 0)$

b. $(3, 4)$

11-101.   Dolores says that the solutions for $x^2 - x + 1 = 0$ are $\frac{1}{2} \pm \frac{i\sqrt{3}}{2}$. Is she correct? Explain your answer.

11-102.   Write a possible equation for the graph at right.

11-103.   Find the solutions to the system at right. The solutions may be real or complex.

$y = x^2 + 2x + 5$

$y = 2x^2 + 4x + 7$

11-104.   Without graphing, find where each of the following curves crosses the x-axis. (Find the *exact* points!)

a. $f(x) = x^2 - x - 12$

b. $f(x) = 2x^2 - 3x - 9$

c. $f(x) = 2x^2 + x - 7$

d. $f(x) = 3x^2 - 2x + 7$

e. $f(x) = 3x^3 + 2x^2 - 8x$

f. $f(x) = 2x^3 + 2x^2 + 13x$

11-105.   Use properties of exponents to rewrite each expression below so that it involves only multiplication and exponents.

a. $\dfrac{(-2x)^3 yz^2}{2^{-1}\sqrt{x}y^{-3}}$

b. $\dfrac{3x^2 y^3}{\sqrt{3x}\sqrt[3]{y}}$

11-106.   The graph of $f(x) = x^2 - 3x - 4$ is shown at right.
Use the graph to solve:

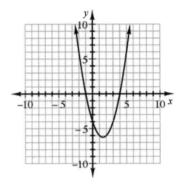

a. $f(x) = 0$

b. $f(x) \geq 0$

c. $f(x) \leq 0$

11-107.   Three bouquet styles from Kris's Flower Shoppe are most popular. Style #1 uses three small bunches of carnations, four lilies, and two small bunches of daisies. Style #2 uses five small bunches of carnations and three small bunches of daisies. Style #3 uses one small bunch of carnations, four lilies, and four small bunches of daisies.

a.   Organize the information into a *styles × flowers* matrix named B.

b.   Carnations cost $2.75 for a small bunch, lilies cost $0.60 each, and daisies cost $1.00 for a small bunch. Organize the costs in a matrix named C.

c.   Which product, BC or CB, makes sense to find the cost of each bouquet? Find that product.

$11.2.6$ How can I graph it quickly?

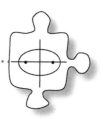

Equation $\leftrightarrow$ Graph for Hyperbolas

In this lesson, you will continue to build your understanding of hyperbolas as you explore the relationships between the graphs of hyperbolas and their equations.

11-108.   Is it necessary to make an $x \rightarrow y$ table in order to graph a hyperbola? What information would be enough to allow you to make a reasonably accurate graph without plotting numerous points? Discuss this with your team and be prepared to share your ideas with the class.

11-109.   As you learned in Lesson 11.2.5, hyperbolas have asymptotes. This is shown in the diagram at right. The steps below will help you find the asymptotes for the hyperbola described by $\frac{x^2}{9} - \frac{y^2}{16} = 1$.

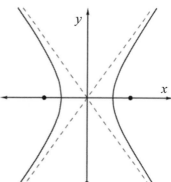

   a.   Start by solving the equation of the hyperbola for y.

   b.   You can see from the diagram that as the value of x becomes extremely large, the curve of the hyperbola approaches the line of the asymptote. As x becomes very large, which number in the equation has little effect on the value of y?

   c.   Try some large numbers for x (such as $x = 100$) with and without subtracting the 1. What do you notice?

   d.   Write the equation of the hyperbola without the -1 under the radical. Then simplify the equation. What lines do the branches of the hyperbola approach as x gets very large? These are the asymptotes of the hyperbola.

   e.   Add the asymptotes to your graph of $\frac{x^2}{9} - \frac{y^2}{16} = 1$.

   f.   What information about the graph of a hyperbola centered at the origin can you find from looking at its equation?

11-110.   Sketch a graph of $\frac{y^2}{36} - \frac{x^2}{25} = 1$ by finding the asymptotes and intercepts.

11-111.   What do you need to know about a hyperbola?

      a.   What do you need to know about a hyperbola to sketch a reasonably accurate graph?

      b.   What do you need to know about a hyperbola to write its equation?

11-112.   Write the equation and sketch a graph of a hyperbola centered at the origin with intercepts $(4, 0)$ and $(-4, 0)$ and asymptotes $y = \pm \frac{9}{4} x$.

11-113.   Write the general equation of a hyperbola centered at the origin with intercepts $(a, 0)$ and $(-a, 0)$ and asymptotes $y = \pm \frac{b}{a} x$.

11-114.   Consider the equation $\frac{x^2}{25} - \frac{y^2}{9} = 1$.

      a.   Use the ideas you have developed in this lesson to help you sketch a graph.

      b.   How could you change the equation to make each of the following transformations?

            i.   The graph moves 4 units to the right.

            ii.   The graph moves 3 units up.

            iii.   The center of the hyperbola is $(-2, 4)$.

            iv.   The hyperbola is rotated $90°$ so that its vertices are on the *y*-axis.

      c.   What information can you get from looking at an equation of *any* hyperbola that can help you sketch a graph?

11-115.   Write the *general equation* of a hyperbola centered at (h, k) with intercepts $(a, 0)$ and $(-a, 0)$ and asymptotes with slope $\pm \frac{b}{a}$.

11-116.   Graph the hyperbolas described by the equations below.

      a. $\frac{(x-2)^2}{4} - \frac{(y+1)^2}{16} = 1$ b. $(y - 4)^2 - \frac{(x+2)^2}{9} = 1$

METHODS AND MEANINGS

MATH NOTES

Equations of Hyperbolas

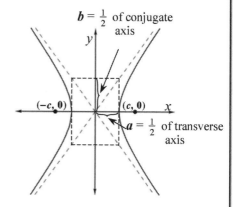

A hyperbola has relationships similar to those of an ellipse. The line connecting the vertices of the two branches is called the **transverse axis**, and a represents the distance from the center to either vertex.

If the center of the hyperbola is at the origin and the vertices are on the x-axis, the equation can be written in the form $\frac{x^2}{a^2} - \frac{y^2}{b^2} = 1$.

The vertices are at the points ($\pm a, 0$), and the asymptotes have equations $y = \pm \frac{b}{a} x$. The foci are on the transverse axis (in this case, the x-axis) at ($\pm c, 0$), with c given by the equation $c^2 = a^2 + b^2$.

If the vertices of the hyperbola are on the y-axis, the transverse axis is vertical and the equation is shown at right.
$$\frac{y^2}{b^2} - \frac{x^2}{a^2} = 1$$

A hyperbola centered at (h, k) with a horizontal transverse axis of length $2a$ and a vertical **conjugate axis** of length $2b$ is given by the equation at right.
$$\frac{(x-h)^2}{a^2} - \frac{(y-k)^2}{b^2} = 1$$

The **eccentricity** is a measure of the shape of the curve; the larger the eccentricity, the more quickly the branches spread apart. Again, the formula is $e = \frac{c}{a}$. Since $c > a$, the eccentricity of a hyperbola is always greater than 1.

To shift the center of the hyperbola to (h, k), replace x and y in the equations with ($x - h$) and ($y - k$), respectively, and adjust the equations of the asymptotes to go through the point (h, k).

11-117. Which of the following equations is the equation of a hyperbola? How can you tell? What is the shape of the graph of the other equation? After you have decided on the shapes, quickly sketch the graphs.

a. $\dfrac{(x-1)^2}{9} + \dfrac{(y+2)^2}{4} = 1$

b. $\dfrac{(y-3)^2}{16} - \dfrac{(x+2)^2}{25} = 1$

11-118. Decide whether each of the following hyperbolas is oriented horizontally or vertically. That is, decide whether the transverse axis is horizontal or vertical. How can you tell?

a. $\dfrac{x^2}{10} - \dfrac{y^2}{5} = 1$

b. $\dfrac{y^2}{6} - \dfrac{x^2}{16} = 1$

c. $\dfrac{(y-2)^2}{10} - \dfrac{(x-5)^2}{7} = 1$

11-119. Change the equation $x^2 + 8x + y^2 - 12y = 12$ to graphing form and sketch a graph.

11-120. Sketch a graph of $y = x^3(x-2)(x+2)^2$.

11-121. Solve the system at right for (x, y, z).

$$2x + y - 2z = 0$$
$$x - y - 4z = -3$$
$$3x + 2y + 2z = -1$$

11-122. A parabola passes through the points $(0, 5)$, $(2, 1)$, and $(6, 17)$.

a. What is its equation?

b. Where is its vertex?

11-123. After graphing $y = 12x^3 + 55x^2 - 27x - 10$ on a graphing calculator you can easily see that one x-intercept is $(-5, 0)$. Use this information to find all of the x-intercepts.

11-124. At McDugal's Golden Parabola, Ramona bought four hamburgers and two milkshakes for $13.50. Inez bought three hamburgers and one milkshake and spent $9.25. What is the cost of a hamburger? A milkshake?

11-125. Solve each ratio problem below for x.

a. Forty-two percent of x is 112.

b. Forty-two is x percent of 112.

c. Twenty-seven is x percent of 100.

d. Twenty-seven percent of 500 is x.

11.3.1 How can I tell which shape?

Identifying and Graphing Conic Sections

In this section, you will learn how to recognize conic sections from their equations and how to sketch graphs quickly. As you work with your team on today's lesson, think about the questions below.

How can we tell what shape the graph will be?

What do we need to know to sketch a graph quickly?

11-126. Carl Conic, cousin of Polly Parabola, was inspired by the success of Professional Parabola Productions and has decided to open his own business, The Courtly Conics Company. He has hired your team to help train his employees to make the right conics according to customers' orders. He has sent your team the following memo:

> *Dear Study Team,*
>
> *My cousin Polly has told me all about your amazing work! I am pleased to hire you to put together the information that I need for the introductory training brochure for my new company, The Courtly Conic Company.*
>
> *Customers will be ordering their conic sections by sending in equations. I need you to explain to my builders how they can tell what type of conic the equation describes and how they can find all of the information from the equation that they need to build the conic correctly.*
>
> *Please have your training instructions on my desk by the end of the day.*
>
> *Thank you,*
> *Mr. Carl Conic*
> *CEO, The Courtly Conics Company*

Your task: Prepare training materials that explain how to recognize what type of equation represents each conic and how to create an accurate graph when given the equation of a conic. Include the general equations for each of the conics in your materials. Use the following equations as examples for the builders.

$$(x-3)^2 + (y-5)^2 = 9 \qquad y = 4(x-2)^2 + 3 \qquad \frac{(x-3)^2}{5} + \frac{(y+2)^2}{16} = 1$$

$$\frac{(x+4)^2}{4} - \frac{(y-2)^2}{25} = 1 \qquad 3(y-1)^2 - x = 4 \qquad \frac{(y+1)^2}{3} - \frac{(x-4)^2}{4} = 3$$

11-127. Organize your training materials into a pamphlet for the builders' use. Use color, arrows, and other math tools to help make your ideas easy to understand.

11-128.   For each equation below, identify the shape of the graph, list all of the necessary information, and sketch a graph.

a. $\frac{(x-1)^2}{9} + \frac{y^2}{4} = 1$

b. $(x-4)^2 + (y+2)^2 = 25$

c. $\frac{(y-2)^2}{36} - \frac{(x-3)^2}{9} = 1$

d. $3x + (y-2)^2 = 10$

11-129.   Complete the square to change the following equations to graphing form. Then sketch the graph of each equation.

a. $f(x) = x^2 + 4x + 6$

b. $x^2 + 6x + y^2 - 8y = 0$

11-130.   Two similar triangles are drawn on a piece of paper. The smaller triangle has an area of 600 square mm and the larger triangle had an area of 960 square mm. If the shortest side of the smaller triangle is 26 mm, how long is the shortest side of the larger triangle?

11-131.   Find the equation of the line that is perpendicular to $y = \frac{1}{2}x - 3$ and passes through the point $(10, 14)$.

11-132.   For the function $f(x) = \frac{\sqrt{x+4}}{2} - 1$, complete parts (a) through (d) below.

a.   Sketch the graph and the inverse.

b.   Find the equation of the inverse function.

c.   Determine the domain and range of the inverse.

d.   Compute $f^{-1}(f(5))$.

11-133.   Solve each equation below.

a. $2^{(x-1)} = 64$

b. $9^3 = 27^{(2x-1)}$

c. $x^6 = 29$

d. $6^x = 29$

11-134. A small rocket is launched from five meters below ground level reaches a height of 3 meters above the ground after 4 seconds. On the way down it is 3 meters above the ground after 8 seconds.

    a.   What are three data points?

    b.   Draw a rough sketch of the height of the rocket over time.

    c.   Find the equation of the parabola based on the data.

    d.   When will the rocket hit the ground?

    e.   What is the domain for this function?

    f.   For what part of the domain is the rocket below ground?

11-135. Solve and check each equation.

    a. $|2x+1| = x+1$ b. $|2x+5| = 3x+4$

11-136. Given the matrices A, B, and C shown at right, calculate each of the following (if possible).

$$A = \begin{bmatrix} 2 & 3 \\ -1 & 4 \end{bmatrix}$$

$$B = \begin{bmatrix} 1 & 5 & 2 \\ 6 & 3 & 0 \end{bmatrix}$$

    a. AB b. BA

    c. $2A+C$ d. $AC - A$

$$C = \begin{bmatrix} -3 & 0 \\ 2 & 3 \end{bmatrix}$$

Graphing Form for Conic Sections

In Lesson 11.3.1, you were able to determine the parameters necessary to sketch a graph because the equations were all given in *graphing form*. But what if they are not given in graphing form?

11-137.   In Chapter 4, you developed a method called **completing the square** to change equations of parabolas and circles to graphing form. With your team, review this method and find the center and radius of each circle below.

a. $x^2 + y^2 + 8x + 6y - 39 = 0$ b. $x^2 + y^2 = 6x - 2y - 5$

11-138.   Norwood is working on conic sections and is trying to change the equation $3x^2 + 24x + 2y^2 - 12y = 6$ to graphing form. He is confused because the x^2 and y^2 terms have coefficients other than 1. He tried rewriting the equation and got $3(x^2 + 8x) + 2(y^2 - 6y) = 6$.

a.   Did he make any mistakes so far? Is his equation equivalent to the original equation? How can you be sure?

b.   He brought the work shown below to his friend Noel, but Noel thinks that he has made a mistake. Noel thinks that he should add 48 and 18 to the right side of the equation instead of 16 and 9. Is Noel correct? Why or why not? What is the correct equation?

$$3(x^2 + 8x + \_\_) + 2(y^2 - 6y + \_\_) = 6$$

$$+16 \qquad\qquad +9$$

$$+16 \quad +9$$

$$3(x + 4)^2 + 2(y - 3)^2 = 31$$

c.   With your team, find a way to rewrite this equation in graphing form and determine what kind of conic section it is. Then sketch a graph.

11-139. Norwood and Noel decided to try their new expertise on another problem. This time they started with the equation $4x^2 - y^2 - 40x - 4y + 80 = 0$.

a. They rewrote the equation to look like $4(x^2 - 10x) - (y^2 + 4y) = -80$. Check their work by simplifying this result. Is it equivalent to their original equation?

b. Then they worked together to complete the square. Their work is shown at right. Why did they add 100 and subtract 4 from the right side? Is the new equation still equivalent to the original one? How can you be sure?

$$4(x^2 - 10x + \underline{\quad}) - (y^2 + 4y + \underline{\quad}) = -80$$
$$+25 \qquad\qquad +4$$
$$+100 \quad -4$$

$$4(x - 5)^2 - (y + 2)^2 = 16$$

c. Finish rewriting the equation and determine the type of conic section it describes. Then sketch a graph.

11-140. Change each of the following equations to graphing form, identify the conic, and sketch the graph.

a. $9x^2 + 4y^2 - 36x + 24y + 36 = 0$

b. $4x^2 - 16x - y + 21 = 0$

c. $16x^2 - 5y^2 - 64x - 30y = 61$

d. $2x^2 + 2y^2 - 12x - 20y = -58$

11-141. LEARNING LOG

In your Learning Log, explain how to change equations of conic sections to graphing form. Be sure to include examples that show how to incorporate negatives correctly. Title this entry "Changing Equations of Conics to Graphing Form" and label it with today's date.

11-142. Change each of the following equations to graphing form, identify the conic, and sketch the graph.

a. $4x^2 - y^2 - 24x - 10y = 5$

b. $x^2 + y^2 + 10x - 4y = -13$

c. $4x^2 + 9y^2 + 24x - 36y = -36$

d. $3x^2 - 12x - y = -17$

11-143. Write a quadratic equation with roots $x = 3 \pm 5i$.

11-144.   In the summer of 1994, a couple was going through their attic and found a $1000 bond
          issued by the State of Nevada in 1865. It read, "Pay to the Bearer" (whoever has
          possession). States issue bonds when they need to borrow money. In 1865, Nevada
          was a new state and in great need of cash, so it issued this bond at an interest rate of
          24% compounded annually.

     a.   Do you think it would have been possible to cash in this bond?

     b.   If $1000 were invested in 1865 at an interest rate of 24% compounded annually,
          how much would the investment be worth in 1994?

     c.   What is the place value of the first digit in the answer to part (b)?

11-145.   Solve the system at right.
$$\frac{z+y}{4} + \frac{z-y}{2} = 1$$
$$\frac{3z-y}{4} + \frac{4z+2y}{11} = 3$$

11-146.   For each equation, state the amplitude, period, vertical shift, horizontal shift, and
          sketch two cycles of the graph.

     a. $y = 3\cos(2x)$ b. $y = \cos 2(x + \frac{\pi}{4})$

11-147.   Rewrite each equation as an equivalent equation using $\log_{10}$. You do not need to find
          a numerical answer. These are sometimes known as **change of base** problems.

     a. $\log_2(3) = x$ b. $\log_5(8) = x$ c. $\log_7(12) = x$ d. $\log_a(b) = x$

11-148.   Use the idea of the previous problem to rewrite $y = \log_4(x)$ so that it could be graphed
          using a graphing calculator.

11-149.   Solve and check each equation.

     a. $\sqrt{x + 20} = x$ b. $\sqrt{x - 2} - \sqrt{2x + 3} = -2$

11-150.   Logarithms are used to measure the "loudness" of sound. Decibels (dB) are
          logarithmic units used to descrbe a ratio of two levels of intensity or pressure. The
          difference between two levels of sound pressure (P_1 and P_2) is defined as
          $10 \log(\frac{P_1}{P_2})$ dB. Usually, when decibels are used to describe just one sound, it is
          assumed that that sound is being compared to a reference level of 20 micropascals.

     a.   How many decibels correspond to doubling the pressure of a sound?

     b.   What is the sound pressure of a sound described as 60 dB?

     c.   What does 0 decibels mean?

     d.   How many times more pressure is in a sound of 40 dB than of 20 dB?

11.3.3 What do they all have in common?

Quadratic Relations

All of the relations you have been studying are members of the family of **quadratic relations**, which are described by the general equation $Ax^2 + By^2 + Cxy + Dx + Ey + F = 0$.

11-151.   Carina figured out that when she makes $C = 1$, $F = -5$, and all other coefficients in $Ax^2 + By^2 + Cxy + Dx + Ey + F = 0$ equal to 0, she gets the equation of a familiar function. What function did she find? Write the equation of her function and sketch a graph.

11-152.   QUADRATIC-RELATION INVESTIGATION

Carina now wonders how many types of graphs can be found for the quadratic relations when $C = 0$, and she wants your team's help.

Your task: With your team, **investigate** the set of quadratic relations given by the general equation $Ax^2 + By^2 + Dx + Ey + F = 0$. Find all families of graphs that are possible. Decide as a team what different values to try for each of the coefficients (*A, B, D, E,* and *F*). For each family of graphs that you find, provide an example of an equation and a graph of that relation. Then use your function-investigation questions to complete a thorough **investigation**. Use the following questions to guide your **investigation**.

Discussion Points

How can we change the equation to a more useful form?

How can we tell what the shape will be?

What values should we try for the coefficients? Which should we make negative?

Could it be a function? How can we tell?

11-153.   It will help to work backward by starting with equations in graphing form, then changing them to standard form $Ax^2 + By^2 + Dx + Ey + F = 0$. Describe the graph for each of the following equations and then transform each equation into standard form. Compare the standard forms with their graphing forms and with the other standard forms.

a. $\frac{(x-1)^2}{9} + \frac{y^2}{4} = 1$

b. $(x-4)^2 + (y+2)^2 = 25$

c. $\frac{(y-2)^2}{36} - \frac{(x-3)^2}{9} = 1$

d. $3x + (y-2)^2 = 10$

e.   Write equations in graphing form for a different orientation and/or location for each of the conics, and transform those equations into standard form.

f.   What **general** statements can you make about equations in standard form and their graphs?

—————   *Further Guidance*   —————
section ends here.

11-154.   LEARNING LOG

What are all of the conic sections? What do they have in common geometrically? What do they have in common algebraically? Work with your team to answer these questions and then record your ideas in your Learning Log. Title this entry "Similarities Among the Conic Sections" and label it with today's date.

11-155.   Explain why it is useful to make $C = 0$ in the general quadratic relation $Ax^2 + By^2 + Cxy + Dx + Ey + F = 0$.

11-156.   Find values of A, B, D, E, and F in the equation $Ax^2 + By^2 + Dx + Ey + F = 0$ to create each of the following conic sections.

a.   Line

b.   Point

c.   Circle

d.   Ellipse

e.   Parabola

f.   Hyperbola

11-157. Identify the shape of the graph of each equation below, change it to graphing form (if necessary), and sketch a graph.

　　a.　$2y^2 - x + 4y + 2 = 0$

　　b.　$5x + 2y - 10 = 0$

　　c.　$4x^2 + 4y^2 + 4x - 24y + 21 = 0$

　　d.　$9x^2 - 16y^2 + 54x - 32y + 29 = 0$

　　e.　$9x^2 + 4y^2 + 54x - 16y + 97 = 0$

　　f.　$4x^2 - y^2 + 24x + 36 = 0$

11-158. Let $p = 2 + 5i$ and $q = 3 - 4i$. Calculate the following values and simplify to $a + bi$ form.

　　a.　$p + q$　　　　b.　$p - q$　　　　c.　$p \cdot q$　　　　d.　$\frac{p}{q}$

11-159. Solve the system of equations at right both graphically and algebraically.

$$x^2 + y^2 = 25$$
$$y = x^2 - 36$$

11-160. Compute the value of each expression below.

　　a.　$(\frac{\sqrt{2}}{2} + \frac{i\sqrt{2}}{2})^2$

　　b.　$(\frac{-\sqrt{2}}{2} - \frac{i\sqrt{2}}{2})^2$

　　c.　Use the results from parts (a) and (b) above to solve $x^2 = i$ for x. (Find the square roots of i.)

　　d.　Locate $\frac{\sqrt{2}}{2} + i\frac{\sqrt{2}}{2}$ and $-\frac{\sqrt{2}}{2} - i\frac{\sqrt{2}}{2}$ on a set of complex axes. What do you notice about their locations?

11-161. Solve and graph each inequality.

　　a.　$|7 - y| \le 3$

　　b.　$3|2m + 1| - 1 > 8$

11-162. The graphs of $f(x) = 2x^2 + 5x - 3$ and $g(x) = x^2 + 4x + 3$ are shown at right. Use the graphs to solve:

　　a.　$f(x) = g(x)$

　　b.　$f(x) > g(x)$

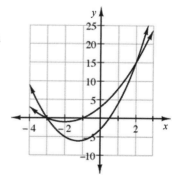

11.3.4 What do I know about conic sections?

Conic Sections Project

In this lesson, you will have a chance to demonstrate your understanding of conic sections by making your own conic section and analyzing it completely.

11-163.   CONIC SECTIONS SCULPTURE PROJECT

How much have you learned about conic sections?

Preparation: To prepare the axes, draw a set of *x*- and *y*-axes on graph paper. To prepare the conic section, first obtain modeling compound and a piece of fishing line from your teacher. Then use the modeling compound to make a cone. Your model will be only part of the "double cone" like the one the class used to create conic sections on the class grapher. Be careful to make your cone regular and to give it smooth sides. When your cone is complete, decide on a slicing angle and carefully slice it with the fishing line. Which conic section have you created?

Your task: Work with your partner to create a stand-alone poster that shows everything you know about your conic section. Be sure to make clear summary statements so that anyone reading your poster can understand your thinking. You will need to place your conic section on your axes and trace it with pencil. Consider the following questions to help you get started.

Discussion Points

Where should we place our shape on the axes?

How can we describe it algebraically? Is there more than one way?

How can we describe it geometrically? Is there more than one way?

Further Guidance

11-164.   As you analyze your conic section, consider the following questions. Note that not all questions apply to all of the conic sections.

- Can you find the foci?
- What is the stretch factor?
- What are the lengths of *a* and *b*?
- What are the equations of the asymptotes (if there are any)?
- What is the equation in graphing form?
- What is the equation in standard form?

- What would be the equation if you rotated the graph 90°? 180°?
- How would the equation change if you shifted the graph?
- Is it a function? If not, could you make it a function? How?
- Is this shape useful for anything in the real world? What?

===   *Further Guidance*   ===
            section ends here.

11-165. Create an equation and its corresponding graph (in any order) for each of the following conic sections.

 a. Circle   b. Line   c. Parabola

 d. Hyperbola   e. Ellipse   f. Two intersecting lines

11-166. Kiesha graphed $y = x(6 - x)$ in a standard calculator viewing window.

 a. What is the best name for her graph?

 b. Jamal has bet Kiesha that with his graphing calculator he can make the graph look like a horizontal line without changing, adding, or deleting functions. Kiesha doesn't think he can do this, but Jamal is sure he can. What **strategy** does Jamal have in mind?

11-167. Find the equation of the line passing through the point $(-2, 5)$ that is perpendicular to the line $y = -5x + 2$.

11-168. Solve the system of equations at right.

$$x^2 + y^2 = 16$$
$$y = x^2 - 4$$

11-169. Multiply and simplify each expression.

 a. $(3 + 2i)(4 + i)$ b. $(2 + 3i)(2 - 3i)$

 c. $(5 - 2i)(5 + 2i)$ d. $(a + bi)(a - bi)$

11-170. Graph at least one full cycle of each graph.

 a. $y = 2 \sin x$ b. $y = \cos (2x)$

 c. $y = -1 + 2 \cos(x)$ d. $y = -1 + 2\sin(x + \frac{\pi}{2})$

11-171.   If $f(x) = x^2 + 7x$, calculate the values described below.

   a. $f(2)$ b. $f(-3)$

   c. $f(i)$ d. $f(-3.5 + 1.5i)$

   e.   Solve $f(x) = 0$.

11-172.   Sketch a graph, $f(x)$, that has the numbers and types of roots for each situation described below.

   a.   5 real roots   b.   3 real and 2 complex roots

   c.   4 complex roots   d.   4 complex and 2 real roots

11-173.   Simplify each expression. Assume the denominator does not equal zero

   a. $\frac{3x+2}{x+2} + \frac{x-5}{2x+4}$ b. $\frac{5}{x^2-4} - \frac{3}{x+2}$

   c. $\frac{2x^2+3x+1}{x^2-4} \div \frac{2x+1}{x+2}$ d. $\frac{x^3-125}{3x^2-13x-10}$

Chapter 11 Closure What have I learned?

Reflection and Synthesis

The activities below offer you a chance to reflect on what you have learned in this chapter. As you work, look for concepts that you feel very comfortable with, ideas that you would like to learn more about, and topics you need more help with. Look for connections between ideas as well as connections with material you learned previously.

①   TEAM BRAINSTORM

With your team, brainstorm a list for each of the following categories. Be as detailed as you can. How long can you make your list? Challenge yourselves. Be prepared to share your team's ideas with the class.

Topics: What have you studied in this chapter? What ideas and words were important in what you learned? Remember to be as detailed as you can.

Connections: How are the topics, ideas, and words that you learned in previous courses connected to the new ideas in this chapter? Again, make your list as long as you can.

Below is a list of the vocabulary used in this chapter. Make sure that you are familiar with all of these words and know what they mean. Refer to the glossary or index for any words that you do not yet understand.

asymptote	circle	complete the square
cone	conic section	conjugate
directrix	ellipse	equidistant
foci	focus	function
graphing form	hyperbola	intersection
line	locus	major axis
minor axis	parabola	perfect square
plane	point	quadratic
relation	system	standard form
transverse		

Make a concept map showing all of the connections you can find among the key words and ideas listed above. To show a connection between two words, draw a line between them and explain the connection, as shown in the example below. A word can be connected to any other word as long as you can **justify** the connection. For each key word or idea, provide a sketch of an example.

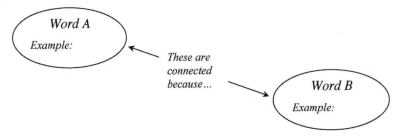

Your teacher may provide you with vocabulary cards to help you get started. If you use the cards to plan your concept map, be sure either to re-draw your concept map on your paper or to glue the vocabulary cards to a poster with all of the connections explained for others to see and understand.

While you are making your map, your team may think of related words or ideas that are not listed above. Be sure to include these ideas on your concept map.

SUMMARIZING MY UNDERSTANDING

This section gives you an opportunity to show what you know about certain math topics or ideas.

With your team, make a list of the **big ideas** of this chapter. Discuss the important ideas of the chapter and try to agree on a short list of no more than five big ideas. Be prepared to share your list in a whole class discussion. When the class has reached agreement on a list, continue with parts (a) and (b) below.

a.   Write your own description of each big idea.

b.   For each big idea, provide one or two representative example problems. Solve each problem completely, using multiple representations, if applicable.

Your teacher may give you a "GO" page to work on (or you can download this from www.cpm.org). "GO" stands for "Graphic Organizer," a tool you can use to organize your thoughts and communicate your ideas clearly.

④ WHAT HAVE I LEARNED?

This section will help you evaluate which types of problems you feel comfortable with and which you need more help with. This section will appear at the end of every chapter to help you check your understanding. Even if your teacher does not assign this section, it is a good idea to try these problems and find out for yourself what you know and what you need to work on.

Solve each problem as completely as you can. The table at the end of this closure section has answers to these problems. It also tells you where you can find additional help and practice on similar problems.

CL 11-174. Find the vertices and sketch a graph of each ellipse.

a. $\frac{x^2}{16} + \frac{y^2}{5} = 1$ b. $5x^2 + 4y^2 = 100$

c. $\frac{(x+2)^2}{9} + \frac{(y-3)^2}{4} = 1$

CL 11-175. Find the equation of each ellipse.

a.
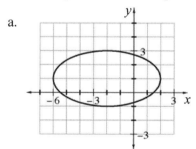

b.
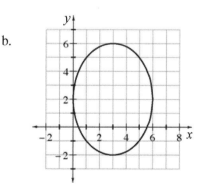

CL 11-176. Using the vertices and slope of the asymptotes as a guide, graph each hyperbola.

    a. $\frac{y^2}{4} - \frac{x^2}{25} = 1$ b. $x^2 - y^2 = 9$ c. $\frac{(x-3)^2}{9} - \frac{y^2}{4} = 1$

CL 11-177. Find the equation of the hyperbola with vertices $(0, \pm 5)$ and asymptotes $y = \pm 2x$.

CL 11-178. Show how to rewrite the equation of the parabola $x^2 + 2x - 8y + 17 = 0$ into the graphing form $(y - 2) = \frac{1}{8}(x + 1)^2$ and then draw the graph.

CL 11-179. For each of the following equations, identify the curve, write the equation in graphing form, and list the following information: center, vertex or vertices, and asymptotes (if there are any).

    a. $2x^2 + y^2 - 4x + 6y - 7 = 0$ b. $3y^2 - x^2 + 12y = 0$

    c. $12x^2 + 8y^2 + 48x - 48y + 24 = 0$

CL 11-180. Find the equation of the parabola that is the set of all points equidistant from the focus $(-3, 1)$ and the directrix $x = -1$.

CL 11-181. Solve each of the following equations, accurate to the nearest 0.001.

    a. $1.8^x = 10$ b. $\log_2 x = 6$

CL 11-182. Find an equation of the parabola that passes through $(2, 11)$, $(-1, -4)$ and $(0, -5)$.

CL 11-183. Sketch a graph of each of the following functions.

    a. $f(x) = \frac{2}{x-1} + 3$ b. $g(x) = -0.5(x + 2)^3 - 3$

    c. $h(x) = |x + 5| - 4$ d. $k(x) = 2\sqrt{x + 1} + 3$

CL 11-184. Find the equation of the exponential function (with an asymptote of $y = 0$) that passes through the points $(-1, 0.6)$ and $(1, 15)$.

CL 11-185. Check your answers using the table at the end of this section. Which problems do you feel confident about? Which problems were hard? Have you worked on problems like these in math classes you have taken before? Use the table to make a list of topics you need help on and a list of topics you need to practice more.

HOW AM I THINKING?

This course focuses on five different **Ways of Thinking**: justifying, generalizing, choosing a strategy, investigating, and reversing thinking. These are some of the ways in which you think while trying to make sense of a concept or attempting to solve a problem (even outside of math class). During this chapter, you have probably used each Way of Thinking multiple times without even realizing it!

Review each of the five Ways of Thinking described in the closure sections of Chapters 1 through 5. Then choose three of these Ways of Thinking that you remember using while working on this chapter. Show and explain where and how you used each one. Describe why thinking in this way helped you solve a particular problem or understand something new. Be sure to include examples to demonstrate your thinking.

Answers and Support for Closure Activity #4
What Have I Learned?

Problem	Solutions		Need Help?	More Practice
CL 11-174.	a. $(\pm 4, 0)$ $(0, \pm\sqrt{5})$	b. $(\pm 2\sqrt{5}, 0)$ c. $(0, \pm 5)$	Lessons 11.2.3 and 11.2.4 Math Notes box in Lesson 11.2.4	Problems 11-81, 11-83, 11-86, 11-99, 11-117, 11-126, 11-128, and 11-153

c. $(-5, 3)$, $(1, 3)$, $(-2, 1)$, and $(-2, 5)$

CL 11-175.	a. $\frac{(x+2)^2}{16} + \frac{(y-1)^2}{4} = 1$		Lessons 11.2.3 and 11.2.4	Problems 11-80 and 11-82
	b. $\frac{(x-3)^2}{9} + \frac{(y-2)^2}{16} = 1$		Math Notes box in Lesson 11.2.4	

Problem	Solutions	Need Help?	More Practice
CL 11-176.	a. 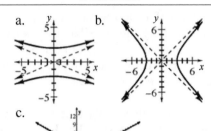 b. c.	Lessons 11.2.5 and 11.2.6	Problems 11-110, 11-114, 11-115, 11-116, 11-117, 11-126, 11-128, and 11-153
CL 11-177.	$\frac{y^2}{25} - \frac{x^2}{6.25} = 1$	Lessons 11.2.5, 11.2.6, Math Notes box in Lesson 11.2.6	Problems 11-112, 11-113, 11-115, and 11-116
CL 11-178.	$8y - 17 = x^2 + 2x$ $8y - 17 + 1 = x^2 + 2x + 1$ $8y - 16 = (x+1)^2$ $8y = (x+1)^2 + 16$ $y = \frac{1}{8}(x+1)^2 + 2$ 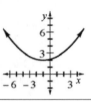	Lesson 11.1.2	Problems 11-20, 11-129, 11-140, 11-142, and 11-157
CL 11-179.	a. ellipse, center $(1, -3)$, vertices $(-2, -3)$, $(4, -3)$, and $(1, -3 \pm 3\sqrt{2})$ $\frac{(x-1)^2}{9} + \frac{(y+3)^2}{18} = 1$ b. hyperbola, center $(0, -2)$, vertices $(0, 0)$ and $(0, -4)$, asymptotes $y = \pm \frac{\sqrt{3}}{3} x - 2$ $\frac{(y+2)^2}{4} - \frac{x^2}{12} = 1$ c. ellipse, center $(-2, 3)$, vertices $(-2 \pm 2\sqrt{2}, 3)$ and $(-2, 3 \pm 2\sqrt{3})$ $\frac{(x+2)^2}{8} + \frac{(y-3)^2}{12} = 1$	Lesson 11.3.2 Math Notes boxes in Lessons 11.2.4 and 11.2.6	Problems 11-138, 11-139, 11-140, 11-142, 11-157

Problem	Solutions	Need Help?	More Practice
CL 11-180.	$x = -\frac{1}{4}(y-1)^2 - 2$	Lesson 11.1.2 Math Notes box in Lesson 11.2.2	Problems 11-18, 11-19, and 11-56
CL 11-181.	a. $x \approx 3.917$ b. $x = 64$	Lessons 7.2.1 and 7.2.2 Math Notes box in Lesson 7.2.1	Problems 7-111, 7-133, 7-139, 7-140, 7-223, CL 7-230, 8-84, and 9-62
CL 11-182.	$y = 3x^2 + 2x - 5$	Lesson 7.1.5 Learning Log entry from problem 7-63	Problems 7-62, 7-64, 7-67, 7-72, 7-80, and 7-178
CL 11-183.	a. b. c. d.	Lesson 4.2.1 Math Notes box in Lesson 4.3.2 Parent Graph Tool Kit	Problems CL 4-157, 5-100, and 8-59
CL 11-184.	$y = 3 \cdot 5^x$	Lesson 7.2.3 Checkpoint 15	Problems 7-125, 7-127, 7-164, CL 7-232, 8-21, and 8-68

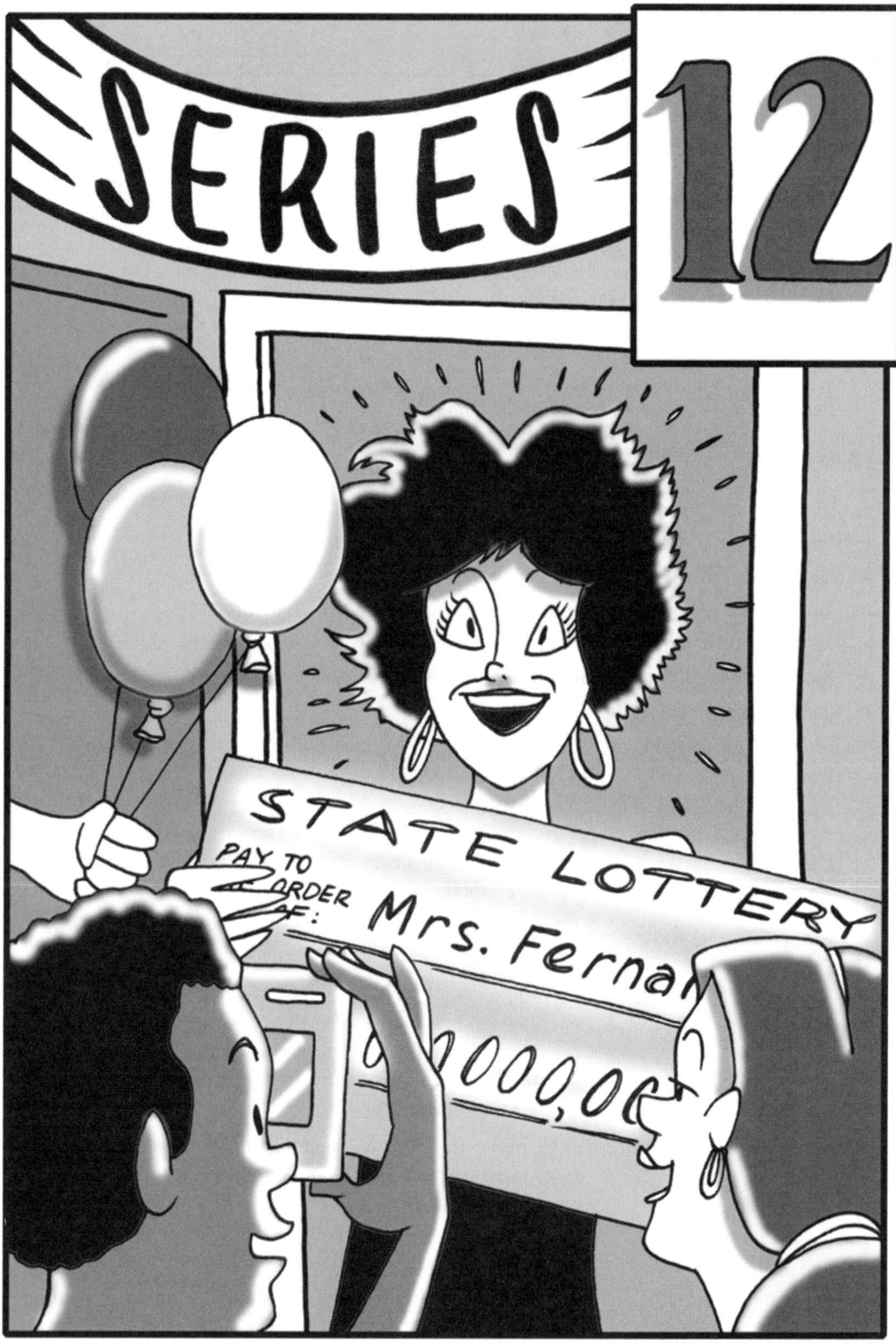
SERIES
12
STATE LOTTERY
PAY TO
ORDER
Mrs. Fernan

CHAPTER 12   Series

In this chapter you will revisit and add to what you learned about arithmetic and geometric sequences. In Sections 12.1 and 12.3 you will use what you know about sequences and multiple representations to write series and find their sums.

In Section 12.2 you will learn a new way to write a mathematical proof called mathematical induction, and in Section 12.4 you will use what you learned about combinations to develop the Binomial Theorem, which is useful for simplifying some algebraic manipulations, as well as solving some probability problems. In Section 12.5, you will use what you learned about series and the Binomial Theorem to approximate a special number, e, the base of the natural logarithms.

In this chapter, you will learn how to:

➢ Recognize the differences between sequences and series.

➢ Find the sum of an infinite geometric series.

➢ Find sums of arithmetic and geometric series for a known value of n.

➢ Use Pascal's triangle and combinations to rewrite certain algebraic expressions.

➢ Apply the Binomial Theorem to some probability problems.

➢ Find an approximation for e.

➢ Use proof by induction.

Guiding Questions

Think about these questions throughout this chapter:

Is there another way to solve this?

How can I represent it?

How can I **generalize** this?

How can I **justify** this generalization?

Chapter Outline

Section 12.1   In this section, you will revisit arithmetic sequences as you learn about arithmetic series and devise methods for finding their sums.

Section 12.2   In this section, you will learn a method of proof called mathematical induction.

Section 12.3   Here, you will revisit geometric sequences as you learn about geometric series and their sums. In addition to finding sums of geometric series where the last term is determined, you will learn how to represent and calculate sums of some infinite series.

Section 12.4   In this section, you will learn about Pascal's Triangle and you will connect it with your knowledge of combinations to develop the Binomial Theorem, which can be used to solve some algebraic, as well as probability problems.

Section 12.5   This section provides an opportunity to use series and the Binomial Theorem to approximate the value of e, the base of the natural logarithms.

12.1.1 How can I find the sum?

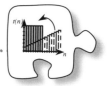

Introduction to Arithmetic Series

A popular amusement park notices that the number of people entering the park every minute increases steadily as the morning passes and the time for the park's famous parade approaches. Assuming no one leaves the park, how many people will be in the park by noon to see the parade? Answering this question requires finding the sum of a sequence of numbers, each number representing the number of people for a particular period of time.

Today your team will consider different ways to find the sum of a sequence of terms. As you work, use the following questions to focus and advance your mathematical discussions.

> What do the terms (of the sequence) represent? What does the sum represent?

> Is there another way to find the sum?

> How can we verify our result?

12-1.   JACKPOT FEVER!

Tonight is the long-anticipated drawing for the largest lottery jackpot in the history of your state. Luckily, there is still time to buy a ticket! Because of the growing jackpot, the number of tickets being sold each hour is climbing, as more people are eager to win.

Lottery officials have been monitoring ticket sales carefully. As the morning progresses, the number of tickets sold each hour are listed in the table below.

Number of hours stores have been open	1	2	3
Number of tickets sold during that hour	1,500,000	1,650,000	1,800,000

a.   The drawing will occur 12 hours after the stores open. Assuming that the number of tickets sold each hour will continue to grow at the same rate until the drawing, how many tickets will be sold before the drawing?

b.   If you have not already done so, look for a shortcut to find this sum. What if, instead of 12 hours, the drawing was going to be 37 hours later? How could you find the total number of tickets sold without adding all 37 numbers by hand? Discuss this with your team and be prepared to share your ideas with the class.

c.   When the stores opened this morning, the jackpot was $23,000,000 and each ticket sold increases the jackpot by $1. How big will the jackpot be when the drawing occurs?

12-2.   SERIES

In problem 12-1, the total number of tickets sold before the drawing is the sum of an arithmetic sequence, where each term in the sequence represents the number of tickets sold in one hour. When the terms of a sequence are added instead of listed, the result is called a **series**. When a sequence is arithmetic, its corresponding series is called an **arithmetic series**. So, the series in problem 12-1 would be written:

$$1,500,000 + 1,650,000 + 1,800,000 + \ldots + 3,150,000$$

Knowing that there is a difference between arithmetic sequences and series, how can you tell which one to use to represent a situation?

A **matrioska**, a set of Russian nested dolls, can help illustrate the difference. These dolls are special because each doll fills the space inside the doll of the next larger size. When the dolls are placed one-inside-the-other, as in the picture, they are "nested."

a.   One way to think of a sequence is as a list of terms that help you relate each term to the other and learn about how the terms are changing. For example, when the dolls are nested, their diameters steadily increase. (Note: Only the top of the innermost doll is shown in the picture.)

   If the smallest doll in the diagram has a diameter of 5 cm, and each doll has a diameter that is 1 cm longer than the next-smallest doll, find a sequence that represents the diameters from shortest to longest.

b.   If the diameters of the nested dolls can represent a sequence, how could the dolls be arranged so that the sum of their diameters is meaningful? In other words, so a series would be an appropriate representation?

   Discuss these questions with your team members and draw a picture of your favorite idea. Then, using the measurements provided in part (a), write the corresponding series and find the sum.

c.   Some sets of Russian dolls have as many as 20 dolls! If the diameters (in millimeters) of a set of 20 dolls can be represented with the sequence below, write the corresponding series and find its sum.

$$t(n) = 5 + 3n$$

12-3.   FINDING THE SUM

When an arithmetic series has many terms, finding its sum can be tedious. It is useful to have **strategies** to find the sum other than just adding all the terms together. To look for a **strategy**, consider a new context.

Flo is preparing to run the 100 meter race at her next track meet. Her coach decides to collect data to learn how well Flo is accelerating (speeding up) at the beginning of the race. The sequence below records how far Flo travels during each second of the first six seconds during practice, in meters.

$$1, 3, 5, 7, 9, 11$$

a.   Find the rule, $t(n)$, for the terms of this sequence.

b.   What does the series in this situation represent? What does the total sum represent?

c.   Flo decided to use square tiles below to represent her distance from the starting line as time passed.

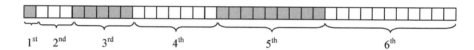

She thought it might help to rearrange her tiles to fit a graph, like the one at right. How is her sequence of rates (in meters per second) shown in this graph? How is her series of increasing distances represented?

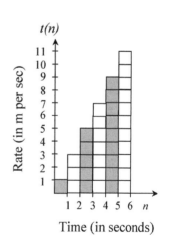

d.   Using the length and width to find the area of the rectangle in part (c) requires adding all the terms in order to find the length. How can the columns in Flo's graph be rearranged to form one big rectangle so the dimensions can be found without having to add *all* of the terms? Discuss this with your team and be prepared to share your ideas with the class.

12-4. For each arithmetic series graphed below, find the sum. Verify your solution.

a.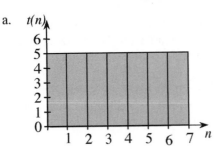

b.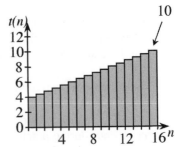

c.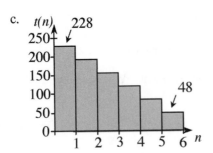

d.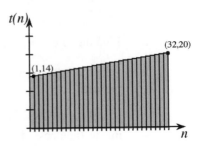

12-5. TEAM CHALLENGE

How much information do you need to be able to write an arithmetic series and find its sum? For each arithmetic series described below, work with your team to write the series, find its sum, or both. If it is not possible, explain why not.

a. What if you know that the first term is 18, the last term is 72, and the common difference is 4.5? What is the series? What is the sum?

b. What if you know that the last term is 21, there are 6 terms, and the sum is 336? What is the series?

c. What if you know that the series has 9 terms and the last term is 18? What is the series? What is the sum?

d. What if the third term of an 18-term series is 29 and the terms are increasing by 10? What is the series? What is the sum?

12-6.   The 300 people who were lined up outside the amusement park had all entered by 8:15, and by 8:30, 550 more had entered. The number who entered each 15 minutes increased steadily by 250 after that, and all were planning to stay for the parade.

a.   How many people entered between 11:45 and 12:00 noon, just in time for the parade?

b.   Represent the problem as a series and write a formula for the nth term.

12-7.   Write a formula for the nth term of each of the following series.

a. $3 + 10 + 17 + ...$ b. $20 + 11 + 2 + ...$

12-8.   If the third term of an arithmetic sequence is 13 and the seventeenth term is –29, what is the eighth term?

12-9.   Change the relation below into graphing form, find the locator point (h, k), and sketch a graph of the relation.

$$x = 2y^2 - 12y + 13$$

12-10.   Divide. $(x^4 - 7x^2 + 3x + 18) \div (x + 2)$

12-11.   Simplify.

a. $(2 + 3i)(2 - 3i) + (2 + 3i)^2$ b. $\frac{2+3i}{2-3i}$

12-12.   Find the sum.

a. $\frac{a}{b} + \frac{c}{d}$ b. $\frac{a}{b} + \frac{c}{d} + \frac{e}{f}$

12-13.   What do you notice about the two problems below when you simplify them?

a. $\dfrac{x^{1/2}}{x^{-3/2}}$

b. $\sqrt{x} \div (\frac{1}{\sqrt{x}})^3$

12-14.   Solve and check your solutions.

a. $\dfrac{4}{m} + \dfrac{3m}{5} = \dfrac{4m+1}{5}$

b. $\dfrac{z}{5} + 4 = \dfrac{3z}{z-2}$

12-15.   Use the symmetry of the unit circle and the knowledge that $\cos\frac{\pi}{4} = \frac{\sqrt{2}}{2}$ to write three other true statements using cosine.

12-16.   One angle of a triangle measures $70°$ and the opposite side has length of 37.2 feet. Another angle of the triangle measures $30°$. Find the measures of the remaining angle and the two remaining sides of the triangle.

12-17.   How many people were in the amusement park in problem 12-6 to watch the noontime parade?

12-18.   Chloe wants to place her matrioska dolls in a row on a windowsill that is 92 cm long. Will her entire set of 20 dolls fit if their diameters in *millimeters* are given by the formula $t(n) = 10 + 3n$?

12-19.   Find the sum of $1 + 6 + 11 + 16 + 21 + \ldots$ if the series has 10 terms.

12-20.   A series has 9 terms, the last term is 18, and the fifth term is 6. What is the series?

12-21.   Is 435 a term in the sequence 3, 11, 19, …? If so, which term is it? If not, **justify** why not.

12-22.   Given the points A (3, 2) and B (–21, 0), determine each of the following.

    a.   The slope of the line $\overrightarrow{AB}$.

    b.   The length of $\overline{AB}$.

    c.   The midpoint of $\overline{AB}$.

    d.   An equation of $\overleftrightarrow{AB}$.

12-23.   A cannon shoots a cannon ball into the air. The barrel of the cannon is located six feet above the ground. After two seconds the ball is 102 feet above the ground. After four seconds it is 70 feet above the ground. Find the equation of the parabola that models the path of the cannon ball.

12-24.   Factor each of the following expressions completely.

    a. $24x^2 - 14x - 20$

    b. $16x^4 - 1$

12-25.   The graph of $y = \frac{1}{x^2}$ is shown at right.

    a.   What is the domain of the function?

    b.   What is the range of the function?

    c.   Solve $\frac{1}{x^2} = 4$

    d.   Solve $\frac{1}{x^2} < 4$

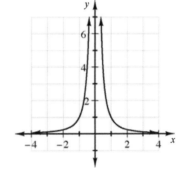

12.1.2 How can I find the sum?

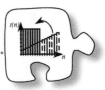

・・・

More Arithmetic Series

In Lesson 12.1.1, you explored ways to use a graph of a series to find its sum without adding every term. Can the **strategies** you developed help you find the sum of a series when you do not have a graph? As you work with your team to answer that question, remember to talk together about how to describe a term or series **generally** and to ask each other if the answers you find make sense.

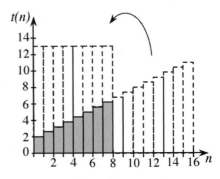

12-26.   While trying to find the sum of an arithmetic series, Antonio rearranged the terms so that the last term is combined with the first term, the second-to-last term is combined with the second term , etc. (as shown at right). Use his graph to answer the questions below.

   a.   How can Antonio be sure that the result of stacking the terms this way will be a rectangle?

   b.   What is the sum of his series? How do you know?

   c.   Which terms of the series form the first column? What is the height of this column?

   d.   Write out Antonio's series.

12-27.   With your team, create a series that has an odd number of terms. How could you apply Antonio's method to this series? Be prepared to share your ideas with the class.

12-28.   Will Antonio's method work for all arithmetic series? Why or why not? Use an example to explain your conclusion.

12-29.   How can Antonio's method be altered to help you find the sum of an arithmetic series without a graph? Work with your team to find the dimensions of the transformed rectangle for each arithmetic series below without graphing the series. Then find the sum.

   a. $11 + 18 + 25 + \ldots + 74$

   b.   14 terms with $t(1) = 8$ and $t(14) = 151$

   c. $t(n) = 6n - 2$, for integer values of n starting at 1 and ending at 25

12-30. Decide if each situation below involves a series or a sequence and give a reason for your choice. Then answer the question.

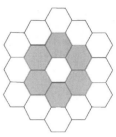

a. Hornets build nests by constructing hexagonal cells around a center, as shown at right. As this hexagonal pattern forms, the first ring of cells has 6 cells, the next has 12, and the next has 18. If a colony of hornets builds 10 rings, how many cells will they have?

b. Thanks to fundraising, the balance of the math club's savings account grows by $55 each month. The balance during the first month of the school year was $190. At the end of the year, the club's treasurer produced a report showing the balance for each month of the school year. What was the balance after the 8th month?

c. Starting on his birthday, Evan's allowance increases $0.25 each week. He decides to save his money in order to buy a new πPod, which costs $180. If his allowance on his birthday is $1.50, will he have enough savings by his next birthday to buy the πPod?

12-31. JACKPOT FEVER RETURNED!

As Ms. Fernandez was standing in line to buy her lottery ticket (see problem 12-1), she noticed that a different state has a jackpot that may go even higher. Then she realized that because of a time difference, it has more hours to grow! She has already predicted that the jackpot in her state will be $50,900,000 when tickets are drawn, and she has to decide quickly if she should buy tickets in the other state.

On a nearby television screen, she sees a news report explaining that the other state started the day with a jackpot of $29,000,000. The news also mentioned that 1,800,000 tickets were sold in the first hour and hourly ticket sales have steadily increased by 20,000 tickets per hour throughout the day. If the drawing in that state occurs 14 hours after stores have opened, which state will have the largest jackpot? Show how you found your answer.

12-32. With your team, find the sum of the arithmetic series $t(1) + t(2) + t(3) + ... + t(n)$?

12-33. LEARNING LOG

Describe how to find the sum of an arithmetic series in your Learning Log. Be sure to include examples in your description. Title this entry "Arithmetic Series" and label it with today's date.

METHODS AND MEANINGS

MATH NOTES

Series

The sum of the terms of a sequence is called a **series**. If the terms have a constant difference (meaning that they increase linearly), then it is an **arithmetic series**. If the terms instead have a constant multiplier (meaning that they increase exponentially), then it is a **geometric series**.

Examples of arithmetic and geometric series are shown below.

arithmetic series: $\qquad\qquad 2+6+10+14+\ldots+(4n-2)$

geometric series: $\qquad\qquad 1+\frac{1}{2}+\frac{1}{4}+\frac{1}{8}+\ldots+\frac{1}{2^n}$

12-34.   Examine each of the series below.

Odd numbers: $1+3+5+\ldots+149$

Even numbers: $2+4+6+\ldots+150$

a.   Write an expression for the nth term of each series.

b.   What is the sum of each series?

12-35.   Consider the series $21+17+13+\ldots+-99$ as you answer the questions in parts (a) through (c) below.

a.   Write an expression for the nth term.

b.   How many terms are in the series? How can you tell?

c.   What is the sum of this series?

12-36.   Given that $(x+1)$ is one of the factors of $3x^3 - 8x^2 - 5x + 6$, find all of the factors.

12-37.   Simplify.

     a. $(1-i)^2$ b. $(1-i)^3$

12-38.   Write the expressions in simplest form.

     a. $(9b^{-6})^{-3/2}$ b. $\dfrac{x}{(\sqrt{x})^{-1}}$

12-39.   Solve.

     a. $5^{x-3} = 120$ b. $\log(2x+1) = -1$

12-40.   Use the symmetry of the unit circle and the knowledge that $\sin\frac{\pi}{3} = \frac{\sqrt{3}}{2}$ to write three other true statements using sine.

12-41.   Graph each ellipse.

     a. $5x^2 + 4y^2 = 100$ b. $\dfrac{(x-2)^2}{25} + \dfrac{(y+3)^2}{9} = 1$

12-42.   Twelve horses raced in the CPM Derby. In how many orders could they finish?

12.1.3 How else can I see it?

General Arithmetic Series

So far, you have developed **strategies** that help to find the sum of a given series for a given number of terms. However, what if the possible number of terms is unknown? For example, in the lottery example from Lessons 12.1.1 and 12.1.2, what if the time of the drawing has not yet been set? How can you find a **general** expression that would represent the total number of tickets sold after any number of hours?

As you work with your team today, pay attention to the different ways to study a series. Many of the **strategies** introduced today may be helpful in the future when thinking about the sum of other types of series. When your team finds a new way to "see" the sum of a series, be sure to share the idea with your classmates.

12-43. Consider the series $1 + 2 + 3 + 4 + ... + n$.

   a. What is the sum of the first 3 terms? The first 10 terms?

   b. What is the sum of the first n terms? That is, find $1 + 2 + 3 + 4 + ... + n$. **Justify** your answer.

   c. Legend has it that long ago, when famous mathematician Carl Gauss was a young student, his teacher tried to keep him busy by giving him the task of finding the sum $1 + 2 + 3 + 4 + ... + 99 + 100$. He stunned his teacher and his classmates by finding the sum quickly without assistance. What is the sum?

12-44. In problem 12-43, you found a **general** rule that gives the sum of the first n counting numbers, but what about other types of numbers? For example, what is the sum of the first n odd numbers? Or the first n even numbers? Find rules for both of these cases below. Look for new **strategies** and **justify** your answer.

   a. Sum of the first n even numbers: $2 + 4 + 6 + 8 + ... + 2n$

   b. Sum of the first n odd numbers: $1 + 3 + 5 + 7 + ... + (2n - 1)$

   c. Use your rules from parts (a) and (b) to find the sum of the first 100 even numbers and then the sum of the first 100 odd numbers.

12-45. Terrell noticed that if he adds the first terms, second terms, third terms, etc. of the two arithmetic series at right, he gets a brand new series!

original series $\rightarrow \begin{cases} 1 + 2 + 3 + 4 + ... + n \\ 2 + 4 + 6 + 8 + ... + 2n \end{cases}$

new series $\rightarrow 3 + 6 + 9 + 12 + ... + 3n$

Problem continues on next page. →

12-45.   *Problem continued from previous page.*

   a.   Describe his new series. Is it arithmetic? How many terms does it have?

   b.   Use the expressions for the sums of the original series to find an expression for the sum of the new (resulting) series.

   c.   Is there another way you could have found the expression for the sum of the series $3+6+9+\ldots+3n$? Be prepared to explain your **strategy** to the class.

   d.   If you have not done so already, verify that your **strategy** in part (c) resulted in an expression equivalent to your expression from part (b).

12-46.   In problem 12-45, you used the sums of two different series to find the sum of a new series. How else can the sum of one series be used to find the sum of another series? Consider this as you work on the problems below.

   a.   How can the sum of $1+2+3+4+\ldots+n$ be used to find the sum of $2+4+6+8+\ldots+2n$? Test your idea algebraically using the expressions for the sums of these series.

   b.   How can the sum of $2+4+6+8+\ldots+2n$ be used to find the sum of $1+3+5+7+\ldots+(2n-1)$? Test your idea algebraically using the expressions for the sums of these series.

12-47.   Flo saw the sum of odd numbers from part (b) of problem 12-44 differently. She decided to represent the arithmetic series with the tile pattern below, where the area of each figure is equal to the term of the series.

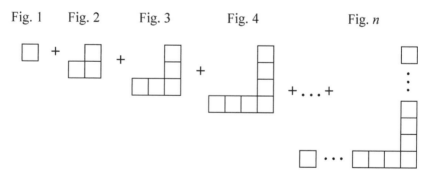

   a.   How many tiles are in the nth term? **Justify** your conclusion.

   b.   What is the sum of the first 3 terms? The sum of the first 5 terms? How can you represent this sum with the tiles?

   c.   What is the sum of the first n terms? Represent the sum algebraically in terms of n and with a diagram with tiles.

   d.   Based on Flo's representation, what is the sum of the first $(n+1)$ odd numbers? **Justify** your answer.

12-48.   Use one or more of the series below to create a new series you have not summed before. Then use the algebraic expressions for the sums to generate an expression for the sum of your new series. Be ready to share your new series and explain its sum to the class.

$$1+2+3+4+\ldots+n$$

$$2+4+6+8+\ldots+2n$$

$$1+3+5+7+\ldots+(2n-1)$$

METHODS AND **M**EANINGS

MATH NOTES

Arithmetic Series

An arithmetic sequence can be represented in general by a formula for its nth term:

$$t(n) = a + (n-1)d$$

The first term (when $n=1$) is a, and the common difference is d.

An arithmetic series is the sum of the terms of an arithmetic sequence.

$$t(1) + t(2) + t(3) + \ldots + t(k)$$

The total sum of this series can be found by adding the first and last terms, multiplying by the number of terms k and dividing by 2,

$$S(k) = \frac{k(t(1) + t(k))}{2}$$

The sum of a series can be represented with the area in the diagram at right, where each column represents a term of the series.

Note that when the diagram is rearranged as shown, the region becomes a rectangle with a height of $t(1) + t(k)$ and a width of $\frac{k}{2}$.

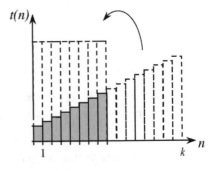

12-49.   Find the sum of the arithmetic series below.

a. $5 + 10 + 15 + 20 + \ldots + 400$ b. $3 + 8 + 13 + 18 + \ldots + 398$

c. $80 + 74 + 68 + 62 + \ldots + 14$

12-50.   Consider the sequence of multiples of 11 that are less than 100. Write them as a series and find the sum.

12-51.   Lorna is looking at the series $5 + 3 + 10 + 8 + 15 + \ldots + 400 + 398$.

"The sequence definitely isn't arithmetic, but it does have a pattern," Lorna told her team, *"I wonder if we can still find the sum of the series?"*

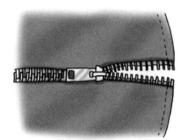

a.   What patterns do you see in Lorna's series? Describe them as completely as you can.

b.   Do you agree with Lorna's statement that this sequence is not arithmetic? **Justify** your conclusion. Do you think it is still possible to find a sum for the series?

c.   *"I think I see it!"* Lorna exclaimed. *"I think we can separate the terms into the two different arithmetic series shown below, kind of like unzipping a zipper."* Her work is shown below.

$$5 + 10 + 15 + \ldots + 395 + 400$$
$$3 + 8 + 13 + \ldots + 393 + 398$$

How can you use Lorna's two series to find the sum of the original series? State the sum and describe your process.

12-52.   A polynomial graph has a double root at $(-2, 0)$, a single root at $(2, 0)$, and passes through $(-1, 6)$. Find the exact equation of the function.

12-53.   Solve each of the following equations without a calculator.

a. $\log_x 17 = 1$ b. $x = \log_4(\frac{1}{2})$

c. $\log_4 x = \frac{1}{2}$ d. $\log_3 81 = x$

12-54.   Solve $\sqrt{x+18} + 2 = x$ and check for extraneous solutions.

12-55.   Solve each equation for $0° \le \theta < 360°$.

a. $2\sin\theta = -1$ b. $\cos^2\theta + 5\cos\theta + 4 = 0$

12-56.   If B is the midpoint of $\overline{AC}$, $A = (-3, 2)$ and $B = (5, -2)$, what are the coordinates of point C?

12-57.   Ernie and Lisa were trying to find the roots of a quadratic function $g(x)$ by solving $g(x) = 0$. Ernie's answer was $-3 \pm \sqrt{\frac{17}{2}}$; Lisa's answer was $\frac{-6 \pm \sqrt{34}}{2}$. Without using a calculator, show that both answers are equivalent and figure out what their original quadratic function $g(x)$ might have been.

12-58.   Write an equation of the ellipse with the given information.

a. x-intercepts at $(\pm 3, 0)$ and y-intercepts at $(0, \pm 6)$.

b. x-intercepts at $(\pm\sqrt{5}, 0)$ and y-intercepts at $(0, \pm 1)$.

12-59.   Twelve students will be chosen at random from the 900 students at Rolling Meadows High School to serve as the Judicial Board for minor student infractions.

a.   How many different Judicial Boards are possible?

b.   Mariko hopes to be on the board. How many possible boards include her?

c.   What is the probability that Mariko is chosen for the board?

12.1.4 How else can I express it?

Summation Notation and Combinations of Series

In this chapter you have focused your work on arithmetic series represented by graphs, algebraically, and geometrically. Today you will be introduced to a new notation for arithmetic series and you will look at methods for writing equations to find sums.

As you work today, keep the following questions in mind to focus your team discussions:

> How does this connect to what we have done before?
>
> How can we simplify it?
>
> How can we describe it?

12-60.   Remember the mathematician Gauss, from Lesson 12.1.3, whose teacher tried to keep him busy by asking him to add up the numbers from 1 to 100? Legend has it that Gauss did not show any of his work (shocking!), but he is commonly said to have used a method that starts with the steps below:

$$S = 1 + 2 + 3 + \ldots + 98 + 99 + 100$$
$$S = 100 + 99 + 98 + \ldots + 3 + 2 + 1$$
$$\overline{2S = 101 + 101 + 101 + \ldots + 101 + 101 + 101}$$

a.   Examine his work. What is he doing? Discuss this with your team, and then summarize each step on your paper.

b.   How can you simplify his resulting equation to find the sum of the series $1 + 2 + 3 + \ldots + 100$? Show and explain on your paper.

c.   How is the process from parts (a) and (b) related to how you have used a graph to find the sum of a series? Discuss with your team and write your conclusions.

d.   Show how to use this **strategy** to find the sum of the series below. Show all of your work.

$$S = 2 + 5 + 8 + 11 + \ldots + 59$$

12-61.   The series in part (d) of problem 12-60 can also be represented using **summation notation**, as shown below:

$$\sum_{c=1}^{20} (-1 + 3c)$$

The symbol "Σ" is the Greek letter "sigma," and indicates that the terms generated as c changes from 1 to 20 are summed. The expression $-1 + 3c$ is the rule for the terms of the series. As you can see in the table at right, when $c = 1$, $t(1) = -1 + 3(1) = 2$, and so on. So, as c changes from 1 to 20, the series below appears:

c	$t(c)$
1	2
2	5
3	8
$\vdots$	$\vdots$
20	59

$$2 + 5 + 8 + \ldots + 59$$

c is referred to as an **index**, which temporarily represents the term number as the series terms are determined. The same series could be written:

$$\sum_{p=1}^{20} (-1 + 3p)$$

It is also possible for the series to be written with a different starting value, such as:

$$\sum_{p=0}^{19} (2 + 3p)$$

a.   Use summation notation to represent the series $15 + 19 + 23 + 27 + 31$.

b.   Expand the series $\sum_{t=1}^{6} t^2$ and find its sum.

12-62.   In problem 12-51 you separated Lorna's complicated series into two different arithmetic series, as shown below.

$$5 + 3 + 10 + 8 + 15 + \ldots + 400 + 398 = 5 + 10 + 15 + \ldots + 400$$
$$+ 3 + 8 + 13 + \ldots + 398$$

a.   Write each arithmetic series using summation notation.

b.   How could you use your expressions from part (a) to write an expression for Lorna's series using summation notation?

12-63.   Find the sum of each arithmetic series described below.

a. $\sum_{t=1}^{10} -5 + 13t$

b.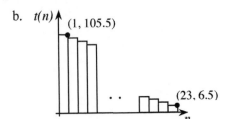

c. $4 + 10 + 16 + 22 + \ldots + (6n - 2)$

d. $\sum_{t=1}^{30} 10 - 5t$

METHODS AND MEANINGS

Summation Notation

MATH NOTES

The capital Greek letter **sigma**, Σ, (equivalent to "S" in English) is used in mathematics as a shorter way to indicate the sum of a series. For example:

$$\sum_{k=1}^{5}(2k-3) = -1+1+3+5+7 = 15$$

Translated, this expression means the sum from $k=1$ to $k=5$ of the terms $2k-3$ equals 15.

Also, the sum of the series $1^2 + 2^2 + 3^2$ can be written $\sum_{k=1}^{3} k^2$.

Note: We call k the **index** and k^2 the **argument** of this summation. The values of the index are consecutive integers only, so the values of k in this second example are 1, 2, and 3.

Review & Preview

12-64.   Write each series in sigma notation and find the sum or an expression for the sum.

a. $47 + 34 + 21 + ... + (-83)$

b. $3 + 10 + 17 + ... + (7n - 4)$

12-65.   Use any method to find the sum of the integers from 100 through 1000. Describe your **strategy**.

12-66.   Use algebra to demonstrate that each pair of expressions in parts (a) and (b) below are equivalent.

a. $\frac{k(k+1)}{2} + k + 1$ and $\frac{(k+1)(k+2)}{2}$

b. $\frac{k(7k-1)}{2} + 7(k+1) - 4$ and $\frac{(k+1)(7k+6)}{2}$

12-67.   For many years mathematicians tried to come up with a formula to generate prime numbers. One candidate was the expression $n^2 + n + 41$, where n is a positive integer. Try at least 3 or 4 numbers. What do you think of the formula? Does it work? Could you prove it?

12-68.   Write each expression in a shorter form.

a. $3(7 \cdot 3^{n-1})$

b. $0.6(10(0.6)^{n-2})$

12-69.   Graph each complex number and find its absolute value. Remember that the absolute value of a complex number is the same as its distance from the origin.

   a. $-2i$ b. $-3+4i$ c. $-2-2i$ d.   4

12-70.   Without a calculator, estimate the value of $2 \log 50$. Explain your logic clearly.

12-71.   What is the solution for the system of equations at right?

$$\frac{7}{13}x + \frac{4}{15}y = 0$$
$$\frac{5}{8}x + \frac{12}{7}y = 0$$

12-72.   Brianna is working on her homework and is asked to state the domain and range for $y = \tan\theta$. She enters the equation on her graphing calculator and sets her Xmin to $-\pi$ and her Xmax to 2π. After looking at its graph, Brianna is still unclear how to state the tangent's domain because of the asymptotes.

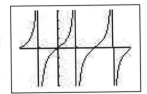

   a.   Explain to Brianna the domain of $y = \tan\theta$ and how to use the graph to make sense of it.

   b.   The second part of Brianna's problem asked her to graph the transformed equation $y = \tan(\theta - \frac{\pi}{2})$. As she entered the equation into her graphing calculator, the screen went blank. (Her batteries were dead.) Explain to Brianna how she can use her first graph to sketch her transformed graph $y = \tan(\theta - \frac{\pi}{2})$. Include a labeled sketch.

   c.   Does this transformation have a different domain from that in part (a)? If so, how is it different? What is the range for each function $y = \tan\theta$ and $y = \tan(\theta - \frac{\pi}{2})$? Justify your answers completely.

12-73.   Use the graph at right to solve $2^x + 1 < 3^x$.

12-74.   Find the equation for an ellipse with vertices $(-2, -3)$, $(10, -3)$, $(4, -2)$, and $(4, -4)$.

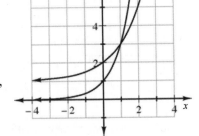

12-75.   Ten points lie on a circle.

   a.   How many chords can be drawn using the given points as endpoints?

   b.   How many triangles can be drawn using the points as vertices?

12.2.1 How can I prove it?

Mathematical Induction

In Section 12.1, you generated expressions that represented the sums of series with n terms. For example, you determined that the series $1 + 3 + 5 + 7 + \ldots + (2n - 1) = n^2$. But is this expression true for all values of n? How can you be convinced? How can you convince others? Your peers? Your teacher? Other math teachers? A mathematician?

Today, you will develop a new way to convince yourself and others that the sum of an indeterminate series (a series with n terms) is valid for any value of n.

12-76.   One way to represent the sum of the series $1 + 3 + 5 + \ldots + (2n - 1)$ is geometrically, using the tile pattern below (from problem 12-44).

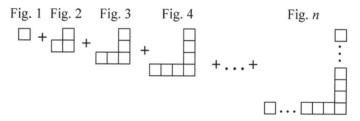

Fig. 1   Fig. 2   Fig. 3   Fig. 4   Fig. n

a.   What is the sum of the first n terms of this series? **Justify** your answer.

b.   Does the sum you found in part (a) work when $n = 1$? What about for $n = 5$? $n = 8$? For each case, write out the corresponding series and test the expression for the sum.

c.   Khalil wonders, *"What if my expression for the sum works for some values of n but not all? It seems to work... but does it always work? How can we show that it must work for all integer values $n \geq 1$?"* Discuss these questions with your team and brainstorm ways to convince yourselves and others that this expression represents the sum of the series $1 + 3 + 5 + \ldots + (2n - 1)$ for all integer values $n \geq 1$.

12-77.   PROOF BY INDUCTION

A **proof** is a convincing logical argument. One form of mathematical proof is called **proof by mathematical induction**. This type of argument is used to demonstrate that a conclusion is true for an infinite set of possibilities (such as an infinite number of values of n). Use the questions below to help you understand the logic behind proof by mathematical induction.

Problem continues on next page. →

12-77.   *Problem continued from previous page.*

a.   In problem 12-70, you demonstrated that $1+3+5+\ldots+(2n-1)=n^2$ when $n=1$, $n=5$, and $n=8$. These demonstrated values can be represented with points on a number line, such as the one below. Is it reasonable to prove that n^2 works for all positive integer values for n by testing them all? Why or why not?

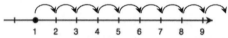

b.   What if you know that whenever the relationship $1+3+5+\ldots+(2n-1)=n^2$ is true for one integer value (we call this value k), it always is true for the value that is one larger ($k+1$)? Discuss with your team how you could use this knowledge to help you prove the relationship must be true for all integer values greater than a demonstrated value. The diagram below may help your discussion.

c.   If you know that the relationship in part (b) is true, what value of n do you need to test in order to use mathematical induction to prove a relationship is true for all positive integers? Why?

12-78.   The core aspect of mathematical induction is proving that whenever a relationship is true for $n=k$, it must be true also for $n=k+1$. This requires starting with an *assumption* that the relationship is true for k in order for it to be proven that the relationship is true for $k+1$. The questions below will help you prove that $1+3+5+\ldots+(2n-1)=n^2$ is true for all $n\geq 1$.

a.   This sum of the first k odd numbers can be represented with the diagram below. One way to extend the series to include the $(k+1)^{th}$ term is to add the $(k+1)^{th}$ figure to both sides. Study the diagram with your teammates. How many tiles are being added to both sides of the equation? That is, how many tiles does the $(k+1)^{th}$ figure have?

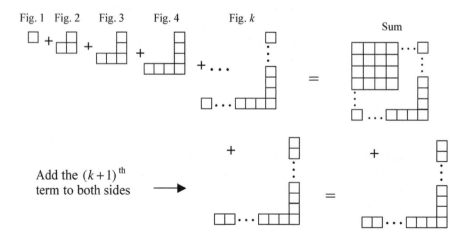

Problem continues on next page. →

Algebra 2 Connections

12-78.   *Problem continued from previous page.*

b.   The right side of the sum above can be represented algebraically with $k^2 + (2k+1)$. Does this sum confirm that the expression $1 + 3 + 5 + \ldots + (2n-1) = n^2$ is true when $n = k+1$? Show how you know algebraically and geometrically.

c.   Since you found that the relationship is true when $n = 1$ (in part (b) of problem 12-76), and you showed that the relationship is true for $n = k+1$ whenever $n = k$ is true, then what conclusion can you draw?

d.   Review the Math Notes box in this lesson for more information about mathematical induction. Add an entry in your Learning Log describing the process of induction. Title this entry "Proof by Induction" and label it with today's date.

12-79.   Does this process work for other finite series, such as $1 + 2 + 3 + \ldots + n = \frac{n(n+1)}{2}$? What if you do not have a geometric representation? Review the process of mathematical induction as you answer the questions below.

a.   According to the relationship $1 + 2 + 3 + \ldots + n = \frac{n(n+1)}{2}$, what should be the sum of the first $(k+1)$ terms?

b.   If you want to prove $1 + 2 + 3 + \ldots + n = \frac{n(n+1)}{2}$ is true for all natural numbers (that is, all positive integers), for what value of n should you demonstrate the relationship is true first? Discuss this with your team, and then show that the relationship is true for that specific value of n.

c.   Assume that the relationship is true for some value k. That is, assume the following:

$$1 + 2 + 3 + \ldots + k = \frac{k(k+1)}{2}$$

With your team, extend the series to include the $(k+1)^{\text{th}}$ term by adding it to both sides of the equation. Then demonstrate that the result on the right is equivalent to the sum of the first $(k+1)$ terms of the series that you found in part (a) above.

d.   Conclude your proof with a statement of what has been proven. Often, these concluding statements begin with "Therefore … ."

12-80.   Prove the following relationships are true for $n \geq 1$ using mathematical induction.

a. $2 + 4 + 6 + \ldots + 2n = n(n+1)$

b. $5 + 8 + 11 + \ldots + (3n+2) = \frac{n(3n+7)}{2}$

c. $1^2 + 2^2 + 3^2 + \ldots + n^2 = \frac{n(n+1)(2n+1)}{6}$

12-81.   EXTENSION

In problem 12-48, you generated a unique series and found an expression for its sum. Now, use mathematical induction to prove that the expression you found will find the sum for any $n \geq 1$.

ETHODS AND MEANINGS

Mathematical Induction for Series

MATH NOTES

Most of the proofs you have written so far have been in geometry, but proof is important in all areas of mathematics. Many theorems in algebra are proved by methods similar to those you used in geometry, but proving the formula for the sum of a series for an infinite set of values of n requires a new strategy called **proof by mathematical induction.**

Mathematical induction can be used to prove that the expression representing the sum of a series is true for all integer values of n greater than a constant, typically $n \geq 1$. To prove the sum of a series using mathematical induction, follow the steps below:

1. Verify by substitution that the relationship is true for a specific value of n, typically $n = 1$.

2. Use substitution to *state* the relationship for $n = k$, and then *assume* it is true. Then extend the relationship to the next integer, $n = k + 1$, by adding the $(k+1)th$ term to both sides of the relationship.

3. Algebraically transform the statement for $n = k$ into the statement $n = k + 1$.

4. Write a concluding statement of what has been proven.

12-82.   Demonstrate that $\frac{3k^2+7k}{2}+3k+5$ is equivalent to $\frac{3k^2+13k+10}{2}$.

12-83.   Find the sum of the first 11 terms of the sequence $21, 26, 31, 36, 41, \ldots$

12-84.   Use summation notation to represent the sum of first ten terms of the arithmetic series $2+4+6+\ldots$. Then find the sum.

12-85.   Use what you know about series to find the sum of all of the multiples of 7 that are between 0 and 500.

12-86.   Factor each of the expressions below, if possible.

   a. $3x^2-18x$ b. $3k^2+13k+10$

   c. $6m^2-13m-5$ d. $9t^2-25$

12-87.   Sketch the graph of $f(x)=5\log(x-2)+3$.

12-88.   Find a polynomial function of degree four with roots: $x=-1, 3, \pm\sqrt{5}$.

12-89.   If Michele knows that $\sin(\frac{7\pi}{6})=-\frac{1}{2}$ and $\cos(\frac{7\pi}{6})=-\frac{\sqrt{3}}{2}$, how can she use this information to find the exact value for $\tan(\frac{7\pi}{6})$? What is it?

12-90.   Graph each hyperbola.

   a. $x^2-y^2=9$ b. $\frac{(x-2)^2}{4}-\frac{(y+1)^2}{9}=1$

12-91.　The booster club sells meals at basketball games. Each meal comes with a choice of hamburger, pizza, hot dog, cheeseburger, or taco, and a choice of root beer, lemonade, milk, tea, or cola. How many different meals can be made?

12-92.　In how many ways can five different French books and three different Spanish books be arranged on a shelf if all the books of one language must remain together?

12-93.　Use mathematical induction to prove that the relationship below is true for $n \geq 1$.

$$9 + 14 + 19 + \ldots + (4n + 5) = n(2n + 7)$$

12-94.　Examine Kari's proof by induction below.

I know $3 + 6 + 9 + \ldots + 3n = \frac{3}{2}n(n+1)$ is true for $n = 2$ because $3 + 6 = \frac{3}{2}(2)(2+1) = 9$. If I assume that $3 + 6 + 9 + \ldots + 3k = \frac{3}{2}k(k+1)$ is true, then:

$$3 + 6 + 9 + \ldots + 3k + 3(k+1) = \frac{3}{2}k(k+1) + 3(k+1)$$
$$= \frac{3}{2}k^2 + \frac{3}{2}k + 3k + 3$$
$$= \frac{3}{2}k^2 + \frac{9}{2}k + 3$$
$$= \frac{3}{2}(k^2 + 3k + 2)$$
$$= \frac{3}{2}(k+1)(k+2)$$

Therefore, the relationship is true for $n = k+1$ whenever it is true for $n = k$.

a.　What did she prove?

b.　How could she adjust her proof so that she can know for sure that the relationship is true for all $n \geq 1$?

12-95.　For the sequence: 5, –2, –9, –16, …

a.　Find $t(50)$, the 50th term.

b.　Find $S(50)$, the sum of the first 50 terms.

12-96.　Use summation notation to write this series: $1 + 4 + 7 + 10 + 13 + 16$.

12-97.   Simplify each of the following expressions.

    a. $5(2 \cdot 5^{n-1})$ b. $0.3(1000(0.3)^{n-3})$

    c. $\frac{1}{3}(2(\frac{1}{3})^{n-5})$ d. $r(ar^{n-2})$

12-98.   Describe the possible values of x that would make each of the following statements true.

    a. $\log x > 3$ b. $\log x < 1$ c. $\log 100 < x$ d. $\log_x 27 > 3$

12-99.   Solve the system of equations at right.

$$x^2 + y^2 = 25$$
$$y = x^2 - 13$$

12-100.   Find the exact value for each of the following trig expressions:

    a. $\cos(\frac{3\pi}{4})$ b. $\tan(\frac{4\pi}{3})$ c. $\sin(\frac{11\pi}{6})$

12-101.   For each equation, identify the curve, write the equation in graphing form, state the locator point, and draw the graph.

    a. $2x^2 + y^2 - 4x + 6y - 7 = 0$ b. $3y^2 - x^2 + 12y = 0$

12-102.   How many committees of three juniors and three seniors can be formed from the student government class of eight juniors and 10 seniors?

12-103.   A bag contains four red pens, six green pens, and two blue pens. If three pens are chosen at random, what is the probability that one of each color is picked?

12.3.1 What about geometric series?

Geometric Series

In this lesson you will work with **geometric series** and develop a method for representing and calculating their sums. Being able to find the sum of a geometric series makes it easy to calculate how much a long-term loan will really cost or how much you will end up paying for something when you buy it on credit. As you work with your team on the problems in this lesson, keep the following discussion questions in mind:

Can we use any of the strategies we already know?

How can we use what we know about systems of equations?

How can we describe what we have done?

How can we generalize what we have done?

12-104.   PICKING A PAYOUT

With a record-setting lottery jackpot projected for noon tomorrow, Hank stood in a very long line to buy a ticket. The man behind him in line tapped him on the shoulder to ask, *"Hey, have you thought about how you'd spend the money if you won?"* Before he could answer, the woman in front interrupted to say, *"First, you have to decide whether you want to get your winnings in one lump sum right away, or if you want to receive them spread out over time. I'm sure one option must be a better deal, but I haven't figured out which one!"*

When Hank got home he immediately went on the Internet and learned that lottery winners do have a choice: receive the winnings in a single payment of 51% of the jackpot right away, or spread payments of the jackpot over 20 years. He also learned that the jackpot is projected to be $50 million! He knew that if he took the single payment he could invest it right away and earn 4% interest on that money.

If he chose to receive the payout over 20 years, the Lottery Commission would invest for him. They guarantee to pay $1,500,000 the first year, and to increase the amount they pay by 5% each year to keep up with inflation.

At lunchtime, Hank called his brother and told him that if his algebra class could figure out the difference between the totals for the two payment methods, he would give that amount to the class if he won the lottery.

a.   If Hank wins the lottery and takes the payments over time, the amounts he will receive each year form a geometric sequence. What is the initial term? What is the growth factor? Write an equation to represent a term in this sequence.

Problem continues on next page. →

12-104.   *Problem continued from previous page.*

   b.   If Hank takes the payments over time, how much will his payout in the 20th year be?

   c.   When you add up the terms of this sequence to find the total over 20 years, you are finding the sum for the geometric series. Show the geometric series.

   d.   With your team, discuss finding a **strategy** for calculating the sum without having to calculate and add all 20 terms. Consider the graphical method of creating rectangles that you used with arithmetic series. Would that work for this kind of series? Explain your thinking.

12-105.   While working on a strategy to solve the lottery problem, Luann's team decided to look at an easier sequence and use fewer terms:

$$t(n) = 2 \cdot 5^{n-1}$$

They wrote out the series for six terms, represented the sum of the series as $S(6)$, and then wrote the series in an equation:

$$2 + 10 + 50 + 250 + 1250 + 6250 = S(6)$$

Then Luann remembered the algebraic **strategy** she used for finding the sum of an arithmetic series where she added the sequence to itself, and manipulated the equations. Is there a similar method you can use for geometric series? Work on this as a team. Is there a way to write the equation down twice and then rewrite the second equation to eliminate some of the terms when the two equations are combined?

12-106.   *"I'm sure that this can be simplified,"* Luann reported to her team. *"But when I try to add the series to itself, like we did with the arithmetic series, it just gets bigger, and there's no clear pattern. If I subtract it from itself I'm left with $0 = 0$."*

   a.   What are some techniques for rewriting an equation that you use when solving systems of equations by elimination? Could these techniques be applied in this situation?

   b.   *"Aha!"* Luann almost shouted.

   "Shhh!" her teammate cautioned, *"What have you got?"*

   "Look! I multiplied both sides of the equation by the multiplier." Luann was really excited about the result. How can you use her results and combine the equations to find the sum $S(6)$?

12-107.   Luann wondered if they could use the same method to write an expression for the general sum of any number of terms of the series:

$$2 + 10 + 50 + \ldots + 2 \cdot 5^{n-1} = S(n)$$

Show how to use her method to write a general expression for the sum. Make a note of what you multiplied by, what was left when you subtracted, and what you finally divided by to get the result.

12-108.   Antonio is working with a new geometric series generated by the equation $t(n) = 30(1.2)^{n-1}$. His sister has challenged him to find the sum of the first 15 terms. He needs your help.

a.   Show Antonio how he can figure out the sum without adding up all of the terms.

b.   Antonio knows his sister will not be satisfied with his answer and she will give him another number of terms to add up. Show him how to write a formula for the sum of the terms of this series.

12-109.   PICKING A PAYOUT . . . continued

Look back to your work on problem 12-104. For your convenience, the two payment options are reprinted below. Recall that the jackpot in question is $50,000,000.

Option 1: Receive a single payment of 51% of the jackpot right away. Invest the money and earn 4% interest compounded annually.

Option 2: Receive payments once a year for 20 years. The first payment would be $1,500,000 and the payments would increase by 5% each year.

Your task: Work with your team to determine which is the best way to collect the money. Should Hank take his winnings immediately and invest the money himself? Or should he choose the guaranteed payout each year for 20 years? In which way would he receive the most money? Be prepared to **justify** your decision with explanations and calculations.

Discussion Points

How will the amount increase over time if he invests it himself?

How can we represent the amount he would receive each year algebraically if he chooses the annual payout?

How much will there be in total after 20 years in each situation?

12-110.   Imagine taking the single payment of 51% of the jackpot.

    a.   How much will you receive?

    b.   If you invest all of the money at a rate of 4% compounded annually, how much can you expect to have after 20 years?

    c.   Is the answer to part (b) the sum of a series?

12-111.   If instead, you choose to take payments spread over 20 years, starting with $1,500,000 in year 1 and growing by 5 percent each year,

    a.   How much money would you receive in year 2? In year 5?

    b.   Write an equation to show how much money you receive in any given year.

    c.   How much money will you have received after 20 years? Be ready to explain your thinking to the class.

12-112.   Which way would you receive more money? How much more? Which way would you choose to receive the funds? Why?

Further Guidance
section ends here.

12-113.   Scott and Greg are looking for summer jobs. Their father, head of the neighborhood beautification committee, says that if they pick up litter from around the neighborhood for a whole day he will pay them $0.15 per piece. Scott realizes that the more litter they pick up the more difficult it will be to find more pieces, so he proposes a different payment scheme. *"How about you give us $0.10 for the first piece, and increase our pay by 2% for each piece after that? Then we'll get paid more for the pieces we work harder to find."*

    a.   Write an equation to generate the series Scott is proposing.

    b.   With Scott's plan, how much will his dad have to pay him for the 100th piece of litter he finds? For the 200th?

    c.   If Scott collects 150 pieces of litter, how much will he have earned in total? What if he picks up 200 pieces?

Problem continues on next page. →

12-113.   *Problem continued from previous page.*

    d.   Greg thinks Scott is crazy to propose an increase of just 2% per piece. After all 2% of 10 cents is just $\frac{2}{10}$ of a cent! Instead, he plans to ask for a one-cent increase for every piece. If their father agrees to this, how much would Greg get paid for the 100th piece he collects? For the 200th piece?

    e.   If the boys each collect 150 pieces of litter, which payment scheme will earn them the most money?

    f.   What if they each pick up a total of 200 pieces?

12-114.   Drought-conscious Darcy is collecting rainwater in order to water her garden through the hot, dry summer. During the last big rainstorm she filled 12 buckets full to the rim! She plans to use one bucket of water each week.

However, Darcy did not count on evaporation. In the sun, each uncovered bucket loses 0.35 gallons of its water volume each week.

    a.   If each bucket starts with 15 gallons in it, how many gallons will be in each of the unused buckets after 2 weeks in the sun? After 7 weeks?

    b.   Is the series arithmetic, geometric, or something else?

    c.   At the end of the 12th week, how many total gallons of water will Darcy have poured on her plants?

12-115.   Hannah is very interested in genealogy, the study of family history. She has traced her family back many years and knows the names of her biological parents, grandparents, great-grandparents, great-great-grandparents, and so on.

    a.   How many people are in each of the first three generations on Hannah's chart? (Assume Hannah herself is the first generation.)

    b.   What kind of sequence does the number of names in each generation form? Is it arithmetic, geometric, or something else? **Justify** your conclusion.

    c.   If Hannah is successful in tracing her true biological ancestors for the last 12 generations, how many names will she have?

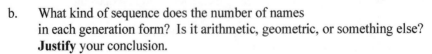

12-116. For each of the problems below, decide if the series is arithmetic, geometric, or something else. Then, find the sum of the series.

a. $\displaystyle\sum_{t=0}^{15} 5(2)^t$

b. $\displaystyle\sum_{p=1}^{17} (20-4p)$

c. $4+8+12+\ldots+392$

d. $\displaystyle\sum_{q=1}^{312} 11q$

e. $2+8+4+10+6+\ldots+84+90$

f. $5+\frac{10}{4}+\frac{10}{8}+\ldots+\frac{10}{4096}$

12-117. Lucy is working with a series that has 12 as its first term and is generated by the expression $t(n)=-9+21n$. The sum of her series is 3429. How many terms are in her series?

12-118. LEARNING LOG

Write an entry in your Learning Log describing what you learned during this lesson. Include information about the differences between geometric sequences and geometric series, and about how to find the sum of a geometric series. What questions do you have about geometric series? Title this entry "Geometric Series" and label it with today's date.

METHODS AND MEANINGS

Geometric Series

A geometric sequence can be represented by a formula for its nth term:

$$t(n) = ar^{n-1}$$

The first term, for which $n=1$, is a, and the common multiplier (or ratio) is r.

A **geometric series** is the sum of the terms of a geometric sequence:

$$t(1) + t(2) + t(3) + \ldots + t(k)$$

The total can be found by multiplying the last term by the common multiplier r, subtracting the first term, and then dividing by $r-1$.

$$S(k) = \frac{r \cdot t(k) - t(1)}{r-1}$$

12-119.   Antonio and Luann were trying to explain their strategy for finding the sum of a
           geometric series to their homework group. They decided to generate a sequence that
           would be easy to add up so they could convince the other students that their **strategy**
           really worked: $t(n) = 3 \cdot 10^{n-1}$.

    a.   The sum of the first six terms of the series is easy to calculate. You can do it in
          your head. Write out the first six terms and find the sum.

    b.   Now explain Luann and Antonio's **strategy** for finding the sum and use your
          answer to part (a) to check your result.

    c.   Represent the first n terms of the series in summation notation, and write an
          expression for the total sum of n terms.

12-120.   According to the school secretary, the size of the
           graduating class of Gauss High has steadily increased since
           it has opened. She claims that the number of graduates
           each year forms the sequence $t(n) = 30 + 12n$, where n is
           the number of years the high school has had students
           graduate. At the end of the year, the administration mails
           out invitations to all previous graduates to attend the
           upcoming graduation ceremony.

    a.   In this situation, what does a sequence represent?
          What does a series represent?

    b.   After the 10th graduation ceremony, how many total graduates should there be?
          Explain how you found your answer.

    c.   The total number of Gauss High
          graduates after n years can be
          represented by the graph at right. If the
          alumni relations committee wants to
          invite all graduates to a party to
          celebrate the nth anniversary of the
          school, how may invitations will they
          need to send?

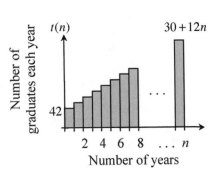

12-121.   Consider the series $8 + 1 + (-6) + (-13) + ... + (-90)$.

    a.   How many terms are there?   b.   What is the sum?

12-122.   Evaluate the sum of the series $\sum_{n=3}^{9} (5n)$. Is the series arithmetic or geometric?

12-123.   Find a polynomial function of degree four with roots: $x = \pm i, 2 \pm \sqrt{3}$.

12-124.   Solve each of the equations below.

   a. $3^x = 141$ b. $2 \cdot 7^{(x-5)} = 12$

12-125.   Give the exact value(s) for each of the unknowns ($0 \le \theta < 2\pi$) in the equations below.

   a. $\sin(\frac{3\pi}{4}) = ?$ b. $\cos(\frac{5\pi}{4}) = ?$ c. $\tan\theta = 1$ d. $\tan(\theta) = -1$

12-126.   State the domain and range for the sine, cosine and tangent functions. Include a sketch as part of your answer.

12-127.   For each equation below, identify the curve, write the equation in graphing form, state the locator point, and draw the graph.

   a. $12x^2 + 8y^2 + 48x - 48y + 24 = 0$ b. $4x^2 + 4y^2 + 16x - 16y + 22 = 0$

12-128.   A bag contains five green marbles and four white marbles. You pick three marbles, one at a time, without replacing them.

   a.   What is the probability of getting white, another white, and then green?

   b.   What is the probability of getting two white and a green in any order?

12-129.   Joe's dad is only 40, but he's already thinking about retiring. If he retires early at age 55, he will receive an annual pension starting at $30,000 and increasing at a rate of 3% each year to account for inflation. If he waits until he is 65, his pension will be a larger percentage of his salary at that time. He figures that it will be about $60,000 to start and the same 3% increase after that for inflation. He wants to know which plan will pay out the largest total by age 80. Show him how to find out the answer to his question.

12-130.   RETURN OF THE BOUNCING BALL

Remember the bouncing ball back in Chapter 2? What if you tossed the ball straight up to a height of 10 meters and then let it bounce 15 times up and down?

a.   How far does the ball travel up and down on the initial toss (before the first bounce)?

b.   If the rebound ratio for the ball is 0.6, write a geometric series to represent the distance it travels up and down by the 15th bounce.

c.   What is the total distance the ball will travel up and down?

12-131.   Ms. Fernandez invested \$50,000 of her lottery winnings into two different mutual funds. At the end of one year, both funds together were worth \$53, 550. One of the funds had produced a return of 8% while the second fund had produced a return of 6.5%. How much money was invested in each fund?

12-132.   Find the exact value for each of the following trig expressions:

a. $\dfrac{\sin(\frac{\pi}{3})}{\cos(\frac{\pi}{3})}$

b. $\tan(\frac{\pi}{3})$

c.   Explain the relationship between the answers from part (a) and (b) above.

12-133.   Find the exact value, if possible, for each of the following trig expressions:

a. $\tan(0)$ b. $\tan(\frac{\pi}{2})$ c. $\tan(\pi)$

d. $\tan(\frac{3\pi}{2})$ e. $\tan(2\pi)$ f. $\tan(4\pi)$

g.   Explain each of your answers as it relates the graph of $y = \tan\theta$.

12-134.   In $\triangle ABC$, if $AB = BC$ and $m\angle ABC = 70°$, then what is $m\angle BAC$?

12-135.   Solve the system of equations at right.

$$\frac{x}{4} + \frac{y}{3} = 1$$
$$2x - \frac{y}{3} = 17$$

12-136.   An exponential function has an asymptote at $y = -10$ and passes through the points (2, 8) and (4, 30.5). Find its equation.

12-137.   Prove $5 + 8 + 11 + ... + (3n + 2) = \frac{n(3n+7)}{2}$ by induction.

12.3.2 What if n is very large?

Infinite Series

What if a bouncing ball continued to bounce forever? How far would it travel? Of course we know that the ball cannot bounce forever, but thinking about the possibility has led to some interesting discoveries. If the ball could bounce forever, the distance for each bounce would be getting smaller and smaller as the number of bounces grew larger and larger. Would the total distance continue to grow to be infinitely large?

12-138.   HOW FAR IS IT?

While we know that a ball cannot bounce forever, imagine that the ball in problem 12-130 could. Or instead, imagine starting at 0 on a number line and moving according to the following rule: move 20 units to the right, and then continue making moves to the right with each move being 0.6 times as long as the previous move.

20   12   7.2   • • •

Your task: With your team, investigate the question below.

How far along the number line will you travel if you keep going and going and going and … ?

Use what you have learned about geometric sequences and try out different values for n. When your team agrees you have answered the question, make up some new infinite geometric series and **generalize** your results to write a **strategy** for finding sums of any infinite geometric series. Prepare a poster to share your team's findings. Include your examples, **generalizations**, and **justifications**. As you work with your team, keep the following discussion questions in mind:

Discussion Points

What patterns do we see as n increases?

What happens when we multiply or divide by numbers smaller than one?

How can we represent this?

Is there a simpler equivalent expression?

Further Guidance

12-139. You already calculated the distance for 15 bounces of the ball in problem 12-130. Calculate the distance for 25 moves along the number line and for several larger values of n. What do you notice about the results as you use larger values for n?

12-140. Calculate the sums of each of the following geometric series for at least two values of n, say $n = 10$ and $n = 30$. What do you notice about the results?

  a. $200 + 100 + 50 + ... + 200(\frac{1}{2})^n$ b. $16 + 24 + 36 + ...16(\frac{3}{2})^n$

  c.   What makes the difference in the results for the series in parts (a) and (b)?

12-141. Replace $t(n)$ and $t(1)$ in the general formula for the sum of a geometric series with $t(n) = ar^{n-1}$ and $t(1) = a$ in order to rewrite the formula in a more convenient form.

$$S(n) = \frac{r \cdot t(n) - t(1)}{r - 1} = \frac{r(ar^{n-1}) - a}{r - 1}$$

  a.   Rewrite the numerator of the new expression for the sum in a simpler form.

  b.   Multiply both numerator and denominator by -1, and rearrange the terms. Will this new expression be equivalent to the original? How do you know?

  c.   Use the distributive property to rewrite the numerator as a product using a as a factor.

12-142. Be sure your result for problem 12-141 is equivalent to the equation $S(n) = \frac{a(1-r^n)}{1-r}$.

  a.   In problem 12-138, $a = 20$ and $r = 0.6$. What happens to the value of r^n as you use larger and larger values for n? And what happens to the value of the expression $1 - r^n$? Discuss these questions with your team.

  b.   For infinite series, the formula can be rewritten as shown below. Use this formula to recalculate the sums of the series in problem 12-139 and part (a) of problem 12-140 part (a), if they were to continue without ending.

$$S(n) = \frac{a}{1-r}$$

  c.   Compare your results for part (b) with your original answers and discuss this with your team.

————— *Further Guidance* —————
section ends here.

12-143.   LEARNING LOG

Write an entry in your Learning Log describing what you learned
during this lesson. Include information about infinite geometric series
and their sums. What questions do you have about series? Title this
entry "Infinite Geometric Series" and label it with today's date.

METHODS AND MEANINGS

Infinite Geometric Series

For an **infinite geometric series** with an initial value of a and a
multiplier (or common ratio) r, and $0 < |r| < 1$, the sum of the series
can be represented:

$$\sum_{n=1}^{\infty} ar^{n-1} = \frac{a}{1-r}$$

For example: When $a = 100$ and the multiplier is $r = 0.2$:

$$100 + 20 + 4 + .8 + \ldots = \frac{100}{1-0.2} = 125$$

Review & Preview

12-144.   A hiker decided to spend his days walking around the country. On the first day he
walked 25 miles, but on the following days he found he could not keep up that pace.
On average he traveled 5% less each day. If he could walk forever, how far would
he go?

12-145.   Find the infinite sum: $0.9 + 0.09 + 0.009 + 0.0009 + \ldots$.

12-146.   Why does the formula for the sum of an infinite geometric series contain the condition
that $0 < |r| < 1$?

12-147.   Find the sum of the first five terms of this series: $3+1+\frac{1}{3}+...$

12-148.   Solve and check.

      a. $\frac{5}{x-1}=4+\frac{x}{2}$ b. $2x=\sqrt{10+6x}$

12-149.   Consider the table at right for the function $f(x)=\log_b x$.

      a.   Complete the table.

      b.   Extend the table to include six more x-values of your choice. Show how you calculated the $f(x)$ values for each.

      c.   Find the base of this logarithmic function and explain how you found it.

x	$f(x)$
1	
2	0.2702
3	0.4283
4	
5	0.6275
6	
7	0.7587
8	
9	
10	
11	0.9349

12-150.   Let $p=2+5i$ and $q=3-4i$. Calculate each of the following and give your answer in the form $a+bi$.

      a. $p-q$ b. $p\cdot q$ c. $\frac{p}{q}$ d. p^2

12-151.   Where is the $\tan\theta$ undefined? Use the unit circle to support your answer.

12-152.   State the sign ($+$ or $-$) of the tangent in each quadrant of the unit circle. **Justify** your answer.

12-153.   Prove by induction: $1+3+5+...+(2n-1)=n^2$

12-154.   From a batch of 500 light bulbs, how many ways can three be tested to see if they are defective?

12.4.1 How can I use combinations?

Pascal's Triangle and the Binomial Theorem

In Chapter 10, you explored several kinds of counting problems:

- *Combinations*: counting where order does not matter and results are not repeated,
- *Permutations*: where order does matter, and results are not repeated,
- *Decision charts*: where order matters and results can be repeated, and
- *A fourth kind of problem*: where order did not matter and results could be repeated, which required considering several subproblems.

You also worked on some problems that did not fit any of these categories exactly. Today you will use combinations as a way of thinking about repeated situations involving *two* alternatives: to choose or not to choose. These situations can be viewed as **binomial.**

For example, when you flip a coin five times, for each flip there are two choices, heads or not heads, and a decision chart gives you $2 \cdot 2 \cdot 2 \cdot 2 \cdot 2$ for the total number of outcomes. But if you want to answer the question, "What is the probability of getting exactly three heads?" or "How many ways are there to get exactly three heads?" you need to think about the number of ways three of the five flips can be heads (and the other two are not heads).

Several of today's problems involve binomial situations where two choices are possible for each of several repeated trials, but first you will consider a problem that may appear to be completely unrelated, looking for patterns in Pascal's Triangle.

12-155. The array of numbers at right is known as Pascal's Triangle. Copy the triangle and add several more rows.

n						
0			1			
1			1	1		
2		1	2	1		
3		1	3	3	1	
4	1	4	6	4	1	
5	1	5	10	10	5	1

a. There are many patterns in the triangle, which continues to grow indefinitely. With your team, find and describe as many patterns as you can. You should be able to describe at least three.

b. Discuss with the class the patterns you found. Write down any patterns your classmates found that your team did not find.

c. The lone number 1 at the top of the triangle is called Row 0. Add rows to your triangle down to row 10, and describe a rule for writing any new row in the triangle.

12-156. Now consider what may appear to be a completely different problem: the algebraic expansion of the binomial expression $(a + b)^n$. Use what you know about polynomial multiplication to complete parts (a) through (d) below.

    a.   Write $(a + b)^2$ in expanded form. In other words, multiply $(a + b)(a + b)$. How many terms are there in the resulting polynomial? What are the coefficients of the terms?

    b.   Write $(a + b)^3$ in expanded form. How many terms are there and what are their coefficients? What did you do to expand the polynomial? With your team, discuss possible ways to carry out the polynomial multiplication quickly.

    c.   How many terms do you think $(a + b)^4$ will have when expanded? Write it in expanded form. What are the coefficients of these terms?

    d.   Based on the patterns in the preceding problems, discuss with your team a possible short cut for writing the answers for parts a-c without multiplying. Use your method to write out the expansion of $(x + y)^5$.

    e.   Describe a method for using Pascal's Triangle to expand $(a + b)^n$.

12-157. Donna has four bracelets in her wardrobe. They can all be worn together, but each is different from the others. Before she goes to bed at night, she sets out the outfit she will wear the next day, including her accessories. How many different ways can she choose the following: 0 bracelets? 1 bracelet? 2 bracelets? 3 bracelets? 4 bracelets?

    a.   How do these possible combinations compare to the 4th row ($n = 4$) of Pascal's Triangle?

    b.   If Donna bought two new bracelets, how many combinations of four bracelets can she choose for her outfit? How can you figure this out without multiplying or using your calculator?

12-158. The Spirit Club (remember them from Chapter 10), recently got a call from the school executive council. They now have 10 volunteers and will need to choose a three-person committee. They need to calculate $_{10}C_3$, the number of possible committees, but they have no calculator with them.

    a.   Al had a thought: *"I remember that the number of three-person committees you can select from 9 is 84. This would be the number of committees the new volunteer will NOT be on because they would be selected from the other nine members."* How would you calculate this number?

Problem continues on next page. →

12-158.   *Problem continued from previous page.*

b.   *"And I also know how many committees the new volunteer WILL be on because I can just add his name to each of the two-member committees I had already selected from 9."* How many possible committees would include the new volunteer?

c.   Without using a calculator (and without multiplying or dividing), explain how Al used parts (a) and (b) to calculate $_{10}C_3$.

d.   How is this related to Pascal's Triangle?

12-159.   Use Pascal's Triangle to expand $(a + b)^3$.

a.   Pascal's Triangle can be used to expand any binomial raised to a power. Use it to expand the expression $(2x + 3)^3$, by substituting $2x$ for a and 3 for b.

b.   Now use Pascal's Triangle to expand $(x - 1)^5$. What will you need to substitute for a and b?

12-160.   LEARNING LOG

Write an entry in your Learning Log explaining Pascal's Triangle and why it is useful. Title this entry "Pascal's Triangle" and label it with today's date.

12-161.   Use Pascal's Triangle to expand $(x + y)^7$.

12-162.   Use the pattern for $(a + b)^3$ to expand $(2x - 3)^3$.

12-163.   Use the pattern for $(a + b)^5$ to write the fourth term of $(w - 4z)^5$.

12-164. George starts a chain letter by sending it to four friends who then send it to four more friends and so on. If George counts as round one and his four friends as round two, how many people will have received the letter after round six?

12-165. Evaluate these infinite geometric series if possible. If it is not possible, explain.

a. $8 + 4 + 2 + \ldots$

b. $3 + 9 + 27 + 81 + \ldots$

12-166. Given the polynomial equation $x^3 - 2x + 1 = 0$, answer the following questions.

a. What integer is a clear solution?

b. What is a factor of $x^3 - 2x + 1$?

c. Solve $x^3 - 2x + 1 = 0$.

12-167. Solve the equations below.

a. $(x+2)^2 - (x-2)^2 = 8$

b. $(x+2)^2 + (x-2)^2 = (2x)^2$

12-168. Explain everything you know about the tangent, including its relationship to the sine and cosine. Be complete using examples and sketches to support your statements.

12-169. Explain each transformation below in terms of the parent graph $y = \tan\theta$.

a. $y = \tan\theta + 1$

b. $y = \tan(\theta + \frac{\pi}{4})$

c. $y = -\tan(\theta)$

d. $y = 4\tan\theta$

12-170. Suppose $|x| < 1$. Consider the infinite sequence $1 + x + x^2 + x^3 + \ldots$.

a. Write an expression for the sum of the sequence.

b. What is the result when you use polynomial division to divide 1 by $1 - x$? Show the first five terms of the quotient.

12.4.2 How can I use the Binomial Theorem?

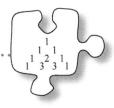

Applying the Binomial Theorem

Knowing the Binomial Theorem not only helps with some algebra multiplication problems, but it can be very useful in solving some probability problems that involve repeated decisions between two alternatives such as True or False, Win or Lose, Heads or Tails, and Hit or Miss.

12-171. Cheryl is playing a game where she tosses four coins in the air. If she has an equal number of heads and tails, she wins. Below is the sample space of all 16 possible outcomes from the tosses.

HHHH	*HTHH*	*THHH*	*TTHH*
HHHT	*HTHT*	*THHT*	*TTHT*
HHTH	*HTTH*	*THTH*	*TTTH*
HHTT	*HTTT*	*THTT*	*TTTT*

a. How many ways can Cheryl win? What is the probability that she wins?

b. The number of ways two heads can be tossed could have been found without the list but instead by using $_4C_2$. How do the 4 and the 2 relate to the problem?

c. How many ways will the coin tosses result in:

    i. 4 heads?   *ii.* 3 heads?   *iii.* 2 heads?   *iv.* 1 head?   *v.* 0 heads?

d. How do your results from part (c) compare to Pascal's Triangle?

e. What is the sum of your answers in part (c)? Why does the result make sense?

12-172. Cheryl wants to know if she could have a better chance of getting two heads if she tossed five coins.

a. Help her answer this question by showing her how to calculate the probability.

b. What if she tossed *n* coins? What would be the total number of possible results? What would be the probability of two heads?

c. What is the probability of getting *k* heads with *n* coins? ($k = 0, 1, 2, 3, ..., n$)

12-173.   Cheryl decided to rewrite her list using a shortcut. When she had three heads and a tail as an outcome, she wrote it as H^3T^1. Her rewritten list is below.

H^4	H^3T	H^3T	H^2T^2
H^3T	H^2T^2	H^2T^2	HT^3
H^3T	H^2T^2	H^2T^2	HT^3
H^2T^2	HT^3	HT^3	T^4

Greg rewrote Cheryl's list as $1H^4$, $4HT^3$, $6H^2T^2$, $4HT^3$, $1T^4$. Then they both said, *"Wow, that looks almost like what you'd get if you used H and T for variables and expanded the algebraic expression $(H+T)^4$! How can that be?"*

What would you get if you expanded this expression? Why is the 4th row of Pascal's Triangle a key to the solution of both of these very different problems?

12-174.   In his homework assignment, Andrew had to expand $(a+b)^9$. He just realized that he did not have the coefficient for the term a^3b^6. He started writing out the first nine rows of Pascal's Triangle when his friend Robbie said he could find the value using combinations. What combination should Andrew use, and what is the coefficient?

12-175.   Rebecca needs to write the 5th term in the expansion of $(a+b)^{11}$.

a.   How many terms are in the expansion?

b.   What is the 5th term of the expansion? (The term is of the form $\_\,a^7b^4$.)

c.   Now Rebecca needs to know the 5th term of $(x-2)^{11}$. How can you use your result from part (b)?

12-176.   In problem 12-173, Greg used $6H^2T^2$ to label the number of ways of tossing two heads out of four coin flips.

a.   If h is the probability of a coin showing heads, and t is the probability of a coin showing tails, what does $6h^2t^2$ represent when $h=\frac{1}{2}$? How does the result compare to your result in part (a) of problem 12-171?

b.   Greg had some trick coins that were weighted so the probability of getting heads was 0.57. What would be the probability of getting two heads using four of Greg's weighted coins?

12-177.   Carrie is the top batter on her softball team. Carrie has a 0.400 batting average, which means she gets a hit 40% of the time (A walk does not count as a time at bat). Carrie comes up to bat 5 times in a game. What is the probability that she will not get a hit?

   a.   If h represents the probability of a hit and m represents the probability of not a hit (an out). Write an expression using h and m that represents the probability of all of the ways that Carrie can get exactly 3 hits in 5 at bats and then calculate the probability.

   b.   Carrie wants to know the probability that she gets at least 3 hits in a game, so she needs to know her probability for 3, 4, or 5 hits. Show her how to calculate the probability of at least 3 hits.

   c.   What is the probability that Carrie gets fewer than 3 hits in a game? You can use your answer to part (b) or calculate this result separately. Discuss which **strategy** to use with your team.

12-178.   Jake was walking across the room carrying 8 dice when he suddenly tripped and the dice went flying. When he went to pick up the dice, he discovered that 5 of them came up 6! What is the probability of rolling exactly 5 sixes with 8 dice?

12-179.   In part (c) of problem 12-172 the probability of getting k heads when flipping n fair coins was represented by $\frac{nC_k}{2^n}$. Using the method of part (a) of problem 12-176, how could you represent the probability of getting k heads when flipping n fair coins? Are the two representations equivalent? Explain why or why not?

ETHODS AND MEANINGS

Binomial Theorem

MATH NOTES

The **Binomial Theorem** can be used to write the expansion of binomial expressions of the form $(a + b)^n$, and to calculate binomial probabilities. For example:

$$(x + 3y)^4$$

$$=_4 C_4 x^4 (3y)^0 +_4 C_3 x^3 (3y)^1 +_4 C_2 x^2 (3y)^2 +_4 C_1 x^1 (3y)^3 +_4 C_0 x^0 (3y)^4$$

$$= 1x^4 + 4x^3(3y) + 6x^2(9y^2) + 4x(27y^3) + 81y^4$$

$$= x^4 + 12x^3 y + 54x^2 y^2 + 108xy^3 + 81y^4$$

In general, $(a + b)^n = {}_nC_n a^n + {}_nC_{n-1} a^{n-1}b + {}_nC_{n-2} a^{n-2}b^2 + \cdots {}_nC_1 ab^{n-1} + {}_nC_0 b^n$.

Probabilities for situations in which there are only two possible outcomes are called **binomial probabilities**. If a and b are binomial probabilities, then $b = 1 - a$.

12-180.   Five coins are tossed. What is the probability that exactly two are heads?

12-181.   What is the third term of $(2x + \frac{1}{4x})^7$?

12-182.   Find the sum of the first six terms of the series $2 + 6 + 18 + 54 + \dots$.

12-183.   Use the pattern for $(a + b)^4$ to expand $(3x + 1)^4$.

12-184.   **Challenge:** Use the general form for the Binomial Theorem to show that the sum of the elements of the nth row of Pascal's Triangle is 2^n .

$$_nC_n + {}_nC_{n-1} + {}_nC_{n-2} + \dots + {}_nC_2 + {}_nC_1 + {}_nC_0 = 2^n$$

12-185.   Solve $\dfrac{x}{2x+1} - \dfrac{1-x}{2x-1} = \dfrac{2x+7}{4x^2-1}$ for x.

12-186.   Rewrite the expression $(x^{-2} - 5y^{-1})^{-1}$ so that it does not have negative exponents.

12-187.   Duong noticed that $_1C_0 + {}_1C_1 = 2^1$. He tried $_2C_0 + {}_2C_1 + {}_2C_2 = 2^2$ and found that it worked also.

   a.   Does $_3C_0 + {}_3C_1 + {}_3C_2 + {}_3C_3 = 2^3$?

   b.   Does $_4C_0 + {}_4C_1 + {}_4C_2 + {}_4C_3 + {}_4C_4 = 2^4$?

   c.   Explain why $_nC_0 + {}_nC_1 + {}_nC_2 + \dots + {}_nC_n = 2^n$.

12-188.   Sketch the graph of $y = 2^{(x+3)}$. Then write the equation of the graph that is four units to the right and five units down from this one.

12-189.   You know that $_nC_r = \dfrac{n!}{(n-r)!r!}$ and $_nC_r = \dfrac{{}_nP_r}{r!}$. Show that the formulas are equivalent.

12-190.   In the past, many states had license plates composed of three letters followed by three digits (0 to 9). Recently, many states have responded to the increased number of cars by adding one digit (1 to 9) ahead of the three letters. How many more license plates of second type are possible? What is the probability of being randomly assigned a license plate containing ALG 2?

12.5.1 What is *e*?

The Number *e*

What you have learned in this chapter about sums of infinite series and the Binomial Theorem will help you with this exploration of the number decimal representation of *e* is 2.718281828…, but this is only an approximation. Like π, the number *e* has been proven to be a **transcendental** number, with a decimal representation that continues infinitely and does not form a repetitive pattern. The number *e* is the base of logarithms known as **natural logarithms** and is important in many areas of science as well as in business and economics.

An approximation for *e* resulted from the work of several mathematicians early in the seventeenth century, about the time that John Napier was in the process of developing logarithms. At that time there was tremendous growth in international trade and increasing involvement in financial deals that involved compound interest. In problem 12-191, you will consider a problem that involves compounding interest over shorter and shorter time intervals.

12-191. Tabitha's uncle gave her $10,000 on her thirteenth birthday. She wants to invest it in a college savings fund. The banker tells her that interest rates have dropped to 3%, but at their bank they will compound the interest at any time interval, daily, even hourly, so their customers can still get a good deal. Tabitha decided to make a table to see how good a deal she could get.

    a.   Tabitha knows that a one year compounding period will result in $10000(1 + .03)^1 = \$10300$, and she can get the amount for semiannual periods by dividing the rate by 2 and then squaring to compound, or $10000(1 + \frac{0.03}{2})^2 = \$10302.25$. Make a table for shorter and shorter compounding periods, quarterly, monthly, daily, and hourly.

    b.   What do you notice about the results? Be prepared to share your observations with the class.

12-192. Tabitha was disappointed, but she decided the daily compounding would have to do. Her friend Veronica was more of a dreamer. She asked, *"What if you could earn 100% interest and compound that?"*

"Wow, that should grow fast!" said Tabitha. *"I've got my calculator. Let's just start with one dollar to make it easy, and we can multiply by any initial amount later."*

Veronica added, *"Yes, and that makes our formula easier."*

    a.   What is the easier version of the formula Veronica is thinking of?

    b.   With your team, make a table for at least 12 values of *n*, including some very large ones.

    c.   Did you try 1,000,000? What do you notice as you use larger numbers for *n*?

12-193. Team Challenge: Investigate the function $f(x) = (1 + \frac{1}{x})^x$.

MᴇᴛHODS AND MᴇᴀɴɪɴɢS

Compound Interest

The formula for compound interest is generally written:

$$A = P(1 + \frac{r}{n})^{nt}$$

Where A is the total amount of money at any time, P is the principle or initial value, r is the annual rate of interest, t is the number of years, and n is the number of times per year the interest is compounded.

For example, if you invest \$5,000 for 20 years at an annual interest rate of 4.8%, compounded monthly:

$$A = \$5000(1 + \frac{0.048}{12})^{12 \cdot 20} = \$5000(1.004)^{240} = \$13,033.50$$

Review & Preview

12-194. Robin and Teryll each have \$8,000 to invest and they disagree about the best place to start a savings account. Teryll found a savings and loan company that will guarantee a rate of 3.9% compounded monthly for the next 10 years. Robin says her bank is much better because they will give her 4% interest compounded semi-annually for the next ten years. In ten years, which account will end up with the greatest amount and how much difference is there?

12-195. Use the Binomial Theorem to write the expansion of each of the following expressions.

    a. $(1 + \frac{1}{n})^3$ b. $(1 + \frac{1}{n})^5$

12-196. Rewrite the expression on the left side of the equation so that it is the same as the one on the right. Explain each algebraic step you take.

$$\frac{(1 - \frac{5}{y})(3 + \frac{2}{z})}{x} = \frac{(y-5)(3z+2)}{xyz}$$

12-197. Prove that the expressions in each of the following pairs are equivalent by showing the algebraic steps needed to rewrite the one on the left so it is the same as the one on the right.

a. $\dfrac{a(a-1)}{7} \cdot \dfrac{1}{a^2}$, $\dfrac{1-\frac{1}{a}}{7}$

b. $\dfrac{x(x-1)(x-b)}{c^2} \cdot \dfrac{1}{x^3}$, $\dfrac{(1-\frac{a}{x})(1-\frac{b}{x})}{c^2}$

c. $\dfrac{n(n-1)}{3!} \cdot \dfrac{1}{n^2}$, $\dfrac{1-\frac{1}{n}}{2!}$

d. $\dfrac{n(n-1)(n-2)}{3!} \cdot \dfrac{1}{n^3}$, $\dfrac{(1-\frac{1}{n})(1-\frac{2}{n})}{3!}$

12-198. Assuming normal conditions, atmospheric pressure P (in lbs. per square inch) can be approximately calculated by using the formula below, where h represents number of feet above sea level.
$$P = 14.7e^{-0.00003h}$$

a. What is normal pressure at sea level?

b. Use the formula to calculate the atmospheric pressure under normal conditions in the mile-high city of Denver, Colorado.

c. The lowest point in Death Valley is 285 feet below sea level. What is the atmospheric pressure in Death Valley under normal conditions?

12-199. You know that the solutions of the general quadratic equation $ax^2 + bx + c = 0$ are

$x = \dfrac{-b \pm \sqrt{b^2 - 4ac}}{2a}$.

a. Find the sum $\dfrac{-b + \sqrt{b^2 - 4ac}}{2a} + \dfrac{-b - \sqrt{b^2 - 4ac}}{2a}$.

b. Find the product $\left(\dfrac{-b + \sqrt{b^2 - 4ac}}{2a}\right)\left(\dfrac{-b - \sqrt{b^2 - 4ac}}{2a}\right)$.

c. How is the sum of the solutions related to the original quadratic equation?

d. How is the product of the solutions related to the original quadratic equation?

12-200. Use what you just proved about the sum and product of the roots of a quadratic equation, in problem 12-199, to write a quadratic equation for each of the following pairs of roots.

a. $-3 + 5i$, $-3 - 5i$

b. $\frac{1}{2} \pm \frac{3}{2}i$

c. $7 \pm \sqrt{3}$

d. $7, -6$

e. $\frac{2}{3}, -\frac{3}{4}$

12.5.2 What is *e*?

Calculating *e* and Using Natural Logarithms

The Binomial Theorem provides another way to think about the number *e*. This particular approach turned out to be very useful because later on it led to some surprising connections with other areas of mathematics.

The beginning of the binomial expansion for $(1+\frac{1}{n})^n$ is written below:

$$(1+\tfrac{1}{n})^n = {_nC_n}(1) + {_nC_{n-1}}(\tfrac{1}{n}) + {_nC_{n-2}}(\tfrac{1}{n^2}) + {_nC_{n-3}}(\tfrac{1}{n^3}) + {_nC_{n-4}}(\tfrac{1}{n^4}) + \dots$$

In problem 12-201 you will use this expansion to further explore the value of *e*.

12-201.   From your work in Chapter 10 you learned that there are several ways to represent combinations. One way is to use the formula:

$$_nC_r = \frac{n!}{(n-r)!\,r!}$$

a.   Rewrite each of the first five terms of the expansion for $(1+\frac{1}{n})^n$ using the combinations formula given above. Check with your team to see that you are all coming up with the same results.

b.   Simplify each of the first two terms completely. Then simplify the other terms by using what you know about dividing factorial expressions to reduce them as far as possible.

c.   By rewriting each term one more time, you will have a version that will help you reason about what will happen for infinitely large values of *n*. Rewrite the third and fifth terms based on the way the fourth term is shown below. Discuss a **justification** for each step with your team, and rewrite the other two.

$$\frac{(n-1)(n-2)}{3!}\cdot\frac{1}{n^2} = \frac{\frac{(n-1)(n-2)}{n^2}}{3!} = \frac{\frac{(n-1)}{n}\,\frac{(n-2)}{n}}{3!} = \frac{(1-\frac{1}{n})(1-\frac{2}{n})}{3!}$$

12-202.   In problem 12-201, you should have written the beginning of the binomial expansion of $(1+\frac{1}{n})^n$ as the following expression:

$$1 + 1 + \frac{1-\frac{1}{n}}{2!} + \frac{(1-\frac{1}{n})(1-\frac{2}{n})}{3!} + \frac{(1-\frac{1}{n})(1-\frac{2}{n})(1-\frac{3}{n})}{4!} + \dots$$

a.   What happens to each factor in the numerators as the value of *n* gets very large? If *n* could be infinitely large, what would each numerator equal? Explain your reasoning.

b.   Rewrite the series of fractions, changing the numerators to what they would be if *n* became an infinitely large number.

12-203.   Euler made the discovery that when n becomes infinitely large $e = \sum\limits_{n=0}^{\infty} \frac{1}{n!}$.

    a.   Is this series arithmetic or geometric? Explain why or why not.

    b.   Calculate the sum of the first 5 terms and then the sum of the first 7 terms. What do you notice?

    c.   Use your calculator to compute the sum $\sum\limits_{n=0}^{12} \frac{1}{n!}$.

12-204.   Consider the function $f(x) = e^x$.

    a.   What is its inverse function, $f^{-1}(x)$?

    b.   Investigate $f(x)$ and $f^{-1}(x)$.

    c.   For what integer values of n is the graph of $f^{-1}(x)$ between the graphs of $y = \log_n x$ and $y = \log_{n+1} x$?

    d.   For what values of x is the graph of $f^{-1}(x)$ above each of the graphs in your answer to part (c)? For what values is it below?

12-205.   The use of e provides a shortcut for calculation of continuously compounding interest. The formula for continuous compounding is $A = Pe^{rt}$, where A is the total amount at any time, P is the original principle, r is the rate of interest, and t is the time period.

    a.   Use this new formula to calculate the amount Tabitha had after investing her $10,000 for one year at 3% annual interest, compounded continuously. How ˒es this compare with her daily compounding result of $10,304.56?

    b.   Suppose a large investment group invested 10 billion dollars at 8% ˍual interest. compounded Compare the amount they would have in one year if the interee compounded continuously with the amount they would earn if the inter˒ daily. ˍnding, rather than daily

    c.   Which investors might benefit from continuoᵛ compounding?

12-206.   Natural logs and exponential functions in base e are often used in formulas. For many problems you can use either the $\boxed{\text{LOG}}$ or the $\boxed{\text{LN}}$ key on your calculator. Solve each of the following problems, first using base 10 logs and then using natural logs.

   a. $10,000(1.08)^x = 20,000$ b. $30,000(0.8)^x = 15,000$

   c.   Interpret the answer for part (a) if the equation represents an amount of money invested at 8% annual interest.

   d.   Interpret the answer to part (b) if the equation represents the price paid for a car that depreciates at 20% per year.

12-207.   Given $\ln 2 \approx 0.69315$ and $\ln 3 \approx 1.0986$, why is $\ln 2 < 1$ and $\ln 3 > 1$? For what value of x does $\ln x = 1$?

12-208.   Use the values for $\ln 2$ and $\ln 3$ given in problem 12-207 to evaluate each of the following expressions. Do **not** use a calculator.

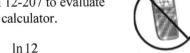

   a. $\ln 6$ b. $\ln 12$

   c. $\ln 16$ d. $\ln \frac{1}{3}$

12-209.   If $p = \ln 2$ and $q = \ln 3$, solve for x in terms of p and/or q.

   $e^x = 2^{10}$ b. $4e^x = 27$

12-210.   Omar was 8 ͻ
   His father inves~ when he received $25,000 dollars from his grandmother's will.
   quarterly. He was h̄ ͙ im in a fund that earned 6% annual interest compounded
   for college. Another fu̅! ͭ ͤ the investment double by the time Omar was ready
   compound continuously. ͭ he same interest rate but the interest would
   ͤ nd was a little riskier, however.

   a.   Write an equation to represei̅ ͤ ͭ

   b.   Which method of compounding the ͥ ͭ ͥ

   c.   Is the difference in doubling time worth the ͭ ͤ hle his money faster?

ctions

12-211. The sum of the digits of a two-digit number is 11, and when the digits are reversed the difference between the new number and the original is 27.

    a.   If you use t to represent the tens digit, and u to represent the units digit, how can you represent one of the numbers?

    b.   How can you represent the number with its digits reversed, still using t and u?

    c.   Use the information from the problem and parts (a) and (b) to write two equations that can be used to solve this problem.

    d.   What are the two numbers?

12-212. Maia had 130 coins, all nickels, dimes, and quarters, in her change jar. Their value totaled $20.80 and she noticed that there were 15 more dimes than nickels. How many of each type of coin did she have?

12-213. Without a graphing calculator, sketch the graph of $f(x) = x^3 + x^2$.

    a.   On another set of axes, sketch the graphs of $g(x) = x^3$ and $h(x) = x^2$ and show how to combine these two graphs to get $f(x)$.

    b.   On a third set of axes, sketch the graphs of $p(x) = x^2$ and $q(x) = x + 1$ and show how to combine the graphs to get the graph of $f(x)$.

12-214. Sketch the graph of $g(x) = (x - 2)^2 - 1$.

    a.   On the same set of axes (in a different color) sketch the graph of $|g(x)| = |(x - 2)^2 - 1|$.

    b.   On a new set of axes sketch the graph of $g(|x|) = (|x| - 2)^2 - 1$

                                                .ed to the original

    c.   Describe how each of the graphs in parts (a) and (b) a⌐ graph of $g(x)$.

Chapter 12 Closure What have I learned?

Reflection and Synthesis

The activities below offer you a chance to reflect on what you have learned in this chapter. As you work, look for concepts that you feel very comfortable with, ideas that you would like to learn more about, and topics you need more help with. Look for connections between ideas as well as connections with material you learned previously.

①   TEAM BRAINSTORM

With your team, brainstorm a list for each of the following categories. Be as detailed as you can. How long can you make your list? Challenge yourselves. Be prepared to ᵇare your team's ideas with the class.

    Topic

What have you studied in this chapter? What ideas and words were ᵑportant in what you learned? Remember to be as detailed as you

   Connections: How ₍
       courses aₗ
        Again, makecs, ideas, and words that you learned in previous
              connected to the new ideas in this chapter?
            ₗng as you can.

ᵢons

② MAKING CONNECTIONS

Below is a list of the vocabulary used in this chapter. Make sure that you are familiar with all of these words and know what they mean. Refer to the glossary or index for any words that you do not yet understand.

arithmetic	binomial theorem	e
geometric	index	infinite
natural logarithm	Pascal's Triangle	proof by induction
series	sigma	summation notation

Make a concept map showing all of the connections you can find among the key words and ideas listed above. To show a connection between two words, draw a line between them and explain the connection, as shown in the example below. A word can be connected to any other word as long as you can **justify** the connection. For each key word or idea, provide a sketch of an example.

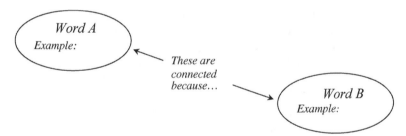

Your teacher may provide you with vocabulary cards to help you get started. If you use the cards to plan your concept map, be sure either to re-draw your concept map on your paper, or to glue the vocabulary cards to a poster with all of the connections explained for others to see and understand.

While you are making your map, your team may think of related words ideas that are not listed above. Be sure to include these ideas on your conce

③　　SUMMARIZING MY UNDERSTANDING

This section gives you an opportunity to show what you know about certain math topics or ideas.

With your team, make a list of the **big ideas** of this chapter. Discuss the important ideas of the chapter and try to agree on a short list of no more than five big ideas. Be prepared to share your list in a whole class discussion. When the class has reached agreement on a list, continue with parts (a) and (b) below.

a.　Write your own description of each big idea.

b.　For each big idea, provide one or two representative example problems. Solve each problem completely, using multiple representations, if applicable.

④　　WHAT HAVE I LEARNED?

This section will help you evaluate which types of problems you feel comfortable with and which you need more help with. This section will appear at the end of every chapter to help you check your understanding. Even if your teacher does not assign this section, it is a good idea to try these problems and find out for yourself what you know and what you need to work on.

Solve each problem as completely as you can. The table at the end of this closure section has answers to these problems. It also tells you where you can find additional help and practice on similar problems.

12-215. Find the sum of each series.

$11 + 12 + 13 + ... + 40$　　　　　b.　$90 + 84 + 78 + ... + 24$

CL 12-216. For this se

$+ 3.3 + 3.6 + 3.9 + 4.2 + ... + 63$,

a.　How many

there?　　　b.　What is the sum of the series?

CL 12-217. A rubber ball is thrown 20 fe
it have traveled after the fifth bo　　　　If it rebounds $\frac{3}{5}$ of the height, how far will

CL 12-218. Write each series using summation ($\sum$) no

b.

a.　$3 + 9 + 12 + ... + 30$

$+ 8 + 11$

CL 12-219. Consider the series $\sum_{n=0}^{\infty} 4\left(-\frac{2}{3}\right)^n$.

   a. Is it arithmetic or geometric? Explain.

   b. Does it have a finite sum? Explain.

   c. If it has a sum, find it.

CL 12-220. Prove by induction: $2+4+6+...+2n = n(n+1)$

CL 12-221. Use the pattern for $(a+b)^4$ to expand $(2m+\frac{1}{m})^4$.

CL 12-222. What term of $(a-b)^8$ contains a^5? What is the whole term?

CL 12-223. For a certain family, the probability of any child having red hair is 25%. If the family has four children what is the probability that exactly one has red hair?

CL 12-224. Check your answers using the table at the end of this section. Which problems do you feel confident about? Which problems were hard? Have you worked on problems like these in math classes you have taken before? Use the table to make a list of topics you need help on and a list of topics you need to practice more.

⑤   HOW AM I THINKING?

This course focuses on five different **Ways of Thinking**: justifying, generalizing, choosing a strategy, investigating, and reversing thinking. These are some of the ways in which you think while trying to make sense of a concept or attempting to solve a problem (even outside of math class). During this chapter, you have probably used each Way of Thinking multiple times without even realizing it!

Review each of the five Ways of Thinking described in the closure sections of Chapters 1 through 5. Then choose three of these Ways of Thinking that you remember using while working on this chapter. Show and explain where and how you used each one. Describe why thinking in this way helped you solve a particular problem or understand something new. Be sure to include examples to demonstrate your thinking.

Answers and Support for Closure Activity #4
What Have I Learned?

Problem	Solutions	Need Help?	More Practice
CL 12-215.	a. 765 b. 684	Lessons 12.1.1, and 12.1.2 Math Notes box in Lesson 12.1.3	Problems 12-19, 12-29, 12-34, 12-35, 12-49, 12-61, 12-63, and 12-83
CL 12-216.	a. 201 b. 6633	Lesson 12.1.1 Math Notes boxes in Lessons 12.1. and 12.1.3	Problems 12-19, 12-20, 12-29, 12-34, 12-35, 12-49, 12-63, 12-64, 12-83, and 12-121
CL 12-217.	92.224 feet	Math Notes box in Lesson 12.3.1	Problems 12-129 and 12-130
CL 12-218.	a. $\displaystyle\sum_{n=1}^{10}(3n)$ b. $\displaystyle\sum_{n=1}^{7}(3n-10)$	Math Notes box in Lesson 12.1.4	Problems 12-61, 12-62, 12-64, 12-84, 12-96, and 12-119
CL 12-219.	a. Geometric, $r=-\frac{2}{3}$ b. yes, $|r|<1$ c. $\frac{12}{5}$	Math Notes boxes in Lessons 12.1.4 and 12.3.2	Problems 12-138, 12-139, 12-144, 12-145, 12-146, 12-147, and 12-165
CL 12-220.	$2=1(1+1)\Rightarrow n=1$ is true $2+4+\cdots+2k+2(k+1)=k(k+1)+2(k+1)$ $\qquad\qquad\qquad= k^2+k+2k+2$ $\qquad\qquad\qquad= k^2+3k+2$ $\qquad\qquad\qquad= (k+1)(k+2)$ $\qquad\qquad\qquad= (k+1)((k+1)+1)$	Lesson 12.2.1	Problems 12-80, 12-93, 12-137, and 12-153
CL 12-221.	$16m^4+32m^2+24+\frac{8}{m^2}+\frac{1}{m^4}$	Lesson 12.4.1	Problems 12-159, 12-162, 12-163, 12-183, and 12-195
CL 12-222.	$-56a^5b^3$	Lesson 12.4.2 Math Notes box in Lesson 12.4.2	Problems 12-174, 12-175, and 12-181
CL 12-223.	$_4C_3(\frac{1}{4})^1(\frac{3}{4})^3=\frac{27}{64}\approx 0.423$	Lesson 12.4.2	Problems 12-177, 12-178, 12-179, and 12-180

ANALYTIC TRIGONOMETRY
13
WELCOME TO
IDENTITY Island
SOMETIMES TRUE
ALWAYS TRUE
NEVER TRUE
Student Field Trip

CHAPTER 13　　　　Analytic Trigonometry

In Chapter 8, you began your study of trigonometric functions as you learned about radians and how to transform the graphs of $y = \sin(x)$, $y = \cos(x)$ and $y = \tan(x)$. In this chapter, you will continue your study of trigonometry, this time **investigating** solutions to trigonometric equations. You will learn about three new trigonometric ratios (secant, cosecant, and cotangent) and their corresponding functions.

By the end of this chapter you will be able to solve a wide variety of trigonometric equations and make statements about how many solutions there are and why, based on the unit circle and the graph.

In this chapter, you will:

➢ Learn about the inverse trigonometric functions and relations.

➢ Learn about the reciprocal trigonometric functions.

➢ Recognize the number of solutions to trigonometric equations for a given domain.

➢ Understand solutions to trigonometric equations algebraically, from the graphs of the functions, and based on the unit circle.

➢ Further develop your algebraic manipulation skills as you rewrite trigonometric expressions and equations.

Guiding Questions

Think about these questions throughout this chapter:

When is it true?

How can I rewrite it?

How many solutions are there?

Is it a function?

How can I solve it?

Chapter Outline

Section 13.1　In this section, you will solve trigonometric equations. You will learn about inverse and reciprocal trigonometric functions. You will also learn how to determine the number of solutions a trigonometric equation has.

Section 13.2　Here, you will identify trigonometric identities (statements that are always true). The identities will allow you to rewrite trigonometric equations, which will expand the range of equations that you are able to solve.

13.1.1 When is it true?

- -

Evaluating Trigonometric Equations

True?
When?

Throughout your study of algebra, you have encountered algebraic statements that are always true, sometimes true, and never true. Then, in Chapter 8, you learned about the trigonometric functions $y = \sin(x)$, $y = \cos(x)$, and $y = \tan(x)$. You learned how to represent these functions in a table, on a graph, and with a unit circle. In this chapter, you will expand your understanding of trigonometric functions and develop **strategies** to determine when trigonometric equations are true. Throughout this chapter all answers should be given in radians unless otherwise stated in the problem.

13-1.   How can you tell which values of x make an algebraic statement is true? For each of the following statements, work with your team to decide if it is always true, sometimes true, or never true. If it is always true, **justify** how you know; if it is sometimes true, give the exact values of x that make it true; and if it is never true, explain why it is never true.

   a. $5(x - 7) = 5x - 35$ b. $2x^2 = 50$

   c. $4x - (3x + 2) = x - 7$ d. $\frac{2}{3}(x - 9) = \frac{3}{4}(2x + 5)$

13-2.   WHEN IS IT TRUE?

   Your teacher will assign your team one of the following equations. Your task is to decide whether the equation is always true, sometimes true, or never true, and to **justify** your decision using as many representations as you can.

   - If the equation is always true, **justify** how you know. Then decide how you could change the equation so that it would never be true.

   - If the equation is sometimes true, find the exact values of x that make it true. Then decide how you could change the equation to make it never true.

   - If the equation is never true, **justify** how you know. Then decide how you could change the equation so that it would be sometimes true.

   a. $\sin(x) = \frac{1}{2}$ b. $\cos(x) = 2$

   c. $\sin(x) = \cos(\frac{\pi}{2} - x)$ d. $\sin(x) = \sin(\frac{\pi}{2} - x)$

   e. $\tan(x) = 0$ f. $2\sin(x) = \sqrt{3}$

   g. $\sin(x) = \frac{3}{2}$ h. $\cos(x) = \sin(\frac{\pi}{2} - x)$

13-3.   Organize your work from problem 13-2 into a poster that will serve as a visual aid for a presentation. Be sure to include all of your **justifications** and reasoning. Use colors, arrows, and other math tools to help make your thinking clear. When you have prepared your poster and presentation, go back to problem 13-2 and evaluate the equations your team did not work on.

13-4.   With your team, discuss the meaning of solutions. Record what you know about the solutions of an equation that are:

a.   Always true.   b.   Sometimes true.

c.   Never true.

13-5.   Decide if each of the following statements are always true, sometimes true, or never true. If a statement is always true, **justify** how you know; if it is sometimes true, give the exact values of x that make it true; and if it is never true, explain why it is never true.

a. $3x - 2 - 4(x+1) = -x - 6$ b. $3x - 5 = 2(x+1) + x$

c. $\sin(x) = \cos(\frac{\pi}{2} - x)$ d. $\tan(x) = 1$

13-6.   Factor each of the following expressions.

a. $x^2 - 4$ b. $y^2 - 81$ c: $1 - x^2$ d. $1 - \sin^2(x)$

13-7.   Solve for x in each of the following triangles. What methods can be used for finding unknown parts of triangles?

a.   b.   c.

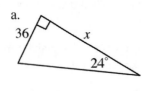

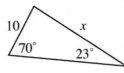

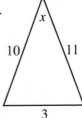

13-8.   Show that $\cos(2x) \neq 2\cos(x)$.

13-9.   Given the function $f(x) = 2 + \sqrt{2x - 4}$, find each of the following.

a.   The domain and range.   b.   The inverse equation.

c.   The domain and range of the inverse.

13-10. Consider the function $f(x) = 3 \sin (x + \frac{\pi}{2}) - 4$.

    a. How is its graph different from $f(x) = \sin(x)$?

    b. Sketch the graph.

13-11. Find the sum of the integers $-10 + -9 + -8 + ... + 40$.

13-12. Find the infinite sum (if possible).

    a. $6 + 3 + \frac{3}{2} + ...$ b. $\sum_{k=1}^{\infty} (\frac{1}{3})^k$

13-13. Graph $\frac{(x-2)^2}{16} + \frac{(y-3)^2}{25} = 1$.

    a. What are the coordinates of the four relocated intercepts? These points, at the top, bottom, left, and right extremes of the ellipse, are called the **vertices** of the ellipse.

    b. Choose two of the four points you found in part (a) and substitute their coordinates into the equation to show that they check.

13-14. If the PEP squad has 12 members, in how many ways can five students:

    a. Line up for a picture in the school newspaper?

    b. Be chosen to visit the rival school before the big game?

13-15. List 3 possible values for h that will make the equation $\cos(x - h) = \sin(x)$ true.

13-16. If $\pi \leq \theta \leq \frac{3\pi}{2}$, what must be true about the sign of:

    a. $\sin(\theta)$ b. $\cos(\theta)$

    c. $\tan(\theta)$ d. $\frac{1}{\cos(\theta)}$

13-17.   Find all values of a for which the equation $ax^2 + 5x + 6 = 0$ has a solution that is a real number. Express a in terms of one or more inequalities.

13-18.   Using a graph of $f(x) = \cos(x)$ for reference, graph $f(x) = |\cos(x)|$.

13-19.   Factor and reduce the rational expression $\frac{5x+10}{x^2+6x+8}$ to simplify. **Justify** each step.

13-20.   Solve each equation.

a. $\sqrt{x+7} + 5 = x$

b. $\frac{a}{a^2-36} + \frac{2}{a-6} = \frac{1}{a+6}$

13-21.   Change the angle measures below from radians to degrees or degrees to radians.

a. $108°$ b. $320°$ c. $\frac{7\pi}{9}$

d. $\frac{19\pi}{12}$ e. $\frac{17\pi}{2}$ f. $260°$

13-22.   Using the intercepts and slopes of the asymptotes as a guide, graph each hyperbola without using a graphing calculator.

a. $\frac{y^2}{4} - \frac{x^2}{25} = 1$

b. $x^2 - y^2 = 9$

13-23.   A jar contains five red, four white, and three blue balls. If three balls are randomly selected, find the probability of choosing:

a.   Two red and one white.   b.   Three white.

c.   One of each color.   d.   All the same color.

e.   One red and two white.   f.   Two of one color and one of another.

13-24.   Expand.

a. $(a+b)^3$ b. $(2m+5)^3$

13.1.2 How many solutions are there?

True?
When?

Solutions to Trigonometric Equations

In Lesson 13.1.1, you recognized that equations can be always true, sometimes true, or never true. In the next few lessons you will focus on trigonometric equations that are sometimes true, as you learn how to solve them and how to determine the number of solutions they have.

13-25. When is the equation $\cos(x) = \frac{1}{2}$ true?

    a.   What do the solutions to this equation represent?

    b.   Solve the equation graphically. How many solutions can you find on the graph?

    c.   Draw a unit circle showing the solutions to $\cos(x) = \frac{1}{2}$. How many solutions do you see?

13-26. Just as taking the square root ($\sqrt{\ }$) can be used to undo a square to solve an equation algebraically, there is an undo (inverse) operation for cosine.

    a.   With your team, see if you can find the undo operation for cosine on your calculator. What does it look like? How can you be sure that it is undoing cosine?

    b.   Use the undo operation for cosine on your calculator to solve the equation $\cos(x) = \frac{1}{2}$. Show where the solution given by the calculator can be seen on the graph and on the unit circle.

13-27. With your team, decide how many solutions there are to the equation $\cos(x) = \frac{1}{2}$. **Justify** your decision using as many representations as you can. How can you write all of them?

13-28. How do all of the solutions to $\cos(x) = \frac{1}{2}$ relate to the one given by $\cos^{-1}(\frac{1}{2})$ on your calculator?

13-29. Find all of the solutions for each equation below. You may use your calculator, but you must represent your solutions graphically and on a unit circle. After you have found all of the solutions, identify which ones lie in the domain $0 \le x \le 2\pi$.

    a. $2\cos(x) + 1 = 0$ b. $\tan(x) = 1$

13-30.   Jeremy used the $\sin^{-1}$ button on his calculator to solve a trigonometric equation and got the solution 37°. He knows that there must be more than one solution. What are the rest of the solutions to Jeremy's equation? Explain how you found them. Use a unit circle and a graph in your explanation.

13-31.   For each of the following equations, find the solutions that lie in the domain $0 \le x \le 2\pi$.

    a. $2\sin(x) - 1 = 0$ b. $2\cos(x) = -\sqrt{3}$

    c. $2\sin(x) = \sqrt{2}$ d. $\cos(x) = 1$

13-32.   Salina, Tamara, and Traci are working on their homework together. Salina tells her friends that she got $\theta = 52°$ for the inverse cosine problem she is working on and asks if they got the same answer. Tamara says she got $\theta = 128°$, and Traci volunteers her answer of $\theta = 308°$. Is it possible that these are all solutions to the same problem? **Justify** your answer.

13-33.   Graph $f(x) = 1 + \tan(x - \frac{\pi}{4})$.

13-34.   What is the inverse of $f(x) = -x + 6$? **Justify** your answer.

13-35.   Simplify then add $\frac{x-2}{x+2} + \frac{2x-6}{x^2-x-6}$. **Justify** each step.

13-36.   Josephina thinks that she has discovered a new pattern, shown at right.

$$\frac{x-1}{x-1} = 1$$

$$\frac{x^2-1}{x-1} = x+1$$

    a.   Check her equations by multiplying. Does her pattern work?

$$\frac{x^3-1}{x-1} = x^2 + x + 1$$

    b,   Based on her pattern, what does $\frac{x^5-1}{x-1}$ equal? Is it true? **Justify** your answer.

$$\frac{x^4-1}{x-1} = x^3 + x^2 + x + 1$$

    c.   Make a conjecture about how to represent the result for $\frac{x^n-1}{x-1}$. You will probably need ", ...," in the middle of your expression.

13-37.   From a class of 28 students, how many different four-person study teams can be formed?

13-38.   Three light bulbs are chosen at random from 15 bulbs, of which five are defective. What is the probability that:

a.   None of the three are defective.   b.   Exactly two are defective.

13-39.   For the sequence $0.52, 0.55, 0.58, ..., 2.02$:

a.   How many terms are there?

b.   What is the sum of the associated series?

13-40.   Find the equation of each ellipse shown below.

a. 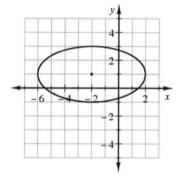   b.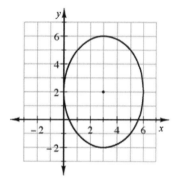

13.1.3 Is it a function?

True?
When?

Inverses of Trigonometric Functions

In Lesson 13.1.2, you learned about using the inverse trigonometric functions to undo operations and solve trigonometric equations. You also learned that the keys for the inverse trigonometric functions on your calculator give you only one of the possible solutions to these equations. In this lesson, you will **investigate** the inverse trigonometric functions more thoroughly. You will determine whether the inverses are also functions.

13-41. Obtain the Lesson 13.1.3 Resource Page from your teacher.

　a. Make a careful graph of $y = \sin(x)$. Is it a function? What are its domain and range?

　b. Graph the line $y = x$.

　c. Reflect the graph of $y = \sin(x)$ across the line $y = x$ to make a graph of its inverse, $x = \sin(y)$. Is it a function? What are its domain and range?

　d: Discuss with your team the restriction you would need to make on the domain of $y = \sin(x)$ so that its inverse is a function.

13-42. Now graph $y = \sin^{-1}(x)$ on your graphing calculaor. How is the result different from the graph that you made? Does it make sense in terms of your answer to part (d) in the problem above? Highlight the portion of your graph that represents the inverse function and label it with its domain and range. Also highlight the portion of the unit circle provided that shows the restriction on the domain of $y = \sin(x)$ required to make its inverse a function.

13-43. Consider the equation $\sin(x) = -\frac{\sqrt{3}}{2}$.

　a. How many solutions does the equation have?

　b. Without using a calculator, find the solutions and show them on the unit circle.

　c. Which solution do you predict your calculator will give? How do you know? Once you have made your prediction, use your calculator to solve $\sin(x) = -\frac{\sqrt{3}}{2}$. Were you correct? (Note that this solution can be written as $\sin^{-1}(-\frac{\sqrt{3}}{2})$.)

13-44. Obtain two more copies of the Lesson 13.1.3 Resource Page from your teacher. Sketch $y = \cos(x)$ and $y = \tan(x)$ on separate axes and label the domain and range of each.

a. Reflect each graph across the line $y = x$ to generate graphs of the inverse relations.

b. Find the domain and range of the relations $x = \cos(y)$ and $x = \tan(y)$.

c. Use your graphing calculator to graph the functions $y = \cos^{-1}(x)$ and $y = \tan^{-1}(x)$. Highlight the portion of your graph that represents the inverse function. Find the domain and range for each function. Also highlight the portion of the unit circle provided that it shows the restrictions on the domain required on $y = \cos(x)$ and $y = \tan(x)$ to make their inverses a function.

13-45. For each of the following problems, find all of the solutions without using a calculator. Use a graph or unit circle to support you answers. Then predict the solution that your calculator will give and use your calculator to check your prediction.

a. $2\cos(x) - 1 = 0$

b. $\tan(x) = \sqrt{3}$

c. $2\sin(x) = \sqrt{3}$

d. $4\sin^2(x) - 3 = 0$

Review & Preview

13-46. Solve each equation for $0° \le \theta \le 360°$, or if you prefer, $0 \le \theta \le 2\pi$. You may need your calculator, but remember that your calculator only gives *one* answer.

a. $\sin(\theta) = 0.5$

b. $\cos(\theta) = -0.5$

c. $4\tan(\theta) - 4 = 0$

d. $3\sin^2(\theta) = 1$

13-47. State the domain and range for each graph below. Then state whether or not it is a function.

a.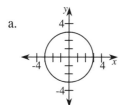

b.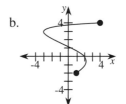

c.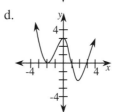

d.

13-48.   Solve each equation. Check for extraneous solutions.

a. $\sqrt{x+7} = x+1$

b. $\frac{2}{x+3} - \frac{1}{x} = \frac{-6}{x^2+3x}$

13-49.   Graph.

a. $(-2, 3, -2)$

b. $3x - 2y - 3z = -6$

13-50.   Solve each system.

a. $\frac{x}{2} + \frac{y}{4} = 4$

$\frac{x}{4} - \frac{3y}{8} = -2$

b. $x + 2y + z = -1$

$4x - y - z = -1$

$-3y = 2z$

13-51.   Divide $(2x^5 - 6x^4 - 2x^2 + 7x - 4) \div (x - 3)$.

13-52.   Find an equation for the ellipse with vertices at $(-4, -5)$, $(1, 7)$, $(6, -5)$, and $(1, -17)$.

13-53.   For the sequence: 7, –2, –11, –20, …

a.   Find $t(40)$, the 40th term.

b.   Find $S(40)$, the sum of the first 40 terms.

13-54.   Find the infinite sum (if possible.)

a. $8 - 6 + \frac{9}{2} - \frac{27}{8} + -\ldots$

b. $\sum_{k=0}^{\infty} \frac{1}{8}(2)^k$

13-55.   Hector missed the beginning of this lesson and he is confused about domains for inverse functions. Describe how the domain for each trigonometric function (sine, cosine, and tangent) is restricted in order to find its inverse function, and explain why this restriction is needed.

13-56.   For each of the following problems, find all of the solutions without using a calculator. Use a graph or unit circle to support you answers. Then predict the solution that your calculator will give and use your calculator to check your prediction.

a. $4\sin(x) + 2 = 0$

b. $2\cos(x) = \sqrt{3}$

c. $\tan(x) + 1 = 0$

d. $4\cos^2(x) - 4 = 0$

13-57.   Explain each transformation below in terms of the parent graph $f(\theta) = \tan\theta$.

a. $f(\theta) = \tan\theta + 1$

b. $f(\theta) = \tan(\theta + \frac{\pi}{4})$

c. $f(\theta) = -\tan(\theta)$

d. $f(\theta) = 4\tan\theta$

13-58.   Quickly sketch each of the following functions.

a. $f(x) = (x-1)^2(x-3)^3(x-5)^2$

b. $g(x) = -(x-1)^2(x-3)^3(x-5)^2$

c.   Express $g(x)$ in terms of $f(x)$.

13-59.   Rewrite each sum below as a single expression.

a. $\frac{1}{2} + \frac{1}{3}$

b. $\frac{3}{2x} + \frac{4}{x^2}$

c. $\frac{x}{x+1} + \frac{3}{x-1}$

d. $\frac{\sin\theta}{\cos\theta} + \frac{1}{\sin\theta}$

13-60.   Rewrite $f(x) = 2x^2 - 4x + 1$ in graphing form. State its domain, range, vertex and line of symmetry. Include a labeled sketch as part of your solution.

13-61.   Solve the following equations. Be accurate to three decimal places. Be sure to check your answers.

a. $7 = 4.2^x$

b. $3x^5 = 126$

c. $14 = 2 \cdot 4^x - 10$

13-62.   Expand.

a. $(a+b)^4$

b. $(3m-2)^4$

13-63.   From a new shipment of 100 video games, how many ways can three games be tested to see if they are defective?

13.1.4 What is the reciprocal?

True?
When?

Reciprocal Trigonometric Functions

In this lesson, you will **investigate** the reciprocal trigonometric functions and their graphs.

13-64.   Your team will **investigate** the graph of the reciprocal of $y = \sin(x)$. Obtain a Lesson 13.1.4A Resource Page from your teacher.

   a.   Using the values on the x-axis as your inputs, complete the table on your resource page and make a careful graph of $y = \sin(x)$.

   b.   Now you will use the values in your table to help you make a graph of the reciprocal of $y = \sin(x)$, which can be written as $y = \frac{1}{\sin(x)}$. Label the third column in your table $\frac{1}{\sin(x)}$. To find the values that go in this column, calculate the reciprocal of each value for $\sin(x)$.

   c.   Where are the outputs for $\sin(0)$, $\sin(\frac{\pi}{2})$, and $\sin(\pi)$ located on the graph? What is true about the reciprocal function at these locations in your table? How would they appear on your graph?

   d.   Now, using a colored pencil, graph $y = \frac{1}{\sin(x)}$ carefully.

   e.   This ratio that is the reciprocal of sine is named **cosecant**. The cosecant function can be abbreviated by $f(x) = \csc(x)$. Label your graph with its name, "Cosecant."

13-65   Is $y = \csc(x)$ a function?

   a.   What are its domain and range?

   b.   What are the intercepts?

   c.   Are there asymptotes? If so, what are their equations?

   d.   Describe the relationship between the sine and cosecant graphs.

Algebra 2 Connections

13-66.   Use your graph to solve each of the following equations in the domain $0 \le x \le 2\pi$.
What do you notice about each of the solutions?

   a. $\sin(x) = \frac{1}{2}$ b. $\csc(x) = 2$

   c. $\sin(x) = 1$ d. $\csc(x) = 1$

   e. $\sin(x) = \frac{\sqrt{3}}{2}$ f. $\csc(x) = \frac{2}{\sqrt{3}}$

13-67.   Is there an inverse cosecant button on your calculator? How could you
use your calculator to solve $\csc(x) = 3.5$?

13-68.   Obtain the Lesson 13.1.4B and Lesson 13.1.4C Resource Pages from your
teacher. Use the same process as you did in problem 13-64 to create graphs of the
reciprocal of the cosine function (named **secant** and abbreviated $f(x) = \sec(x)$) and
the reciprocal of the tangent function (named **cotangent** and
abbreviated $f(x) = \cot(x)$). What are the domains and ranges for these functions?

13-69.   For each of the following equations, work with your team to decide if it is always true,
sometimes true, or never true. If it is always true, **justify** how you know; if it is
sometimes true, give the exact values of x that make it true; and if it is never true,
explain why it is never true. Hint: Use what you have learned above and the idea of
rewriting to get started.

   a. $\sin^2(x)\csc(x) = \frac{\sqrt{3}}{2}$ b. $\sec^2(x) = \frac{2}{\cos(x)}$

   c. $\tan(x)\sec(x)\sin(x) = 0$ d. $\sec^2(x)\cos(x) = 0$

   e. $\cos(x)\sec(x) = 1$

METHODS AND MEANINGS

Inverses of Trigonometric Functions

To find an inverse function for a trigonometric function, the domain of the original function had to be restricted. For each function the restriction is different.

For sine, restricting the domain to $-\frac{\pi}{2} \leq x \leq \frac{\pi}{2}$ leads to the inverse function, $y = \sin^{-1} x$ with domain $-1 \leq x \leq 1$ and range $-\frac{\pi}{2} \leq y \leq \frac{\pi}{2}$.

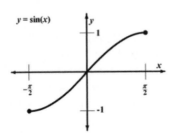 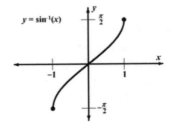

For cosine, restricting the domain to $0 \leq x \leq \pi$ gives a good piece of the graph close to the origin, and gives an inverse function $y = \cos^{-1} x$, with domain $-1 \leq x \leq 1$ and range $0 \leq y \leq \pi$.

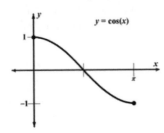 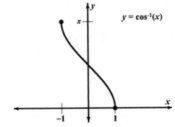

For tangent, the restriction is $-\frac{\pi}{2} < x < \frac{\pi}{2}$, so the domain for the inverse tangent $y = \tan^{-1} x$ is all real numbers and the range is $-\frac{\pi}{2} < y < \frac{\pi}{2}$.

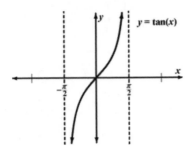 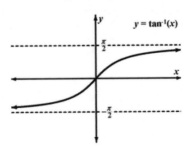

13-70. Using the triangle on the right, find:

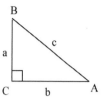

    a. $\sin A$ b. $\sec A$

    c. $\csc B$ d. $\tan B$

13-71. Solve each equation below for x if $-2\pi \le x \le 2\pi$.

    a. $4\sin^2(x) = 1$ b. $3\tan^2(x) = 1$

13-72. Solve $2\sin(x)\cos(x) + \cos(x) = 0$. Give your answers in degrees or radians.

13-73. Solve for x in the figure at right.

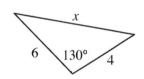

13-74. If the cost of a CD now averages \$15.95 and in 4 years will cost \$21.95, what is the annual multiplier and the annual percent increase?

13-75. Multiply the expressions in parts (a) through (d).

    a. $(a+b)(a^2 - ab + b^2)$ b. $(x-2)(x^2 + 2x + 4)$

    c. $(y+5)(y^2 - 5y + 25)$ d. $(x-y)(x^2 + xy + y^2)$

    e.   What did you notice about these products?

    f.   Make up another multiplication problem that will follow the same pattern.

13-76. Parts (a) through (d) of problem 13-75 represent a general pattern known as the **sum and difference of cubes**. Use this pattern to factor each of the following polynomials.

    a. $x^3 + y^3$ b. $x^3 - 27$ c. $8x^3 - y^3$ d. $x^3 + 1$

    e.   Make up another problem involving the sum or difference of cubes and show how to factor it.

13-77.   Find the equation of a cubic function that has $y = x^3$ as its parent graph, a locator point at $(-6, -10)$, and passes through the origin.

13-78.   For each of the following equations, identify the curve, write the equation in graphing form, and describe any of the following terms that apply: center, vertex or vertices, and asymptotes.

a. $9x^2 - 16y^2 - 32y = 160$ b. $y^2 - 2y + 3x = 5$

c. $16 + 6x - x^2 - y^2 = 0$

13-79.   Find the equation of a hyperbola with vertices $(0, \pm 7)$ and asymptotes $y = \pm 2x$.

13-80.   From the 13 spades in a deck of cards, four are selected. Find the probability that:

a.   Exactly one card is a "face" card (Jack, Queen, or King).

b.   The cards form a sequence (A, 2, 3, 4; 2, 3, 4, 5; ...; J,Q, K, A).

13-81.   Using the triangle on the right, find:

a. $\sec B$ b. $\tan A$

c. $\cot A$ d. $\csc A$

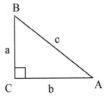

13-82.   Solve $2\sin(x)\cos(x) - \sin(x) = 0$ in the domain $0 \le x \le 2\pi$. Give answers in degrees or radians.

13-83.   If $f(x) = 2x^2 - 3$ and $g(x) = x + 1$, find $f(g(x))$.

13-84.   Without using a calculator, simplify and evaluate each of the following log expressions. Your result should be an expression without logarithms.

a. $\log(4) + \log(25)$ b. $\dfrac{7^{\log_7(3)}}{\log_5 5^4}$

13-85.   Use the sum or difference of cubes and what you already know about factoring to factor the following expressions as completely as possible.

a. $x^5 + 8x^2 y^3$

b. $8y^6 - 125x^3$

c. $x^6 - y^6$ (Note: This is tricky. If you start it as the difference of two cubes, you will not be able to factor it completely. Think of it as the difference of two squares and then factor the factors as the sum and difference of two cubes.)

13-86.   Write an equation for the curve at right. Then sketch the graph of the inverse of this graph and write its equation.

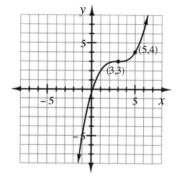

13-87.   An exponential function has an asymptote at $y = 5$ and passes through the points $(2, 5.64)$ and $(-1, 15)$. Find the equation of the function.

13-88.   What is the fifth term of each expansion?

a. $(a + b)^9$

b. $(2x + y)^8$

13-89.   Sure Shot Jane can hit the bull's eye with a bow and arrow 90% of the time. If she shoots five arrows, what is the probability that three or more arrows hit the bull's eye?

13.2.1 How can I rewrite it?

· ·

Trigonometric Identities

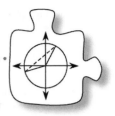

To solve many trigonometric equations, it is first necessary to rewrite the equation in a simpler form. In this lesson, you will solve trigonometric equations graphically and will develop methods for rewriting those equations so that you can solve them algebraically.

13-90. Consider the equation $2 \sin(x) \cos(x) = \frac{1}{2}$ for the domain $0 \le x \le 2\pi$.

    a. Do you have tools to solve this equation algebraically?

    b. Use your graphing calculator to graph $y = 2 \sin(x) \cos(x)$ and $y = \frac{1}{2}$ in the domain $0 \le x \le 2\pi$. Copy the graph onto your paper and use it to approximate the solutions to $2 \sin(x) \cos(x) = \frac{1}{2}$. How many solutions are there in this domain?

    c. Crystal was working on this problem and noticed that the graph of $y = 2 \sin(x) \cos(x)$ looked just like the graph of a regular cyclic function. She thought it must be possible to write a different equivalent equation for this graph. Work with your team to write a cyclic equation for this graph. Is there more than one? If so, which is the simplest?

    d. Using your equivalent equation from part (c), rewrite the equation $2 \sin(x) \cos(x) = \frac{1}{2}$ and solve it algebraically. How do your solutions compare to those you approximated from your graph?

    e. Write an algebraic statement showing that these two expressions are equivalent. This is called the **Double Angle Identity** for the sine.

13-91. DISCOVERING IDENTITIES GRAPHICALLY

The graphs of some other trigonometric functions can be used to rewrite the functions and create new identities. Use a method similar to the method used in problem 13-90 to rewrite each of the following equations. Then use your result to write a new identity.

$y = \cos(-x)$ $y = \sin(-x)$ $y = \cos\left(\frac{\pi}{2} - x\right)$ $y = \sin\left(\frac{\pi}{2} - x\right)$

$y = \sin^2(x)$ $y = \cos^2(x)$ $y = \cos^2(x) - \sin^2(x)$ $y = \cos^2(x) + \sin^2(x)$

13-92. Obtain the Lesson 13.2.1 Resource Page from your teacher. This resource page will be referred to as your Identity Tool Kit. Record each identity you have discovered along with its **justification**.

     Algebra 2 Connections

13-93.   Use your new identities to help you rewrite and solve the following equations in the given domains.

    a. $2\cos\left(\frac{\pi}{2}-x\right)=1$ for all x b. $\cos^2(x)-\sin^2(x)=\frac{\sqrt{3}}{2}$ for $0\le x\le 2\pi$

13-94.   One of the identities that you discovered in problem 13-91 is $\cos^2(x)+\sin^2(x)=1$. This is called the **Pythagorean Identity**, and it is one of the most useful identities you will learn.

    a.   Work with your team to explore the following question: Why is $\cos^2(x)+\sin^2(x)=1$ called the Pythagorean Identity? Does it have anything to do with the Pythagorean theorem? Be prepared to share your ideas with the class.

    b.   Two more very useful identities can come directly from the Pythagorean Identity. To discover the first related identity, divide both sides of the equation by $\cos^2(x)$. For the second related identity, divide both sides of the equation by $\sin^2(x)$. Add these two new identities to your Identity Tool Kit (Lesson 13.2.1 Resource Page).

13-95.   Rewrite each of the following expressions in a simpler form.

    a. $\cos^2(\theta-\pi)+\sin^2(\theta-\pi)$ b. $\cos^2(2w)-\sin^2(2w)$

    c. $\frac{\sin\theta}{\cos\theta}$

13-96.   An isosceles triangle has sides with lengths 10, 10, and 5 cm. What are the measures of the angles in the triangle?

13-97.   Solve for x in *degrees*.

    a. $2\sin(x)=1$ b. $\cos^2(x)+4\cos(x)+4=0$

13-98.   Divide $6x^3-5x^2+5x-2$ by $(2x-1)$.

13-99.   Divide $x^4-7x^2+3x+18$ by $(x+2)$.

13-100. Each labeled point on the graph below is either a maximum or a minimum.

a. Find the period and amplitude of the graph.

b. Find an equation for the graph.

c. Use one of the labeled points to check your equation.

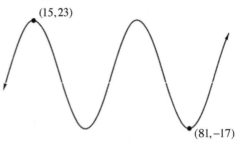

(15, 23)

(81, −17)

13-101. Find the equation of an ellipse with center at the midpoint of a segment with endpoints at $(-2, -3)$, $(10, -3)$ and congruent to $x^2 + 36y^2 = 36$.

13-102. Rewrite the Pythagorean Identity as many ways as you can. One way to change the identity would be to solve the equation for one trigonometric function. Another way is to use factoring. Try several different ways.

13-103. If $\pi \le \theta \le \frac{3\pi}{2}$ and $\sin\theta = -\frac{3}{5}$, find $\cos\theta$. Use what you know about the Pythagorean Identity and the unit circle to get started.

13-104. Rewrite each of the following expressions in terms of either $\sin(\theta)$ or $\cos(\theta)$.

a. $\tan(\theta)$ b. $\csc(\theta)$ c. $\cot(\theta)$ d. $\sec(\theta)$

13-105. Given the points $(2, 9)$ and $(4, 324)$:

a. Write the equation of a line that passes through them.

b. Write the equation of an exponential function with an asymptote at $y = 0$ that passes through them.

13-106. Without graphing, determine where the graphs of $f(x) = 2x^2 - 3x + 1$ and $g(x) = 4x - 2$ intersect.

13-107. Simplify each rational expression below.

a. $\dfrac{\frac{x+1}{2x}}{\frac{x^2-1}{x}}$ b. $\dfrac{\frac{4}{x+3}}{\frac{1}{x}+3}$

13-108. Hospital records show that 10% of all the cases of a certain disease are fatal. If five patients suffer from this disease, find the probability that:

a. All will recover.   b. At least three will die.

13.2.2 How can I prove it?

Proving Trigonometric Identities

13-109. Polly Parabola and Carl Conic have a cousin named Thomas Trig. Functions of America, Professional Parabola Productions, and The Courtly Conic Company have enjoyed such huge success that Thomas has decided to open a company called Identity Island. However, to do this, he needs some help and has sent your team the following memo.

> *Dear Study Team,*
>
> *My goal for Identity Island is to be able to offer a wide selection of trigonometric identities to interested customers. I found a list of identities on the Internet, but I know that lots of information on the Internet is false! I cannot afford to be embarrassed in front of my potential customers by offering identities that are not true.*
>
> *I need your help. I need a solid algebraic proof on file for each identity that we offer. Please submit a report by the end of the day that demonstrates each of the identities algebraically.*
>
> *I have the utmost faith in your team's abilities. Thank you for your time!*
>
> *Sincerely,*
>
> *Thomas Trig*

Your task: Work with your team to demonstrate algebraically whether or not each of the identities below is always true, never true or sometimes true. To prove some of the identities you will need to refer to the identities that you developed in Lesson 13.2.1.

a. $\cot(x) + \tan(x) = \sec(x)\csc(x)$

b. $(1 - \sin x)(1 + \sin x) = \frac{1}{1 + \tan^2(x)}$

c. $\frac{1}{\sec^2(x)} + \frac{1}{\csc^2(x)} = 1$

d. $\sec^2(x) - \csc^2(x) = \tan^2(x) - \cot^2(x)$

e. $\frac{\sec(x)}{\tan(x) + \cot(x)} = \sin(x)$

f. $\sin^2(x)\cot^2(x) + \cos^2(x)\tan^2(x) = 1$

g. $\frac{\csc^2(x) - 1}{\csc^2(x)} = \cos^2(x)$

h. $\frac{\sin x}{\cos x} + \frac{\cos x}{\sin x} = 2$

13-110. A 125-foot redwood tree is leaning 20° off vertical toward the north. How long will its shadow be when the noon sun is 68° above the horizon? (When the sun is 68° above the horizon, the angle the sunlight makes with the ground is 68°.)

13-111. Divide each of the following polynomials, $P(x)$, by $D(x)$ to find the quotient $Q(x)$ and then rewrite the polynomial in the form $P(x) = D(x) \cdot Q(x) + R$, where R is the remainder.

a. $P(x) = 2x^4 - x^2 + 3x + 5$

$D(x) = x - 1$

b. $P(x) = x^5 - 2x^3 + 1$

$D(x) = x - 3$

13-112. Without using a calculator, solve each equation below in the domain $0 \le x \le 2\pi$.

a. $\sin(x) = -1$

b. $2\cos(x) - 1 = 0$

c. $\tan(x) = 1$

d. $2\sin(x) = 4\sin(x) + 1$

13-113. Solve for x.

a.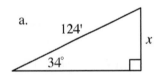

b.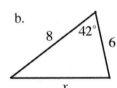

13-114. If two dice are thrown and the numbers that come up are added to calculate a total number of points, what is the probability that each of the following events will occur?

a. Five points.

b. Seven points.

c. Five points before seven points.

13-115. Simplify each expression.

a. $\dfrac{2x^2 - x - 3}{3x^2 - 11x + 6}$

b. $\dfrac{x^3 - 8}{4x^3 - 3x^2 - 10x}$

13-116. Solve.

a. $\log_7(3x - 2) = 2$

b. $2^x \cdot 2^{x-2} - 16^2 = 0$

13-117.   Graph each of following relations. Some of the equations may need to be changed to a more useful form.

a. $\dfrac{(x-2)^2}{9} - \dfrac{(y+3)^2}{4} = 1$

b. $\dfrac{y^2 - 2y + 1}{4} - \dfrac{x^2 + 6x + 9}{25} = 1$

c. $4(x^2 - 10x + 25) - 16(y^2 + 6y + 9) = 64$

13-118.   Prove that each of the following equations is an identity. In other words, prove that they are each true for all values for which the functions are defined.

a. $(\sin\theta + \cos\theta)^2 = 1 + 2\sin\theta\cos\theta$

b. $\tan\theta + \cot\theta = \sec\theta\csc\theta$

c. $(\tan\theta\cos\theta)(\sin^2\theta + \dfrac{1}{\sec^2\theta}) = \sin\theta$

13-119.   Solve $\dfrac{2+\sin^2\theta}{3} = \dfrac{3}{4}$ in the domain $0 \le \theta \le 2\pi$. Show your solutions on a unit circle.

13-120.   If the side lengths of $\triangle ABC$ are $a = 9$, $b = 10$, and $c = 5$, calculate the measure of the largest angle.

13-121.   Write an equation for the curve shown at right. Is it a function? **Justify** your answer.

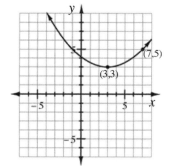

13-122.   Solve for x, correct to three decimal places.

a $27 = 6^x$

b. $27 = \dfrac{1}{6^x}$

c. $27 = \dfrac{1}{(\frac{1}{6})^x}$

d.   Show that $\dfrac{1}{(\frac{1}{6})^x} = 6^x$.

13-123.   Solve each system of equations. Explain the graphical implications of your answer.

a. $3x - 2y = -10$
     $4x + y = 49$

b. $7x - 2y = 11$
     $14x - 4y = 3$

13-124.   Find a polynomial function of degree three with roots $x = 3, 1 \pm i$. Express your answer in standard form.

13-125.   For each of the following equations, identify the curve, write the equation in graphing form, and list the following information: center, focus or foci, and asymptotes. Refer to the Math Notes boxes in Lessons 11.2.2, 11.2.4, and 11.2.6 for definitions

a. $2x^2 + y^2 - 4x + 6y - 7 = 0$

b. $3y^2 - x^2 + 12y = 0$

c. $12x^2 + 8y^2 + 48x - 48y + 24 = 0$

13.2.3 What about sums and differences?

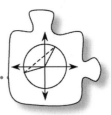

Angle Sum and Difference Identities

In this lesson you will use your knowledge of relationships in the unit circle to develop four new identities called the Angle Sum and Difference Identities.

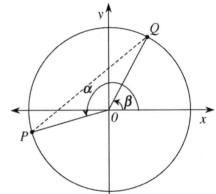

13-126.   Danny and Damian were working on finding identities. They thought it would be useful to look at the sums and differences of angles. They started with a unit circle and created the angles α and β as shown at right. They recognized that they had formed a triangle, $\triangle POQ$.

   a.   Write the measure of the obtuse angle in $\triangle POQ$ in terms of α and β.

   b.   Danny and Damian each realized that they can calculate the length of side PQ of their triangle, but they wanted to use two different methods. What are the two methods they could be thinking of?

   c.   Danny wanted to use the idea of distance between points P and Q to calculate the length. In order to do that, he needs to label the coordinates of points P and Q. Based on angles α and β, represent the coordinates of each point using trigonometric functions.

   d.   Use your answer from part (c) to write an expression for the distance between points P and Q.

   e.   Damian realized that since this is a unit circle, the lengths of OP and OQ are both one unit, so he wanted to use the Law of Cosines. Use the Law of Cosines to write an expression for the length of side PQ.

   f.   Since the expressions you wrote for parts (c) and (d) both represent the length of PQ, what equation can you write? Simplify your equation to write a formula for $\cos(\alpha - \beta)$. This is called the **Angle Difference Identity** for cosine. Add this to your Identity Tool Kit (Lesson 13.2.1 Resource Page).

13-127.   Danny and Damian were so pleased with this result that they wanted to keep going. They wanted to know how they could rewrite $\cos(\alpha + \beta)$. As they were thinking about this, Damian had a realization. *"I know how we could figure it out!"* he exclaimed. *"We could use the identity we already found to rewrite $\cos(\alpha - (-\beta))$, since that's the same thing as $\cos(\alpha + \beta)$."* Work with your team to use this idea to find the **Angle Sum Identity** for cosine.

13-128.   *"So now we have the sum and difference formulas for cosine, but what about for sine?"* Damian asked. Danny pondered this for a while and then remembered an identity he thought they could use to figure these out. *"Don't we have an identity that relates sine to cosine?"* he asked.

a.   Which identity is Danny thinking of?

b.   Danny and Damian realized that they could use this to rewrite $\sin(\alpha + \beta)$. Work with your team to rewrite $\sin(\alpha + \beta)$ and find the **Angle Sum Identity** for sine.

c.   Now work with your team to develop the **Angle Difference Identity** for the sine. Be prepared to share your **strategies** with the class.

ⓂETHODS AND MEANINGS

MATH NOTES

Trigonometric Identities

Identities are equations that are true for all values for which the functions are defined.

$$\cos(-x) = \cos(x) \qquad \sin(-x) = -\sin(x)$$

Reciprocal Trigonometric Functions:

$$\csc(x) = \frac{1}{\sin(x)} \qquad \sec(x) = \frac{1}{\cos(x)} \qquad \cot(x) = \frac{1}{\tan(x)}$$

Pythagorean Identities:

$$\sin^2(x) + \cos^2(x) = 1 \qquad \tan^2(x) + 1 = \sec^2 x \qquad 1 + \cot^2(x) = \csc^2(x)$$

Co-function Identities:

$$\sin(x) = \cos\left(\tfrac{\pi}{2} - x\right) \qquad \cos(x) = \sin\left(\tfrac{\pi}{2} - x\right) \qquad \sec(x) = \csc\left(\tfrac{\pi}{2} - x\right)$$

$$\csc(x) = \sec\left(\tfrac{\pi}{2} - x\right) \qquad \tan(x) = \cot\left(\tfrac{\pi}{2} - x\right) \qquad \cot(x) = \tan\left(\tfrac{\pi}{2} - x\right)$$

Angle Sum and Difference Identities:

$$\sin(x + y) = \sin(x)\cos(y) + \cos(x)\sin(y)$$

$$\sin(x - y) = \sin(x)\cos(y) - \cos(x)\sin(y)$$

$$\cos(x + y) = \cos(x)\cos(y) - \sin(x)\sin(y)$$

$$\cos(x - y) = \cos(x)\cos(y) + \sin(x)\sin(y)$$

Double Angle Identities:

$$\sin(2x) = 2\sin(x)\cos(x)$$

$$\cos(2x) = \cos^2(x) - \sin^2(x)$$

13-129.   Write $\frac{\pi}{12}$ as the difference of two special angles. Then use the appropriate angle difference formula to find the exact sine and cosine of $\frac{\pi}{12}$.

13-130.   Write each angle as the sum or difference of two special angles and then find the exact sine or cosine.

    a. $\sin\frac{7\pi}{12}$ b. $\cos\frac{11\pi}{12}$

13-131.   Show how to derive the double angle formulas for $\sin(2x)$ and $\cos(2x)$ by substituting x for both α and β in the formulas for $\sin(\alpha+\beta)$ and $\cos(\alpha+\beta)$, then simplifying.

13-132.   Consider the function $f(x)=\cos(x+\frac{\pi}{2})$.

    a.   Make a complete graph of $f(x)$.

    b.   Write a simpler trig function that is represented by the same graph.

    c.   Now use the angle sum identity to expand and simplify $\cos(x+\frac{\pi}{2})$.

    d.   Does your work in part (c) agree with your graphical results from parts (a) and (b)? Explain.

13-133.   Express $\frac{\cos x}{1-\tan x}-\frac{\sin x}{\cot x-1}$ in terms of $\sin x$ and $\cos x$ and then simplify.

13-134.   Latisha had graphed the polynomial $y=x^3-5x^2+8x-6$ during class and remembered that it had one real root at $x=3$. Explain how you could use division to find the other roots, and then find them.

13-135.   Each of the following sums is the beginning of an arithmetic series. Find the nth term of each series, for the specified value of n.

    a. $(-2)+(-5)+(-8)+...,\ n=12$ b. $9+15+21+...,\ n=20$

13-136.   Without using a calculator, solve these two problems from a college entrance exam.

    a.   If $x^{-4/3}+1=17$, find $x^{-1/3}$.   b.   If $\log(A)=a$, find $\log(\frac{A}{100})$.

13-137.   In a certain family, the probability of any one child having dark hair is $\frac{3}{4}$. If the family has three children, what is the probability that exactly one has dark hair?

13-138.   Graph the following equations. Some of them will need to be changed into a more useful form.

   a. $\dfrac{(x+2)^2}{9} + \dfrac{(y-3)^2}{4} = 1$ b. $\dfrac{x^2+2x+1}{16} + \dfrac{y^2+6y+9}{25} = 1$

   c. $4(x^2 - 10x + 25) + 9(y^2 - 8y + 16) = 36$

Chapter 13 Closure What have I learned?

Reflection and Synthesis

The activities below offer you a chance to reflect on what you have learned in this chapter. As you work, look for concepts that you feel very comfortable with, ideas that you would like to learn more about, and topics you need more help with. Look for connections between ideas as well as connections with material you learned previously.

①   TEAM BRAINSTORM

         With your team, brainstorm a list for each of the following categories. Be as detailed as you can. How long can you make your list? Challenge yourselves. Be prepared to share your team's ideas with the class.

         Topics: What have you studied in this chapter? What ideas and words were important in what you learned? Remember to be as detailed as you can.

         Connections: How are the topics, ideas, and words that you learned in previous courses connected to the new ideas in this chapter? Again, make your list as long as you can.

Below is a list of the vocabulary used in this chapter. Make sure that you are familiar with all of these words and know what they mean. Refer to the glossary or index for any words that you do not yet understand.

$\cos^{-1}$	cosecant	cotangent
identity	reciprocal	secant
$\sin^{-1}$	solution	$\tan^{-1}$

Make a concept map showing all of the connections you can find among the key words and ideas listed above. To show a connection between two words, draw a line between them and explain the connection, as shown in the example below. A word can be connected to any other word as long as you can **justify** the connection. For each key word or idea, provide a sketch of an example.

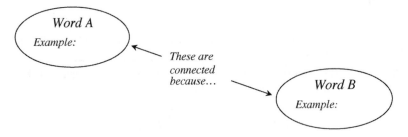

Your teacher may provide you with vocabulary cards to help you get started. If you use the cards to plan your concept map, be sure either to re-draw your concept map on your paper or to glue the vocabulary cards to a poster with all of the connections explained for others to see and understand.

While you are making your map, your team may think of related words or ideas that are not listed above. Be sure to include these ideas on your concept map.

③ SUMMARIZING MY UNDERSTANDING

This section gives you an opportunity to show what you know about certain math topics or ideas.

With your team, make a list of the **big ideas** of this chapter. Discuss the important ideas of the chapter and try to agree on a short list of no more than five big ideas. Be prepared to share your list in a whole class discussion. When the class has reached agreement on a list, continue with parts (a) and (b) below.

a. Write your own description of each big idea.

b. For each big idea, provide one or two representative example problems. Solve each problem completely, using multiple representations, if applicable.

④ WHAT HAVE I LEARNED?

This section will help you evaluate which types of problems you feel comfortable with and which you need more help with. This section will appear at the end of every chapter to help you check your understanding. Even if your teacher does not assign this section, it is a good idea to try these problems and find out for yourself what you know and what you need to work on.

Solve each problem as completely as you can. The table at the end of this closure section has answers to these problems. It also tells you where you can find additional help and practice on similar problems.

CL 13-139. Decide whether each of the following statements is sometimes true, always true, or never true. If it is sometimes true, give the values for x that make it true; if it is always true or never true, **justify** how you know.

a. $\cos(x) = \frac{3}{4}$

b. $2\tan(x) = 0$

c. $\sin(x) = \frac{5}{2}$

d. $\sin(x) = \cos(\frac{\pi}{2} - x)$

CL 13-140. Solve each of the following equations in the domain $0 \le x < 2\pi$.

a. $2\cos(x) = 1$

b. $4\tan(x) + 4 = 0$

c. $2\sin^2(x) - \sin(x) - 1 = 0$

d. $\csc(x) = -2$

CL 13-141. Explain why the graph of $y = \sec(x)$ has asymptotes.

CL 13-142. Solve each of the following equations in the domain $0 \le x \le 2\pi$.

a. $\cot(x) = 1.2$

b. $\cos(x) = -1$

c. $\frac{1}{4}\csc(x) = \sin(x)$

d. $\cos(2x) = \frac{1}{2}$

CL 13-143. Rewrite each expression as an equivalent expression that has only one trigonometric function.

a. $\sin(x) \cdot \csc(x) - \sin^2(x)$

b. $\frac{1 - \sin^2(x)}{\cot^2(x)}$

c. $\tan(x) \cdot \cot(x) - \cos^2(x)$

d. $\sin^2(x) \cdot (1 + \tan^2 x)$

CL 13-144. Show that the identity $\frac{1}{\cos(x)} - \cos(x) = \tan(x)\sin(x)$ is true.

CL 13-145. Using radian measure, represent all possible solutions to each equation.

a. $\tan(x) = \sqrt{3}$

b. $\cos(x) = -\frac{\sqrt{2}}{2}$

c. $\sin(x) = \frac{\sqrt{3}}{2}$

d. $\cot(x) = -1$

CL 13-146. Start with the expression $\sin(x + \frac{\pi}{2})$.

a. Use the angle sum identity to expand and simplify.

b. What other equation has a graph that is the same as the graph of $y = \sin(x + \frac{\pi}{2})$?

CL 13-147. Graph each of the following functions.

a. $y = 3\sin 2(x - \frac{\pi}{4}) + 1$

b. $f(x) = -2\cos(x + \frac{\pi}{12}) - 1$

CL 13-148. Find the roots of the function $f(x) = x^4 + x^3 + 2x - 4$.

CL 13-149. Check your answers using the table at the end of this section. Which problems do you feel confident about? Which problems were hard? Have you worked on problems like these in math classes you have taken before? Use the table to make a list of topics you need help on and a list of topics you need to practice more.

⑤   HOW AM I THINKING?

This course focuses on five different **Ways of Thinking**: justifying, generalizing, choosing a strategy, investigating, and reversing thinking. These are some of the ways in which you think while trying to make sense of a concept or attempting to solve a problem (even outside of math class). During this chapter, you have probably used each Way of Thinking multiple times without even realizing it!

Review each of the five Ways of Thinking described in the closure sections of Chapters 1 through 5. Then choose three of these Ways of Thinking that you remember using while working on this chapter. Show and explain where and how you used each one. Describe why thinking in this way helped you solve a particular problem or understand something new. Be sure to include examples to demonstrate your thinking.

Answers and Support for Closure Activity #4
What Have I Learned?

Problem	Solutions	Need Help?	More Practice
CL 13-139.	a. True when $x \approx 0.72 + 2\pi n$ radians or when $x \approx 5.56 + 2\pi n$ radians. b. True for $x = \pi n$ radians. c. Never true. The range of sine is $-1 \le y \le 1$. d. Always true.	Lesson 13.1.1	Problems 13-2, 13-5, 13-15, 13-25, and 13-69
CL 13-140.	a. $\frac{\pi}{3}, \frac{5\pi}{3}$ b. $\frac{3\pi}{4}, \frac{7\pi}{4}$ c. $\frac{7\pi}{6}, \frac{11\pi}{6}, \frac{\pi}{2}$ d. $\frac{7\pi}{6}, \frac{11\pi}{6}$	Lessons 13.1.2, 13.1.4 and 13.2.1	Problems 13-31, 13-46, 13-56, 13-66, 13-71, 13-72, 13-82, 13-112, and 13-119
CL 13-141.	$y = \sec(x)$ is the same as $y = \frac{1}{\cos(x)}$, so whenever cosine is 0, secant will be undefined.	Lesson 13.1.4	Problems 13-64, and 13-65
CL 13-142.	a. $x \approx 0.69$ radians or $x \approx 3.84$ radians b. $x = \pi$ c. $x = \frac{\pi}{6}, \frac{5\pi}{6}, \frac{7\pi}{6}, \frac{11\pi}{6}$ d. $x = \frac{\pi}{6}, \frac{5\pi}{6}, \frac{7\pi}{6}, \frac{11\pi}{6}$	Lessons 13.1.2 and 13.1.4 Math Notes box in Leson 13.2.3	Problems 13-66, 13-67, 13-71, 13-72, 13-82, 13-112, and 13-119
CL 13-143.	a. $\cos^2(x)$ b. $\sin^2(x)$ c. $\sin^2(x)$ d. $\tan^2(x)$	Lessons 13.2.1 and 13.2.2 Math Notes box in Leson 13.2.3	Problems 13-95, 13-104, 13-109, 13-133
CL 13-144.	$\frac{1}{\cos(x)} - \cos(x) = \frac{1}{\cos(x)} - \frac{\cos^2(x)}{\cos(x)}$ $= \frac{1-\cos^2(x)}{\cos(x)} = \frac{\sin^2(x)}{\cos(x)} = \frac{\sin(x)}{\cos(x)} \cdot \sin(x)$ $= \tan(x)\sin(x)$	Lessons 13.2.1 and 13.2.2 Math Notes box in Leson 13.2.3	Problems 13-109, and 13-118

Problem	Solutions	Need Help?	More Practice
CL 13-145.	a. $\frac{\pi}{3} + \pi n$ b. $\frac{3\pi}{4} + 2\pi n$, $\frac{5\pi}{4} + 2\pi n$ c. $\frac{\pi}{3} + 2\pi n$, $\frac{2\pi}{3} + 2\pi n$ d. $-\frac{\pi}{4} + \pi n$ or $\frac{3\pi}{4} + \pi n$	Lesson 13.1.2	Problems 13-29, 13-31, 13-43, 13-45, 13-46, 13-56, 13-66, 13-71, and 13-112
CL 13-146.	a. $\sin(x)\cos(\frac{\pi}{2}) + \cos(x)\sin(\frac{\pi}{2})$ $= \cos(x)$ b. $y = \cos(x)$	Lesson 13.2.3 Math Notes box in Leson 13.2.3	Problems 13-128, 13-129, and 13-130
CL 13-147.	a. b.	Lessons 8.1.2, 8.1.7, 8.2.1, 8.2.3, and 8.2.4	Problems 8-115, 8-127, 8-140, 8-143, 8-145, 8-146 8-153, 8-159, 8-161, and 13-10
CL 13-148.	$x = 1, -2, \pm\sqrt{2}i$	Lesson 9.3.2 Math Notes Box in Lesson 9.3.2	Problems, 9-140, 9-149, CL 9-185, 10-50, 11-93, 11-123, 12-166

Algebra 2 Checkpoint Materials

Notes to Students (and their Teachers)

Students master different skills at different speeds. No two students learn exactly the same way at the same time. At some point you will be expected to perform certain skills accurately. Most of the Checkpoint problems incorporate skills that you should have been developing in Algebra 1 and geometry. If you have not mastered these skills yet it does not mean that you will not be successful in this class. However, you may need to do some work outside of class to get caught up on them.

Starting in Chapter 2 and finishing in Chapter 9, there are eighteen problems designed as Checkpoint problems. Each one is marked with an icon like the one above. After you do each of the Checkpoint problems, check your answers by referring to this section. If your answers are incorrect, you may need some extra practice to develop that skill. The practice sets are keyed to each of the Checkpoint problems in the textbook. Each has the topic clearly labeled, followed by the answers to the corresponding Checkpoint problem and then some completed examples. Next, the complete solution to the Checkpoint problem from the text is given, and there are more problems for you to practice with answers included.

Remember, looking is not the same as doing! You will never become good at any sport by just watching it, and in the same way, reading through the worked examples and understanding the steps is not the same as being able to do the problems yourself. How many of the extra practice problems do you need to try? That is really up to you. Remember that your goal is to be able to do similar problems on your own confidently and accurately. This is your responsibility. You should not expect your teacher to spend time in class going over the solutions to the Checkpoint problem sets. If you are not confident after reading the examples and trying the problems, you should get help outside of class time or talk to your teacher about working with a tutor.

Two other sources for help with the Checkpoint problems and the other new topics in Algebra 2 are the *Parent's Guide with Review (Algebra 1)* and the *Parent's Guide with Review (Algebra 2)*. These resources are available free of charge from the Internet at www.cpm.org.

Checkpoint Topics

1. Using the Slope-Intercept Form of a Line to Solve a System of Equations
2. Solving Systems of Linear Equations in Two Variables
3. Multiplying Polynomials
4. Simplifying Expressions with Positive Exponents
5. Factoring Quadratic Expressions
6. Writing the Equation of a Line Given Two Points
7. Finding the x- and y-intercepts of a Quadratic Function
8. Finding the Slope of a Line through Two Points and the Distance Between the Points
9. Using Function Notation and Identifying the Domain and Range
10. Solving for One Variable in an Equation with Two or More Variables
11. Integral and Rational Exponents
12. Graphing Linear Inequalities
13. Solving Rational Equations
14. Completing the Square and Finding the Vertex for a Parabola
15. Writing and Solving Exponential Equations
16. Solving Absolute Value Equations and Inequalities
17. Finding an Equation for the Inverse of a Function.
18. Solving a System of Equations in Three Variables

Answer to Problem 2-47: (3, 2)

If an equation of a line is written in the form $y = mx + b$, then the y-intercept is the point $(0, b)$. The slope of the line is the coefficient of x, represented in the general form of the equation as m. Therefore, in the equation $y = \frac{3}{2}x + 7$, the slope is $\frac{3}{2}$ and the y-intercept is $(0, 7)$.

First review how to use the information in slope-intercept equations to graph a line.

Example 1: Without making a table, graph $y = \frac{2}{3}x - 2$.

Solution: We start by identifying the slope and y-intercept. The slope is $\frac{2}{3}$ and the y-intercept is $(0, -2)$. (Before continuing, imagine what the line will look like). To graph the line, first find and mark the y-intercept. The fact that the slope is positive tells us the direction of the line is upward left to right. Then, knowing that the slope is $\frac{2}{3}$, we can find another point on the line by starting at the y-intercept, moving our pencil up vertically two units and then horizontally (to the right) three units. Just remember that the slope is positive! After moving vertically two units and horizontally three units, we arrive at another point on the line. Draw the line through the two points.

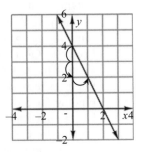

Answer: You should get a graph like the one shown at right.

Example 2: Without making a table, graph $y = 4 - 2x$.

Solution: Do not let the form of the equation fool you. The slope is -2 (the coefficient of x) and the y-intercept is 4 (the constant value). Rearranging the order of the terms does not change their meaning. As in example 1, start by graphing the y-intercept. Then slide your pencil down 2 and to the right 1.

Answer: You should get a graph like the one shown at right.

If the equation is not already in slope/intercept form (also known as "y-form") then the equation must first be solved for y.

Example 3: If you wanted to graph $2x + 5y = 10$, then you would solve for y to get $y = \frac{10-2x}{5}$ or $y = -\frac{2}{5}x + 2$. Then you can see that the y-intercept is (0, 2) and the slope is $-\frac{2}{5}$.

Two special cases to remember are vertical and horizontal lines.

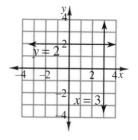

$y = 2$ is a horizontal line (the slope is zero) passing through the y-axis at (0, 2), as shown in the graph at right.

$x = 3$ is a vertical line (the slope is undefined) passing through the x-axis at (3, 0), as shown in the graph at right.

Now we graph to solve a system of linear equations, as shown in the following example.

Example 4: Graph each line and find the intersection of $x + y = 5$ and $y = \frac{1}{3}x + 1$.

Solution: The first equation needs to be solved for y to get $y = -x + 5$. Then you can see that the y-intercept is (0, 5) and the slope is -1. The second equation has a y-intercept of (0, 1) and a slope of $\frac{1}{3}$.

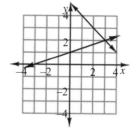

Answer: After graphing the two lines, you can see that they intersect at the point (3, 2), as shown at right.

Solving Algebraically

A solution to a system of equations is a point that lies on both graphs. In other words, it is an x- and a y-value that make both equations true. So, for the solution, we know that the y-value in the first equation has to be equal to the y-value in the second. When both equations are given in y-form, we can then set them equal and use algebra to solve.

Example 5: Find the point of intersection of $y = 5 - x$ and $y = \frac{1}{3}x + 1$ algebraically.

Solution: Since both equations are solved for y, we can set them equal and solve for x, as shown at right. We can then substitute $x = 3$ into either equation to find y. Choosing the first, we get $y = 5 - 3 = 2$.

$$5 - x = \frac{1}{3}x + 1$$
$$4 = \frac{4}{3}x$$
$$3 = x$$

Answer: (3, 2)

Here are some more to try. Solve each system by graphing. Then use algebra to check your solution.

a. $y = -x + 8$
$y = x - 2$

b. $y = -x + 3$
$y = x + 3$

c. $y = -3x$
$y = -4x + 2$

d. $y = -x + 5$
$y = \frac{1}{2}x + 2$

e. $y = 2$
$y = -4x + 3$

f. $3x + 3y = 4 + x$
$y = \frac{4}{3} - \frac{2}{3}x$

g. $y = 2$
$2x + y = 4$

h. $x = 3$
$3x + 3y = 0$

i. $2x + 3y = 0$
$2x - 3y = 0$

j. $3x - 2y = 4$
$2y = 3x - 6$

Answers:

a. (5, 3)

b. (0, 3)

c. (2, –6)

d. (2, 3)

e. $(\frac{1}{4}, 2)$

f. same line

g. (1, 2)

h. (3, –3)

i. (0, 0)

j. no solution / parallel lines

Checkpoint Number 2

Problem 2-101

Solving Systems of Linear Equations in Two Variables.

Answer to Problem 2-101: $(3, 2)$

You can solve systems of equations using a variety of methods. For linear systems, you can graph, use the Substitution Method, or use the Elimination Method. Each method works best with certain forms of equations. Following are some examples and then we will return to the original problem. Although the method that is easiest for one person may not be easiest for another, the most common methods are shown on the next two pages.

Example 1: Solve the system of equations $x = 4y - 7$ and $3x - 2y = 1$.

Solution: For this, we will use the *Substitution* Method. Since the first equation tells us that x is equal to $4y - 7$, we can substitute $4y - 7$ for x in the second equation. This allows us to solve for y, as shown at right.

$$3(4y - 7) - 2y = 1$$
$$12y - 21 - 2y = 1$$
$$10y - 21 = 1$$
$$10y = 22$$
$$y = \tfrac{22}{10} = 2.2$$

Then substitute $y = 2.2$ into either original equation and solve for x: Choosing the first equation, we get $x = 4(2.2) - 7 = 8.8 - 7 = 1.8$.

Answer: The solution to the system is $x = 1.8$ and $y = 2.2$ or $(1.8, 2.2)$.

Example 2: Solve the system of equations $y = \tfrac{3}{4}x - 1$ and $y = -\tfrac{1}{3}x - 1$.

Solution: *Graphing*: Generally graphing is not the most efficient way to solve a system of linear equations. In this case, both equations are written in y-form so we can see that they have the same y-intercept. Since lines can cross only at one point, no points or infinite points, and these lines have different slopes (they are not parallel), the y-intercept must be the only point of intersection. We did not actually graph here, but we used the principles of graphs to solve the system. Substitution will work nicely as well.

Answer: $(0, -1)$

Example 3: Solve the system $x + 2y = 16$ and $x - y = 2$.

Solution: For this, we will use the *Elimination* Method. We can subtract the second equation from the first and then solve for y, as shown at right.

$$x + 2y = 16$$
$$-(x - y = 2)$$
$$0 + 3y = 14$$
$$3y = 14$$
$$y = \tfrac{14}{3}$$

Then substitute $y = \tfrac{14}{3}$ into either original equation and solve for x. Choosing the second equation, we get $x - \tfrac{14}{3} = 2$, so $x = 2 + \tfrac{14}{3} = \tfrac{20}{3}$.

Answer: The solution to the system is $(\tfrac{20}{3}, \tfrac{14}{3})$.

Example 4: **Solve the system** $x + 3y = 4$ **and** $3x - y = 2$.

Solution: For this, we will use the *Elimination* Method, only we will need to do some multiplication first. If we multiply the second equation by 3 and add the result to the first equation, we can eliminate y and solve for x, as shown at right.

$$\begin{array}{r} x + 3y = 4 \\ + \ 9x - 3y = 6 \\ \hline 10x \quad\ = 10 \\ x = 1 \end{array}$$

We can then find y by substituting $x = 1$ into either of the original equations. Choosing the second, we get $3(1) - y = 2$, which solves to yield $y = 1$.

Answer: The solution to this system is $(1, 1)$.

Now we can return to problem 2-101.

Example 5: **Solve the following system of linear equations in two variables.** $5x - 4y = 7$
$2y + 6x = 22$

For this system, you can use either the Substitution or the Elimination Method, but each choice will require a little bit of work to get started.

Substitution Method: Before we can substitute, we need to isolate one of the variables. In other words, we need to solve one of the equations for either x or for y. If we solve the second equation for y, it becomes $y = 11 - 3x$. Now we substitute $11 - 3x$ for y in the first equation and solve for x, as shown at right.

$$\begin{array}{r} 5x - 4(11 - 3x) = 7 \\ 5x - 44 + 12x = 7 \\ 17x - 44 = 7 \\ 17x = 51 \\ x = 3 \end{array}$$

Since we know that $y = 11 - 3x$, and we know that $x = 3$, we can substitute to find that $y = 11 - 3(3) = 2$.

Elimination Method: Before we can eliminate a variable, we need to rearrange the second equation so that the variables line up, as shown at right. Now we see that we can multiply the second equation by 2 and add the two equations to eliminate y and solve for x, as shown below right.

$$\begin{array}{r} 5x - 4y = 7 \\ 6x + 2y = 22 \end{array}$$

$$\begin{array}{r} 5x - 4y = 7 \\ + \ 12x + 4y = 44 \\ \hline 17x \quad\ = 51 \\ x = 3 \end{array}$$

We can then substitute $x = 3$ into the first equation to get $5(3) - 4y = 7$. Simplifying and solving, we get $-4y = -8$ and thus $y = 2$.

Answer: $(3, 2)$

Here are some more to try. Find the solution to these systems of linear equations. Use the method of your choice.

a. $y = 3x - 1$
    $2x - 3y = 10$

b. $x = -0.5y + 4$
    $8x + 3y = 31$

c. $2y = 4x + 10$
    $6x + 2y = 10$

d. $3x - 5y = -14$
    $x + 5y = 22$

e. $4x + 5y = 11$
    $2x + 6y = 16$

f. $x + 2y = 5$
    $x + y = 5$

g. $2x - 3 = y$
    $x - y = -4$

h. $y + 2 = x$
    $3x - 3y = x + 14$

i. $2x + y = 7$
    $x + 5y = 12$

j. $y = \frac{3}{5}x - 2$
    $y = \frac{x}{10} + 1$

k. $2x + y = -2x + 5$
    $3x + 2y = 2x + 3y$

l. $4x - 3y = -10$
    $x = \frac{1}{4}y - 1$

Answers:

a:. $(-1, -4)$

b. $(\frac{7}{2}, 1)$

c. $(0, 5)$

d. $(2, 4)$

e. $(-1, 3)$

f. $(5, 0)$

g. $(7, 11)$

h. $(-8, -10)$

i. $(\frac{23}{9}, \frac{17}{9})$

j. $(6, 1.6)$

k. $(1, 1)$

l. $(-\frac{1}{4}, 3)$

Checkpoint Number 3

Problem 2-152

Multiplying Polynomials

Answers to problem 2-152:

a. $2x^3 + 2x^2 - 3x - 3$

b. $x^3 - x^2 + x + 3$

c. $2x^2 + 12x + 18$

d. $4x^3 - 8x^2 - 3x + 9$

The product of polynomials can be found by using the distributive property. Using generic rectangles or, in the case of multiplying two binomials, the FOIL method can help you to keep track of the terms to be sure that you are multiplying correctly.

Example 1: Multiply $(3x - 2)(4x + 5)$.

Solution 1: In multiplying binomials, such as $(3x - 2)(4x + 5)$, you can use a generic rectangle. You would consider the terms of your original binomials as the dimensions (length and width) of the rectangle. To find the area of each piece, you would multiply the terms that represent the length and width of that piece. To get your final answer, you would add the areas of each of the interior pieces and simplify by combining like terms. This process is shown in the diagram below.

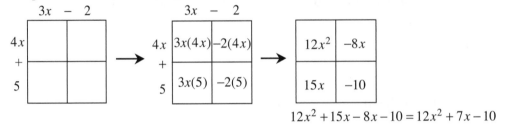

$$12x^2 + 15x - 8x - 10 = 12x^2 + 7x - 10$$

Solution 2: You might view multiplying binomials with generic rectangles as a form of *double distribution*. The $4x$ is distributed across the first row of the generic rectangle and then the 5 is distributed across the second row of the generic rectangle. Some people write it this way:

$$(3x - 2)(4x + 5) = (3x - 2)4x + (3x - 2)5 = 12x^2 - 8x + 15x - 10 = 12x^2 + 7x - 10$$

Solution 3: Another approach to multiplying binomials is to use the mnemonic "F.O.I.L," which is an acronym for First, Outside, Inside, Last.

F. Multiply the FIRST terms of each binomial. $(3x)(4x) = 12x^2$

O. Multiply the OUTSIDE terms. $(3x)(5) = 15x$

I. Multiply the INSIDE terms. $(-2)(4x) = -8x$

L. Multiply the LAST terms of each binomial. $(-2)(5) = -10$

Finally we combine like terms to get $12x^2 + 15x - 8x - 10 = 12x^2 + 7x - 10$.

Answer: $12x^2 + 7x - 10$

Now we can go back and try problem 2-152 using a variety of methods.

Example 2: Multiply $(x+1)(2x^2-3)$ and simplify.

Solution: We can use F.O.I.L. here. Multiplying the **first** terms, we get $(x)(2x^2)=2x^3$. Multiplying the **outside** terms, we get $(x)(-3)=-3x$. Multiplying the **inside** terms, we get $(1)(2x^2)=2x^2$. Multiplying the **last** terms, we get $(1)(-3)=-3$. Adding these results, we get $2x^3-3x+2x^2-3$. Generally, answers are expressed in with terms in order of decreasing powers of x, so we can rearrange terms for our answer.

Answer: $2x^3+2x^2-3x-3$

Example 3: Multiply $(x+1)(x-2x^2+3)$ and simplify.

Solution: This is a good candidate for using a generic rectangle, as shown at right. After calculating the area of each individual cell, we find our expression by adding them together to get $x^3-2x^2+x^2+3x-2x+3$ and then combining like terms to get our simplified answer.

	x^2	$-2x$	$+3$
x	x^3	$-2x^2$	$3x$
$+1$	x^2	$-2x$	3

Answer: x^3-x^2+x+3

Example 4: Multiply $2(x+3)^2$ and simplify.

Solution: Here we write out the factors and use the distributive property, as shown in the solution at right.

$$2(x+3)(x+3)$$
$$=(2x+6)(x+3)$$
$$=(2x+6)(x)+(2x+6)(3)$$
$$=2x^2+6x+6x+18$$
$$=2x^2+12x+18$$

Answer: $2x^2+12x+18$

Example 5: Multiply $(x+1)(2x-3)^2$ and simplify.

Solution: Write out the factors. Multiply two of the factors together and then multiply that result by the third factor. This process is shown at right.

$$(x+1)(2x-3)(2x-3)$$
$$=(2x^2-x-3)(2x-3)$$
$$=4x^3-6x^2-2x^2+3x-6x+9$$
$$=4x^3-8x^2-3x+9$$

Answer: $4x^3-8x^2-3x+9$

Here are some more to try. Multiply and simplify.

a. $(2x+3)(x-7)$

b. $(4x-2)(3x+5)$

c. $(x-2)(x^2+3x+5)$

d. $(x+8)(x-12)$

e. $4(3x-5)^2$

f. $(2x+y)(2x-y)$

g. $(2x+3)^2$

h. $(5x-8)(2x+7)$

i. $(x+3)(x^2-4x+7)$

j. $(x+7)(x-11)$

k. $-8x^2(5x^2+7)$

l. $(2x+y)(x+1)^2$

Answers:

a. $2x^2-11x-21$

b. $12x^2+14x-10$

c. x^3+x^2-x-10

d. $x^2-4x-96$

e. $36x^2-120x+100$

f. $4x^2-y^2$

g. $4x^2+12x+9$

h. $10x^2+19x-56$

i. $x^3-x^2-5x+21$

j. $x^2-4x-77$

k. $-40x^4-56x^2$

l. $2x^3+4x^2+2x+x^2y+2xy+y$

Checkpoint Number 4

Problem 3-55

Simplifying Expressions with Positive Exponents

Answers to problem 3-55:

a. $16x^8y^4$ b. $-\dfrac{y^3}{12}$ c. $\dfrac{16x^7}{3y}$ d. $125x^5y^3$

There are three basic patterns for expressions with bases that are the same and positive exponents. They are summarized below with some examples.

1. $x^a x^b = x^{a+b}$ Examples: $x^3 x^4 = x^{3+4} = x^7$; $2^7 2^4 = 2^{11}$

2. $\dfrac{x^a}{x^b} = x^{a-b}$ Examples: $\dfrac{x^{10}}{x^4} = x^{10-4} = x^6$; $\dfrac{2^4}{2^7} = 2^{-3}$

3. $(x^a)^b = x^{ab}$ Examples: $(x^4)^3 = x^{4\cdot3} = x^{12}$; $(2x^3)^4 = 2^4 \cdot x^{12}$
$= 16x^{12}$

Now we can return to problem 3-55. Simplify each expression.

Example 1: Simplify $(2x^2y)^4$.

Solution: $(2x^2y)^4 = 2^4 x^{2\cdot4} y^{1\cdot4} = 16x^8y^4$

Example 2: Simplify $\dfrac{-3x^2y^3}{(-6x)^2}$.

Solution: $\dfrac{-3x^2y^3}{(-6x)^2} = \dfrac{-3x^2y^3}{36x^2} = -\dfrac{y^3}{12}$

Example 3: Simplify $\dfrac{(2x^2y)^4}{3xy^5}$.

Solution: $\dfrac{(2x^2y)^4}{3xy^5} = \dfrac{16x^8y^4}{3xy^5} = \dfrac{16x^7}{3y}$

Example 4: Simplify $5(5xy)^2(x^3y)$.

Solution: $5(5xy)^2(x^3y)$
$= 5(25x^2y^2)(x^3y)$
$= 125x^5y^3$

Here are some more to try. Use the properties of exponents to write each of the following expression in simpler form.

a. $3x^2 \cdot x$

b. $\dfrac{n^{12}}{n^3}$

c. $(x^3)^2$

d. $(-2x^2)(-2x)$

e. $\dfrac{-8x^6y^2}{-4xy}$

f. $(2x^3)^3$

g. $(10^3)^4$

h. $3^2 \cdot 3^5$

i. $\dfrac{10^5}{10^3}$

j. $(x^2y^3)(x^3y^4)$

k. $(x^3)^4$

l. $\dfrac{6x^2y^3}{2xy}$

m. $-3x^2(4x^3)$

n. $(2x^2)^3$

o. $(x^3y)^2(2x)^3$

p. $\dfrac{m^{16}y^{31}}{m^{12}y^{17}}$

q. $(6x^3z)^3$

r. $(3x^2)^2(6x^4)$

s. $(5x)^2(3y)^3$

t. $(3x^{11}z^5)^2$

u. $(2b)^5(3k^2)^2$

v. $(\dfrac{3x^2}{6x^5})^3$

w. $(6x^2)(24x^3)$

x. $\dfrac{6x^2y^3}{2xy}$

Answers:

a. $3x^3$

b. n^9

c. x^6

d. $4x^3$

e. $2x^5y$

f. $8x^9$

g. 10^{12}

h. 3^7

i. 10^2

j. x^5y^7

k. x^{12}

l. $3xy^2$

m. $-12x^5$

n. $8x^6$

o. $8x^{12}y^2$

p. m^4y^{14}

q. $216x^9z^3$

r. $54x^8$

s. $675x^2y^3$

t. $9x^{22}z^{10}$

u. $288b^5k^4$

v. $\dfrac{1}{8x^9}$

w. $144x^5$

x. $3xy^2$

Checkpoint Number 5
Problem 3-111
Factoring Quadratic Expressions

Answers to Problem 3-111:

    a. $(2x+1)(2x-1)$ b. $(2x+1)^2$

    c. $(2y+1)(y+2)$ d. $(3m+1)(m-2)$

Factoring quadratics means changing the expression into a product of factors or to find the dimensions of the generic rectangle that represents the quadratic. You can use diamond problems with generic rectangles or just guess and check with F.O.I.L. or the distributive property to factor. Here are some examples using diamonds and rectangles:

Example 1: Factor $x^2 + 6x + 8$.

Solution: Multiply the x^2-term by the constant term and place the result in the top of the diamond. This will be the product of the two sides. Then place the x-term at the bottom of the diamond. This will be the sum of the sides. Then find the two terms that multiply to give the top term in the diamond and add to give the bottom term in the diamond, in this case $2x$ and $6x$. This tells us how the x-term is split in the generic rectangle. Once we have the area of the generic rectangle we can find the dimensions by looking for common factors among rows and columns. Study the example below.

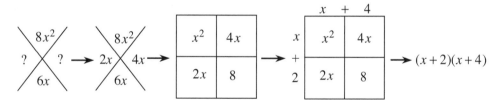

Example 2: Factor $5x^2 - 13x + 6$.

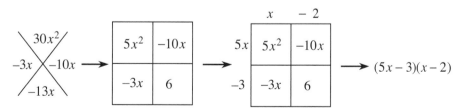

Now we can go back to problem 3-111. Factor each quadratic.

a.

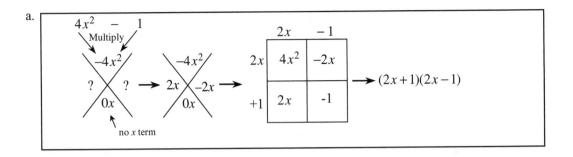

b.

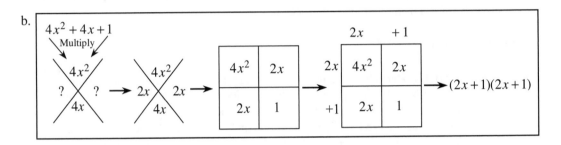

c.

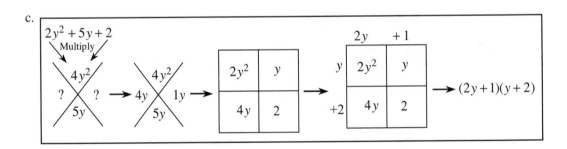

d.

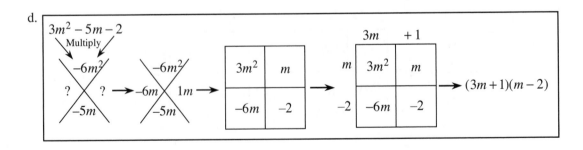

Here are some more to try. Factor each expression.

a. $2x^2 + 7x - 4$

b. $7x^2 + 13x - 2$

c. $3x^2 + 11x + 10$

d. $x^2 + 5x - 24$

e. $2x^2 + 5x - 7$

f. $3x^2 - 13x + 4$

g. $64x^2 + 16x + 1$

h. $5x^2 + 12x - 9$

i. $8x^2 + 24x + 10$

j. $6x^3 + 31x^2 + 5x$

Answers:

a. $(x + 4)(2x - 1)$

b. $(7x - 1)(x + 2)$

c. $(3x + 5)(x + 2)$

d. $(x + 8)(x - 3)$

e. $(2x + 7)(x - 1)$

f. $(3x - 1)(x - 4)$

g. $(8x + 1)^2$

h. $(5x - 3)(x + 3)$

i. $2(4x^2 + 12x + 5) = 2(2x + 1)(2x + 5)$

j. $x(6x^2 + 31x + 5) = x(6x + 1)(x + 5)$

Checkpoint Number 6
Problem 4-29
Writing the Equation of a Line Given Two Points.

Answers to problem 4-29:

a. $y = -x + 3$

b. $y = -\frac{3}{4}x + 12$

c. $y = \frac{1}{3}x - \frac{5}{3}$

The equation of a line can be written in the form $y = mx + b$, where m represents the slope and b represents the y-intercept. One way to find the equation is to calculate the slope and then solve, substitute in into the general equation for m, and then solve for b, the y-intercept. Another method is to use the two points to write two equations involving m and b and then solve the system. Below is an example of each method.

Example 1: Find an equation of the line that passes through the points (6, 5) and (9, 2).

Solution 1: Using the points we make a generic slope triangle, as shown at right, and find the slope to be $m = -\frac{3}{3} = -1$. Substituting -1 for m in the general equation gives $y = -1x + b$.

We can substitute any point we know that is on the line for x and y to solve for b. Substituting the point (9, 2), we get $2 = -1(9) + b$. Solving for b gives $2 = -9 + b$. Therefore $b = 11$.

Solution 2: Substituting both points given into the general equation for x and y gives the system at right. Subtracting the second equation from the first gives $3 = -3m$, so $m = -1$. Now we can find b by substituting m into either equation in our system. Using the first equation, $5 = 6(-1) + b$. Solving for b gives $b = 11$.

$$5 = 6m + b$$
$$2 = 9m + b$$

Answer: The equation of the line is $y = -x + 11$.

Now we can return to the problem 4-29.

Example 2: Write an equation for the line that passes through points (–1, 4) and (2, 1).

Solution: Using the first method described above, we make a generic slope triangle, shown at right, and find the slope to be $m = -\frac{3}{3} = -1$. Substituting this value into the general equation, we get $y = -1x + b$. We then substitute -1 for x and 4 for y (from the first point given – we could also have used the second), to get $4 = -1(-1) + b$. Solving this for b, we get $b = 3$.

Answer: The equation of the line is $y = -x + 3$.

Example 3: Find an equation for the line that passes through points (–8, 18) and (4, 9).

Solution: Using the second method described above, we substitute the x- and y-values from both of the given points into the general equation $y = mx + b$ to get the system shown at right. Multiplying the second equation by two and then adding it to the first gives $36 = 3b$, which implies that $b = 12$. We can now find m by substituting $b = 12$ into either equation in our system. Choosing the second equation, we get $9 = 4m + 12$, which gives $4m = -3$. Therefore $m = -\frac{3}{4}$.

$$18 = -8m + b$$
$$9 = 4m + b$$

Answer: The equation of the line is $y = -\frac{3}{4}x + 12$.

Example 4: Find an equation of the line that passes through points $(-1, -2)$ and $(11, 2)$.

Solution: This time, we make a generic triangle without the axes. The lengths of each leg of the triangle can be calculated by subtracting the x- and y-values of the two points. We can see that the difference in y-values is 4 and the differences in x-values is 12. Thus, the slope is $\frac{4}{12} = \frac{1}{3}$. In order to find b,

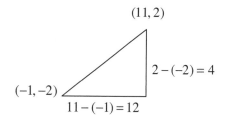

we substitute this value into our general equation, which yields $y = \frac{1}{3}x + b$. Substituting in the values of the second point gives $2 = \frac{1}{3} \cdot 11 + b$, which solved to give $b = 2 - \frac{11}{3} = -\frac{5}{3}$.

Answer: The equation of the line is $y = \frac{1}{3}x - \frac{5}{3}$.

Here are some more to try. Find the equation of the line through the given points.

a. (2, 3) and (1, 2) b. (–3, –5) and (–1, 0)

c. (4, 2) and (8, –1) d. (1, 3) and (5, 7)

e. (0, 4) and (–1, –5) f. (–3, 2) and (2, -3)

g. (4, 2) and (–1, –2) h. (3, 1) and (–2, –4)

i. (4, 1) and (4, 10)

Answers:

a. $y = x + 1$ b. $y = \frac{5}{2}x + \frac{5}{2}$ c. $y = -\frac{3}{4}x + 5$

d. $y = x + 2$ e. $y = 9x + 4$ f. $y = -x - 1$

g. $y = \frac{4}{5}x - \frac{6}{5}$ h. $y = x - 2$ i. $x = 4$

Checkpoint Number 7

Problem 4-80

Finding the x- and y-intercepts of a Quadratic Function

Answers to Problem 4-80: y-intercept: $(0, -17)$, x-intercepts: $(-2 + \sqrt{21}, 0)$ and $(-2 - \sqrt{21}, 0)$.

The y-intercepts of an equation are the points at which the graph crosses the y-axis. To find the y-intercept of an equation, substitute $x = 0$ into the equation and solve for y. For example:

> Find the y-intercept for the equation $y = x^2 + 4x - 12$.
> If $x = 0$, then $y = (0)^2 + 4(0) - 12 = -12$. The y-intercept is $(0, 12)$.

The x-intercepts of an equation are the points at which the graph crosses the x-axis. To find the x-intercepts of an equation, substitute $y = 0$ into the equation and solve for x. For a quadratic, you can do this by factoring and using the Zero Product Property or by using the Quadratic Formula, as well as other methods. Here are two examples:

Example 1: Find the x-intercepts of the graph of the equation $y = x^2 + 4x - 12$.

Solution: If $y = 0$, then:

$$0 = x^2 + 4x - 12$$

By factoring and using the Zero Product Property:

$$0 = (x + 6)(x - 2)$$
$$x + 6 = 0 \quad \text{or} \quad x - 2 = 0$$
$$x = -6 \quad \text{or} \quad x = 2$$

Answers: The x-intercepts are (–6, 0) and (2, 0).

Example 2: Find the x-intercepts of the graph of the equation $y = 2x^2 - 3x - 3$.

Solution: If $y = 0$, then:

$$0 = 2x^2 - 3x - 3$$

Since we cannot factor the trinomial we use the Quadratic Formula to solve for x.

If $ax^2 + bx + c = 0$ then:

$$x = \frac{-b \pm \sqrt{b^2 - 4ac}}{2a} .$$

Substitute $a = 2$, $b = -3$, $c = -3$.

$$x = \frac{-(-3) \pm \sqrt{(-3)^2 - 4(2)(-3)}}{2(2)}$$

Simplify.

$$x = \frac{3 \pm \sqrt{9 + 24}}{4} = \frac{3 \pm \sqrt{33}}{4}$$

Find $\sqrt{33}$ approximately:

$$\approx \frac{3 \pm 5.745}{4} , \text{ so } \frac{3 + 5.745}{4} \text{ and } \frac{3 - 5.745}{4}$$

Answers: Simplify the fractions and the x-intercepts are approximately $(2.19, 0)$ and $(-0.69, 0)$.
They can be expressed in exact form as $(\frac{3 + \sqrt{33}}{4}, 0)$ and $(\frac{3 - \sqrt{33}}{4}, 0)$.

Now we can find the x- and y-intercepts for any quadratic equation.

Example 3: Find the x and y intercepts of the graph of $y = x^2 + 4x - 17$.

Solution: To find the y-intercept, let $x = 0$ so $y = (0)^2 + 4(0) - 17 = -17$.
To find the x-intercept, let $y = 0$ so $0 = x^2 + 4x - 17$.
Since we cannot factor we use the Quadratic Formula with $a = 1$, $b = 4$ and $c = -17$.

$$x = \frac{-4 \pm \sqrt{4^2 - 4(1)(-17)}}{2(1)} = \frac{-4 \pm \sqrt{16 + 68}}{2} = \frac{-4 \pm \sqrt{84}}{2} = \frac{-4 \pm 2\sqrt{21}}{2} = -2 \pm \sqrt{21}$$

Answers: The y-intercept is $(0, -17)$. The x-intercepts are $(-2 \pm \sqrt{21}, 0)$, or approximately
$(2.58, 0)$ and $(-6.58, 0)$.

Here are some more to try. Find the x and y intercepts for the graphs of each equation.

a. $y = 2x^2 - 9x - 35$ b. $y = 2x^2 - 11x + 5$

c. $3x^2 + 2 + 7x = y$ d. $8x^2 + 10x + 3 = y$

e. $y + 2 = x^2 - 5x$ f. $(x - 3)(x + 4) - 7x = y$

g. $-4x^2 + 8x + 3 = y$ h. $0.009x^2 - 0.86x + 2 = y$

i. $y = 2x^3 - 50x$ j. $y = 3x^2 + 4x$

Answers:

a. $(7, 0)$, $(-\frac{5}{2}, 0)$, and $(0, -35)$ b. $(5, 0)$, $(\frac{1}{2}, 0)$, and $(0, 5)$

c. $(-\frac{1}{3}, 0)$, $(-2, 0)$, and $(0, 2)$ d. $(-\frac{3}{4}, 0)$, $(-\frac{1}{2}, 0)$, and $(0, 3)$

e. $(\frac{5 \pm \sqrt{33}}{2}, 0)$ or $(\approx 5.37, 0)$, $(\approx -0.37, 0)$, and $(0, -2)$

f. $(\frac{-8 \pm \sqrt{84}}{2}, 0)$ or $(\approx 7.58, 0)$, $(\approx -1.58, 0)$, and $(0, -12)$

g: $(\frac{-8 \pm \sqrt{112}}{-8}, 0)$ or $(\approx -0.32, 0)$, $(\approx 2.32, 0)$, and $(0, 3)$

h. $(\frac{0.86 \pm \sqrt{0.6676}}{0.018}, 0)$ or $(\approx 2.39, 0)$, $(\approx 93.17, 0)$, and $(0, 2)$

i. $(0, 0)$, $(5, 0)$, $(-5, 0)$, and $(0, 0)$ j. $(0, 0)$, $(-\frac{4}{3}, 0)$, and $(0, 0)$

Checkpoint Number 8
Problem 4-122
Finding the Slope of a Line through Two Points
and the Distance Between the Points

Answers to problem 4-122:

    a.   The slope is 1 and the distance is $\sqrt{32} = 4\sqrt{2} \approx 5.66$ units.

    b.   The slope is $\frac{1}{2}$ and the distance is $\sqrt{45} = 3\sqrt{5} \approx 6.71$ units.

    c.   The slope is $\frac{37}{28}$ and the distance is $\sqrt{2153} \approx 46.40$ units.

    d.   The slope is 1 and the distance is $\sqrt{1250} = 25\sqrt{2} \approx 35.36$ units.

A generic right triangle is a useful diagram to help compute either the slope of the line connecting two points or the distance between the points. The slope is the ratio of the length of the vertical leg of the triangle over the length of the horizontal leg. (Remember to check whether the slope should be negative or positive.) The distance between the points is the length of the hypotenuse, which can be found using the Pythagorean theorem. Here are two examples.

Example 1: **Find the slope of the line that passes through (–2, 3) and (3, 5). Also, find the distance between the points.**

Solution: Using an accurate graph, the length of the legs can be seen as 2 and 5. Notice that the line slopes in the positive direction. That is, a point moving along this line from left to right moves upward.

$$\text{slope} = \frac{\textit{Vertical Change}}{\textit{Horizontal Change}} = \frac{2}{5}$$

The distance d can be found by $d^2 = 2^2 + 5^2 = 29$. Solving for d, we find $d = \sqrt{29} \approx 5.39$.

Find the slope and the length of the line segment that connects (–7, 20) and (3, –5).

Solution: For this problem, we sketch a generic graph and draw in a triangle. By looking at the change in y-values (from 20 to – 5), we can see that the vertical change is 25. By looking at the change in x-values (from –7 to 3), we can see that the horizontal change is 10. We can also see that the line slopes in the negative direction. That is, a point moving along this line from left to right moves downward.

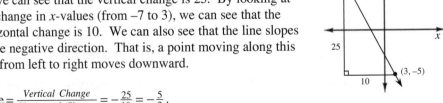

$$\text{slope} = \frac{\textit{Vertical Change}}{\textit{Horizontal Change}} = -\frac{25}{10} = -\frac{5}{2}.$$

The length of the line segment is the same as the distance between the points. It can be found by $d^2 = 25^2 + 10^2 = 725$. Solving for d, we find $d = \sqrt{729} \approx 26.92$.

The following examples are from problem 4-122. Use a generic rectangle to find the slope of the line through the two given points and then find the distance between the two points.

Example 3: **Find the slope of the line through $(0,0)$ and $(4,4)$ and then find the distance between the points.**

Solution: We start by drawing the graph at right. Then we can see that the vertical change is 4 and the horizontal change is also 4. Thus, the slope is $\frac{4}{4} = 1$. Applying the Pythagorean theorem, the distance between the points is
$d = \sqrt{4^2 + 4^2} = \sqrt{32} = 4\sqrt{2} \approx 5.66$.

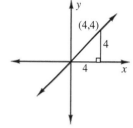

Answer: The slope is 1 and the distance is $\sqrt{32} = 4\sqrt{2} \approx 5.66$ units.

Example 4: **Find the slope of the line through $(-2,4)$ and $(4,7)$ and then find the distance between the points.**

Solution: We start by drawing the graph at right. We can calculate the horizontal change by subtracting 4 from 7, resulting in 3. We can calculate the horizontal change by subtracting -2 from 4, resulting in 6. Thus the slope is $\frac{3}{6} = \frac{1}{2}$. Applying the Pythagorean theorem, the distance between the points is $d = \sqrt{6^2 + 3^2} = \sqrt{45} \approx 6.71$.

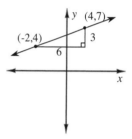

Answer: The slope is $\frac{1}{2}$ and the distance is $\sqrt{45} = 3\sqrt{5} \approx 6.71$ units.

Example 5: **Find the slope of the line through $(12,18)$ and $(-16,-19)$ and then find the distance between the points.**

Solution: Sometimes people prefer to use formulas that represent the diagram. Using the points $(12, 18)$ and $(-16, -19)$:

slope $= \frac{y_2 - y_1}{x_2 - x_1} = \frac{-16 - 12}{-19 - 18} = \frac{-28}{-37} = \frac{28}{37}$

distance $= \sqrt{(x_2 - x_1)^2 + (y_2 - y_1)^2} = \sqrt{(-16 - 12)^2 + (-19 - 18)^2}$
$= \sqrt{(-28)^2 + (-37)^2} = \sqrt{2153} \approx 46.4$

$y_2 - y_1$ and $x_2 - x_1$ represent the lengths of the vertical and horizontal legs respectively.

Answer: The slope is $\frac{28}{37}$ and the distance is approximately $\sqrt{2153} \approx 46.4$ units.

Example 6: **Find the slope of the line through (–12, 5) and (6, –2) and then find the distance between the points.**

Solution: In this case, we apply the formulas again.

slope $\quad = \frac{y_2 - y_1}{x_2 - x_1} = \frac{-2-5}{6-(-12)} = \frac{-7}{18}$

distance $\quad = \sqrt{(x_2 - x_1)^2 + (y_2 - y_1)^2}$

$\quad\quad\quad = \sqrt{(6-(-12))^2 + (-2-5)^2} = \sqrt{18^2 + (-7)^2} = \sqrt{373} \approx 19.31$

Answer: The slopes is $-\frac{7}{18}$ and the distance is $\sqrt{373} \approx 19.31$ units.

Here are some more to try. Find the slope of the line through the two given points and then find the distance between the two points.

a.	(1, 2) and (4, 5)	b.	(7, 3) and (5, 4)
c.	(–6, 8) and (–4, 5)	d.	(5, 0) and (0, 1)
e.	(10, 2) and (2, 24)	f.	(–6, 5) and (8, –3)
g.	(–3, 5) and (2, 12)	h.	(–6, –3) and (2, 10)
i.	(–15, 39) and (29, –2)		

Answers:

a.	$m = 1, \ d = \sqrt{18}$	b.	$m = -\frac{1}{2}, \ d = \sqrt{5}$
c.	$m = -\frac{3}{2}, \ d = \sqrt{13}$	d.	$m = -\frac{1}{5}, \ d = \sqrt{26}$
e.	$m = -\frac{11}{4}, \ d = \sqrt{548}$	f.	$m = -\frac{4}{7}, \ d = \sqrt{260}$
g.	$m = \frac{7}{5}, \ d = \sqrt{74}$	h.	$m = \frac{13}{8}, \ d = \sqrt{233}$
i.	$m = -\frac{41}{44}, \ d = \sqrt{3617}$		

Checkpoint Number 9

5-39

Using Function Notation and Identifying the Domain and Range

Answers to problem 5-39:

    Domain: all real numbers; Range: $y \geq 0$;

    a. $g(-5) = 8$ b. $g(a+1) = 2a^2 + 16a + 32$

    c. $x = 1$ or $x = -7$ d. $x = -3$

We should first review some vocabulary and notation.

An equation is called a **function** if there exists *no more than one* output for each input. If an equation has two or more outputs for a single input value, it is not a function. The set of possible inputs of a function is called the **domain**, while the set of all possible outputs of a function is called the **range**.

Functions are often given names, most commonly "*f*," "*g*," or "*h*." The notation $f(x)$ represents the output of a function, named *f*, when *x* is the input. It is pronounced "*f* of *x*." The notation $g(2)$, pronounced "*g* of 2," represents the output of function *g* when $x = 2$.

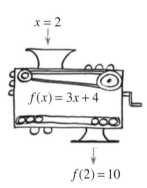

Similarly, the function $y = 3x + 4$ and $f(x) = 3x + 4$ represent the *same function*. Notice that this notation is interchangeable, that is $y = f(x)$. In some textbooks, $3x + 4$ is called the **rule** of the function. The graph of $f(x) = 3x + 4$ is a line extending forever in both the *x* (horizontal) and the *y* (vertical) directions, so the domain and range of $f(x) = 3x + 4$ are all real numbers.

Examples 1 through 3: For each function below, give the domain and range. Then calculate $f(2)$ and solve $f(x) = 3$.

Example 1: $f(x) = |x - 1| - 2$

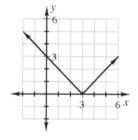

Solution: We start by graphing the function, as shown at right. Since we can use any real number for *x* in this equation, the domain is all real numbers. The smallest possible result for y is –2, so the range is $y \geq -2$. By looking at the graph or substituting $x = 2$ into the equation, $f(2) = |2 - 1| - 2 = -1$. To solve $f(x) = 3$, find the points where the horizontal line $y = 3$ intersects the graph or solve the equation $3 = |x - 1| - 2$, which yields $x = -4$ or $x = 6$.

Example 2: $f(x)$ **is given by the graph below.**

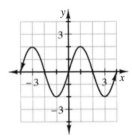

The arrows indicate that the graph continues indefinitely right and left and we see no disruption in the smooth function, so the domain is all real numbers. All of the y-values fall between -2 and 2, so the range is $-2 \le y \le 2$. We can see from the graph that when $x = 2$, the value of the function appears to be 0, or $f(2) \approx 0$. Since $-2 \le y \le 2$, the value of the function never gets as high as 3, so $f(x) = 3$ has no solution.

Example 3: $f(x) = \sqrt{x+3}$

Solution: Again, we start by making a graph of the function, which is shown at right. Since the square root of a negative number does not exist, we can only use x-values of -3 or larger. Thus, the domain is $x \ge -3$. We can see from the graph and the equation that the smallest possible y-value is zero, so the range is $y \ge 0$. Looking at the graph gives an approximate answer when $x = 2$ of $y \approx 2.25$. Or, by substituting $x = 2$ into the equation, we get $f(2) = \sqrt{2+3} = \sqrt{5}$. To solve $f(x) = 3$, find the point where $y = 3$ intersects the graph or solve $3 = \sqrt{x+3}$, which gives $x = 6$.

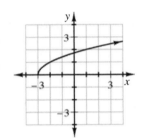

Now we can return to problem 5-39.

Example 4: Given $g(x) = 2(x+3)^2$, **state the domain and range, calculate** $g(-5)$ **and** $g(a+1)$, **and then find the value of** x **when** $g(x) = 32$ **and when** $g(x) = 0$.

Solution: The graph is a parabola opening upward with vertex $(-3,0)$, as shown at right. Thus, the domain is all real numbers and the range is $y \ge 0$.

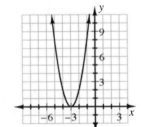

$$g(-5) = -2(-5+3) = 2(-2)^2 = 8$$

$$g(a+1) = 2(a+1+3)^2 = 2(a+4)^2$$
$$= 2(a^2 + 8a + 16) = 2a^2 + 16a + 32$$

If $g(x) = 32$, then $32 = 2(x+3)^2$. Dividing both sides by 2, we get $16 = (x+3)^2$. Taking the square root of both sides gives $\pm 4 = x+3$, which leads to the values $x = 1$ or -7.

If $g(x) = 0$, then $0 = 2(x+3)^2$. Diving both sides by two or applying the Zero Product Property gives $0 = (x+3)^2$ and then $0 = x+3$. Thus $x = -3$.

Here are some more to try.

For each graph given in parts (a) through (c), describe the domain and range.

a. 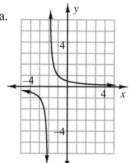   b. 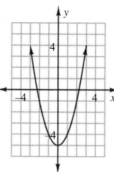   c.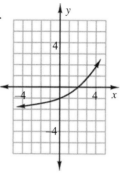

d.   If $f(x) = 3 - x^2$, calculate $f(5)$ and $f(3a)$.

e.   If $g(x) = 5 - 3x^2$, calculate $g(-2)$ and $g(a+2)$.

f.   If $f(x) = \frac{x+3}{2x-5}$, calculate $f(2)$ and $f(2.5)$.

g.   If $f(x) = x^2 + 5x + 6$, solve $f(x) = 0$.

h.   If $g(x) = 3(x-5)^2$, solve $g(x) = 27$.

i.   If $f(x) = (x+2)^2$, solve $f(x) = 27$.

Answers:

a.   **Domain: $x \neq -2$, Range: $y \neq 0$**

b.   **Domain: all real numbers, Range: $y \geq -5$**

c.   **Domain: all real numbers, Range: $y > -2$**

d. $f(5) = 22$, $f(3a) = 3 - 9a^2$

e. $g(-2) = -7$, $g(a+2) = -3a^2 - 12a - 7$

f: $f(2) = -5$, **not possible**

g. $x = -2$ **or** $x = -3$

h. $x = 8$ **or** $x = 2$

i. $x = -2 \pm \sqrt{27}$

Checkpoint Number 10

Problem 5-84

Solving for One Variable in an Equation with Two or More Variables

Answers to Problem 5-84:

a. $y = \frac{1}{3}x - 4$

b. $y = \frac{6}{5}x - \frac{1}{5}$

c. $y = (x+1)^2 + 4$

d. $y = x^2 + 4x$

When we want to solve for one variable in an equation with two or more variables it usually helps to start by simplifying, such as removing parentheses and fractions. Next isolate the desired variable in the same way as you solve an equation with only one variable. Here are two examples.

Example 1: Solve $\frac{x-3y}{4} + 2(x+1) = 7$ **for** y.

Solution: First multiply all terms by 4 to remove the fraction and then simplify, as shown at right. Then, to isolate y, we subtract $9x$ from both sides to get $-3y = -9x + 20$. Dividing both sides by -3 results in $y = 3x - \frac{20}{3}$.

$$(4)\frac{x-3y}{4} + 4(2)(x+1) = 4(7)$$
$$x - 3y + 8x + 8 = 28$$
$$9x - 3y = 20$$

Answer: $y = 3x - \frac{20}{3}$

Example 2: Solve $x + 2\sqrt{y+1} = 3x + 4$ **for** y.

First, we isolate the radical by subtracting x from both sides to get $2\sqrt{1+y} = 2x + 4$ and then dividing both sides by 2 to get $\sqrt{1+y} = x + 2$. Then, we remove the radical by squaring both sides, as shown at right. Lastly, we isolate y by subtracting 1 from both sides of the equation.

$$(\sqrt{y+1})^2 = (x+2)^2$$
$$y + 1 = (x+2)(x+2)$$
$$y + 1 = x^2 + 4x + 4$$

Answer: $y = x^2 + 4x + 3$

For each of the following examples (from Problem 5-84), we will solve the equation for y.

Example 3: $x - 3(y+2) = 6$

$$x - 3y - 6 = 6$$
$$x - 3y = 12$$
$$-3y = -x + 12$$
$$y = \frac{-x+12}{-3} \text{ or } y = \frac{1}{3}x - 4$$

Example 4: $\frac{6x-1}{y} - 3 = 2$

$$\frac{6x-1}{y} = 5$$
$$(y)\frac{6x-1}{y} = 5(y)$$
$$6x - 1 = 5y$$
$$y = \frac{6x-1}{5} \text{ or } y = \frac{6}{5}x - \frac{1}{5}$$

Example 5: $\sqrt{y-4} = x+1$

$(\sqrt{y-4})^2 = (x+1)^2$

$y-4 = (x+1)^2$

$y = (x+1)^2 + 4$ or $x^2 + 2x + 5$

Example 6: $\sqrt{y+4} = x+2$

$(\sqrt{y+4})^2 = (x+2)^2$

$y+4 = x^2 + 4x + 4$

$y = x^2 + 4x$

Here are some more to try. Solve each equation for y.

a. $2x - 5y = 7$

b. $2(x+y)+1 = x-4$

c. $4(x-y)+12 = 2x-4$

d. $x = \frac{1}{5}y - 2$

e. $x = y^2 + 1$

f. $\frac{5x+2}{y} - 1 = 5$

g. $\sqrt{y+3} = x-2$

h. $(y+2)^2 = x^2 + 9$

i. $\frac{x+2}{4} + \frac{4-y}{2} = 3$

j. $\sqrt{2y+1} = x+3$

k. $x = \frac{2}{4-y}$

l. $x = \frac{y+1}{y-1}$

Answers:

a. $y = \frac{2}{5}x - \frac{7}{5}$

b. $y = -\frac{1}{2}x - \frac{5}{2}$

c. $y = \frac{1}{2}x + 4$

d. $y = 5x + 10$

e. $y = \pm\sqrt{x-1}$

f. $y = \frac{5}{6}x + \frac{1}{3}$

g. $y = x^2 - 4x + 1$

h. $y = \pm\sqrt{x^2 + 9} - 2$

i. $y = \frac{1}{2}x - 1$

j. $y = \frac{1}{2}x^2 + 3x + 4$

    or $y = \frac{1}{2}(x+4)(x+2)$

k. $y = \frac{4x-2}{x}$ or $y = 4 - \frac{2}{x}$

l. $y = \frac{x+1}{x-1}$

Checkpoint Number 11

Problem 6-48

Integral and Rational Exponents

Answers to problem 6-48:

a. $x^{1/5}$
b. x^{-3}
c. $x^{2/3}$
d. $x^{-1/2}$

The following properties are useful for simplifying expressions with integral (positive or negative whole numbers) or rational (fractional) exponents.

$x^0 = 1$ Examples: $2^0 = 1$, $(-3)^0 = 1$, $(\frac{1}{4})^0 = 1$

(Note that 0^0 is undefined.)

$x^{-n} = \frac{1}{x^n}$ Examples: $x^{-3} = \frac{1}{x^3}$, $y^{-4} = \frac{1}{y^4}$, $4^{-2} = \frac{1}{4^2} = \frac{1}{16}$

$\frac{1}{x^{-n}} = x^n$ Examples: $\frac{1}{x^{-5}} = x^5$, $\frac{1}{x^{-2}} = x^2$, $\frac{1}{3^{-2}} = 3^2 = 9$

$x^{a/b} = (x^a)^{1/b} = (\sqrt[b]{x})^a$ Examples: $5^{1/2} = \sqrt{5}$

or : $16^{3/4} = (\sqrt[4]{16})^3 = 2^3 = 8$

$x^{a/b} = (x^{1/b})^a = (\sqrt[b]{x})^a$ $4^{2/3} = \sqrt[3]{4^2} = \sqrt[3]{16} = 2\sqrt[3]{2}$

We can apply these patterns to problem 6-48, which asked us to rewrite each of the following expressions as a power of x.

a. Using the fourth property above, $\sqrt[5]{x} = x^{1/5}$.

b. Using the second property above, $\frac{1}{x^3} = x^{-3}$.

c. Using the fourth property above, $\sqrt[3]{x^2} = x^{2/3}$.

d. Using the second and fourth properties above, $\frac{1}{\sqrt{x}} = \frac{1}{x^{1/2}} = x^{-1/2}$.

Here are some exercises to try. Use integral or rational exponents to rewrite each expression without negative or fractional exponents and simplify. You should not need a calculator for any of these.

a. x^{-5} b. m^0 c. 4^{-1} d. y^{-3}

e. 5^{-2} f. 5^0 g. y^{-7} h. $(x^3y^4)^{-2}$

i. $x^{-1}y^{-8}$ j. $x^{-4}y^{-2}(x^{-3}y^{-6})^0$ k. $25^{1/2}$

l. $25^{-1/2}$ m. $2^{1/2}$ n. $(\frac{1}{27})^{-1/3}$ o. $x^{3/2}$

p. $9^{3/2}$ q. $(x^3y^6)^{1/3}$ r. $16^{-3/4}$ s. $(m^2)^{-3/2}$

t. $(x^3y^6)^{1/2}$ u. $(9x^3y^6)^{-2}$

Answers:

a. $\frac{1}{x^5}$ b. 1 c. $\frac{1}{4}$ d. $\frac{1}{y^3}$

e. $\frac{1}{25}$ f. 1 g. $\frac{1}{y^7}$ h. $\frac{1}{x^6y^8}$

i. $\frac{1}{xy^8}$ j. $\frac{1}{x^4y^2}$ k. 5 l. $\frac{1}{5}$

m. $\sqrt{2}$ n. 3 o. $\sqrt{x^3} = x\sqrt{x}$ p. 27

q. xy^2 r. $\frac{1}{8}$ s. $\frac{1}{m^3}$ t. $xy^3\sqrt{x}$

u. $\frac{1}{81x^6y^{12}}$

Answer graph to problem 7-73, part (a):

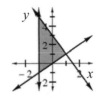

Graphing inequalities is very similar to graphing equations. First you graph the line that you would graph if the inequality were an equation. You must determine if the line is solid (included) or dashed (not included) and which side of the line should be shaded. Here are two examples of graphing a system of inequalities.

Example 1: On graph paper, graph and shade the solution region for the systems of inequalities at right.

$$y \le \tfrac{2}{5}x$$
$$y > 5 - x$$

Solution: We will address the inequality $y \le \tfrac{2}{5}x$ first. We start by graphing the equation $y = \tfrac{2}{5}x$. We can graph it using the slope, $\tfrac{2}{5}$, and y-intercept, $(0, 0)$. Since the inequality contains the solutions to the equation (the symbol is $\le$, not $<$), we draw the graph as a solid, rather than dashed, line.

Test point: $(0, 1)$

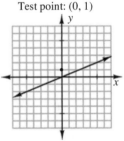

Once it is graphed, we notice that the line divides the grid into two regions. We must determine which region contains the solutions to the inequality $y \le \tfrac{2}{5}x$. We choose a point in either region and test whether or not it makes the original inequality true. Using $(0, 1)$ as the test point:

$$1 \overset{?}{\le} \tfrac{2}{5}(0) \quad \text{FALSE!}$$

Since $(0, 1)$ makes the inequality false, we can assume that all points above the line make the inequality false, and that the points below the line must make it true. Therefore, we shade the area below the line to show that all points in this region are solutions.

Test point: $(0, 1)$

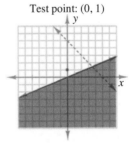

Next we do the same thing for the second inequality. First we graph the equation on the same set of axes. The slope is -1 and the y-intercept is $(0, 5)$. This inequality does not contain the solutions to the equation (the symbol is $>$, and not $\ge$). We show this by drawing a dashed, rather than solid, line. This line has also divided the grid into two regions and we must choose a point as to test to determine which region contains the solutions. Again, using $(0, 1)$ as the test point:

$$1 \overset{?}{>} 5 - 0 \quad \text{FALSE!}$$

Example continues on next page. →

Continued from previous page.

Since our test point made the inequality false, we can conclude that point on the opposite side of this line would make the inequality true. So for the second inequality we shade above the line and to the right.

Answer: The region where the shading overlaps contains solutions to both inequalities in this system. We indicate this by shading this region more darkly, as in the graph at right.

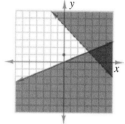

Now we can return to problem 7-73.

Example 2: Graph the system of inequalities $y \leq -2x + 3$, $y \geq x$, and $x \geq -1$.

Solution: Start by looking at the equation of the line that marks the edge of each inequality. The first has slope -2 and y-intercept $(0, 3)$. Checking $(0, 1)$ gives a true statement so we shade below the solid line. The second line has slope 1 and y-intercept $(0, 0)$. Again checking $(0, 1)$ gives a true statement, so we shade above the solid line. The third is a vertical line at $x = -1$. Checking a point tells us to shade the right side. The overlapping shading is a triangle with vertices $(-1, 5)$, $(1, 1)$, and $(-1, -1)$.

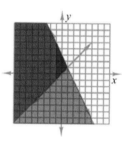

Here are a few more to try. Graph and shade the solution region for each system of inequalities below.

a. $y \leq -x + 2$

   $y \leq 3x - 6$

b. $y \geq \frac{2}{3}x + 4$

   $y \leq \frac{7}{12}x + 5$

c. $x < 3$

   $y \geq -2$

d. $y \leq 4x + 16$

   $y \geq -\frac{4}{3}x - 4$

Answers:

a.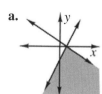

b.

c.

d.

Checkpoint Number 13
Problem 7-145
Solving Rational Equations

Answers to problem 7-145:

a. $x = \pm 2\sqrt{3}$

b. $x = 2$

c. $x = \frac{2}{9}$

d. $x = \frac{-1 \pm \sqrt{13}}{6} \approx 0.434$ or -0.768

To solve rational equations (equations with fractions) it is usually best to first multiply everything by the common denominator to remove the fractions, a method known as **fraction busters**. After you have done this, you can solve the equation using your usual strategies. Following are a few examples.

Example 1: Solve $\frac{24}{x+1} = \frac{16}{1}$.

Solution: The common denominator in this case is $(x+1)$. Multiplying both sides of the equation by $(x+1)$ removes all fractions from the equation. You can then simplify and solve for x. This process is demonstrated at right.

$$(x+1)(\tfrac{24}{x+1}) = (x+1)(\tfrac{16}{1})$$
$$24 = 16(x+1)$$
$$24 = 16x + 16$$
$$8 = 16x$$
$$x = \tfrac{1}{2}$$

Answer: $x = \frac{1}{2}$

Example 2: Solve $\frac{5}{2x} + \frac{1}{6} = 8$.

Solution: Again, we multiply both sides of the equation by the common denominator, which, in this case, is $6x$. We must be careful to remember to distribute so that we multiply each term on both sides of the equation by $6x$. Then we simplify and solve, as shown at right.

$$6x(\tfrac{5}{2x} + \tfrac{1}{6}) = 6x(8)$$
$$6x \cdot \tfrac{5}{2x} + 6x \cdot \tfrac{1}{6} = 48x$$
$$15 + x = 48x$$
$$15 = 47x$$
$$x = \tfrac{15}{47}$$

Answer: $x = \frac{15}{47}$

Now we can return to problem 7-145. Solve each of the following rational equations.

Example 3: $\frac{x}{3} = \frac{4}{x}$

$$3x(\tfrac{x}{3}) = 3x(\tfrac{4}{x})$$
$$x^2 = 12$$
$$x = \pm\sqrt{12} = \pm 2\sqrt{3}$$
$$x \approx \pm 3.46$$

Example 4: $\frac{x}{x-1} = \frac{4}{x}$

$$x(x-1)(\tfrac{x}{x-1}) = x(x-1)(\tfrac{4}{x})$$
$$x^2 = 4(x-1)$$
$$x^2 - 4x + 4 = 0$$
$$(x-2)(x-2) = 0$$
$$x = 2$$

Example 5: $\frac{1}{x}+\frac{1}{3x}=6$

$$3x(\frac{1}{x}+\frac{1}{3x})=3x(6)$$
$$3x(\frac{1}{x})+3x(\frac{1}{3x})=18x$$
$$3+1=18x$$
$$x=\frac{2}{9}$$

Example 6: $\frac{1}{x}+\frac{1}{x+1}=3$

$$x(x+1)(\frac{1}{x}+\frac{1}{x+1})=x(x+1)(3)$$
$$x(x+1)(\frac{1}{x})+x(x+1)(\frac{1}{x+1})=x(x+1)(3)$$
$$x+1+x=3x^2+3x$$
$$0=3x^2+x-1$$
Using the Quadratic Formula,
$$x\approx-0.434,\ -0.768$$

Here are some more to try. Solve each of the following rational equations.

a. $\frac{3x}{5}=\frac{x-2}{4}$

b. $\frac{4x-1}{x}=3x$

c. $\frac{2x}{5}-\frac{1}{3}=\frac{137}{3}$

d. $\frac{4x-1}{x+1}=x-1$

e. $\frac{x}{3}=x+4$

f. $\frac{x-1}{5}=\frac{3}{x+1}$

g. $\frac{x+6}{3}=x$

h. $\frac{2x+3}{6}+\frac{1}{2}=\frac{x}{2}$

i. $\frac{3}{x}+\frac{5}{x-7}=-2$

j. $\frac{2x+3}{4}-\frac{x-7}{6}=\frac{2x-3}{12}$

Answers:

a. $x=-\frac{10}{7}$

b. $x=\frac{1}{3},1$

c. $x=115$

d. $x=0,4$

e. $x=-6$

f. $x=\pm4$

g. $x=3$

h. $x=6$

i. $x=\frac{3\pm\sqrt{51}}{2}$

j. $x=-13$

✓ Checkpoint Number 14

Problem 8-17

Completing the Square and Finding the Vertex for a Parabola.

Answers to problem 8-17:

Graphing form: $y = 2(x-1)^2 + 3$ Vertex: $(1, 3)$

If a parabola is in graphing form then the vertex can be found easily and a sketch of the graph can be made quickly. If the equation of the parabola is not in graphing form the equation can be rearranged. One way to rearrange the equation is by completing the square.

Following are three examples:

Note that the first two examples are the same as problems 4-123 and 4-125, which are shown in Chapter 4 with algebra tiles. Refer back to the pictures and explanations for those problems if they seem useful to you.

First, recall that $y = x^2$ is the parent equation for parabolas and the general equation for parabolic functions can be written in graphing form as $y = a(x-h)^2 + k$ where (h, k) is the vertex, and relative to the parent graph the function has been:

- Vertically stretched, if the absolute value of a is greater than 1
- Vertically compressed, if the absolute value of a is less than 1
- Reflected across the x-axis, if a is less than 0.

Example 1: Complete the square to change $y = x^2 + 8x + 10$ into graphing form and name the vertex.

Solution: We need to make $x^2 + 8x$ into a perfect square. To do this, take half of the coefficient of the x-term and square it. This is the number that would make a perfect square. As you can see from the calculations at right, for this example, this number is 16.

$$y = x^2 + 8x + 10$$
$$y = (x^2 + 8x + ?) + 10$$
$$? = (\tfrac{8}{2})^2 = 16$$

In order to create a perfect square, we add that number . But in order to make sure our new equation is equivalent to the original, we have to subtract 16 as well. Thus, our new form of the equation would look like $y = (x^2 + 8x + 16) + 10 - 16$, which can be rewritten as $y = (x+4)^2 - 6$. Now we can see that the vertex is $(-4, -6)$.

Example 2: Complete the square to change $y = x^2 + 5x + 2$ into graphing form and name the vertex.

Solution: We need to make $x^2 + 5x$ into a perfect square. Again, we take half of the coefficient of x and square it, as shown at right. In this case, we find that we should add $\frac{25}{4}$ to the expression in parentheses, but then we must subtract $\frac{25}{4}$ again to preserve the equality. This can be written as $y = (x^2 + 5x + \frac{25}{4}) + 2 - \frac{25}{4}$, which can be simplified to $y = (x + \frac{5}{2})^2 - \frac{17}{4}$ or $y = (x + 2.5)^2 - 4.25$. The vertex is $(-2.5, -4.25)$,

$$y = x^2 + 5x + 2$$
$$y = (x^2 + 5x + ?) + 2$$
$$? = (\tfrac{5}{2})^2 = \tfrac{25}{4}$$

Example 3: Complete the square to change $y = 2x^2 - 6x + 2$ into graphing form and name the vertex.

Solution: This problem is a little different because we have $2x^2$. First we must factor the 2 out of the x-terms. Then we make $x^2 + 3x$ into a perfect square as before.

Since $\frac{9}{4}$ is needed to make $x^2 + 3x$ into a perfect square, we add that inside the parentheses. Since all of the amounts in the parentheses are being multiplied by 2, we have really added $2(\frac{9}{4}) = \frac{9}{2}$, so we must subtract $\frac{9}{2}$, to keep the equation equivalent. This process is shown at right.

$$y = 2x^2 - 6x + 2$$
$$y = 2(x^2 - 3x) + 2$$
$$y = 2(x^2 - 3x + \tfrac{9}{4}) + 2 - 2 \cdot \tfrac{9}{4}$$
$$y = 2(x - \tfrac{3}{2})^2 - \tfrac{5}{2}$$

Answer: Graphing form: $y = 2(x - \frac{3}{2})^2 - \frac{5}{2}$ or $y = 2(x - 1.5)^2 - 2.5$; Vertex: $(1.5, -2.5)$.

We can now go back to problem 8-17:

Example 4: Complete the square to change the equation $y = 2x^2 - 4x + 5$ to graphing form, identify the vertex of the parabola, and sketch its graph.

Solution: First we must factor the 2 out from the x-terms. Then we make the $x^2 - 2x$ into a perfect square as before. The coefficient of x in this case is –2, half of which is – 1. Since $(-1)^2 = 1$, we see that a 1 is needed to make the expression in parentheses into a perfect square. Again, since everything inside the parentheses is being multiplied by 2, we must subtract $2(1) = 2$ to keep the value the same. See this process at right.

$$y = 2x^2 - 4x + 5$$
$$y = 2(x^2 - 2x) + 5$$
$$y = 2(x^2 - 2x + 1) + 5 - 2(1)$$
$$y = 2(x - 1)^2 + 3$$

To sketch the graph, we start by plotting the vertex, (1, 3). Then we can plot the next few points by recognizing that the shape of this parabola is the shape of $y = x^2$ stretched by a factor of 2. Therefore, the points one unit to the left and right of the vertex will be 2 units higher than the vertex, which gives the points (0, 5) and (2, 5). The points two units to the left and right of the vertex will be 8 units higher, which gives the points (–1, 11) and (3, 11). Thus we get the graph at right.

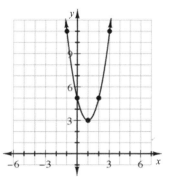

Answer: Graphing form: $y = 2(x - 1)^2 + 3$; Vertex: (1, 3); See graph above right.

Here are some more to try. Complete the square to write each equation in graphing form. Then state the vertex and the stretch factor and sketch a graph.

a. $y = x^2 - 6x + 9$

b. $y = x^2 + 3$

c. $y = x^2 - 4x$

d. $y = x^2 + 2x - 3$

e. $y = x^2 + 5x + 1$

f. $y = x^2 - \frac{1}{3}x$

g. $y = 3x^2 - 6x + 1$

h. $y = 5x^2 + 20x - 16$

i. $y = -x^2 - 6x + 10$

Answers:

a. $(3, 0)$; $a = 1$

b. $(0, 3)$; $a = 1$

c. $(2, -4)$; $a = 1$

d. $(-1, -4)$; $a = 1$

e. $(-\frac{5}{2}, -5\frac{1}{4})$; $a = 1$

f. $(\frac{1}{6}, -\frac{1}{36})$; $a = 1$

g. $(1, -2)$; $a = 3$

h. $(-2, -36)$; $a = 5$

i. $(-3, 19)$; $a = -1$

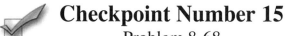

Checkpoint Number 15

Problem 8-68

Writing and Solving Exponential Equations

Answers to problem 8-68:

a. The more rabbits you have, the more new ones you get, a linear model would grow by the same number each year. A sine function would be better if the population rises and falls, but more data would be needed to apply this model.

b. $R = 80,000(5.4772...)^t$

c. ≈ 394 million

d. 1859, it seems okay that they grew to 80,000 in 7 years, *if* they are growing exponentially.

e. No, since it would predict a huge number of rabbits now. The population probably leveled off at some point or dropped drastically and rebuilt periodically.

Exponential functions are equations of the form $y = ab^x + c$ where a represents the initial value, b represents the multiplier, c represents the horizontal asymptote. x often represents the time. Some problems just involve substituting in the given information and doing calculations. If you are trying to solve for the time (x), then you will usually need to use logarithms. If you need to find the multiplier (m), then you will need roots. Note that we often assume that $c = 0$, unless we are told otherwise.

Example 1: Lunch at out favorite fast food stands cost $6.50. The price has steadily increased 4% per year for many years.

Question 1: What will lunch cost in 10 years?

Solution: In this case, we can use $6.50 as the initial value, the multiplier is 1.04, so the equation for the situation is $y = 6.50(1.04)^x$. The time we are interested in here is 10 years. Substituting into the equation, $y = 6.50(1.04)^{10} = \$9.62$

Question 2: What did it cost 10 years ago?

Solution: Using the same equation, only using -10 for the years, $y = 6.50(1.04)^{-10} = \$4.39$

Question 3: How long before lunch costs $10?

Solution: Again, we use the same equation, only this time we know the y-value, but not the value of x. To solve for x, we use logarithms, as shown in the work at right.

Answer: About 11 years.

$$\$10 = 6.50(1.04)^x$$

$$1.04^x = \tfrac{10}{6.5}$$

$$\log 1.04^x = \log(\tfrac{10}{6.5})$$

$$x\log 1.04 = \log(\tfrac{10}{6.5})$$

$$x = \frac{\log(\tfrac{10}{6.5})}{\log 1.04} \approx 11$$

Example 2: Tickets for a big concert first went on sale three weeks ago for $60. This week people are charging $100. Write an equation that represents the cost of the tickets w weeks from the time that they went on sale. Assume that they continue to increase in the same way.

Solution: To find the multiplier, we can use what we are given. The initial value is $60, the time is 3 weeks, and the final value is $100. This gives $100 = 60k^3$. Solving for k gives $k = \sqrt[3]{\frac{100}{60}} \approx 1.186$.

Answer: The equation is approximately $y = 60(1.186)^w$.

We now solve parts (b), (c), and (d) of problem 8-68.

Example 3: When rabbits were first brought to Australia, they had no natural enemies. There were about 80,000 rabbits in 1866. Two years later, in 1868, the population had grown to over 2,400,000!

    b. **Write an exponential equation for the number of rabbits t years after 1866.**

Solution: For 1866, 80000 would be the initial value, time would be 2 years, and the final amount would be 2400000, which gives the equation $2400000 = 80000m^2$. Solving for m, we get $30 = m^2$ so $m = \sqrt{30} \approx 5.477$. Thus the equation is approximately $R = 80,000(5.477)^t$

    c. **How many rabbits do you predict would have been present in 1871?**

Solution: The initial value is still 80,000, the multiplier ≈ 5.477, and now the time is 5 years. This gives $80,000(5.477)^5 \approx 394$ million.

    d. **According to your model, in what year was the first pair of rabbits introduced into Australia?**

Solution: In this situation, we use 2 as the initial value, 80000 as the final value, and the multiplier is still 5.477 but the time is not known. Using these values, we get $80000 = 2(5.477)^x$, which is solved at right. The answer 6.23 tells us that approximately 6.23 years had passed between the time of the first pair of rabbits, and the time when there were 80000. Thus, rabbits would have been introduced sometime in 1859.

$$80000 = 2(5.477)^x$$
$$40000 = (5.477)^x$$
$$\log(5.477)^x = \log 40000$$
$$x\log(5.477) = \log 40000$$
$$x = \frac{\log(40000)}{\log(5.477)} \approx 6.23$$

Here are some more to try:

  a.   A video tape loses 60% of its value every year it is in the store. The video costs
       $80 new. Write a function that represents its value in t years. What is it worth
       after 4 years?

  b.   Inflation is at a rate of 7% per year. Janelle's favorite bread now costs $1.79.
       What did it cost 10 years ago? How long before the cost of the bread doubles?

  c.   A bond that appreciates 4% per year will be worth $146 in five years. Find the
       current value.

  d.   Sixty years ago, when Sam's grandfather was a kid, he could buy his friend
       dinner for $1.50. If that same dinner now costs $25.25 and inflation was
       consistent, write an equation that will give you the costs at different times.

  e.   A two-bedroom house in Omaha is now worth $110,000. If it appreciates at a
       rate of 2.5% per year, how long will it take to be worth $200,000?

  f.   A car valued at $14,000 depreciates 18% per year. After how many years will
       the value have depreciated to $1000?

Answers:

  a. $y = 80(0.4)^t$, **$2.05**   b.   **$91, 10.2 years**

  c.   **$120**   d. $y = 1.50(1.048)^x$

  e.   **24.2 years**   f.   **13.3 years**

Checkpoint Number 16

Problem 8-129

Solving Absolute Value Equations and Inequalities

Answers to problem 8-129:

    a. $x = 1$ or $x = -4$ b. $-\infty < x < \infty$

Absolute value can be defined as a distance from a reference point. The patterns shown below can help solve absolute value equations and inequalities.

Patterns: Examples:

$|x| = k$ means: $x = k$ or $x = -k$ $|x| = 5$ means $x = 5$ or $x = -5$.

                                                  (5 and -5 are both 5 units from zero.)

$|x| < k$ means: $-k < x < k$ $|x| < 5$ means $-5 < x < 5$.

                                                  (The numbers between -5 and 5 are fewer than 5 units from zero)

$|x| > k$ means: $x > k$ or $x < -k$ $|x| > 5$ means $x > 5$ or $x < -5$.

                                                  (The numbers greater than 5 and less than -5 are more than 5 units from zero.)

If the expression inside the absolute value is more complicated, you can still use one of the three basic patterns above, as you can see in the examples below. (Note that $\le$ and $\ge$ follow the same patterns as the pure inequality.)

Example 1: Solve $|2x + 3| = 7$.

Solution: If $|2x + 3| = 7$, then the quantity $(2x + 3)$ must be equal to either 7 or -7, as can be seen in the first pattern above. Therefore, we can set up and solve the two equations show at right to find that $x = 2$ or $x = -5$.

$$2x + 3 = 7 \quad \text{or} \quad 2x + 3 = -7$$
$$2x = 4 \qquad\qquad 2x = -10$$
$$x = 2 \qquad\qquad\quad x = -5$$

Example 2: Solve $|2x + 3| \le 7$.

Solution: If $|2x + 3| \le 7$, then the quantity $(2x + 3)$ must be less than 7 and greater than -7, as can be seen in the second pattern above. Therefore, we can set up and solve the inequalities shown at right to find that $-5 \le x \le 2$.

$$-7 \le 2x + 3 \le 7$$
$$-10 \le 2x \le 4$$
$$-5 \le x \le 2$$

Now we can go back and try problem 8-129.

Example 3: Solve $2|2x+3|=10$.

Solution: Start by isolating the absolute value to get $|2x+3|=5$. Using the first pattern, this can be rewritten as $2x+3=5$ or $2x+3=-5$. Solving each of these equations yields $x=1$ or $x=-4$.

Example 4: Solve $-|x+3|<10$.

Solution: Again, we want to start by isolating the absolute value. Here it is important to know that dividing by a negative changes the inequality sign. Therefore, dividing both sides of this inequality by –1, we get $|x+3|>-10$. Since an absolute value is always positive, this inequality will be true for any real value of x. Therefore $-\infty<x<\infty$.

Here are some more to try. Solve each absolute value equation or inequality.

a. $|x-2|+10=8$

b. $15-|x+1|=3$

c. $-3|x+6|+12=0$

d. $|2x+7|=0$

e. $|x+4|\geq 7$

f. $|x|-5\leq 8$

g. $|4r-2|>8$

h. $-2|x-3|+6<-4$

i. $|4-d|\leq 7$

Answers:

a. **no solution**

b. $x=11$ or $x=-13$

c. $x=-2$ or $x=-10$

d. $x=-\frac{7}{2}$

e. $x\geq 3$ or $x\leq -11$

f $-13\leq x\leq 13$

g. $r<-\frac{3}{2}$ or $r>\frac{5}{2}$

h. $x>8$ or $x<-2$

i. $-3\leq d\leq 11$

Checkpoint Number 17
Problem 9-23
Finding an Equation for the Inverse of a Function

Answers to problem 9-23:

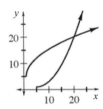

a. $f^{-1}(x) = \frac{1}{3}(\frac{x-5}{2})^2 + 1 = \frac{1}{12}(x-5)^2 + 1$ for $x \geq 5$

b. See graph at right.

To find the equation for the inverse of a function, you can interchange the x and y variables and then solve for y. This also means that the coordinates of points that are on the graph of the function will be reversed on the graph of the inverse. Here are some examples:

Example 1: Write the equation for the inverse of $y = 2(x+3)$.

Solution: We can interchange the x and the y to get $x = 2(y+3)$ as the equation of the inverse. To get our final answer, we solve for y, as shown at right.

$$(y+3) = \frac{x}{2}$$
$$y = \frac{x}{2} - 3$$

Answer: $y = \frac{x}{2} - 3$

Example 2: Write the equation for the inverse of $y = \frac{1}{2}(x+4)^2 + 1$.

Solution: Again, we can interchange the x and the y to get the equation of the inverse and then solve for y to get our answer in y-form, as shown at right.

$$x = \frac{1}{2}(y+4)^2 + 1$$
$$\frac{1}{2}(y+4)^2 = x - 1$$

Answer: $y = \pm\sqrt{2x-2} - 4$. Note that because of the $\pm$, this inverse is not a function.

$$(y+4)^2 = 2x - 2$$
$$y + 4 = \pm\sqrt{2x-2}$$
$$y = \pm\sqrt{2x-2} - 4$$

Example 3: Write the equation for the inverse of $y = -\frac{2}{3}x + 6$.

Solution: Interchanging the x and the y, we get $x = -\frac{2}{3}y + 6$. Solving for y gives
$y = -\frac{3}{2}(x-6) = -\frac{3}{2}x + 9$.

Answer: $y = -\frac{3}{2}x + 9$

Example 4: Write the equation for the inverse of $y = \sqrt{x-2} + 3$.

Solution: Again, we exchange x and y and then solve for y, as shown at right.

The original function is half of a sleeping parabola, so the inverse is only half of a parabola as well. Thus the domain of the inverse is restricted to $x \geq 3$.

$$x = \sqrt{y-2} + 3$$
$$\sqrt{y-2} = x - 3$$
$$y - 2 = (x-3)^2$$
$$y = (x-3)^2 + 2$$

Answer: $y = (x-3)^2 + 2$ in the domain $x \geq 3$.

We can now return to problem 9-23:

Example 5: Find the equation for the inverse of the function $y = 2\sqrt{3(x-1)} + 5$. Then sketch the graph of both the original and the inverse.

$$x = 2\sqrt{3(y-1)} + 5$$

Interchanging x and y we get $x = 2\sqrt{3(y-1)} + 5$. We then solve for y, as shown at right. This equation can then be simplified to get $y = \frac{(x-5)^2}{12} + 1$.

$$2\sqrt{3(y-1)} = x - 5$$

$$\sqrt{3(y-1)} = \frac{x-5}{2}$$

Note that the domain and range of the inverse are the interchanged domain and range of the original function. In other words, the original function has a domain of $x \geq 1$ and range of $y \geq 5$. The domain of the inverse, then, is $x \geq 5$ and the range is $y \geq 1$.

$$3(y-1) = (\tfrac{x-5}{2})^2$$

$$y - 1 = \tfrac{1}{3}(\tfrac{x-5}{2})^2$$

$$y = \tfrac{1}{3}(\tfrac{x-5}{2})^2 + 1$$

As you can see by the graph at right, the points on the inverse graph, have interchanged coordinates from the points on the graph of the original function. For example, two points on the original graph are $(1, 5)$ and $(4, 11)$. The corresponding points on the graph of the inverse are $(5, 1)$ and $(11, 4)$.

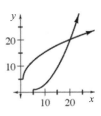

Answer: $y = \frac{(x-5)^2}{12} + 1$ in the domain $x \geq 5$.

Here are some more to try. Find the equation for the inverse of each function.

a. $y = 3x - 2$

b. $y = \frac{x+1}{4}$

c. $y = \frac{1}{3}x + 2$

d. $y = x^3 + 1$

e. $y = 1 + \sqrt{x+5}$

f. $y = 3(x+2)^2 - 7$

g. $y = 2\sqrt{x-1} + 3$

h. $y = \frac{1}{2+x}$

i. $y = \log_3(x+2)$

Answers:

a. $y = \frac{x+2}{3}$

b. $y = 4x - 1$

c. $y = 3x - 6$

d. $y = \sqrt[3]{x-1}$

e. $y = (x-1)^2 - 5$

f. $y = \sqrt{\frac{x+7}{3}} - 2$

g. $y = (\frac{x-3}{2})^2 + 1$

h. $y = \frac{1}{x} - 2$

i. $y = 3^x + 2$

Checkpoint Number 18

Problem 9-127

Solving a System of Equations in Three Variables

Answer to problem 9-127: $(6, -2, -8)$

To solve a system of equations in three variables using elimination you can use the same basic process as you would with two variables. Choose any variable to eliminate and then you are left with two equations in two variables. Continue to solve in the usual way. To solve using matrix multiplication you need to change the system into matrices and then isolate the variable matrix by using the inverse matrix on the graphing calculator. Here is an example of each method.

Example 1: Solve for (x, y, z)

$$5x - 4y - 6z = -19$$
$$-2x + 2y + z = 5$$
$$3x - 6y - 5z = -16$$

Method One — Elimination

Choose a variable to eliminate. We choose z and decide to use the first two equations. We multiply the second equation by 6 to get $-12x + 12y + 6z = 30$ and add it to the first, as shown at right.

$$-12x + 12y + 6z = 30$$
$$\underline{5x - 4y - 6z = -19}$$
$$(A) \quad -7x + 8y = 11$$

Then we must also eliminate z using a different combination of two equations. We choose to multiply the second by 5 to get $-10x + 10y + 5z = 25$ and add it to the third.

$$-10x + 10y + 5z = 25$$
$$\underline{3x - 6y - 5z = -16}$$
$$(B) \quad -7x + 4y = 9$$

Now we have two equations with two variables. We can subtract line (B) from line (A) to eliminate x and find y.

$$(A) \quad -7x + 8y = 11$$
$$(B) \quad \underline{-(-7x + 4y = 9)}$$
$$4y = 2$$
$$y = \tfrac{1}{2}$$

We substitute the value we got for y into equation (A) to get $-7x + 8(\tfrac{1}{2}) = 11$. This gives $-7x = 7$ and $x = -1$.

Then we go back to any of the original equations and substitute the values for x and y to find z. Using the first one:

$$5(-1) - 4(\tfrac{1}{2}) - 6z = -19$$
$$-7 - 6z = -19$$
$$-6z = -12$$
$$z = 2$$

The solution is $(-1, \tfrac{1}{2}, 2)$.

Method Two–Matrices

First we write the problem as a matrix equation.

$$\begin{bmatrix} 5 & -4 & -6 \\ -2 & 2 & 1 \\ 3 & -6 & -5 \end{bmatrix} \cdot \begin{bmatrix} x \\ y \\ z \end{bmatrix} = \begin{bmatrix} -19 \\ 5 \\ -16 \end{bmatrix}$$

We use a graphing calculator to left-multiply both sides of the equation by the inverse of the coefficient matrix. (For help with how to do this with your calculator, refer to the Lesson 7.3.3 Resource Page or consult the manual for your calculator.)

$$\begin{bmatrix} x \\ y \\ z \end{bmatrix} = \begin{bmatrix} 5 & -4 & -6 \\ -2 & 2 & 1 \\ 3 & -6 & -5 \end{bmatrix}^{-1} \cdot \begin{bmatrix} -19 \\ 5 \\ -16 \end{bmatrix}$$

This gives:

$$\begin{bmatrix} x \\ y \\ z \end{bmatrix} = \begin{bmatrix} -1 \\ 0.5 \\ 2 \end{bmatrix}$$

The solution is $(-1, \frac{1}{2}, 2)$.

We can now go back and solve problem 9-127.

Example 2: Use elimination or matrix multiplication to solve this system of equations:

$$x + y - z = 12$$
$$3x + 2y + z = 6$$
$$2x + 5y - z = 10$$

Method One

To eliminate z, we add the first two equations:

$$x + y - z = 12$$
$$+(3x + 2y + z = 6)$$
$$\overline{\quad 4x + 3y \quad = 18 \ (A)}$$

We can eliminate z again by adding the second and the third:

$$3x + 2y + z = 6$$
$$2x + 5y - z = 10$$
$$\overline{\quad 5x + 7y \quad = 16 \ (B)}$$

Now we can multiply equation (A) by 5 to get
$5(4x + 3y = 18) \Rightarrow 20x + 15y = 90$ and (B) by -4 to get
$-4(5x + 7y = 16) \Rightarrow -20x - 28y = -64$ and add the results to eliminate x:

$$20x + 15y = 90$$
$$-20x - 28y = -64$$
$$\overline{\quad -13y = 26}$$
$$y = -2$$

Substituting $y = -2$ into (A) gives $x = 6$. Substituting $y = -2$ and $x = 6$ in any of the original equations gives $z = -8$.

Method Two

We rewrite the system as the matrix equation at right.

$$\begin{bmatrix} 1 & 1 & -1 \\ 3 & 2 & 1 \\ 2 & 5 & -1 \end{bmatrix} \cdot \begin{bmatrix} x \\ y \\ z \end{bmatrix} = \begin{bmatrix} 12 \\ 6 \\ 10 \end{bmatrix}$$

We isolate the variable matrix:

$$\begin{bmatrix} x \\ y \\ z \end{bmatrix} = \begin{bmatrix} 1 & 1 & -1 \\ 3 & 2 & 1 \\ 2 & 5 & -1 \end{bmatrix}^{-1} \cdot \begin{bmatrix} 12 \\ 6 \\ 10 \end{bmatrix}$$

We use the graphing calculator to calculate the inverse and multiply to get $\begin{bmatrix} x \\ y \\ z \end{bmatrix} = \begin{bmatrix} 6 \\ -2 \\ -8 \end{bmatrix}$

The solution is $x = 6$, $y = -2$, $z = -8$.

Here are some more to try. Solve these systems of equations.

a. $x + y + z = 34$
$3x + 2y + 4z = 95$
$x + 2y + 3z = 56$

b. $x - 2y + 3z = 8$
$2x + y + z = 6$
$x + y + 2z = 12$

c. $5x + y + 2z = 6$
$3x - 6y - 9z = -48$
$x - 2y + z = 12$

d. $4x - y + z = -5$
$2x + 2y + 3z = 10$
$5x - 2y + 6z = 1$

e. $x + y = 2 - z$
$-y + 1 = -z - 2x$
$3x - 2y + 5z = 16$

f. $a - b + 2c = 2$
$a + 2b - c = 1$
$2a + b + c = 4$

g. $-4x = z - 2y + 12$
$y + z = 12 - x$
$8x - 3y + 4z = 1$

h. $3x + y - 2z = 6$
$x + 2y + z = 7$
$6x + 2y - 4z = 12$

i. $4x + 4y - 5z = -2$
$2x - 4y + 10z = 6$
$x + 2y + 5z = 0$

Answers:

a. **(17, 12, 5)**

b. **(–1, 3, 5)**

c. **(–1, –3, 7)**

d. **(–1, 3, 2)**

e. **(–3, 0, 5)**

f. **no solution**

g. **(–3, 5, 10)**

h. **infinite solutions**

i. $(\frac{1}{2}, -\frac{3}{4}, \frac{1}{5})$

Glossary

3-dimensional coordinate system   In three dimensions the z-axis is perpendicular to the x-y plane at $(0, 0)$. Points in 3-dimensions are represented with coordinates (x, y, z). The first octant where x,-y, and-z are positive is shown at right with the point $(2, 3, 1)$. (p. 307)

absolute value   The absolute value of a number is the distance of the number from zero. Since the absolute value represents a distance without regard to direction, it is always a positive real number. For example, $|-7| = 7$, and $|7| = 7$. The absolute value of a complex number is its distance from zero in the complex plane. For a complex number $a + bi$, $|a + bi| = \sqrt{a^2 + b^2}$. For example, $|3 - 2i| = \sqrt{3^2 + (-2)^2} = \sqrt{13}$. (pp. 193, 464, 466)

additive identity   The number 0 is called the additive identity because adding 0 to any number does not change the number. An additive identity matrix or 0 matrix is a matrix of all 0's. (pp. 352, 362)

additive inverse   The additive inverse of a number is the number we can add to that number to get the additive identity, 0. So, for the number 5, the additive inverse is -5; for the number -13, the additive inverse is 13. For any number x, the additive inverse is $-x$. (p. 352)

algebraic representation   Algebraic representation generally means representing the mathematical relationships using numbers, a variable or variables, and operation symbols in equations, or inequalities.

algebraic strategies   Using algebraic strategies means to write an algebraic representation of the problem and then to rewrite those expressions to get equivalent, but more useful results that lead to a solution for the problem or that reveal more information to help solve it. (pp. 221, 224)

amplitude   The amplitude of a cyclic graph is one-half the distance between the highest and lowest points. In the graph at right, a is the amplitude. (pp. 421, 423)

angle   An angle is formed by two rays joined at a common endpoint (the vertex). In geometric figures, angles are usually formed by two segments with a common endpoint.

angles of rotation.   Angles with one vertex at the origin and formed by counter-clockwise rotation from the positive x-axis, are referred to as angles of rotation in standard position. For an angle θ, in standard position, the positive x-axis is the initial ray and the terminal ray may point in any direction. The measure of such an angle may have any real value. (p. 403)

appreciation   An increase in value. (p. 151)

arccosine of x   See "cosine inverse ($\cos^{-1} x$)." (pp. 675, 679)

arcsine of x　See "sine inverse ($\sin^{-1} x$)." (p. 678)

arctangent of x　See "tangent inverse ($\tan^{-1} x$)." (p. 679)

area　For a 2-dimensional region, the number of non-overlapping square units needed to cover the region. Also see "surface area."

area model　An area model or diagram is one way to represent the probabilities of the outcomes for a sequence of two events. The total area is one, and the probabilities are represented by proportional parts. In the example, P(S) and P(not S) are the dimensions of the right side. The probabilities that A will occur or not occur depending on when S occurs are the top and bottom of the rectangle. The area of each part is the probability of each possible sequence of two events. (p. 502)

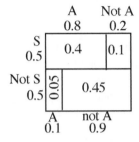

argument　Used with sigma notation for sequences to describe the nth term. In the expression, $\sum_{k=1}^{10}(2k+1)$ the expression $2k+1$ is the argument. (p. 627)

arithmetic sequence　In an arithmetic sequence the difference between sequential terms is constant. Each term of an arithmetic sequence can be generated by adding the common difference to the previous term. For example in the sequence, 4, 7, 10, 13, ..., the common difference is 3. (pp. 71, 75, 83)

arithmetic series　An arithmetic series is the sum of the terms of an arithmetic sequence. Given the arithmetic sequence $3, 7, 11, ..., 43$, the corresponding arithmetic series is $3+7+11+...+43$. (pp. 610, 618, 622)

arrange, arrangement　We arrange a set of objects or make an arrangement when we put them in a particular order, in a line, in a row, around a circle, on a shelf, in a stack, around a table... (pp. 523, 525, 530)

asymptote　A line that the graph of a curve approaches so that the distance between the graph and the line gets as small as you wish. We often graph functions, which have vertical and/or horizontal asymptotes. For example the asymptotes for the graph of $f(x)=\frac{1}{x+25}$ are $x=-25$ and $y=0$. (Asymptotes are more completely defined in later courses.) (pp. 116, 118, 181, 183, 289)

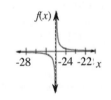

axes　In a coordinate plane, the two perpendicular number lines that intersect at the origin (0, 0). The x-axis is horizontal and the y-axis is vertical. In 3-dimensions a third number line, the z-axis is perpendicular to the x-y plane at the origin (0, 0, 0). (p. 307) See "coordinate axes" and "3-dimensional axes" for illustration.

The Binomial Theorem The formula for the expansion of $(x+y)^n$ is called the Binomial Theorem. (p. 655)

$$(x+y)^n = {_n}C_n x^n + {_n}C_{n-1} x^{n-1} y + {_n}C_{n-2} x^{n-2} y^2 + \ldots + {_n}C_1 xy^{n-1} + {_n}C_0 y^n$$

For example, $(x+y)^3 = {_3}C_3 x^3 + {_3}C_2 x^2 y + {_3}C_1 xy^2 + {_3}C_0 y^3 = 1x^3 + 3x^2 y + 3xy^2 + 1y^3$

boundary curve A curve that marks the "edge" of the graph of an inequality. For a strict inequality ($<$ or $>$) the curve is dotted to show that points on the curve are not included in the graph; for $\leq$ or $\geq$ the curve is solid to show that the points on the curve are included. The graph of intersection of $y < x^2 + 4x + 3$ and $y \geq 2x^2 + 5x - 3$ is shown at right. (p. 247)

boundary line The line that marks the "edge" of the graph of a linear inequality. For a strict inequality ($<$ or $>$) the line is dotted to show that points on the line are not included in the graph; for $\leq$ or $\geq$ the line is solid to show that the points on the line are included. The graph of $y > \frac{2}{3}x - 3$ is at right. (p. 247)

boundary point On a number line graph, a point that represents the largest or smallest value in the set of real numbers or the largest or smallest number that is not in the set. When the boundary point is in the set to be represented it marked with a solid dot; when it is not in the set we use a "hollow dot." Examples for $-1.5 < x < 4$ and $x \geq -4$ are shown at right. (pp. 236, 238)

circle In a plane, the set of all points equidistant from a single point. The general equation of a circle is $(x-h)^2 + (y-k)^2 = r^2$ where the point (h, k) is the center of the circle of radius r. (pp. 198, 206, 566, 567, 576)

circular functions The periodic functions based on the unit circle, including $y = \sin x$, $y = \cos x$, and $y = \tan x$. See "sine function," "cosine function," and "tangent function."

coefficient When variable(s) are multiplied by a number, the number is called a coefficient of that term. The numbers that are multiplied by the variables in the terms of a polynomial are called the coefficients of the polynomial. For example, 3 is the coefficient of $3x^2$. (p. 440)

combination A combination is the number of ways we can select items from a larger set without regard to order. For instance, choosing a committee of 3 students from a group of 5 volunteers is a combination since the order in which committee members are selected does not matter. We write ${_n}C_r$ to represent the number of combinations of n things taken r at a time (or n choose r). For instance, the number of ways to select a committee of 3 students from a group of 5 is ${_5}C_3$. You can use Pascal's Triangle to find ${_5}C_3$ or use permutations and divided by the number of arrangements $\frac{{_5}P_3}{{_3}P_3} = \frac{5!}{3!2!}$. Formulas for combinations include: ${_n}C_r = \frac{{_n}P_r}{r!} = \frac{n!}{r!(n-r)!}$. (pp. 523, 530)

common difference The difference between consecutive terms of an arithmetic sequence or the *generator* of the sequence. When the common difference is positive the sequence increases; when it is negative the sequence decreases. In the sequence $3, 7, 11, \ldots, 43$, the common difference is 4. (pp. 75, 83)

common ratio   Common ratio is another name for the multiplier or *generator* of a geometric sequence. It is the number to multiply one term by to get the next one. In the sequence: 96, 48, 24, … the common ratio is $\frac{1}{2}$. (p. 83)

complete graph   A complete graph is one that includes everything that is important about the graph (such as intercepts and other key points, asymptotes, or limitations on the domain or range), and that makes the rest of the graph predictable based on what is shown. For example, a complete graph of the equation $y = \frac{1}{3}(x-2)^2(x+3)$ is shown at right. (p. 9)

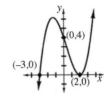

completing the square   A standard procedure for rewriting a quadratic equation from standard form to graphing (or vertex) form is called completing the square. Completing the square is also used to solve quadratic equations in one variable. For example, the expression $x^2 - 6x + 4$ starts with the first two terms of $(x-3)^2$. To "complete the square" we need to add 9 to $x^2 - 6x$. Since the original expression only adds 4, completing the square would increase the expression by 5, so $(x-3)^2 - 5$ is an equivalent form that is useful for solving or graphing. (pp. 202, 206, 387)

complex conjugates   The complex number $a + bi$ has a complex conjugate $a - bi$. Similarly, the conjugate of $c - di$ is $c + di$. What is noteworthy about complex numbers conjugates is that both their product $(a+bi)(a-bi) = a^2 - b^2i^2 = a^2 + b^2$ and their sum $(a+bi)+(a-bi) = 2a$ are real numbers. If a complex number is a zero (or root) of a real polynomial function, then its complex conjugate is also a zero (or root). (p. 460)

complex numbers   Numbers written in the form $a + bi$ where a and b are real numbers, are called complex numbers. Each complex number has a real part, a, and an imaginary part, bi. Note that real numbers are also complex numbers with $b = 0$, and imaginary numbers are complex numbers where $a = 0$. (pp. 455, 456)

complex plane   A set of coordinate axes with all the real numbers on the horizontal axis (the real axis) and all the imaginary numbers on the vertical axis (the imaginary axis) defines the complex plane. Complex numbers are graphed in the complex plane using the same method we use to graph coordinate points. Thus, the complex number $1 + 3i$ is located at the point $(1, 3)$ in the complex plane. (p. 466)

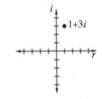

composite function   A function that is created as the result of using the outputs of one function as the inputs of another can be seen as a composite function. For example the function $h(x) = |\log x|$ can be seen as the composite function $f(g(x))$ where $f(x) = |x|$ and $g(x) = \log x$. See "composition." (p. 292)

composition   When the output of one function is used as the input for a second function, a new function is created which is a composition of the two original functions. If the first function is $g(x)$ and the second is $f(x)$, the composition can be written as $f(g(x))$ or $f \circ g(x)$. Note that the order in which we perform the functions matters and $g(f(x))$ will usually be a different function. (p. 274)

compound interest Interest that is paid on both the principal and the previously accrued interest. (pp. 125, 658, 661)

compress A term used informally to describe the relationship of a graph to its parent graph when the graph increases or decreases more slowly than the parent. For example, the solid parabola shown at right is a compressed version of its parent, shown as a dashed curve. (pp. 170, 175)

conditional probability The probability of outcome B occurring, given that outcome A has already happened is called the conditional probability of B, given A (the usual notation is $P(B|A)$). One way to calculate the conditional probability of B given A, is to divide the probability of both outcomes A and B by the probability of outcome A alone, or $P(B|A) = \frac{P(A \text{ and } B)}{P(A)}$. In many situations it is possible to calculate the conditional probability directly from the data by counting the number of possibilities for outcome B once outcome A has occurred. (pp. 506, 516)

cone If you have a circle in a plane and a point P, not in that plane, the solid obtained by joining all of the points inside or on the circle to P is a circular cone. P is called the *apex* of the cone. A *standard* cone is a circular cone with its apex P directly over the center of the circle. For the purpose of defining the conic sections visualize two standard cones, one upside down on top of the other, touching at their apexes and both extending infinitely, one upwards and one downwards. (p. 554)

conic section Circles, ellipses, hyperbolas and parabolas are known as conic sections. They are given this name because each curve can be found by taking a section or slice of a cone. (pp. 554, 561)

conjugate Every complex number $a + bi$ has a conjugate, $a - bi$, and both the sum and product of the conjugates are real. Similarly, an irrational number that can be written $a + \sqrt{b}$ where a and b are rational, has a conjugate, $a - \sqrt{b}$, and the product and sum of these conjugates are rational. (p. 460)

conjugate axis The axis of a hyperbola that does not contain the vertices. It is perpendicular to the transverse axis at the center of the hyperbola. The distance from the center to the end of the conjugate axis is represented as b in the general equation. (p. 585) See "hyperbola."

continuous For this course, when the points on a graph are connected and it makes sense to connect them, we say the graph is continuous. Such a graph will have no holes or breaks in it. This term will be more completely defined in a later course. (pp. 62, 86)

coordinate axes For two dimensions, two perpendicular number lines, the x- and y-axes, that intersect where both are zero and that provide the scale(s) for labeling each point in a plane with its horizontal and vertical distance and direction from the origin $(0, 0)$. In three dimensions, a third number line, the z-axis, is perpendicular to a plane and intersects it at origin $(0, 0, 0)$. The z-axis provides the scale for the height of a point above or below the plane. See "3-dimensional coordinate system." (p. 307)

coordinates   The numbers in an ordered pair (a, b) or triple (a, b, c) used to locate a point in the plane or in space in relation to a set of coordinate axes. (pp. 22, 307)

cosecant   The cosecant is the reciprocal of the sine. (p. 682)

cosine   In a right triangle (as shown at right) the ratio $\frac{adjacent\ side}{hypotenuse}$ is known as the cosine of the acute angle. At right, $\cos B = \frac{a}{c}$ since the side length a is adjacent to angle B. On a unit circle the cosine of an angle is the x-coordinate of the point the where the terminal ray of an angle in standard position intersects the unit circle. (pp. 392, 407)

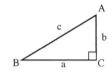
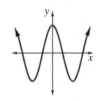

cosine function   The cosine of angle θ, denoted $\cos\theta$, is the x-coordinate of the point on the unit circle reached by a rotation angle of θ radians in standard position. The general equation for the cosine function is $y = a\cos b(x - h) + k$. This function has amplitude a, period $\frac{2\pi}{b}$, horizontal shift h, and vertical shift k. (p. 409)

cosine inverse ($\cos^{-1} x$)   Read as the inverse of cosine x, $\cos^{-1} x$ is the measure of the angle with cosine x. We can also write $y = \arccos x$. Note that the notation refers to the inverse of the cosine function, *not* $\frac{1}{\cos x}$. Because $y = \cos^{-1} x$ is equivalent to $x = \cos y$ and there are infinitely many angles y such that $\cos y = x$, the inverse *function* is restricted to select the *principal* value of y such that $0 \leq y \leq \pi$. The graph of the inverse cosine function is at right. (p. 684)

cotangent   The cotangent is the reciprocal of the tangent. The graph of the cotangent function is at right. (p. 683)

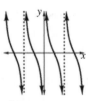

cubic   A cubic polynomial is a polynomial with degree 3. (pp. 182, 207)

cycle   One cycle of a graph of a trigonometric function is the shortest piece that represents all possible outputs. The length of one cycle is the distance along the x-axis needed to generate all possible output values or the distance around the unit circle needed to generate all possible outcomes. (p. 379)

cyclic function   The term cyclic function is sometimes used to describe trigonometric functions, but it also includes any function that sequentially repeats its outputs at regular intervals. (p. 412)

decision chart   A decision chart is a method for organizing a counting problem that could be represented by a symmetric tree diagram. Begin by asking how many decisions need to be made, and then mark a space for each decision. Fill in each space with the number of possibilities for that decision. For example a child has a set of 26 blocks, each with a different letter of the alphabet on it. How many three-letter arrangements could he make by lining up any three of his blocks? There are three decisions, with 26 choices for the first letter, 25 for the second, and 24 for the third. To calculate the total number of possibilities the numbers in the decision chart must be multiplied.

$$\underline{26} \cdot \underline{25} \cdot \underline{24}$$

The decision chart is a short way to represent a tree with 26 branches at stage one, 25 at stage two, and 24 at stage three. (pp. 514, 521)

Algebra 2 Connections

degree   One degree is an angle measure that is $\frac{1}{360}$ of a full circle or $\frac{\pi}{180}$ radians. (p. 399)

degree of a polynomial   The degree of a monomial is the sum of the exponents of its variables. For example, the degree of $3x^2y^5z$ is 8. For a polynomial the degree is the degree of the monomial term with the highest degree. Example: for the polynomial $2x^5y^2 - 4x^4z^6 + x^7z$ the degree is 10. (p. 440)

degree of a polynomial in one variable   The highest power of the variable. The degree of a polynomial function also indicates the maximum number of factors of the polynomial and provides information for predicting the number of "turns" the graph can take. (p. 440)

dependent variable   The variable whose value is determined by the value of another variable. For a given value of the independent variable, or input, the value of the dependent variable is the output. In an ordered pair, the variable occurring second is the dependent variable. The dependent variable is usually graphed in relation to the vertical axis. (pp. 6, 13, 199)

depreciation   A decrease in value possibly because of normal wear and tear, age, decay, decrease in price. (p. 151)

directrix   A line used to define a conic section. A parabola can be defined as the locus of points equidistant from a line, which is its directrix and a point, which is its focus. (p. 556)

discrete graph   A graph that is made up of separate points. (p. 62)

discriminant   For any quadratic equation $ax^2 + bx + c = 0$, $b^2 - 4ac$ is called the discriminant. If $b^2 - 4ac \geq 0$, the roots of the quadratic are real. If the discriminant is less than 0, the roots are imaginary or complex. (p. 460)

distance formula   An application of the Pythagorean Theorem to find the distance between two points in a plane. The distance between any two points (x_1, y_1) and (x_2, y_2) is $\sqrt{(x_2 - x_1)^2 + (y_2 - y_1)^2}$. In the example at right the distance is $\sqrt{4^2 + 5^2}$. (p. 200)

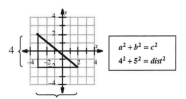

Distributive Property   The basis for rewriting products as sums and sums as products. For numbers or algebraic expressions A, B, and C, $A(B + C) = AB + AC$. (pp. 94, 99)

domain   The domain of a function is the set of possible values for the independent variable or the set of possible input values. It consists of every number that x can represent for the function, in other words every number that has an output. (pp. 16, 18, 199)

double root   A root of a function that occurs exactly twice. If an expression of the form $(x - a)^2$ is a factor of a polynomial, then the polynomial has a double root at $x = a$. The graph of the polynomial does not pass through the x-axis at $x = a$ but is tangent to the axis at $x = a$. (p. 446)

double root

eccentricity   The eccentricity of an ellipse is a measurement reflecting its "roundness." The eccentricity, e, is found with the formula $e = \frac{c}{a}$, where $c^2 = a^2 - b^2$, and a and b are the lengths of the semi-major and semi-minor axes. For a hyperbola, the eccentricity is a measure of the shape of the curve; the larger the eccentricity the more quickly the branches spread apart. The formula is also $e = \frac{c}{a}$. Note that since $c > a$, the eccentricity of a hyperbola is always greater than 1; ellipses have eccentricity less than 1. Parabolas have eccentricity equal to 1, and circles have eccentricity equal to 0. (pp. 576, 585)

elimination to solve a system of equations   The key step in the elimination method of solving equations is to add or subtract both sides of the equations to eliminate one of the variables. For example in the equations at right the variable, y, is eliminated when the two equations are added to get $13x = -13$. (p. 66)

$$5x - 3y = 1$$
$$8x + 3y = -14$$

ellipse   The set of all points for which the sum of their distances from two fixed points, the foci, remains constant. You can visualize an ellipse as a circle that has been stretched vertically or horizontally. The general form of the equation of an ellipse (with a horizontal major axis) is $\frac{(x-h)^2}{a^2} + \frac{(y-k)^2}{b^2} = 1$. The line through the two vertices of the ellipse in the long direction is called the major axis of the ellipse, and the distance from the center of the ellipse to one end of the major axis is called the semi-major axis. The shortest length across the center of the ellipse is the minor axis, and half this length is the semi-minor axis. If a is the length of the semi-major axis, b the semi minor axis, c the distance from the center to either focus, and (h, k) is the center, then the equation of the ellipse can be written

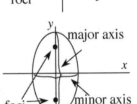

$$\frac{(x-h)^2}{a^2} + \frac{(y-k)^2}{b^2} = 1, \text{ if the major axis is horizontal or}$$

$$\frac{(x-h)^2}{b^2} + \frac{(y-k)^2}{a^2} = 1, \text{ if the major axis is vertical.}$$

In either case, b is defined by $c^2 = a^2 - b^2$, and the eccentricity is $e = \frac{c}{a}$.
(pp. 570, 571, 575, 576)

equally likely   Outcomes or events are considered to be equally likely when they have the same probability. (pp. 497, 502, 510)

equation   A mathematical sentence in which two expressions have an equal sign between them. (linear pp. 11, 173, exponential p. 123, quadratic p. 177, square root p. 154)

equidistant   The same distance or length. For example, all the points on a circle are equidistant from its center and that distance is the length of the radius. (p. 566)

equilateral   A polygon is equilateral if all its sides have equal length. The example at right is an equilateral hexagon.

equivalent   Two algebraic expressions are equivalent if they have the same value for any legitimate substitution for their variables. Two equations are equivalent if they have the same solutions. (pp. 94, 98, 119)

Algebra 2 Connections

evaluate To evaluate an expression with variables, substitute the value(s) given for the variable(s) and perform the operations according the order of operations. For example, to evaluate the expression $x^3 - x^2$ for $x = -3$, substitute -3 for x, $(-3)^3 - (-3)^2 = -27 - 9 = -36$.

event Used in relation to calculating probabilities, an event is a set of outcomes or an outcome of some action that has alternative possibilities. (pp. 510, 515)

expected value The expected value for an outcome is the product of the probability of the outcome and the value placed on that outcome. The expected value of an event is the sum of the expected values for its possible outcomes. For example, in a lottery where 7 numbers are drawn from 77 and you have to have chosen all seven to win, the probability that your ticket is the $1,000,000 winner is $\frac{1}{2404808340}$ and the expected value is $0.000416. (pp. 497, 499, 510)

experimental probability A data-based probability arrived at by conducting trials and recording the results. When a die is rolled 20 times the experimental probability of getting a 6 is the number of times 6 comes up over the total number or rolls 20. (p. 537)

exponential function An exponential function has an equation of the form $y = ab^x$ for the domain of all real numbers and range positive real numbers , where a is the initial value and b is the multiplier or base. The general form for an exponential function is $f(x) = ab^{x+h} + k$. An example of an exponential function is graphed at right. (pp. 55, 125, 151)

expression An algebraic representation that contains one or more numbers and/or variables and may include operations and grouping symbols. Some examples of algebraic expressions are $x^5 - 4x^2 + 8$, $\sqrt{a^2 + b^2}$, $\frac{x-9}{2} - 10 + \frac{1}{y}$, x. (pp. 101, 102, 103)

extraneous solution Sometimes in the process of solving equations, multiplying or squaring expressions involving a variable will lead to a numerical result that does not make the original equation true. This false result is called an extraneous solution. For example, in the process of solving the equation $\sqrt{x+3} = 9 - x$ both sides of the equation are squared to get $x + 3 = x^2 - 19x + 81$ which has solutions 6 and 13. 6 is a solution of the original equation, but 13 is extraneous, because $\sqrt{13+3} \neq 9 - 13$. (pp. 224, 360)

$f^{-1}(x)$ Read this as "f inverse of x," the inverse function for $f(x)$. (p. 231)

factor A factor is part of a product. A polynomial expression $p(x)$ is a factor of another polynomial expression $P(x)$ when there is a polynomial $q(x)$ such that $p(x)q(x) = P(x)$. In the equation $3x^2 - 9x + 6 = 3(x - 2)(x - 1)$, the expressions $(x - 2)$, $(x - 1)$, and 3 are factors. (pp. 23, 149, 475)

Factor Theorem States that if a is a root of a polynomial then $x - a$ is a factor, and if $x - a$ is a factor then a is a root. For example, the polynomial $x^2 - 5x - 6 = (x - 6)(x + 1)$ and the roots are 6 and -1.

factorial A shorthand notation for the product of a list of consecutive positive integers from the given number down to 1: $n! = n(n-1)(n-2)(n-3) \cdot \ldots \cdot 3 \cdot 2 \cdot 1$. For example, $5! = 5 \cdot 4 \cdot 3 \cdot 2 \cdot 1 = 120$. (pp. 515, 521)

fair game   A game in which the expected values for each player are equal. If you pay to play a game then the game is fair if the cost to play equals the expected value. For example, player A and player B are rolling a die to see how far to move in a board game. If the die comes up 1, 2, 3, or 4, player A moves that many spaces. If the die comes up 5 or 6 player B gets to move that many spaces. Player A has an expected value of moving $\frac{1}{6}+\frac{2}{6}+\frac{3}{6}+\frac{4}{6}=\frac{10}{6}$ spaces on each turn. Player B has an expected value of moving $\frac{5}{6}+\frac{6}{6}=\frac{11}{6}$ spaces per turn, so this game is not fair. (pp. 497, 510)

family of functions   A group of functions that have at least one common characteristic. For example we describe all cubic functions, $y=a(x-h)^3+k$ as the family of functions with parent graph $y=x^3$. All are cubic polynomials and all of the graphs are similar in shape. The set of all equations $y=mx+7$ describes the family of linear functions with y-intercept 7. (pp. 189, 207)

feasible region   Used to describe the intersection of the graphs of a set of inequalities that represent the constraints or parameters of a problem situation. The feasible region represents the points with coordinates that satisfy the given conditions. (pp. 241, 245)

focal length   The distance c from the vertex to the focus of a parabola is called the focal length. In a hyperbola or an ellipse focal length is the distance c, from the center to one focus. See "focus of a parabola," "foci of an ellipse," and "foci of a hyperbola." (p. 568)

foci of an ellipse   Every ellipse has two points on its major axis called the foci of the ellipse. For any point (x, y) on the ellipse, the sum of the distances from each focus to (x, y) is a constant. An ellipse with its center at the origin, x-intercepts of $(\pm a, 0)$ and y-intercepts $(0, \pm b)$, where $a > b$, has its foci at $(\pm c, 0)$, with $c^2 = a^2 - b^2$. When the center is $(0, 0)$ and the major axis is on the y-axis the foci are $(0, \pm c)$. (pp. 570, 571) See "ellipse. "

foci of a hyperbola   Each hyperbola has two points on its transverse axis called the foci of the hyperbola. For any point (x, y) on the hyperbola, the difference between the distances from each focus to (x, y) is constant. A hyperbola with it center at the origin, x-intercepts $(\pm a, 0)$ and asymptotes $y = \pm \frac{b}{a}x$ has its foci at $(\pm c, 0)$, with $c^2 = a^2 + b^2$. When the center is $(0, 0)$ and the transverse axis is on the y-axis the foci are $(0, \pm c)$. (p. 585) See "hyperbola."

focus of a parabola   A parabola is defined to be the set of points in the plane, each of which is the same distance from a fixed point (the focus) as it is from a fixed straight line (the directrix). Also, if rays parallel to the line of symmetry enter into the interior of the parabola to intersect the parabola and reflect so that the angle of incidence equals the angle of reflection, then all such rays intersect at the focus of the parabola. (pp. 556, 568) See "parabola."

fractional exponents   Raising a number to a fractional exponent indicates a power as well as a root. $x^{a/b} = \sqrt[b]{x^a} = (\sqrt[b]{x})^a$. (pp. 143, 144, 148)

function   A relationship in which for each input there is exactly one output. For example, $y = x^2$ is a function because each input for x determines one output. $x^2 + y^2 = 25$ is not a function, because, for example, when $x = 4$, y could be either 3 or –3. (pp. 6, 197, 199)

function notation   A convenient way to represent a function or to write a rule to show what a function machine does is to name the function with a letter and put the variable that represents the inputs in parentheses, for example $f(\ )$.   When the variable is x, this will be $f(x)$.   Read it "f of x" to mean the output of the function when the operations of f are performed on the input x. (p. 231)

general equation   If $y = f(x)$ is a parent equation, then the general equation for that function is given by $y = af(x-h)+k$ where (h, k) is the point corresponding to $(0, 0)$ in the parent graph and, relative to the parent graph, the function has been: 1) vertically stretched if the absolute value of a is greater than 1; 2) vertically compressed if the absolute value of a is less than 1; and/or 3) reflected across the x-axis if a is less than 0. (pp. 189, 207)

general quadratic equation for conic sections   The equation $ax^2 + by^2 + cx + dy + e = 0$, in which a and b are not *both* equal to zero is a general equation that could represent a parabola, an ellipse, a hyperbola, a circle, or a pair of lines depending on the values of the coefficients. This equation represents conic sections with axes parallel to the x- or y-axes. The general equation $ax^2 + bxy + cy^2 + dx + ey + f = 0$ includes conics with axes that are not parallel to the x- or y-axes. (p. 593)

generalize   Based on several specific examples describe common characteristics, patterns, or relationships and make a conjecture that can be tested on other examples. Use variables to represent a situation or relationship. (pp. 2, 26, 214)

generator   The generator of a sequence tells what you do to each term to get the next term. Note that this is different from the function for the nth term of the sequence. The generator only tells you how to find the following term, when you already know one term. In an arithmetic sequence the generator is the common difference; in a geometric sequence it is the multiplier or common ratio. (p. 69)

geometric sequence   A geometric sequence is a sequence that is generated by a multiplier. This means that each term of a geometric sequence can be found by multiplying the previous term by a constant. For example: 5, 15, 45... is the beginning of a geometric sequence with generator (common ratio) 3. In general a geometric sequence can be represented $a,\ ar,\ ar^2, ... + ar^{n-1}$. (pp. 71, 79, 80, 81)

geometric series (sum)   The sum of a geometric sequence is a geometric series, for example: $5 + 15 + 45 + ...$ The sum of the first n terms of a geometric sequence, $a + ar + ar^2 + ar^3 + ... + ar^{n-1}$ is given by the formula at right. (pp. 618, 636, 641, 647)

$$S = \frac{a(r^n - 1)}{r-1}$$

graph   The graph of an equation is the set of points representing the coordinates that make the equation true. The direction to "graph an equation" or "draw a graph" means use graph paper, scale your axes appropriately, label key points, and plot points accurately. This is different from *sketching* a graph. The equation $y = \frac{1}{3}(x-2)^2(x+3)$ is graphed at right. (p. 9)

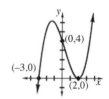

graphing form   A form of the equation of a function or relation that clearly shows key information about the graph. For example: the graphing form for the general equation of a quadratic function (also called vertex form) is $y = a(x - h)^2 + k$. The vertex (h, k), orientation (whether a is positive or negative) and amount of stretch or compression based on $|a| > 1$ or $|a| < 1$ can be appear in the equation. (pp. 176, 177)

growth factor   One way to analyze how the output value in a mathematical relation changes as the input value increases. Growth can be represented by constant addition, as the slope of a linear function or the constant difference in an arithmetic sequence, or by multiplication as the base of an exponential function or the multiplier in a geometric sequence. (p. 11)

(h, k) In this course h and k are used as parameters in general equations for families of functions $f(x) = af(x - h) + k$ and families of relations to represent the horizontal and vertical shifts of the parent graph. The point (h, k) represents location of a point that corresponds to $(0, 0)$ for parent graphs where $(0, 0)$ is on the graph. For circles, ellipses, and hyperbolas, (h, k) represents the center of the shifted graph. (pp. 190, 207, 576, 585)

half-life   When material decays, the half-life is the time it takes until only half the material remains. (p. 131)

horizontal shift   Used with parent graphs and general equations for functions and relations such as $y = a(x - h)^2 + k$. It is the amount a graph is moved left or right in relation to its parent graph, in this case $y = x^2$. The horizontal shift will be h units to the right if h is positive, to the left if h is negative. (p. 175)

hyperbola   A hyperbola has relationships corresponding to those of an ellipse. A hyperbola is made up of two branches. The line connecting the vertices of the two branches is called the transverse axis, and the letter a is used to represent the distance from the center to either vertex. For the equation at top right the center of the hyperbola is at the origin. The vertices are $(\pm a, 0)$ and the asymptotes have the equations $y = \pm \frac{b}{a} x$. The foci are on the transverse axis, in this case the x-axis, at $(\pm c, 0)$ with c given by the equation $c^2 = a^2 + b^2$. For a hyperbola, the eccentricity is a measure of the shape of the curve; the larger the eccentricity the more quickly the branches spread apart. Eccentricity is given by the formula $e = \frac{c}{a}$. Note that since $c > a$, the eccentricity of a hyperbola is always greater than 1. If the vertices are on the y-axis the foci are on the y-axis at $(0, \pm c)$, and the equation is written as shown in the lower equation at right. Everything else is the same *except* the asymptotes have slopes $\pm \frac{a}{b}$. b is also known as the length of the semi-conjugate axis. (pp. 579, 583)

$$\frac{x^2}{a^2} - \frac{y^2}{b^2} = 1$$

$$\frac{y^2}{a^2} - \frac{x^2}{b^2} = 1$$

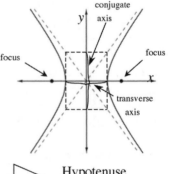

hypotenuse   The longest side of a right triangle, the side opposite the right angle.

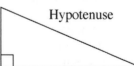

Hypotenuse

identity (trigonometric)   Equations that are true for all values for which the functions are defined. For example $\sin^2 x + \cos^2 x = 1$ which is true for all values of x, or $\cot x = \frac{1}{\tan x}$ which is true whenever the tangent and cotangent are defined. (p. 688)

identity element   The identity element for addition is the number we can add to any number and not change that number's "identity" or value. For addition, the identity element is 0; $a+0=a$ for any number, a. For multiplication, the identity element is 1, because $1 \cdot x = x$ for any number x. (p. 362)

identity matrix   An m by m matrix, often labeled I, with zero in every entry except those on the upper-left to lower-right diagonal. On that diagonal, each entry $m_{ij} = 1$. For any m by m matrix, M, $MI = IM = M$. The identity matrix for a 2 by 2 matrix is shown at right. (p. 362) $\begin{bmatrix} 1 & 0 \\ 0 & 1 \end{bmatrix}$

imaginary numbers   The set of numbers that are solutions of equations of the form $x^2 =$ (a negative number) are called imaginary numbers. They are not positive, negative, or zero. The imaginary number i is a solution of the equation $x^2 = -1$, so $i^2 = -1$. In general, imaginary numbers follow the rules of real number arithmetic (e.g. $i + i = 2i$). Multiplying the imaginary number i by every possible real number yields all possible imaginary numbers. (pp. 454, 456)

independent events   When the probability of two events happening equals the product of their probabilities, the events are said to be independent. For example, the probability of landing on red on two consecutive spins of a roulette wheel is $\frac{9}{19} \cdot \frac{9}{19} = \frac{81}{361}$. (pp. 506, 516)

independent variable   In a function, the independent variable is the input variable. The variable occurring first in an ordered pair. (pp. 6, 13, 199)

index (plural indices)   In summation notation, the indices are the numbers below and above the sigma that indicate which term to start with and which to end with. For a series they show the first and last replacement values for n. When the symbol above sigma is ∞ the series continues without ending. Example: $\sum_{n=1}^{8} 5n - 7 = -2 + 3 + 8 + ... + 33$. (pp. 626, 627)

inequality   A mathematical statement that shows a relationship between two values or expressions where one is greater than (>) the other, or less than (<) the other, or just not equal ($\neq$) to the other. (p. 243)

inequalities with absolute value   If k is any positive number, an inequality of the form: $|f(x)| > k$ is equivalent to the statement $f(x) > k$ or $f(x) < -k$; and $|f(x)| < k$ is equivalent to the statement $-k < f(x) < k$. For example, you can solve the inequality, $|5x - 6| > 4$ by solving the two inequalities $5x - 6 > 4$ or $5x - 6 < -4$. (p. 243)

infinite geometric series   An infinite geometric series is a geometric series which never ends. The sum of such a series with an initial value a and common ratio r, with $-1 < r < 1$, is given by the formula at right. (p. 647) $S = \dfrac{a}{1-r}$

inflection point   A point at which a graph changes concavity. Concavity refers to whether the graph opens upward or downward. So an inflection point is a point at which a graph changes from opening upward to opening downward, or vice versa. The graph of $y = x^3$ has an inflection point, otherwise known as a point of inflection, at $x = 0$.

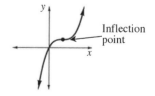

Glossary

initial ray   When an angle of rotation is drawn in standard position, the positive *x*-axis is called the initial ray. (p. 403) See "angle and angle of rotation."

initial value   The initial value of a sequence is the first term of the sequence. (pp. 69, 86)

input   A replacement value for a variable in a function or relation. The first number in an ordered pair. The set of all possible input values is the domain of a function. (p. 6)

integer   Any whole number or the opposite of a whole number: ... $- 3, -2, -1, 0, 1, 2, 3, ...$ (p. 475)

integral roots   Roots (or zeros) of functions that are integers. (p. 475)

intercepts   Points where a graph crosses the axes. *x*-intercepts are points at which the graph crosses the *x* axis and *y*-intercepts are points at which the graph crosses the *y* axis. On the graph at right the *x*-intercept is (3, 0) and the *y*-intercept is (0, 6). (p. 11)

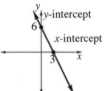

interest   An amount paid which is a percentage of the principal. For example, a savings account may offer 4% annual interest rate, which means they will pay $4.00 in interest for a principal of $100 kept in the account for one year. (p. 125)

intersection   A point of intersection is a point that the graphs of two or more equations have in common. Graphs may intersect in one, two, several, many or no points. The set of coordinates of a point of intersection are a solution to the equation for each graph. (pp. 17, 21, 222, 223, 224)

inverse circular functions   See "inverse trigonometric functions." (p. 684)

inverse function   A function that "undoes" what the original function does. It can also be seen as the *x*-*y* interchange of the function. The inverse of a function performs in reverse order the inverse operation for each operation of the function. The graph of an inverse function is a reflection of the original function across the line $y = x$. For example, $y = x^3 + 2$ is equivalent to $x = \sqrt[3]{y - 2}$, its inverse function is written $y = \sqrt[3]{x - 2}$. (p. 268)

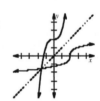

inverse operations   Subtraction is the inverse operation for addition and vice versa, division for multiplication, square root for squaring, and more generally taking the nth root for raising to the nth power.

inverse trigonometric functions   For each trigonometric function $\sin(x)$, $\cos(x)$, and $\tan(x)$, there is an inverse function written $\sin^{-1}(x)$, $\cos^{-1}(x)$, and $\tan^{-1}(x)$. Note: this symbol does not mean $\frac{1}{\sin(x)}$. It is a new function that "undoes" the original trig function, thus giving a specific angle measure when the input is $\sin x$, $\cos x$, or $\tan x$. For example: $\sin^{-1}(-\frac{1}{2}) = -\frac{\pi}{6}$. Note that the range of the inverse function is restricted to outputs for *y* such that $-\frac{\pi}{2} \le y \le \frac{\pi}{2}$ for $\sin x$, $-\frac{\pi}{2} < y < \frac{\pi}{2}$ for $\tan x$ and $0 \le y \le \pi$ for $\cos x$. (p. 684) Also see "cosine inverse," "sine inverse," and "tangent inverse."

investigating a function   To investigate a function means to make a complete graph of the function and to write down everything you know about the function. Some things to consider are: domain, range, intercepts, asymptotes, inverse, and symmetry. (p. 32, 34)

isosceles triangle   A triangle with two sides of equal length.

isometric dot paper   Useful for graphing three dimensional figures. The pattern of dots on the paper enhances the 3-dimensional appearance of the x-, y-, and z-axes. (p. 308)

justify   To give a logical reason supporting a statement or step in a proof. More generally to use facts, definitions, rules, and/or previously proven conjectures in an organized sequence to convincingly demonstrate that your claim is valid. (p. 109)

key point   An important point on a graph. Often an x- or y-intercept, a starting or ending point, a maximum or minimum point. Sometimes a point not on the graph that serves to locate an asymptote. (p. 9)

Law of Cosines   For any $\triangle ABC$, $a^2 = b^2 + c^2 - 2bc\cos A$ (pp. 28, 276)

Law of Sines   For any $\triangle ABC$, $\frac{\sin A}{a} = \frac{\sin B}{b} = \frac{\sin C}{c}$ (pp. 28, 276)

left-multiply   Since multiplication of matrices is not commutative the product AB may not equal BA. If we start with matrix A and we want the product BA we must left-multiply matrix A by matrix B. The order of the multiplication matters; therefore, we specify whether we are multiplying on the left side of the matrix or on the right, which would be right-multiplying. (p. 366)

line   Graphed, a line is made up of an infinite number of points, is one-dimensional and extends without end in two directions. In two dimensions a line is the graph of an equation of the form $ax + by = c$. (pp. 11, 167, 190)

line of best fit   The line that best approximates several data points. For this course we place the line by visually approximating its position. An example is shown in the graph at right.

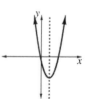

line of symmetry   A line that divides a figure into two congruent shapes which are reflections of each other across the line. (p. 167)

linear equation   An equation with at least one variable of degree one and no variables of degree greater than one. The graph of a linear equation of two variables is a line in the plane. $ax + by = c$ is the standard form of a linear equation. (p. 11)

linear function   A polynomial function of degree one or zero, with general equation $f(x) = a(x - h) + k$. The graph of a linear function is a line. (p. 38)

linear inequality   An inequality with a boundary line represented by a linear equation. (pp. 247, 326)

linear programming A method for solving a problem with several conditions or constraints that can be represented as linear equations or inequalities. (pp. 241, 245)

locator point A locator point is a point which gives the position of a graph with respect to the axes. For a parabola, the vertex is a locator point. (p. 181)

locus The location of a set of points that fit a given description. For example: A circle with center $(5, -2)$ and radius 3 is described as the locus of points that are a distance of three units from the point $(5, -2)$. (p. 566)

Log-Power Property (p. 330) See "Power Property of Logs."

Log-Product Property (pp. 334, 335) See "Product Property of Logs."

Log-Quotient Property (pp. 334, 335) See "Quotient Property of Logs."

logarithm An exponent. In the equation $y = 2^x$, x is the logarithm, base 2, of y, or $\log_2 y = x$. (pp. 282, 283)

logarithmic and exponential notation $m = \log_b(n)$ is the logarithmic form of the exponential equation $b^m = n$ $(b > 0)$. (p. 283)

logarithmic functions Inverse exponential functions. The base of the logarithm is the same base as that of the exponential function. For instance $y = \log_2 x$ can be read as "y is the exponent needed for base 2 to get x," and is equivalent to $x = 2^y$. The short version is stated "log, base 2, of x," and written $\log_2 x$. (pp. 281, 285, 286)

major axis The longer axis of an ellipse. The distance from the center of the ellipse to the end of the major axis is the semi-major axis, represented as a in the general equation. (pp. 574, 576) See "ellipse."

mathematical induction In this course, a method of proof that can be used to prove that a formula is true for any natural number ($n = 1, 2, 3, \ldots$) Such a proof consists of the following steps: (i) Verify that the formula is true for $n = 1$. (ii) Write the general statement of the formula for $n = k+1$. (iii) Show and justify the reasoning needed to move from the result for $n = k$ to get to the next case where $n = k + 1$. (pp. 629, 632)

matrix A rectangular array of numbers or algebraic expressions enclosed in square brackets. Usually a matrix is denoted by a capital letter. The plural is "matrices." Each matrix has horizontal rows and vertical columns. The number of rows and columns describe the matrix, so if a matrix has m rows and n columns we say the matrix has dimension m by n. We often write that $m_{i, j}$ is the entry in the ith row and the jth column. In the 3×3 matrix at right, $m_{2,3} = 2$. (p. 351)

$$\begin{bmatrix} 3 & 0 & -1 \\ 12 & 5 & 2 \\ 1 & -2 & 1 \end{bmatrix}$$

maximize Make as large as possible. (pp. 242, 246)

maximum point The highest point on a graph. For example, the vertex of a downwardly oriented parabola. (pp. 242, 246)

maximum value   The largest value in the range of a function. For example, the *y*-coordinate of the vertex of a downwardly oriented parabola. (pp. 242, 246)

mean   The average for a set of data. The mean is found by summing all the numbers and dividing the sum by the number of pieces of data. (p. 94)

median   The middle score of a set of data. The median is found by arranging the numbers from highest to lowest and finding the number in the middle. If the number of values is even, the median is the average (mean) of the two middle numbers. (p. 94)

minimize   Make as small as possible. (pp. 242, 246)

minimum point   The lowest point on a graph. For example, the vertex of an upwardly oriented parabola. (p. 242, 246)

minimum value   The smallest value in the range of a function. For example, the *y*-coordinate of the vertex of an upwardly oriented parabola. (pp. 242, 246)

minor axis   The shorter axis in an ellipse. The length of the semi-minor axis, the distance from the center to the end of the minor axis, is represented by b in the general equation. (pp. 574, 576) See "ellipse."

multiplicative inverse   The multiplicative inverse for a non-zero number is the number we can multiply by to get the multiplicative identity, 1. For example, for the number 5, the multiplicative inverse is $\frac{1}{5}$; for the number $\frac{2}{3}$ the multiplicative inverse is $\frac{3}{2}$. The multiplicative inverse for a complex number, such as $3 - i$, is $\frac{1}{3-i} = \frac{3}{\sqrt{10}} + \frac{1}{\sqrt{10}}i$. The multiplicative inverse for a square matrix is the matrix we can multiply by to get the identity matrix. (pp. 364, 366)

multiplier   In a geometric sequence the number multiplied times each term to get the next term is called the multiplier or the common ratio or generator. The multiplier is also the number you can multiply by in order to increase or decrease an amount by a given percentage in one step. For example, to increase a number by 4%, the multiplier is 1.04. We would multiply the number by 1.04. The multiplier for decreasing by 4% is 0.96. (pp. 79, 80, 83, 86)

negative exponents   Raising a number to a negative exponent is the same as taking the reciprocal of the number. $x^{-a} = \frac{1}{x^a}$ for $x \neq 0$. (pp. 132, 148)

non-function   A relation that has more than one output for one or more of its inputs. (pp. 197, 198)

order   In a counting problem the order in which events occurs is sometimes important. For example, when an outcome ABC is considered to be different from BAC the different arrangements of A, B, and C are being counted as different results and the order of the events is important in determining the number of results. (pp. 523, 530) See "permutations."

ordered pair   A pair of numbers written (x, y) used to represent the coordinates of a point in an *xy*-plane where *x* represents the horizontal distance from 0 and *y* is the vertical. The input and output values of a function or relation can be represented as ordered pairs were *x* is the input, and *y* is the output.

ordered triple   Three real numbers written in order (x, y, z) represent a point in space or replacement values for a situation involving three variables. See "3-dimensional coordinate axes." (p. 312)

orientation   Used informally in this course to describe some graphs. For example the direction a parabola opens might be referred to as its orientation. When describing the graph of a polynomial function, a positive orientation would mean the graph eventually continues upward as the value of x increases, as in the example above right. A negative orientation would mean it eventually heads downward as the value of x continues to increase, as in the example below right. (pp. 175, 445)

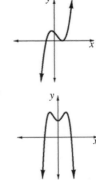

outcome   Used to describe the result of an event in counting and probability problems. For example, when rolling one six-sided die, the possible outcomes are the numbers 1, 2, 3, 4, 5, and 6. (pp. 497, 502, 510)

output   Used to describe the result of applying a function or relationship rule to an input value. When a function is represented by a function machine the output is the number that comes out of the machine. For the function $f(x) = x^2 - 73$ when the input is 10, the output is 27. Function notation shows how the function operates on the input to produce the output: $f(10) = 10^2 - 73 = 27$. (p. 6)

parabola   The set of all points that are equidistant from a single point (the focus) and a line (the directrix). The general equation for a parabola that is a function (or a quadratic function) in graphing (or vertex) form, is $y = a(x - h)^2 + k$. The general equation of a quadratic function in standard form is $y = ax^2 + bx + c$. A general equation for parabolas that are not functions, "sleeping" parabolas, is $x - h = a(y - k)^2$. (pp. 168, 171, 179, 181-183, 199, 555, 556, 568)

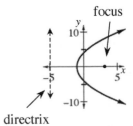
focus

directrix

parallel   Two lines in a plane are parallel if they never intersect. Parallel lines have the same slope. Two line segments in a plane are parallel if the lines they lie on lines that never intersect. Two lines in space are parallel if they lie in the same plane and they do not intersect. There is a constant distance between parallel lines.

parameter   In a general equations where x and y represent the inputs and outputs of the function, variables such as a, b, c, m, h, and k are often referred to as parameters, and they are often replaced with specific values. For example: in the equation $y = a(x - h)^2 + k$ representing all parabolas that are functions, the a, h, and k are (variable) parameters that give the shape and location, while x and y are the independent and dependent variables. (pp. 38, 115, 143, 175, 413)

parent graph   The simplest version of a family of graphs. For instance, the graph of $y = x^2$, is considered the parent graph for parabolas that are functions. (p. 182)

Pascal's Triangle   The array of numbers at right. The triangular pattern continues downward. This array shows all the values of $_nC_r$ where n is the row number when the vertex is $_0C_0$. r is the number of places to the right in row n (when the counting begins with 0). For instance, $_5C_2$ is equal to 10. (p. 649)

```
        1
      1   1
    1   2   1
  1   3   3   1
1   4   6   4   1
1  5  10  10  5  1
```

percentile   A percentile ranking indicates the percentage of scores which are below the score in question. For example, if you scored at the 90th percentile on a test, your score was higher than the scores of 90% of the other test takers.

perfect square   Usually, a quadratic polynomial $ax^2 + bx + c$ that can be rewritten as the second power of a binomial, $(cx + d)^2$. For example, $x^2 - 6x + 9$ is a perfect square that can be rewritten as $(x - 3)^2$. Also, any polynomial of even degree that can be rewritten as the square of one polynomial factor. For numbers, a whole number that can be written as the second power of another whole number. For example, 1, 4, 9, 16, and 25 are perfect squares.

perimeter   The distance around the exterior of a figure on a flat surface. For a polygon the perimeter is the sum of the lengths of its sides. The perimeter of a circle is called its circumference.

period   The length of one cycle of a graph, as shown by the dashed line in the graph at right. (pp. 416, 423)

periodic function   A function which has a repetitive section or cycle such as the sine, cosine and tangent functions. In a periodic function, the cyclic pattern continues forever both to the left and to the right. (p. 423)

permutation   A permutation is an arrangement in which the order of selection matters. For example a batting line-up is a permutation because it is an ordered list of players. If each of five letters, A, B, C, D, E is printed on a card, the number of 3-letter sequences can you make by selecting three of the five cards is a permutation. Permutations can be represented with tree diagrams, decision charts, and their value calculated by using the formula for $_nP_r = \frac{n!}{(n-r)!}$. In the example given above, $_5P_3 = \frac{5!}{2!} = \frac{5 \cdot 4 \cdot 3 \cdot 2 \cdot 1}{2 \cdot 1} = 5 \cdot 4 \cdot 3 = 60$. (pp. 518, 520, 525)

perpendicular   Two lines, rays, or line segments that intersect to form a right angle. A line and a plane can also be perpendicular if the line does not lie in the plane, but intersects it and forms a right angle with every line in the plane that passes through the point of intersection.

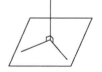

plane   A plane is an undefined term in geometry. It is a two-dimensional flat surface that extends without end. It is made up of points and has no thickness. The part of a plane outlined by its xy-, xz- and yz-traces is often used to represent a plane on a 3-dimensional coordinate system. (pp. 312, 320)

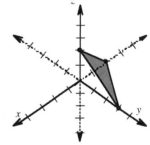

point   An undefined term in geometry. A point has no dimensions but can be located by its coordinates on a number line, in a plane, or in space.

point-slope form $y - k = m(x - h)$ is called the point slope form of a linear equation or function because it shows the slope m and a point (h, k) that is on the graph of the line. For example, given a line that has slope $\frac{5}{3}$ and contains the point with coordinates $(3, -4)$ its equation can be written $y + 4 = \frac{5}{3}(x - 3)$. (p. 190)

polynomial   An algebraic expression that involves at most the operations of addition, subtraction, and multiplication. A polynomial in one variable is an expression that can be written as the sum of terms of the form: (any number) $\cdot$ $x^{\text{(whole number)}}$. These polynomials are usually arranged with the powers of x in order, starting with the highest, left to right. The numbers that multiply the powers of x are called the coefficients of the polynomial. See "degree of a polynomial" for an example. (pp. 437, 440, 441, 451)

Power Property of Logs $\log_m(a^n) = n\log_m(a)$. For example, $\log_3 625 = 4\log_3 5$. (pp. 330, 335)

principal   Initial investment or capital. An initial value.

probability   The probability that an event A. with a finite number of equally likely outcomes, will occur is the number of outcomes for event A divided by the total number of equally likely outcomes. This can be written as $\frac{\textit{number of outcomes for event A}}{\textit{total number of possible outcomes}}$. A probability p is a ratio, $0 \leq p \leq 1$. (p. 510)

Product Property of Logs $\log_m(a \cdot b) = \log_m(a) + \log_m(b)$. For example, $\log_3 30 = \log_3 5 + \log_3 6$. (p. 334)

profit   The amount of money after expenses have been accounted for. (pp. 241, 242, 245)

proof by induction   (pp. 629, 632) See "mathematical induction."

proportion   Equal ratios are described as a proportion. For example, the equation $\frac{x-8}{2x+1} = \frac{5}{6}$.

Pythagorean Identity   For trigonometric functions, $\cos^2 x + \sin^2 x = 1$ for any value of x. (pp. 689, 695)

quadratic equation   Any equation where at least one term has degree 2 and no term has degree higher than 2. The standard equation $Ax^2 + By^2 + Cxy + Dx + Ey + F = 0$ represents all quadratic relations in one or two variables. (pp. 23, 171, 177, 188)

quadratic formula   This formula gives you the solutions $x = \frac{-b \pm \sqrt{b^2 - 4ac}}{2a}$, for a quadratic equation in one variable that can be written in the standard form $ax^2 + bx + c = 0$. (p. 23)

quadratic function   A quadratic equation that can be written $y = ax^2 + bx + c$ is also a quadratic function where x is the independent variable and y is the dependent variable. Its graph is a parabola with a vertical orientation. The graphing form of a quadratic function is $f(x) = a(x - h)^2 + k$. (pp. 177, 188)

quadratic relation   The conic sections are quadratic relations. See "general quadratic equation," "quadratic equations," "parabola," "ellipse," and "hyperbola." (p. 593)

quotient   The result of a division problem is a quotient with a remainder (which could be 0). When a polynomial $p(x)$ is divided by a polynomial $d(x)$ the a polynomial $q(x)$ will be the quotient with a remainder $r(x)$. The product of $q(x)$ and $d(x)$ plus the remainder $r(x)$ will equal the original polynomial. $p(x) = d(x)q(x) + r(x)$. (p. 472)

Quotient Property of Logs $\log_m(\frac{a}{b}) = \log_m(a) - \log_m(b)$. For example, $\log_3 \frac{37}{5} = \log_3 37 - \log_3 5$. (p. 334)

radian measure   An arc of a unit circle equal to the length of the radius of the circle is one radian. The central angle for this arc has measure one radian. 1 radian = $\frac{180}{\pi}$ degrees. (p. 399)

range   The range of a function is the set of possible outputs for a function. It consists of all the values of the dependent variable, that is every number that y can represent for the function $f(x) = y$. (pp. 18, 199)

ratio   The comparison of two quantities or expressions by division. (p. 83)

rational number   A number that can be written as a fraction $\frac{a}{b}$ where a and b are integers and $b \neq 0$. (p. 453)

rational equation   An equation that includes at least one rational expression. For example, $5 - \frac{x+2}{x} = 7$. (p. 347)

rational expression   An expression in the form of a fraction in which the numerator and denominator are polynomials. For example, $\frac{x-7}{x^2+8x-9}$ is a rational expression.

rational function   A function that contains at least one rational expression. For example, $f(x) = \frac{5}{x-3}$.

real numbers   The set of all rational numbers and irrational numbers is referred to as the set of real numbers. Any real number can be represented by a point on a number line. (pp. 17, 199, 456)

rebound height   The height a ball reaches after a bounce. (pp. 60, 64)

rebound ratio   The ratio of the height a ball bounces after one bounce to the height from which it dropped. (pp. 60, 64)

reciprocal   The multiplicative inverse of a number or an expression. (p. 682)

rectangular numbers   The terms of the sequence 0, 2, 6, 12, 20, …. These numbers are called rectangular because they count the number of dots in rectangular arrays with the dimensions $n(n+1)$ where $n = 0, 1, 2, 3, 4, …$

recursive definition   For a sequence, a recursive definition is a rule that gives the first term and then tells us how to get the next term of the sequence from the term or terms that precede it. For example, in the Fibonacci sequence $1, 1, 2, 3, 5, 8, …$, the next term is the sum of the previous two terms.

reference angle   For every angle of rotation in standard position, the reference angle is the angle in the first quadrant $0 \le \theta \le \frac{\pi}{2}$ whose cosine and sine have the same absolute values as the cosine and sine of the original angle. (p. 403)

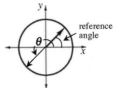

reflect vertically   Used here to mean reflect a graph across the x-axis so that every point (x, y) on the original graph becomes $(x, -y)$ on the reflection. The graph of $y = -x^2$ is a vertical reflection of $y = x^2$. (p. 207)

relation   Functions are also relations, but relations are not necessarily functions. The equations for parabolas, ellipses, hyperbolas, and circles are all relations but only the equations that describe vertically oriented parabolas are functions. (pp. 6, 199)

relative maximum (minimum)   A function that has a "peak" (or "valley") at a point P is said to have a relative maximum (minimum) at the point P. This is the point where the function changes direction.

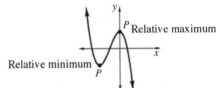

remainder   When dividing polynomials in one variable, the remainder is what is left after the constant term of the quotient has been determined. The degree of the remainder must be less than the degree of the divisor.   In the example below the remainder is $3x - 3$.
$(x^4 + 3x^3 - x^2 + x - 7) \div (x^2 + x + 1) = x^2 + 2x - 4 + \frac{3x-3}{x^2+x+1}$. (p. 472) Also see "quotient."

repeated root   A root of a polynomial that occurs more than once. The root r will occur as many times as $(x - r)$ is a factor of the polynomial. (p. 446) See "double root" and "triple root."

repetition   An important criterion to consider when counting outcomes of an event. Whether an outcome can be repeated determines the number of alternatives that would include that outcome. For example: If A, B, and C are letters written on cards, the number of arrangements possible will be $3 \cdot 2 \cdot 1$. But if you ask how many arrangements of A, B, and C could appear on a license plate, the answer will be $3 \cdot 3 \cdot 3$. Arrangements that involve repetition of a letter, such as AAA or CAC are counted when counting possible license plates. (pp. 523, 529)

reversing   To reverse your thinking can be described as "thinking backward." It sometimes means starting at the end of a problem and working backward to the beginning. It is useful to think this way when you want to undo a process or understand a concept from a new direction. Thinking about inverse functions involves reversing your thinking. Writing polynomials, given their zeros is another example. (pp. 263, 286)

rewrite   To rewrite an equation or expression is to write an equivalent equation or expression. Rewriting could involve using the Distributive Property, following the order of operations, using properties of 0 or 1, substitution, inverse operations, Properties of Logarithms, or use of trigonometric identities. We usually rewrite in order to change expressions or equations into more useful forms or sometimes, just simpler forms. (pp. 68, 97, 101, 144, 222, 244)

right-multiply   Since multiplication of matrices is not commutative the product *AB* may not equal *BA*. If we want the product *BA* we can right-multiply matrix *B* by matrix *A* or we can left-multiply matrix *A* by matrix *B*. The order of the multiplication matters; therefore, we specify whether we are left-multiplying or right-multiplying. See "left-multiply." (p. 366)

right angle   An angle with measure 90°.

right triangle   A triangle with a right angle.

roots of a function   The number *r* is a root (or zero) of the function $f(x)$ if $f(r) = 0$. A root may be a real or a complex number. Real roots occur where the graph of the function $f(x)$ crosses the *x*-axis. Complex roots must be found algebraically. (pp. 144, 446, 447)

rule   An algebraic representation or a written description of a mathematical relationship. (pp. 123, 135)

sample space   With probability, all the possible outcomes. (pp. 501, 510)

secant   The reciprocal of the cosine. (p. 683)

sequence   A function in which the independent variable is a positive integer (sometimes called the "term number"). The dependent variable is the term value. A sequence is usually written as a list of numbers. For example, the arithmetic sequence 5, 8, 11, ... (pp. 69, 71, 83)

series   The sum of the terms of a sequence. (pp. 610, 618, 636)

sigma   The Greek letter Σ which is used to mean sum. Using Σ provides a way to write a short, compact mathematical representation for a series. (p. 626) See "summation notation."

similar   Two figures are similar if they have the same shape, but are not necessarily the same size. The ratios of the lengths of corresponding sides of similar figures are equivalent.

simple interest   Interest paid on the principal alone. (p. 125)

simplify   To rewrite an expression or equation as an equivalent expression or equation in a form that is considered to be simpler or less cumbersome than the original. (p. 133) See "rewrite."

sine   In a right triangle (as shown at right) the ratio $\frac{opposite\ side}{hypotenuse}$ is known as the sine of the acute angle. **At right,** $\sin B = \frac{b}{c}$ since the side length *b* is opposite angle *B*. (p. 407)

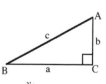

sine function   For any real number θ, the sine of θ, denoted $\sin\theta$, is the *y*-coordinate of the point on the unit circle reached by a rotation angle of θ radians in standard position. The general equation for the sine function is $y = a\sin b(x - h) + k$. This function has amplitude *a*, period $\frac{2\pi}{b}$, horizontal shift *h*, and vertical shift *k*. (pp. 383, 409, 423)

sine inverse ($\sin^{-1} x$) Read as the inverse of sine x, $\sin^{-1} x$ is the measure of the angle with sine x. We can also write $y = \arcsin x$. Note that the notation refers to the inverse of the sine function, *not* $\frac{1}{\sin x}$. Because $y = \sin^{-1} x$ is equivalent to $x = \sin y$ and there are infinitely many angles y such that $\sin y = x$, the inverse *function* is restricted to select the *principal* value of y such that $-\frac{\pi}{2} \leq y \leq \frac{\pi}{2}$. The graph of the inverse function, $y = \sin^{-1} x$ with $\frac{\pi}{2} \leq y \leq \frac{\pi}{2}$ is at right. (p. 684)

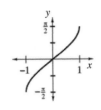

sketch To sketch the graph of an equation means to show the approximate shape of the graph in the correct location with respect to the axes with key points clearly labeled. (p. 8)

"sleeping" parabola A "sleeping" parabola is a parabola which opens to the left or right, rather than upward or downward. These parabolas are not the graphs of functions. (p. 199)

slope The ratio of the vertical change to the horizontal change between any two points on a line. For any two points (x_1, y_1) and (x_2, y_2) on a given line, the slope is $\frac{y_2 - y_1}{x_2 - x_1}$. For example, the slope of a line between points with coordinates $(3, -5)$ and $(-7, 2)$ is $\frac{2-(-5)}{-7-3} = -\frac{7}{10}$. (pp. 11, 200)

slope-intercept form A linear equation written in the form $y = mx + b$ is written in slope-intercept form. In this form, m is the slope of the line and the point $(0, b)$ is the y-intercept. (p. 11)

solution Of an equation or inequality is a number or expression that makes the equation or inequality true when substituted for the variable. To find the numerical solution means to identify all the numbers that make a mathematical equation or inequality true. There may be any number of solutions for an equation or inequality, from 0 to infinitely many. Solutions to equations and inequalities in one variable are single numbers. For two variables they are ordered pairs, for three variables ordered triples. Equations with no solutions, such as $|x - 5| = -3$, are never true. Equations with one, several, or many solutions, such as $x(x + 3)(x - 7) = 0$ are sometimes true, and equations or identities such as $5(2x - 4) = 10x - 20$ are always true. (pp. 224, 225, 226, 229, 250, 443, 447)

standard form (linear function) A linear equation written in the form $Ax + By = C$ is written in standard form. For linear functions, $B \neq 0$. (p. 11)

standard form (quadratic function) The standard form for the equation of a quadratic function is $y = ax^2 + bx + c$ where $a \neq 0$. (p. 177)

standard form (quadratic relations in general) The standard for parabolas, ellipses, and hyperbolas with axes parallel to the x- or y-axes is $Ax^2 + By^2 + Cx + Dy + E = 0$. (p. 593)

standard window The graphing window on a calculator set to show the x- and y-axes for values $-10 \leq x \leq 10$ and $-10 \leq y \leq 10$.

stretch factor   Used to describe the effect of a in the graphing form of a quadratic, cubic, absolute value, or exponential function. For $a > 1$ or $a < -1$ the outputs increase or decrease faster than the outputs for the parent functions, and the graphs are described as being stretched upwards or downwards in relation to the parent graph. (pp. 170, 175)

subproblems   A large problem can sometimes be separated into smaller or simpler problems called "subproblems" so that the solution of these subproblems leads to the solution of the larger problem. (p. 529)

substitution   Replacing a variable or expression with a number, another variable, or another expression. For example, when evaluating the function $f(x) = 5x - 1$, for $x = 3$, substitute 3 for x to get $f(3) = 5(3) - 1 = 14$. (p. 56)

substitution to solve a system of equations   A method for solving a system of equations by replacing one variable with an expression involving the remaining variable(s). (p. 56)

summation notation   A convenient way to represent a series is to use summation notation. The Greek letter sigma, Σ, indicates a sum. For example, $\sum_{n=1}^{4} 3n = 3(1) + 3(2) + 3(3) + 3(4) = 30$.

The numbers below and above the sigma are called the indices. The index below, $n = 1$, tells us what value to start with for n. The top index tells us how high the value can go. In the example shown above, n starts at 1 and increases to 4. (pp. 626, 627)

surface area   The sum of all the areas of the surfaces of a three-dimensional figure or object.

symmetry   A figure that appears not to change when reflected across a line is said to have reflection symmetry. A figure that appears not to change when rotated through an angle of less than $360°$ is described as having rotation symmetry. (p. 167)

system of equations   A system of equations is a set of equations with more than one unknown or variable. The systems we solve most often in this course have two or three equations and two or three variables. Systems of equations are often solved using substitution or elimination to reduce the number of variables. A system of quadratic equations is shown at right. (pp. 17, 223, 224, 229, 232, 250)

$$y = x^2 + 8x - 4$$
$$y = 2x^2 + 5x - 8$$

tangent   In a right triangle (at right) the ratio $\frac{opposite\ side}{adjacent\ side}$ is known as the tangent of an acute angle. At right, $\tan B = \frac{b}{a}$ since the side of length b is opposite angle B and the side length a is adjacent to (or next to) angle B. The function $f(\theta) = \tan(\theta) = \frac{y}{x}$ where (x, y) are the coordinates of the point on the unit circle where the radius makes an angle of θ with the positive horizontal axis. (pp. 405, 407)

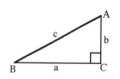

tangent function   For any real number θ, the tangent of θ, denoted $\tan\theta$, is the slope of the line containing the ray which represents a rotation of θ radians in standard position. The general equation for the tangent function is $y = a\tan b(x - h) + k$. This function has period of $\frac{\pi}{b}$, vertical asymptotes at $\frac{\pi}{2b} + h \pm \frac{n\pi}{b}$ for $n = 1, 2, ...$, horizontal shift h, and vertical shift k. (p. 405)

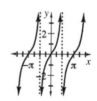

tangent inverse ($\tan^{-1} x$)   Read as the inverse of tangent x, $\tan^{-1} x$ is the measure of the angle that has tangent x. We can also write $y = \arctan x$. Note that the notation refers to the inverse of the tangent function, *not* $\frac{1}{\tan x}$. Because $y = \tan^{-1} x$ is equivalent to $x = \tan y$ and there are infinitely many angles y such that $\tan y = x$, the inverse *function* is restricted to select the *principal* value of y such that $\frac{\pi}{2} < x < \frac{\pi}{2}$. The graph of the inverse tangent function is at right. (p. 679)

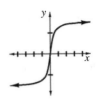

term   A single number, variable, or product of numbers and variables. A monomial is a term. Also a component of a sequence. (p. 75)

term number   In a sequence, a number that gives the position of a term in the sequence. A replacement value for the independent variable in a function that determines the sequence. See "sequences." (p. 92)

terminal ray   When an angle of rotation is drawn in standard position, the positive x-axis is called the initial ray and the ray that determines the angle is called the terminal ray. (p. 407) See "angle."

theoretical probability   A probability calculation based on counting possible outcomes. (p. 540)

transverse axis   In a hyperbola, the line connecting the vertices of the two branches. (p. 585) See "hyperbola."

tree diagram (or model)   Tree diagrams are useful for representing possible outcomes of probability experiments. For example, the tree diagram at right represents the possible outcomes when a coin is flipped twice. (pp. 497, 502)

triangular numbers   The terms of the sequence 0, 1, 3, 6, 10, ... are known as the triangular numbers. These numbers are called triangular because they count the number of points in a sequence of triangular patterns. Each number also represents the sum of the first n integers ($n \geq 0$).

trigonometric ratios   (p. 28) See "sine," "cosine," "tangent," "secant," "cosecant," and "cotangent."

triple root   A root of a function that occurs exactly three times. If an expression of the form $(x - a)^3$ is a factor of a polynomial, then the polynomial has a triple root at $x = a$. The graph of the polynomial has an inflection point at $x = a$. (p. 446)

undoing   Using inverse operations and reversing the order of operations to solve an equation in one variable or to "undo" a function rule in order to write its inverse. For example, in the equation $y = x^3 - 7$, add y and write the cube root. (pp. 222, 263, 264)

unit circle   A circle with a radius of one unit is called a unit circle. (pp. 390, 402)

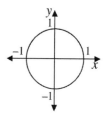

variable   A symbol used to represent one or more numbers. In this course, letters of the English alphabet are used as variables in addition to the Greek letters, θ, α, and β. (p. 38)

vertex   For a parabola that is a function, the vertex of a parabola is the lowest or highest point of the graph of the parabola. The vertex of a parabola locates its position with respect to the axes. It is the lowest or highest point of the graph of the parabola. In general, the vertex is the turning point for a graph. (p. 168) See "parabola," "ellipse," "hyperbola," "absolute value," for other graphs with vertices (the plural of vertex).

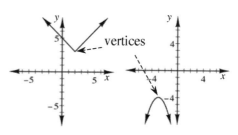

vertex form   The vertex form for the equation of a quadratic function (also called graphing form) is written $y = a(x - h)^2 + k$. (p. 177)

vertical shift   Used to describe the location of a graph in relation to its parent graph, the shift is the vertical distance (up or down) of each point on the graph from the corresponding point on the parent graph. For example, each point on the graph of $y = x^2 + 2$ is two units higher that its corresponding point on $y = x^2$. In a general equation such as $y = a(x - h)^2 + k$ the vertical shift is represented by k. (p. 175)

volume   For a 3-dimensional figure the number of non-overlapping cubic units that will fit inside. (p. 25)

x-intercept   A point where a graph intersects the x-axis. In two dimensions, the coordinates of the x-intercept are $(x, 0)$. In three dimensions they are $(x, 0, 0)$. (pp. 11, 446, 447) See "intercept."

x-y interchange   The result of exchanging the x and y variables and then solving for y. The resulting equation is the inverse of the original function. (pp. 276, 283)

x → y table   A table that represents pairs of related values. The input value x appears in the first row or column, and the output value, y, appears in the second. The $x \to y$ table at right contains input and output pairs for the equation $y = x^2 - 3$. (p. 8)

x	y
-3	6
-2	1
-1	-2
0	-3
1	-2
2	1

y-intercept   A point where a graph intersects the y-axis. In two dimensions the coordinates of the y-intercept are $(0, y)$. In three dimensions, the coordinates are $(0, y, 0)$. (p. 11) See "intercept."

zero factorial   Zero factorial is 1, $0! = 1$. (pp. 522, 526, 543)

zero power   The result of raising any number (except zero) to the zero power is 1. $x^0 = 1$ for any number $x \neq 0$. (pp. 132, 148)

Zero Product Property   When the product of two or more factors is zero, at least one of the factors must equal zero. Used to solve equations in factored form. For example, given the equation $(x-4)(x+5) = 0$ you can see that 4 and -5 are solutions and that they are the only possible solutions because there are no other numbers that make either factor zero. (p. 23)

zeros of a function   The roots of a function or the values of x for which the function value $y = 0$. The x-intercepts of the graph of a function in the real plane are zeros. These are also called the roots of the function. A function can have complex zeros. These complex zeros cause $y = 0$, but they are not x-intercepts since they do not exist in the real plane. (p. 447) See "roots of a function."

Index
Student Version and Additional Resources

Many of the pages referenced here contain a definition or an example of the topic listed, often within the body of a Math Notes box. Others contain problems that develop or demonstrate the topic. It may be necessary to read the text on several pages to fully understand the topic. Also, some problems listed here are good examples of the topic and may not offer any explanation. The page numbers below reflect the pages in the Student Version. References to Math Notes boxes are bolded.

PG indicates page numbers from the Parent Guide with Extra Practice.

SSD indicates a web-based resource available at: www.cpm.org/teachers/state_stds_supplements.htm.

An electronic copy of the Parent Guide with Extra Practice is also available for free download at: www.cpm.org/teachers/resources.htm.

Since the time of this printing, additional recourses may have been added. Please check the websites above for the most complete list.

B

Base 10 logarithms, 288, 329; PG 82
Binomial Theorem, **655**; PG 169
   application, 653
Bouncing Ball Lab, 60, 64
Boundary, 236; PG 67
   curve, **247**
   line, **247**
   point, 236, 238; PG 67
Building With Yarn, 3
Bunny problem, 53

C

Candy Dish Investigation, 537
Casino Dice Game, 538
Causation, SSD: Displaying Data
Change of base, 592
Choose, **525**, **530**; PG 145
Choosing a strategy, 2
Circle
   general equation, 206; PG 50
Coefficient, **440**; PG 123
Cofunction Identities, **695**
Column, 348, **351**; PG 98
Combinations
   counting, 523, **530**; PG 145
   definition, 523; PG 145
   notation, **530**; PG 145
Common difference, 75, **83**; PG 15
Common ratio, **83**; PG 15
Complete graph, 9; PG 3
Completing the square, 202, 206, 387,
   736; PG 53, 151
Complex
   number, **199**, 455, **456**; PG 128
      absolute value, 464, **466**
      arithmetic operations, 454, 458,
      479
      graphing, **466**
      plane, 464, **466**
      root, 458, **460**; PG 129
      solutions, 458; PG 128
Complex axes, 463
Complex conjugate, **460**; PG 129
Complex fraction, 331; SSD: Rational
   Expressions
Composite function, 292
Composition of functions, **274**; PG 77

Compound interest, 125, **658**;
   PG 29
   continuous, 661
Compress
   horizontal, 175; PG 43
   vertical, 170, 175; PG 43
Conditional probability, 506,
   516
Cone, 554; PG 151
Conic section, 554, 561; PG 151
   ellipse, **571**, **576**; PG 151
   hyperbola, **585**; PG 151
   orientation, **580**
   parabola, **555**, **558**; PG 151
Conjugate
   complex, **460**
   axis, 585
Continuous
   function, 86
   graph, **62**; PG 14
Cooling Corpse Lab, 342
Coordinate system
   three-dimensional, 307;
      PG 87
Correlation, SSD: Displaying
   Data
Cos x
   graphing, 392; PG 109
   inverse, 675, 679; PG 174
   investigation, 392; PG 109
Cosecant, 682; PG 175
Cosine, 392
   inverse, **684**; PG 109
Cosine of θ, **407**; PG 109
Cotangent, 683; PG 175
Counting
   combinations, 523, **530**;
      PG 139
   factorial, **521**; PG 139
   permutations, 518, **525**;
      PG 139
Cross-sections
   conic sections, 561; PG 152
Cube root, 137, 144
Curve fitting, 143, 147; PG 34
Cyclic, 379
Cyclic function, 412; PG 173

Graphing form (of a quadratic), 176,
177, 736; PG 46
Growth factor, **11**

H
Half-life, 131; PG 30
Horizontal asymptote, **118**; PG 7
Horizontal compression, 175; PG 44
Horizontal shift, 175; PG 44
Hyperbola, 579, 583; PG 6
    conjugate axis, **585**
    eccentricity, **585**
    foci, **585**
    general equation, **585**
    transverse axis, **585**
    vertices, **585**

I
Identity matrix
    additive, 362
    multiplicative, 362; PG 100
Imaginary
    numbers, 453, **454**, **456**; PG 128
    graphing, 466
    roots, 458; PG 129
Independent events, 506, **516**
Independent variable, **6**, 13, **199**
Index, 626, **627**; PG 160
Induction, 629, **632**; PG 163
    proof by, 629; PG 163
Inequalities
    absolute value, 236, 237, **243**, 742
    graphing, 235, 236, **247**, 732;
        PG 67
    linear, 236, 247; PG 68
    system, 237
    solving, 235; PG 67
Inequality notation, 18; PG 68
Infinite geometric series
    sum, **647**; PG 167
Infinity, 17
Initial term, **92**
Initial value, 69, **86**; PG 15
Input, **6**; PG 1
Integral root, 475; PG 134
Integral Zero Theorem, **478**; PG 134

Intercepts
    average of, 176, 177; PG 53
    x-intercept, 11, 720; PG 3
    y-intercept, 11, 720; PG 3
Interest
    compound, 125; PG 29
    simple, 125
Intersection, 17, 21, 222, 223,
    224; PG 3, 61
Inverse, 267, **269**, 272, **276**,
    744; PG 77, 78
    absolute value, 279
    additive, 352
    cosine, 675, 679; PG 173
    equation, 272, 443, 744;
        PG 77
    exponential, 282; PG 81
    exponential function, 277,
        278, 281; PG 81
    function, 268, 744; PG 77
    graphing, 267, 268, **269**,
        276, 744; PG 78
    notation, **269**, **276**; PG 77
    relations, 268
    sine, 678; PG 174
    tangent, 679; PG 174
    trigonometric functions, **684**;
        PG 173
    variation, SSD
Inverse cosine
    graph, **684**; PG 173
Inverse function, 272; PG 77
Inverse sine
    graph, **684**; PG 174
Inverse tangent
    graph, **684**; PG 174
Investigating, 2, 47
Investigating a function
    introduction, 32, 34; PG 6
Irrational numbers, **453**

J
Joint variation, SSD

L

Law of Cosines, **28**, **276**
Law of Sines, **28**, **276**
Laws of exponents, 132, **148**,713, 730;
      PG 31
Learning log, 18
Left multiply, **366**
Line, forms
      of symmetry, 167
      parent equation of, 190
      point-slope, 190; PG 13
      slope-intercept, **11**, 704; PG 3
      standard, **11**
Line of symmetry, 265, 268
Linear equation, **11**, 704; PG 3
Linear function, 38
    sequence, 77
Linear inequalities, 247
    graphing, 326, 732; PG 69
Linear programming, 241, 245;
      PG 69
List, systematic, **502**
Locator point, 181; PG 44
Locus, 566
    definition, 566
Logarithm, 282, **283**; PG 81
    base, **283**; PG 81
    base 10, 288, 329; PG 82
    definition, **335**; PG 81
    general equation, 289
    graphing, 281, 285, 286; PG 81
    introduction, 278; PG 81
    inverse relationship, **335**; PG 81
    notation, **283**; PG 81
    power property, 335; PG 93
    power rule, 330; PG 93
    product property, 334, **335**; PG 94
    quotient property, 334, **335**;
      PG 94
    solving equations, 329; PG 93
Logarithmic form, 283; PG 81
Looking inside, 222

M

Major axis, 574, **576**
Mathematical induction, 629,
      632; PG 163
Mathematical model
    cubic
      Game Tank Lab, 484
    exponential
      The Bouncing Ball Lab,
        60, 64
      Fast Cars Lab, 151
      The Penny Lab, 130
    linear programming
      The Toy Factory Lab,
        241
    logarithm
      *Case of the Cooling
        Corpse*, 342
    parabola, 179
    probability
      Casino Dice Game, 538
      *The Candy Dish
        Investigation*, 537
    trigonometric
      Pendulum Experiment,
        379
Matrix, **351**; PG 98
    column, 348, **351**; PG 98
    dimensions, **351**; PG 98
    entry, **351**; PG 98
    introduction, 348; PG 98
    left inverse, **366**
    left-multiply, **366**
    multiplication, 349, **351**,
      354, **356**; PG 98
    multiplicative inverse, 364,
      366; PG 100
    right inverse, **366**
    right-multiply, **366**
    row, 348, **351**; PG 98
    zero, 352
Matrix equation, 362, 364, 747;
      PG 100
Maximize, 242, 246; PG 69
Mean, 94; SSD: Measures of
      Central Tendency
Measures of Central Tendency,
      SSD
Median, 94; SSD: Measures of
      Central Tendency

Point-slope form, 190; PG 13
Polynomial, 437, **440**, 441; PG 123
    division, 469, **472**; PG 132
    general equation, **451**
    graph, 445; PG 124
    minimum degree, 445
    multiplication, 710
    notation, **451**; PG 123
Polynomial Function Investigation,
    438
Population, 53
Power property of logarithms, 335;
    PG 93
Power Property of Logs, 330; PG 93
Presentation, 10
Probability, **510**; PG 139
    conditional, 506
    independent events, 506
Probability models, **502**; PG 139
    area model, **502**; PG 139
    systematic list, **502**
    tree diagram, **502**; PG 139
Problem-solving strategies, 2, 3
Product property of logarithms, 334;
    PG 94
Profit, 241, 242, 245; PG 70
Proof, 629; PG 163
Proof by induction, 629, **632**; PG 163
Pythagorean Identity, 689, **695**

Q

Quadratic
    Shrinking Target, 165
Quadratic equation, **23**
    factoring, **23**, 715
    general form, 171, **177**; PG 44
    graphing/vertex form, **177**; PG 44
    solving, **23**, 188, 720; PG 20
    standard form, **177**; PG 53
Quadratic Formula, **23**, 720; PG 128
Quadratic function
    finding intercepts, 188, 720;
        PG 45
Quadratic relations, 593
Quadratic sequence, 73
Quarterly interest, 127
Quartile, 154
Quotient property of logarithms, 334;
    PG 94

R
Rabbit problem, 53
Radian, **399**; PG 107
    convert to degrees, 399;
        PG 107
    mode, 398
Radical expressions
    operations with, SSD
    simplifying, SSD
Range, 18, 199, 725; PG 2
Ratio
    common, **83**; PG 15
Rational equation
    solving, 347, 734; PG 187
Rational exponents, 275, 730
Rational expressions
    operations with, PG 181;
        SSD
Rational numbers, **453**
Real
    root, 455, **460**; PG 130
Real numbers, 17, **199**, **456**
Real world problems
    exponential growth and
        decay, 138–141,
        338–343
    polynomials, 450, 484
    systems with, 232, 241
Rebound ratio, 60, 64
Reciprocal trigonometric
    functions, 682, **695**;
        PG 175
    cosecant, 682, **695**; PG 175
    cotangent, 683, **695**; PG 175
    secant, 683, **695**; PG 175
Recorder/Reporter, 4
Reference angle, **403**; PG 109
Region, 236, 238, **247**; PG 69
Relation, **6**, **199**
Remainder, 472
Resource manager, 4
Reverse, 263, 286
Reversing, 2
Rewrite, 68, 97, 101, 144, 222,
    244; PG 20
Richter scale, 504
Right multiply, **366**
Rochambeau
    Rock, Paper, Scissors, 497

Algebra 2 Connections

V

Variable, 38; PG 34
    dependent, **6**, **199**
    eliminating, **66**; PG 34
    independent, **6**, **199**
Variation
    direct, SSD
    inverse, SSD
    joint, SSD
Vertex, 168
    ellipse, 575
    form of a quadratic, **177**; PG 44
    hyperbola, **585**
    parabola, 168, 736; PG 44
Vertical asymptote, **118**; PG 7
Vertical compression, 170, 175;
    PG 43
Vertical shift, 175; PG 43
Vertical stretch, 170, 175; PG 43

W

Ways of Thinking, 2, 47

X

$x \rightarrow y$ table, 8
x-intercept, **11**, 446, 447, 720;
    PG 3
x-y interchange, 276, **283**;
    PG 77

Y

$y = x$, 268; PG 78
y-form, 68; PG 63
y-intercept, **11**, 720; PG 3

Z

Zero factorial, 522, 526;
    PG 145
    definition, **543**; PG 145
Zero power, 132, **148**
Zero Product Property, **23**, 720
Zeros (of a function), **44**